W9-BVX-990

NATIONAL GEOGRAPHIC SOCIETY

Research Reports

NATIONAL GEOGRAPHIC SOCIETY

Research Reports

VOLUME 12

On research and exploration projects
supported by the National Geographic Society,
the initial grant for which
was made in the year

1971

Compiled and edited by
Paul H. Oehser, John S. Lea, and Nancy Link Powars
under the direction of the
Committee for Research and Exploration

NATIONAL GEOGRAPHIC SOCIETY
WASHINGTON, D. C.

NATIONAL GEOGRAPHIC SOCIETY

Washington, D. C.

Organized "for the increase and diffusion of geographic knowledge"

GILBERT HOVEY GROSVENOR (1875-1966)

Editor, 1899-1954; President, 1920-1954

Chairman of the Board, 1954-1966

THE NATIONAL GEOGRAPHIC SOCIETY is chartered in Washington, D. C., in accordance with the laws of the United States, as a nonprofit scientific and educational organization for increasing and diffusing geographic knowledge and promoting research and exploration. Since 1890 the Society has supported more than 2,200 explorations and research projects, adding immeasurably to man's knowledge of earth, sea, and sky. It diffuses this knowledge through its monthly journal, NATIONAL GEOGRAPHIC; more than 50 million maps distributed each year; its books, globes, atlases, filmstrips and educational films; *National Geographic* WORLD, a magazine for children age 8 and older; information services to press, radio, and television; technical reports; exhibits in Explorers Hall; and a nationwide series of programs on television.

• • • •

International Standard Book No. ISBN 0-87044-345-3
Library of Congress Catalog Card No. 68-26794

Statement by the Chairman

The National Geographic Society was founded in 1888 by a group composed largely of Washington scientists to increase and diffuse geographic knowledge and to promote research and exploration. The Society's activities toward achieving its second objective date from 1890, when the society sponsored a geographic and geologic expedition to study the Mount St. Elias Range of Alaska. Since then it has made more than 2,200 grants in support of approximately 1,700 projects in research and exploration. The work has encompassed the broad scope of geography, including such scientific disciplines as geology, paleontology, astronomy, geophysics, oceanography, biology, anthropology, archeology, ethnology, and geographic exploration. The research program has increased as the Society has grown, until today the budget of the Society provides $2,500,000 annually in support of the program.

To assist in the task of selecting from among the hundreds of applicants those best qualified to continue the high standards of accomplishment set by recipients of grants during the past nine decades, the Society has assembled the panel of distinguished scientists and scholars listed above.

This is the twelfth in a series of volumes that as projected will eventually contain summary reports on the results of all the research and exploration projects sponsored by the Society since it was established. These are being published volume by volume, as rapidly as the material can be assembled. The present volume contains 77 accounts covering work done under grants made during the year 1971. In some instances, when a continuing research program has been supported by grants over a number of years, and a breakdown of results by year is found impracticable, it has seemed best to include only one résumé for the entire project, with cross references to the main account inserted in other volumes as appropriate. Volumes now in print (1980) cover the following years: 1890-1954, 1955-1960, 1961-1962, and one volume for each of the years 1963 through 1970.

In presenting the reports no attempt has been made to standardize the style and specific approach of the investigator, other than to confine each account to reasonable space limitations. In many cases fuller but scattered reports on the work have been, or will be, published elsewhere—in the technical scientific journals, occasionally in the *National Geographic,* or in book form. Published accounts emanating from the research projects are included in the literature references, which each author has been encouraged to supply.

Although the editors of these Reports make every reasonable effort to obtain a report from every grantee, so that the results of all projects supported in a given year will be accounted for in the volume for that year, circumstances occasionally interfere. In some instances these delayed reports will be published in later volumes as appropriate. Grantees generally have been most cooperative in this publication project, and the Committee for Research and Exploration takes this opportunity to thank them for their support. In the years to come we shall be calling on them in similar fashion, and we solicit their continued help.

Experience with the previous volumes of this series has convinced us that the presentation of research findings as given in these books is of significant value to the scientific community. Scholars the world over find this record of the accumulating results of National Geographic Society research grants of real assistance in their own investigations and in the preparation of scientific publications. The general reader also gains new and important knowledge about the current state of research related to geography from each of these volumes.

Contents

Statement by the Chairman, Committee for Research and Exploration v

Studies of Pre-Columbian American Diseases, 1971-1976. By *Marvin J. Allison* 1

Microflora of Arctic Sea Ice. By *Spencer Apollonio* 13

Investigation of Submerged Beachrock Deposits off Bimini, Bahamas. By *John A. Gifford* and *Mahlon M. Ball* 21

Progress of Plant Successions on Soufrière Volcano, St. Vincent Island, West Indies, 1972. By *John Stanley Beard* 39

Nocturnal Orientation in the Ashy Petrel and Cassin's Auklet. By *Bruce L. Manion* 47

Behavior of Vertebrate Populations on Abandoned Strip-mine Areas. By *Fred J. Brenner* 67

Conventionality of Territorial Leks in a Population of Uganda Kob. By *Helmut K. Buechner* 75

Distribution, Mobility, and Behavior of the Red Sea Garden Eel. By *Eugenie Clark* 91

Three Surging Glaciers, St. Elias Mountains, Canada. By *Sam G. Collins* 103

Spectroscopy of Volcanic Flames and Fume. By *Dale P. Cruikshank* and *David Morrison* 117

A Study of Fossil Old World Monkeys of the Circum-Mediterranean Region. By *Eric Delson* 125

Excavations at Tell Keisan (Israel). By *Jacques Briend* 129

Photographic Record in Color of Live Deep-sea Cephalopods. By *P. Noel Dilly* 145

Postfledgling Activities of Juvenile Bald Eagles as Determined by Radio Telemetry. By *Thomas C. Dunstan* 149

The Battle of Lepanto Search and Survey Mission, Greece, 1971-1972. By *Peter Throckmorton, Harold E. Edgerton,* and *Eletherios Yalouris* 161

Petrology and Origin of the Mount Stuart Batholith, Cascade Mountains, Washington. By *Erik H. Erikson, Jr.* 175

The "Acropolis" of Aphrodisias in Caria: Investigations and Excavations of the Theater and the Prehistoric Mounds, 1971-1977. By *Kenan T. Erim* 185

Occultation of Beta Scorpii and Companion by Jupiter, May 13, 1971. By *David S. Evans* 205

Petrology of Andean Metamorphic Rocks from Colombia and Ecuador. By *Tomas Feininger* 213

Laysan Albatross: Mortality, Survival, Breeding, and Changes in Breeding Populations. By *Harvey I. Fisher* 219

Excavations at Rattlers Bight—A Late Maritime Archaic Settlement and Cemetery in Hamilton Inlet, Labrador. By *William W. Fitzhugh* 223

Biology of Snail-killing Flies of the Pacific Northwest (Diptera: Sciomyzidae). By *Benjamin A. Foote* 233

Mountain Gorilla Research, 1971-1972. By *Dian Fossey* 237

The Bakhtiyārī Tribe: Its Organization and Role in Iran. By *G. R. Garthwaite* 257

Papyrus and the Ecology of Lake Naivasha. By *John J. Gaudet* 267

Thermal Ecology of the American Alligator *(Alligator mississippiensis)*. By *Frederick R. Gehlbach* 273

Collections, Observations, and Illustrations of the Flora of Tierra del Fuego, 1971-1973. By *Rae Natalie Prosser Goodall* 275

Reproductive Cycles and Biogeographic Relationships of Tropical *Anolis* Lizards. By *George C. Gorman* 283

Archeological Investigations at Chalcatzingo, 1972, 1973. By *David C. Grove* 287

Systematics and Evolution of the Family Thelotremataceae (Lichens) in the Lesser Antilles. By *Mason E. Hale, Jr.* 305

Chromosomes, Speciation, and Evolution of Mexican Iguanid Lizards. By *William P. Hall III* 309

The Paleoecology of Dry Cave, New Mexico. By *Arthur H. Harris* 331

Morphological and Ecological Studies of Sponges in Pacific Reef Caves. By *Willard D. Hartman* and *Henry W. Reiswig* 339

Archeological Investigations at the Murray Springs Clovis Site, Arizona, 1971. By *C. Vance Haynes, Jr.* 347

Source of the Colossi of Memnon on the Theban Plain, Egypt. By *Robert F. Heizer* 355

Studies on the Terrestrial Hermit Crab *(Coenobita clypeatus)*. By *Alex Henderson* and *Syd Radinovsky* 361

Mass-nesting of Pacific Ridley Turtles on Nancite Beach, Santa Rosa National Park, Costa Rica. By *David A. Hughes* and *Joseph D. Richard* 369

Description and Function of *Anolis limifrons* Social Displays. By *Thomas A. Jenssen* 377

Seamounts in the Austral Islands Region. By *Rockne H. Johnson* 389

Population Ecology of the Flamingos of the World. By *M. Philip Kahl* 407

Conservation of the Kyrenia Ship, 1971-1972. By *Michael L. Katzev* 417

Reproductive Performance of Fish-eating Birds at Eagle Lake, California. By *James R. Koplin* 427

Polar-bear Den Surveys in Svalbard, 1972 and 1973. By *Thor Larsen* 445

Demographic and Social-anthropological Study of the Hambukushu of Botswana. By *Thomas John Larson* 455

Early Man Research in East Africa, 1971. By *Mary D. Leakey* 459

Domestic Architecture and Village Layout in Mainland Greece, About 2200-800 B.C. By *William A. McDonald* and *Stanley E. Aschenbrenner* 463

An Ecocene Flamingo Nesting Area, Sweetwater County, Wyoming. By *Paul O. McGrew* 473

Behavior of the Reef Sharks of Rangiroa, French Polynesia. By *Donald R. Nelson* and *Richard H. Johnson* 479

Volcanic Gas and Petrologic Investigations of Galápagos Islands Calderas. By *Bert E. Nordlie* 501

The Tlapanec Indians of Tlacoapa, Guerrero, Mexico. By *Marion Oettinger, Jr.*, and *Patricia Amanda Parsons* 517

Field Investigations of Yak in the Nepal Himalaya. By *Richard P. Palmieri* 529

Geographic Variation in the Frequency of Spontaneous Tumors in Fern Gametophytes. By *Carl R. Partanen* 535

Behavior, Songs, and Populations of Parasitic Finches. By *Robert B. Payne* 541

Research on the Behavior of Various Species of Whales. By *Roger S. Payne* 551

Ethnographic Research on *Afkodre,* Surinam. By *B. Edward Pierce* 565

Ecology of the Golden-rumped Elephant-shrew *(Rhynchocyon chrysopygus)* of Kenya. By *Galen B. Rathbun* 573

Livelihood Mobility and Economic Diversity in Three Villages of Trinidad. By *Bonham C. Richardson* 579

The Flax Genus *Linum.* By *Claude M. Rogers* 587

Energy and Water Budget Studies in the Tundra. By *Wayne R. Rouse* 591

Archeological Research on the Island of Cozumel, Mexico. By *Jeremy A. Sabloff* and *William L. Rathje* 595

Excavation of Oligocene Marine Fossil Beds Near Charleston, South Carolina. By *Albert E. Sanders* 601

The Taiwan Pheasant Project. By *Sheldon R. Severinghaus* 623

Asian Woodpecker Studies. By *Lester L. Short* 631

Biology of the Precambrian Genus *Kakabekia:* Geographic and Microenvironmental Determinations in the Distribution of Living *K. barghoorniana.* By *B. Z. Siegel* and *S. M. Siegel* 639

In Search of the Primitive Bamboos. By *Thomas R. Soderstrom* and *Cleofé E. Calderón* 647

Aspects of Mbotgate Life Style. By *E. Richard Sorenson* 655

Crown-of-thorns Starfish *(Acanthaster planci)* Investigations in Micronesia, July 1971 through March 1972. By *Walter A. Starck II* 665

Excavation of Protohistoric Arikara Indian Cemetery Near Mobridge, South Dakota, 1971. By *T. Dale Stewart* 677

Biography of Joseph Francis Rock (1884-1962): Scientist-Explorer. By *Stephanne B. Sutton* 687

Desert Gazelles: Energetic and Water Cost of Locomotion. By *C. Richard Taylor* 689

Biotic Succession of Lodgepole-pine Forests of Fire Origin in Yellowstone National Park. By *Dale L. Taylor* 693

Systematics, Ecology, and Distribution of Annual Killifish in Northern South America. By *Jamie E. Thomerson* 703

Photographing Pre-Columbian Gold Artifacts of Panama. By *Reina Torres de Araúz* 709

Observations on the Biology of Marsupials in Colombia and Venezuela. By *C. Hugh Tyndale-Biscoe* 711

Migration Studies of the Monarch Butterfly in North America. By *Fred A. Urquhart* and *Norah R. Urquhart* 721

Investigation of Cave Deposits of Quaternary and Holocene Origin: The Muleta Expedition, 1971-1973. By *William H. Waldren* 731

Ancient Environments and Age of Non-glaciated Terrain in Southeastern Alaska. By *Ian A. Worley* 733

Appendix 749

Index 763

Editor's Note

The accounts in this volume are arranged alphabetically under the name of the principal investigator, who is not necessarily the senior author named in the Table of Contents. A full list of the 1971 grants on which these are based is to be found in the Appendix (p. 313) of *National Geographic Society Research Reports, 1966 Projects,* published in 1973.

The following accounts published in *National Geographic Society Research Reports, 1968 Projects, 1969 Projects,* and *1970 Projects* deal with research that continued into 1971 and was supported by grants in that year. Since these accounts cover this 1971 research, no further treatment of it is required in the present volume.

"An Ecological Study of the Pika *(Ochotona princeps)* in the Western United States," by Richard D. Bates, *1970 Projects,* pp. 29-43.

"Biotelemetry Capability for Biological Research," by John J. Craighead, Joel R. Varney, and Jay S. Sumner, *1969 Projects,* pp. 103-109.

"Early People and Extinct Animals at China Lake, California," by Emma Lou Davis, David E. Fortsch, and Carol Panlaqui, *1970 Projects,* pp. 83-92.

"The Shape of Geographos and Other Asteroids," by J. L. Dunlap and Tom Gehrels, *1970 Projects,* pp. 125-134.

"Exploration by Sonar and Coring of the Helice Site, Greece," by Harold E. Edgerton and Peter Throckmorton, *1970 Projects,* pp. 135-141.

"Biosystematic and Evolutionary Study of the *Capsicum pubescens* Complex," by W. Hardy Eshbaugh, *1970 Projects,* pp. 143-162.

"Behavior of Free-ranging Chimpanzees, Tanzania, 1969-1971," by Jane Goodall, *1970 Projects,* pp. 207-215.

"Biology of the Kaibab Squirrel," by Joseph G. Hall, *1970 Projects,* pp. 223-230.

"Archeological and Paleoecological Investigations at Guadalupe Pueblo, Sandoval County, New Mexico: A Preliminary Report," by Cynthia Irwin-Williams and Lonnie C. Pippin, *1970 Projects,* pp. 309-330.

"Population Ecology of Key Deer," by Willard D. Klimstra, James W. Hardin, and Nova J. Silvy, *1969 Projects,* pp. 313-321.

"A Comparison of the Spacing Patterns of Polar Bears on Islands and Mainland Coasts in Hudson and James Bays," by Brian M. Knudsen, *1970 Projects,* pp. 353-355.

"Lower Pleistocene Hominids from Lake Turkana, North Kenya, 1970-1972," by Richard E. F. Leakey, *1970 Projects,* pp. 363-376.

"Studies of the Natural History of the American Bison," by Dale F. Lott, *1969 Projects,* pp. 399-404.

"Speciation among Small Mammals of the Apostle Islands," by Richard F. Meierotto, *1970 Projects,* pp. 389-397.

"Breeding Biology of Cackling Geese and Associated Species on the Yukon-Kuskokwim Delta, Alaska," by Peter G. Mickelson, *1970 Projects,* pp. 399-404.

"Mesozoic and Tertiary Vertebrates of Baja California, 1968-1971," by William J. Morris, *1968 Projects,* pp. 305-316.

"The Chan Chan-Moche Valley Archeological Project, Peru," by Michael E. Moseley, *1970 Projects,* pp. 413-425.

"Excavation of the Phoenician and Roman Cities at Sarepta (Modern Sarafand, Lebanon)," by James B. Pritchard, *1969 Projects,* pp. 455-472.

"Ecology and Behavior of High-altitude Mammals in South Asia," by George B. Schaller, *1970 Projects,* pp. 461-478.

"Archeological Investigations in the Grand Canyon," by Douglas W. Schwartz, *1969 Projects,* pp. 545-555.

"Biology of Northern American Accipters in Arizona and New Mexico," by Noel F. R. Snyder and Helen A. Snyder, *1970 Projects,* pp. 487-491.

"Vision and Orientation in Aquatic Animals," by Talbot H. Waterman, *1970 Projects,* pp. 547-566.

Reports on the 1971 grants listed below were not available at the time this volume went to press. They will appear in later volumes as they are received.

953: To Ivan Polunin, University of Singapore, Singapore, for a study of the behavior of Asian *Pteroptyx* fireflies.

975: To Dr. Delbert Wiens, University of Utah, Salt Lake City, Utah, for a study of the biogeographical affinities and chromosomal relationships of African mistletoes.

996: To Barry W. Prather, Michigan State University, East Lansing, Michigan, for continuation of a geophysical and volcanological investigation of the Mount Rainier summit crater area, started in 1970 under grant no. 884.

Libraries and institutions regularly receiving copies of these reports will note that this one bears the volume number 12 and that this practice of numbering will henceforth be used to identify subsequent volumes. For their convenience, the earlier ones may be considered to bear numbers as follows:

Vol. No.	*Covering grant years*	*Date Issued*
1	1890-1954	1975
2	1955-1960	1972
3	1961-1962	1970
4	1963	1968
5	1964	1969
6	1965	1971
7	1966	1973
8	1967	1974
9	1968	1976
10	1969	1978
11	1970	1979

To aid researchers, the Society's grants made from 1966 onward are listed numerically in the *Research Reports* volumes as indicated below:

Grants (year made)	*In volume*	*(project year)*
550 - 600 (1966)	4	(1963)
601 - 670 (1967)	5	(1964)
671 - 743 (1968)	5	(1964)
744 - 822 (1969)	6	(1965)
823 - 917 (1970)	6	(1965)
918 - 1036 (1971)	7	(1966)
1037 - 1136 (1972)	8	(1967)
1137 - 1285 (1973)	9	(1968)
1286 - 1421 (1974)	10	(1969)
1422 - 1568 (1975)	11	(1970)
1569 - 1701 (1976)	11	(1970)
1702 - 1844 (1977)	12	(1971)
1845 - 1974 (1978)	12	(1971)

Studies of Pre-Columbian American Diseases, 1971-1976

Principal Investigator: Marvin J. Allison, Medical College of Virginia Commonwealth University, Richmond, Virginia.[1]

Grant Nos. 971, 1147, 1306, 1594. In support of a study of pre-Columbian diseases.

This Peruvian-American cooperative study was initiated to evaluate medical and dental problems of man in a given area of the world over a relatively long period of time, approximately 5,000 years. Thus our studies begin with hunter-fishermen-gatherers, who had cotton but no ceramics, and continue through pre-Columbian agriculturists, Colonial Indians, and in some cases, modern man.

The study was done in the Regional Museum of Ica and the Medical College of Virginia, utilizing material scientifically excavated from coastal sites in the Departments of Lima and Ica in Peru, as well as some material from Tarapaca in northern Chile. The total number of individuals studied to date was: Huacho, 23 (mummies); Ica, 173 (mummies) plus 1,000 (skeletons and teeth); Tarapaca, 75 (mummies); and Ica (Modern Man), 40.

The material came from more than 20 cemeteries located in nearly 10 different valleys separated by over 1,000 kilometers. The common denominator of this area is the coastal climate and desert way of life as opposed to the Andean or jungle way of life. Thus these people had many common habits of dress, eating, and social structure. Intruders from the mountains appeared at different intervals and are easily recognizable archeologically as well as anthropologically.

All material used in this study was of known source and archeological association. Representative samples were selected from each excavation for

[1] Grateful acknowledgement is extended to the many persons who assisted and worked with me at various times during the years of this project: Colleagues and students at the Medical College of Virginia, at the Regional Museum of Ica, Peru, and at other institutions both in this country and in South America. I regret that it is not feasible to mention them all by name, but without their generous help this research would not have been possible. Dr. T. Dale Stewart, physical anthropologist of the Smithsonian Institution, gave freely of his advice and expertise to help resolve many problems in the area of bone pathology and physical anthropology.

carbon-14 as well as archeological dating. Where feasible the following studies were undertaken on the individual:

A. Physical anthropology
   1. Measurements and indices
   2. Nonmetric variants and other possible genetic markers
   3. Serological studies of red and white cell antigens
   4. Age, sex, and hair color

B. Evaluation of childhood conditions of health using Harris's lines

C. Mutilations
   1. Head deformations
   2. Tattoos
   3. Ear piercing

D. Study of diseases
   1. Congenital
   2. Metabolic
   3. Infections
   4. Neoplastic
   5. Circulatory
   6. Trauma
   7. Odontogenic
   8. Parasitic

E. Chemical studies
   1. Heavy metal intoxication in miners
   2. Heavy metals and other toxic elements in foodstuffs

F. Serological studies for microbial identification

The limiting factor throughout was the quality of the material. We were most fortunate in having enough good material in each area to enable us to evaluate a sufficient number of individuals to determine trends.

Table 1 compares the mortality of the ancient and the modern inhabitants of the Department of Ica. The ages at death of the modern people were collected from the gravestones of individuals who died in the preantibiotic era from 1923 to 1927.

The distribution of deaths between the ancient and modern preantibiotic population of the Department of Ica has a number of interesting points of discussion. The modern population lived longer than the ancient population—for males over 40, 32 percent as opposed to 8 percent; for females over 50, 38 percent as opposed to 13 percent. These end points were limited to the method of aging the ancient population. Actually in both the ancient and modern populations the females lived longer; in the modern group 3 females lived over 100 years, the oldest to age 104.

Childhood mortality was higher for males in both the ancient and modern groups. During the period from birth to the first 30 days of life mortality was double that of modern man, but then it was very similar until the 7th to 12th month period, when the modern children had a fourfold increase in mortality over the ancient children group. Possibly this high mortality is connected with a difference in the time of weaning, the ancient children group being weaned after 24 months. Certainly from 24 months to 6 years there is a period

TABLE 1. Mortality, Department of Ica, Peru

Ancient Inhabitants 265 B.C. to A.D. 1600
Modern Inhabitants A.D. 1923 to A.D. 1927

Age	*Number (pct.) of males*		*Number (pct.) of females*	
	Ancient	*Modern*	*Ancient*	*Modern*
1–30 days	2 (4.2)	6 (3.8)	4 (5.1)	1 (0.8)
1–3 months	1 (2.1)	5 (3.1)	1 (1.3)	3 (2.3)
4–6 "	2 (4.2)	5 (3.1)	2 (2.5)	2 (1.5)
7–12 "	2 (4.2)	17 (10.6)	2 (2.5)	2 (1.5)
13–18 "	3 (6.3)	9 (5.6)	3 (3.8)	3 (2.3)
19–24 "	1 (2.1)	8 (5.0)	0 (0)	10 (7.5)
3–4 years	4 (8.3)	13 (8.1)	4 (5.1)	2 (1.5)
5–6 "	8 (16.7)	3 (1.9)	2 (2.5)	5 (3.8)
7–8 "	2 (4.2)	3 (1.9)	4 (5.1)	0 (0)
9–10 "	2 (4.2)	1 (0.6)	0 (0)	1 (0.8)
Totals: Children	27 (56)	70 (44)	22 (28)	50 (38)
11–20 years	4 (8.3)	8 (5.0)	11 (13.9)	8 (6.1)
21–30 "	2 (4.2)	12 (7.5)	11 (13.9)	6 (4.6)
31–40 "	11 (22.7)	18 (11.2)	21 (26.5)	10 (7.6)
41–50 "	4 (8.3)	11 (6.9)	4 (5.1)	7 (5.3)
51–60 "		11 (6.9)	10 (12.7)	6 (4.6)
61–70 "		6 (3.8)		16 (12.2)
71–80 "		13 (8.1)		8 (6.1)
81–90 "		9 (5.6)		10 (7.6)
91–100 "		2 (1.3)		7 (5.3)
101+ "		0 (0)		3 (2.3)
Totals: Adults	21 (44)	90 (56)	57 (72)	81 (62)
Totals	48 (100)	160 (100)	79 (100)	131 (100)

TABLE 2. ABO Frequencies in 136 Pre-Columbian and 70 Colonial Mummies

Culture	*Number of individuals*	*A No. (%)*	*B No. (%)*	*AB No. (%)*	*O No. (%)*
Huacho	10	3 (30)	–	1 (10)	6 (60)
Paracas	16	5 (31.3)	1 (6.1)	5 (31.3)	5 (31.3)
Nazca	7	–	–	3 (42.9)	4 (57.1)
Huari	36	9 (25)	1 (2.8)	10 (27.8)	16 (44.4)
Ica	23	3 (13.1)	1 (4.3)	2 (8.7)	17 (73.9)
Inca	5	–	–	–	5 (100)
Chile Atacamenas	39	4 (10.3)	–	–	35 (89.7)
Subtotal	136	24 (17.6)	3 (2.2)	21 (15.4)	88 (64.8)
Ica Colonial	32	8 (25)	–	–	24 (75)
Inca Colonial	26	3 (11.5)	–	1 (3.8)	22 (84.7)
Chile Atacamenas Colonial	12	1 (9)	–	–	11 (91)
Subtotal	70	12 (17.1)	–	1 (1.4)	57 (81.5)
Total	206	36 (17.5)	3 (1.5)	22 (10.7)	145 (70.3)

of high mortality among the ancient children groups, particularly in the male children.

Once adulthood was reached there was a higher mortality from ages 11 to 30 in the ancient female group but not in the modern group. The 31- to 40-year period of life had the largest number of deaths for the adult life of ancient males and females as well as modern males; but modern females peaked at 61 to 70 years of age.

The conclusions that may be reached from such a table is that infant mortality was higher in ancient times, but the practice of weaning earlier in modern times or possible early pregnancy after delivery resulted in an increased mortality in children from the 7th to the 12th month. On the other hand, peak mortality in ancient times among children occurred around 5 years of age. In general, male children had a higher mortality than female children. Among the adults in the ancient group there was a somewhat higher mortality among females during the childbearing years, but this was not seen among modern females. In both groups the female lived longer than the male.

Our physical-anthropology studies lead us to believe that the pre-Columbian inhabitants of Ica were comparable in size with the modern rural non-European inhabitants. A review of our ABO blood-group data in table 2 and our HL-A (white cell) data indicates variations in these genetic markers within the populations studied. The presence of all ABO blood-group antigens in the Americas 5,000 years ago is a new discovery, and the frequency of AB blood group must lead us to consider a different historical development of the ABO system. In our opinion further investigations will probably reveal the sequence as being O, AB, which later split into A and B. Such a system would explain the Cis AB group currently known to exist in modern man, especially in the Orient, as a holdover of an earlier blood group. A comparative study of the ABO and HL-A tables reveals that these two systems tend to support each other, reinforcing the differences among the cultures. These markers also have proved of value to establish blood relationships among individuals from the same or neighboring cemeteries, a task that was formerly impossible.

A study of the body at the time of death generally allows only for an evaluation of disease present at that moment. X-ray studies of the tibia will often allow an evaluation of health conditions during the period of growth of this bone (the first 16 years of life), as periods of poor health due to starvation or disease will cause a striation to appear on the X-ray due to overcalcification. Calculations can be made to determine at what age these lines appear, and comparisons of health conditions may then be inferred. The healthiest group of individuals, that is to say, those with the fewest lines, were from a fishing-gathering group 5,000 years old. It is probable that they had a high protein diet, for as agriculture became more common and people probably moved into closer contact, urban environment childhood illness increased. This was especially striking on the coast where the frequency was much higher than that seen in the mountains. The phenomenon of spongy hyperostosis seen in coastal children and not in the mountains leads us to consider malaria as a possible agent responsible for this difference, although as yet malaria has not been demonstrated in pre-Columbian America.

Among the diseases that we successfully demonstrated as existing in pre-Columbian America were tuberculosis and hookworm infestation due to *Ancylostoma duodenale;* both had been considered imports of the Europeans and Negro slaves. Our first case of tuberculosis was in an 8-year-old boy from the Nazca culture around A.D. 700. He showed many of the manifestations of tuberculosis, Pott's disease, psoas abscess, renal disease, pericarditis, and the terminal event, a miliary tuberculosis. Since then we have additional cases in the Paracas, Huari, Inca, and Atacamena cultures, dating back from 600 B.C. Since most of those cases were bone tuberculosis and since this comprises only about 5–8 percent of the total cases of tuberculosis, this disease must have been extremely common in pre-Columbian America and among the primary causes of death. Another common cause of death was pneumonia. Thus if this is included with tuberculosis, death due to respiratory infectious disease must be considered the major cause of death.

We found several cases of gastrointestinal disease—a hookworm infestation due to *Ancylostoma duodenale*—and a case of typhoid fever. A relatively large study of feces for ova and parasites was projected.

We found one teenage girl with a rather typical lupus erythematosis including the presence of viruslike particles in the kidneys. These particles are commonly seen in modern cases of this disease. Another rather rare disease was a case of Bartonellosis or Carrion's disease in which typical bacteria were demonstrated in the tissues by utilizing the electron microscope.

Two types of what might be termed occupational diseases were seen. In a fishing preceramic cultural group from Huacho a number of ear-canal osteomas were seen, probably associated with work in the water. We noted these also in some of our Paracas material, another culture in part associated with fishing in the ocean. The second occupational illness was pneumoconiosis and silicosis due to silver mining. This was noted in a group of Colonial Indians who had been mining silver in Tarapaca, northern Chile.

Several congenital diseases were found, in utero dislocation of the hip, hydrocephalus, and scoliosis (torsion of the vertebral column). A number of other congenital defects were noted that produced no disease; among these were spina bifida occulta and winged vertebrae.

Arthritis, both the infectious and degenerative types, was noted in many cases. Degenerative osteoarthritis began early in most cultural groups; lesions at times visible in the late teens and early twenties that we don't usually see now before 50 years of age.

Two hernias were noted, one, in a miner, involving the stomach with a large diaphragmatic hernia; the second was in an individual from the Atacamena culture and death was due to the strangulation of two loops of the jejunum by a diaphragmatic hernia.

One feature of considerable interest to us was that in 75 mummies examined from the Atacamena cultures we found two cases of gall-bladder disease where death was due to gallstones. In Peru in none of the mummies were we able to find a single case of gallstones in over twice that number of mummies. The American Indian in general is very susceptible to the development of gallstones, but it would appear that here we have another difference in the Indian in Chile and Peru that cannot be easily explained at this moment.

Metabolic diseases are difficult to diagnose in mummies, but we found two examples in our studies. The first was a case of thyroid disease (goiter) in which the gland was considerably enlarged and calcified with a considerable thickening of the calvarium indicative of a probable hypothyroidism. The second was a congenital disease of the calcium metabolism, primary generalized hyperostosis, that results in greatly thickened bones two to three times heavier than normal.

The frequency of trauma was evaluated and found to increase 500 percent during the post-Columbian period. Trauma of the skull was treated surgically in pre-Columbian times in Peru by trepanization. We published an evaluation of this on our material from the Regional Museum of Ica.

We have had a number of studies on dental disease published and changes were noted in the different cultures with respect to caries, enamel development, and alveolar bone loss. Similar studies were done on the mastoid process and auditory canal where surprising little ear disease was noted.

We have looked carefully for neoplasms but except for the usual benign osteomas of the skull have found nothing of interest.

There were a number of skin diseases manifested in the form of a rash. One of these was a generalized candidiasis that today would be seen in diabetics. Another was associated with a fulminating pneumonia that gives the appearance of being typhus, but has not yet been confirmed. We found an ulcerative, pigmented skin lesion in a youth suggestive of chromoblastomycosis, but this too is being further studied.

An interesting spin-off of these studies has been the opportunity to evaluate toxic and heavy metal levels in foodstuffs associated with the graves. We are currently measuring levels of lead, silver, arsenic, selenium, mercury, and antimony over a span of about 1,000 years. Normal levels of these substances vary considerably in modern material. Much of this is attributed to industrial contamination. Here for the first time we have an opportunity to determine levels from an industrially uncontaminated environment. Samples used are vegetable and animal, including Pacific Ocean fish.

REFERENCES

Papers and Books

ALLISON, MARVIN J.; CASTRO, N.; and HOSSAINI, ALI A.

1976. ABO blood groups in Peruvian mummies. Amer. Journ. Phys. Anthrop., vol. 44, pp. 55-62.

ALLISON, MARVIN J.; GERSZTEN, ENRIQUE; SOTIL, RAND; and PEZZIA, ALEJANDRO

1976. Primary hyperostosis in ancient Peru. Med. Coll. Virginia Quart., vol. 12, pp. 49-51.

ALLISON, MARVIN J.; KLURFELD, D.; and GERSZTEN, ENRIQUE

1975. Demonstration of erythrocytes and hemoglobin products in mummified tissue. Paleopathology Newsletter, no. 11, pp. 7-8.

ALLISON, MARVIN J.; MENDOZA, DANIEL; and PEZZIA, ALEJANDRO

1973. Documentation of a case of tuberculosis in pre-Columbian America. Amer. Rev. Resp. Dis., vol. 107, pp. 985-991.

1974. A radiographic approach to childhood illness in pre-Columbian inhabitants of southern Peru. Amer. Journ. Phys. Anthrop., vol. 40, pp. 409-415.

ALLISON, MARVIN J., and PEZZIA, ALEJANDRO

1973. Preparation of the dead in pre-Columbian coastal Peru, pt. 1. Paleopathology Newsletter, no. 4, pp. 10-12.

1974. Preparation of the dead in pre-Columbian coastal Peru, pt. 2. Paleopathology Newsletter, no. 5, pp. 7-9.

1976. Treatment of head wounds in pre-Columbian and Colonial Peru. Med. Coll. Virginia Quart., vol. 12, pp. 74-79.

ALLISON, MARVIN J.; PEZZIA, ALEJANDRO; GERSZTEN, ENRIQUE; GIFFLER, RONALD F.; and MENDOZA, DANIEL

1974. Aspiration pneumonia due to teeth—a report of two cases 950 A.D. and 1973 A.D. South. Med. Journ., vol. 67, pp. 479-483.

ALLISON, MARVIN J.; PEZZIA, ALEJANDRO; and MENDOZA, DANIEL

1974. A case of Carrion's disease associated with human sacrifice from the Huari culture of southern Peru. Amer. Journ. Phys. Anthrop., vol. 41, pp. 295-300.

ALLISON, MARVIN J.; PEZZIA, ALEJANDRO; HASEGAWA, L.; and GERSZTEN, ENRIQUE

1974. A case of hookworm infestation in a pre-Columbian American. Amer. Journ. Phys. Anthrop., vol. 41, pp. 103-105.

ASHWORTH, JOEL T.; ALLISON, MARVIN J.; GERSZTEN, ENRIQUE; and PEZZIA, ALEJANDRO
1976. The pubic scars of gestation and parturition in a group of pre-Columbian and Colonial Peruvian mummies. Amer. Journ. Phys. Anthrop., vol. 45, pp. 85-89.

DALTON, HARRY P.; ALLISON, MARVIN J.; and PEZZIA, ALEJANDRO
1976. The documentation of communicable diseases in Peruvian mummies. Med. Coll. Virginia Quart., vol. 12, pp. 43-48.

ELZAY, RICHARD P.; ALLISON, MARVIN J.; and PEZZIA, ALEJANDRO
1977. A comparative study of the dental health status of five pre-Columbian cultures. Amer. Journ. Phys. Anthrop., vol. 46, pp. 135-140.

GERSZTEN, ENRIQUE; ALLISON, MARVIN J.; MUNIZAGA, JUAN; and KLURFELD, D.
1976. Diaphragmatic hernia of the stomach in a Peruvian mummy. Bull. New York Acad. Med., vol. 52, pp. 601-604.

GERSZTEN, ENRIQUE; ALLISON, MARVIN J.; PEZZIA, ALEJANDRO; and KLURFELD, D.
1976. Thyroid disease in a Peruvian mummy. Med. Coll. Virginia Quart., vol. 12, pp. 52-53.

HOSSAINI, ALI A., and ALLISON, MARVIN J.
1976a. Paleoserologic studies: ABO and histocompatibility antigens in mummified American Indians. Med. Coll. Virginia Quart., vol. 12, pp. 67-73.
1976b. Distribution of HL-A antigens and ABO blood groups in pre-Columbian mummies. The reticuloendothelial system in health and disease. Pp. 101-110 *in* "Advances in Experimental Medicine and Biology," vol. 73A, Sherwood M. Reichard, Mario R. Escobar, and Herman Friedman, eds. Plenum Press, New York.

MARTINEZ, A. J.; FULTZ, D.; ALLISON, MARVIN J.; GERSZTEN, ENRIQUE; STANLEY, D. C.
1975. Electron microscopic study of tissues from pre-Columbian Americans. 33d Ann. Proc. Electron Micr. Soc. Amer., Las Vegas, Nevada (G. W. Bailey, ed.).

MUNIZAGA, JUAN; ALLISON, MARVIN J.; and GERSZTEN, ENRIQUE
1975. Pneumoconiosis in miners from a 16th-century mining community. Bull. New York Acad. Med., vol. 51, pp. 1281-1393.

SAWICKI, V. A.; ALLISON, MARVIN J.; DALTON, HARRY P.; and PEZZIA, ALEJANDRO
1976. Presence of salmonella antigens in feces from a Peruvian mummy. Bull. New York Acad. Med., vol. 52, pp. 805-813.

SAWYER, DANIEL R; ALLISON, MARVIN J.; ELZAY, RICHARD P.; and PEZZIA, ALEJANDRO
1976. Morphological characteristics of the pre-Columbian dentition, I: Shovel-shaped incisors, Carabelli's cusp, and protostylid. Med. Coll. Virginia Quart., vol. 12, pp. 54-63.

SAWYER, DANIEL R.; ALLISON, MARVIN J.; and PEZZIA, ALEJANDRO
1976. Talon cusp: A clinically significant anomaly in a primary incisor from pre-Columbian America. Med. Coll. Virginia Quart., vol. 12, pp. 52-53.

Abstracts

ALLISON, MARVIN J., and GERSZTEN, ENRIQUE

1973. Enfermedades Americanas pre-Colombianas, pt. 1: Infecciones bacterianas. Presented at 9th Congress, Latin American Pathology Society, Mérida, Yucatán.

1976. Healing in trauma and trephanization in Peruvian mummies. Presented at 65th Annual Meeting, International Academy of Pathology, Boston, March.

ALLISON, MARVIN J.; GERSZTEN, ENRIQUE; and MUNIZAGA, JUAN

1976. Occupational diseases in miners in Colonial Peru. Presented at 45th annual meeting of American Association of Physical Anthropologists, St. Louis, April.

ALLISON, MARVIN J.; GERSZTEN, ENRIQUE; and PEZZIA, ALEJANDRO

1975. Tuberculosis in pre-Columbian Americans. Presented at International Academy of Pathology, New Orleans.

ALLISON, MARVIN J.; MENDOZA, DANIEL; and PEZZIA, ALEJANDRO

1972. Una aproximación radiográfica de las enfermedades infantiles en los habitantes pre-Colombinos del sur del Perú. Presented at 3d Peruvian Congress of Radiology.

ALLISON, MARVIN J.; SOTIL, RAUL; and GERSZTEN, ENRIQUE

1975. Hiperostosis generalizada primaria un caso del Perú pre-Colombino. Presented at Congressos Integrados de Patologia, Recife, Brasil.

CONNER, G. R.; GRANT, G. C.; and ALLISON, MARVIN J.

1975. The determination of lead and silver in Chilean mummy tissues. Presented at International Conference on Heavy Metals in the Environment, Toronto.

GERSZTEN, ENRIQUE, and ALLISON, MARVIN J.

1973. Enfermedades Americanas pre-Colombianas, pt. 2: Infestiones parasitarias. Presented at 9th Congress Latinamerican Pathology Society, Mérida, Yucatán.

1975. Enfermedades ocupacionales y traumaticos durante la época colonia. Presented at Congressos Integrados de Patología, Recife, Brasil, November.

1976. Occupational diseases in Peruvian mummies. Presented at 65th annual meeting of International Academy of Pathology, Boston, March.

GOODALE, FAIRFIELD; ASHWORTH, JOEL; ALLISON, MARVIN J.; and GERSZTEN, ENRIQUE

1975. Osteitis pública en momias Peruanas. Presented at Congressos Integrados de Patología, Recife, Brasil.

HOSSAINI, ALI A.; ALLISON, MARVIN J.; and KHORRAMI, A.

1975. HL-A antigens in mummies from Peru and Chile. Presented at International Society of Blood Transfusion, Helsinki, Finland.

KHORRAMI, A.; ALLISON, MARVIN J.; and HOSSAINI, ALI A.

1975. Studies on HL-A antigens of contemporary Americans and pre-Columbian South Americans. Presented at Virginia Academy of Science, Harrisonburg, Virginia.

Seminars and Symposia

ALLISON, MARVIN, J., and GERSZTEN, ENRIQUE
1975. Nuevos metodos en paleopatología. Seminar, San Marcos University, Lima, Peru, November.

ALLISON, MARVIN J.; GERSZTEN, ENRIQUE; DALTON, HARRY P.; and MARTÍNEZ, J.
1975. Paleopathology of Peruvian mummies. Symposium, ASCP and CAP meeting, Chicago, Illinois, September.

ALLISON, MARVIN J.; GERSZTEN, ENRIQUE; MENDOZA, DANIEL; and TORREALVA, DANIEL
1973. La salud en el Perú pre-Colombino. Symposium for Archeologists, Lima, Peru.

Exhibits and Television Programs

ALLISON, MARVIN J.
1974. Consulting the expert: Pathology of mummies. Educational TV program, Station 57, 1974.

ALLISON, MARVIN J.; GERSZTEN, ENRIQUE; and DALTON, HARRY P.
1974a. Paleopathology of pre-Columbian Americans. Exhibit at meeting of International Academy of Pathology, San Francisco.
1974b. Paleopathology of pre-Columbian Americans. Exhibit of the month, Armed Forces Institute of Pathology, Washington, D. C.
1974c. Pathology in Peruvian mummies. Exhibit at ASCP meeting, Washington, D. C.
1975. Medical anthropology of Peruvian mummies. Exhibit at ASCP and CAP meeting, Chicago, September.
1976. Paleopathology of ancient Peru. Exhibit at International Congress, International Academy of Pathology, Washington, D. C.

ALLISON, MARVIN J., and PEZZIA, ALEJANDRO
1975. Paleopathology. UPTV television program, England.

MARVIN J. ALLISON

Microflora of Arctic Sea Ice

Principal Investigator: Spencer Apollonio, New England Regional Fishery Management Council, Peabody, Massachusetts.

Grant No.921: For a study of the composition, variation, and ecology of microflora of Arctic sea ice.

The presence of an abundant and diverse population of microscopic flora on the bottom of Arctic and Antarctic sea ice has been known for many years from anecdotal reports (e.g., Sutherland, 1852; Scott, 1905). It is only quite recently that specific and quantitative information has been available on either Arctic (e.g., Apollonio, 1961, 1965; Meguro et al., 1967) or Antarctic ice flora (e.g., Bunt, 1963; Burkholder and Mandelli, 1965).

The significance of these peculiar communities of plants in the polar ecosystems is still unclear, although there has been some limited speculation (e.g., Andriashev, 1968) on their importance in the marine food chains. There has also been limited work (e.g, Bunt, 1967) on the physiological adaptations necessary for existence in such a seemingly improbable habitat.

Background of the Present Work

Prior to this work, published quantitative reports of the presence of ice algae under winter conditions (i.e., in snow-covered, intact, unbroken, and unmelted sea ice) in the North American Arctic existed only from Point Barrow, Alaska (Meguro (et al., 1967), and Jones Sound, Northwest Territories, Canada (Apollonio, 1961, 1965). My earlier unpublished work on the Arctic Ocean itself (1957-1958) and on its coastal periphery in Dumbell Bay, Ellesmere Island, Northwest Territories, Canada (1959) only suggested the probability of an ice flora in the Arctic Ocean. This possibility was not supported by or was contrary to reports (e.g., Gran, 1904; Mohr and Tibbs, 1963) from other areas of the Arctic Ocean to the effect that ice flora was negligible or nonexistent in the ocean itself.

General Purpose of the Project

The primary purpose of the present work was relatively simple, namely, to expand our very limited knowledge of the geographical distribution and species composition of the ice flora in the Canadian Arctic and to determine whether in fact an ice flora does exist in significant abundance in the Arctic Ocean—or at least on its coastal perimeter. Further, it was intended to describe the transition, if any, of the magnitude and species composition of the ice flora, by a series of samplings at fairly close intervals, from Jones Sound, the area of known occurrence, to the Arctic Ocean.

It was intended to make this series of samples along the west coast of Ellesmere Island from lat. 76°30′ to 83°00′ N., a distance of nearly 400 geographical miles. This particular location, also, would permit sampling of various types of sea ice, from the relatively thin (± 1.5 meters) annual ice of Jones Sound to the thicker, and probably older, ice of the Arctic Ocean itself. The samples could thereby provide some information on the variations, if any, of the flora with various kinds of sea ice at high Arctic latitudes.

It was hoped, also, to provide some information on the seasonal changes of the ice flora, to sample a peculiar, isolated habitat, to obtain additional samples of a previously reported relict species, and to provide some additional, although indirect, knowledge of the physiology of the flora by measuring chemical characteristics (dissolved organic carbon) of the ice habitat.

These latter three objectives are summarized at greater length, as follows: The area of work off Ellesmere Island gave access to a unique habitat that offered interesting sampling possibilities. The several fiords (e.g., Disraeli Fiord) of northern Ellesmere Island were, until not more than 3,000 years ago (Hattersley-Smith et al., 1970), in free and open connection with the surface waters of the Arctic Ocean (Keys et al., 1969, MS.). At that time, presumably, they would share in common with the adjacent Arctic Ocean any ice flora that may have then been present. In the last several hundred or few thousand years, however, the Ward Hunt Ice Shelf has effectively cut off surface (±40 meters) circulation between the Arctic Ocean and the fiords. Any ice flora in the fiords might reflect, either in quantity or species composition, the effect of that isolation. It was therefore planned to sample Lake A (Hattersley-Smith et al., 1970), Disraeli Fiord, and the adjacent Arctic Ocean for species comparison with the question of the effect of extended isolation on the flora in mind.

In his report on earlier samples taken by the author in Jones Sound, Bursa (1965) noted that the samples contained so-called discoasters, apparently a relict species of a group of unicellular, nanno-planktonic plants (Coccolithophoridae?) considered characteristic of warm oceanic waters; discoasters were previously considered to have become extinct at the Pliocene-Pleistocene transition, and are used by marine sedimentologists to delineate, by the presence or absence of their remains, that time period, or transition, in oceanic bottom cores. Since Bursa's report is the only reference to living discoasters, it was hoped that the present work would yield additional specimens, for further study, of a group of organisms previously thought to be extinct.

Finally, samples of sea ice were to be preserved in a frozen state for measurement of dissolved organic carbon. There was evidence from unpublished work at the Woods Hole Oceanographic Institution (R.R.L. Guillard, personal communication) that unicellular plants living at low light intensities (as under snow and thick sea ice) might supplement, in some way, their activities by organic carbon. In addition, there are data to suggest (e.g., Ignatiades and Fogg, 1973) that such plants, at low light intensities or low temperatures, might secrete a significant fraction of their photosynthetic products in some form of organic carbon. There is a likelihood that such excreted products could accumulate in the immediate vicinity of the ice algae—in the intercrystalline spaces of sea ice—thus lending itself to convenient measurement, and making possible inferences on the physiological consequences of life in the ice habitat.

Methods

The method of sampling ice algae was previously described (Apollonio, 1961). Briefly, it entails coring through the ice and retrieving the lower surface with the attached ice flora. The chlorophyll and chlorophyll-derivatives were measured by C. S. Yentsch (Yentsch and Menzel, 1963). A. S. Bursa, Arctic Unit, Fisheries Research Board of Canada, undertook the identification of the species composition of the ice flora. Organic carbon in samples of frozen sea ice was measured by N. W. Corwin (Woods Hole Oceanographic Institution) by the method of Strickland and Parsons (1968).

Travel from the Eskimo village of Grise Fiord on Jones Sound along the west and north coasts of Ellesmere Island to Cape Columbia was undertaken with the indispensable aid of Akeeagok and Tookiekee, natives of Grise Fiord, using two snowmobiles provided by Massey-Ferguson, Ltd., Toronto.

Results and Discussion

Samples were taken in Jones Sound off Grise Fiord village, in Baumann Fiord, Eureka Sound, Slidre Fiord, Nansen Sound, in the Arctic Ocean off Ward Hunt Island, in Lake A on Ellesmere Island, and in Disraeli Fiord. In general, the ice flora in 1971 was either nonexistent (e.g., Baumann Fiord) or at very low concentrations (e.g., Slidre Fiord). Specific data are given in table 1. Compared with chlorophyll concentrations previously found in April-June in Jones Sound (Apollonio, 1965) and Point Barrow (Meguro et al., 1967), these are very low values. They confirm the visual impression during the sampling that the ice flora was very poorly developed throughout the area.

TABLE 1. Summary of Chlorophyll *a* and Dissolved Organic Carbon Data from Arctic Sea Ice, Ellesmere Island, Northwest Territories, April and May 1971

Date	*Location*	*Ice thickness (meters)*	*Snow depth (cm)*	*Chlorophyll* a *(mg/m³)*	*Dissolved organic carbon (mg/L)*
April 30-May 7	Slidre Fiord	2.3±	20.0±	0.117-0.237	2.22-5.78
May 8-10	Nansen Sound	2.6±	10.0±	27.05	3.15
May 14-15	Arctic Ocean	0.9-1.6±	2.5±	6.54-7.12	2.29-6.58

The high chlorophyll value found (27.05 mg/m^3) was far less than values (100-1000 mg/m^3) commonly observed in Jones Sound in the springs of 1961-1963. The samples from Jones Sound in 1971 showed negligible if any chlorophyll concentrations. In several other sampling areas, similarly, there was no visible or measurable chlorophyll. In 1961-1963 almost invariably snow-covered sea ice samples produced visually obvious and substantial chlorophyll concentrations. In 1971 none of the samples, except only those from the ice in the Arctic Ocean off Ward Hunt Island, showed visible chlorophyll.

Those samples from the Arctic Ocean were taken from ice that was relatively thin and, clearly, quite recently formed and with negligible snow cover. But it is obvious in table 1 that there is no clear correlation between thickness of sea ice and chlorophyll concentration; the thickest ice contained both the least and the most chlorophyll. Further, unlike previous experience in Jones Sound, in 1971 there was no obvious correlation between snow depth and chlorophyll concentrations. The work in Jones Sound suggested a direct relation between snow depth and chlorophyll concentration (Apollonio, 1965).

In reporting the chlorophyll values, C. S. Yentsch noted "the acid ratios are high for most samples indicating that very little phaeophytin is present," i.e., that the few plants present appear to be healthy, with very few breakdown derivatives of normal chlorophyll.

The list of cryoflora of Ellesmere Island is given below. Dr. Bursa commented on the results of his identifications: "The algal-sea-ice samples from

Ellesmere Island were very poor. . . . However, these data are of some significance since no records are available from this high region." No discoasters were found in any of the samples.

April 30, Slidre Fiord, Eureka Weather Station.
Ebria tripartita, Navicula sp., *Nitzschia delicatissima,* starch and detritus.

May 7, Slidre Fiord, Eureka Weather Station.
Gyrosigma sp., phytodetritus, starch and oil.

May 10, Nansen Sound.
Navicula frigida, N. latissima.

May 14, Ward Hunt Island.
Amphiprora hyperborea, Chaetoceros certosporum, C. diadema, C. simplex, Euglena sp., *Eutreptia,* sp., *Fragilaria oceanica* f. *circularis, Gymodinium catenatum* v. *simplex, Gyrodinium grenlandicum, Hapterriceros* sp. (a new benthic diatom), *Licmophora* sp., *Navicula vanhoffeni, Nitzschia pungens, N. seriata, Stylodinium* sp., *Synedra* sp., *Thalassiosira gravida, T. nordenskioldi, Thalassiothrix longissima.*

May 14, Ward Hunt Island.
Cyclotella menenighiana, Fragilaria nana, F. oceanica, Gymnodinium sp., *Nitzschia pungens.*

May 15, Ward Hunt Island.
Amphidinium sp, *Chlorella* sp., *Euglena* sp., *Eutreptia* sp., *Fragilaria oceanica, Gymnodinium catenatum* f. *simplex, Nitzchia lineola, Stauroneis grani, N. pungens,* starch.

May 15, Disraeli Fiord.
None.

The samples clearly demonstrate the presence of a relatively abundant (for 1971) ice flora on new ice on the periphery of the Arctic Ocean. The samples taken from the ocean north of Ward Hunt Island were by far the richest of any in the series, but only in a comparative sense.

Traveling and sampling conditions within Disraeli Fiord inside the Ward Hunt Iceshelf, an area of particular interest, were not conducive to extensive sampling in the time available. Entrance into the fiord was difficult because of deep, soft snow which made travel extremely slow and laborious. The surface ice was thick (>2 meters), extremely friable, and difficult to core satisfactorily. The samples taken in "Lake A" and in Disraeli Fiord gave no visual evidence of chlorophyll—nor were ice algae detected in the microscopic examination.

The dissolved organic carbon data (table 1) are of interest if only because there are no other such data from the North American Arctic. The samples all show relatively high values, and bear no obvious relation to the apparent variability of the associated ice flora; the carbon values from Slidre Fiord, where a very poor flora was found, are comparable to the carbon values associated with the relatively abundant ice flora on the periphery of the Arctic Ocean. The values are somewhat higher than the values reported (e.g., Duursma, 1961; Menzel and Ryther, 1970) from surface waters of other oceans but there do not appear to be unusual concentrations of organic carbon in the lower surface of the ice as is the case with inorganic nutrients (phosphates; Apollonio 1965).

The significance of the carbon measurements lay in hypotheses suggesting (1) that micro-algae photosynthesis under low light intensities might be enhanced by the presence of dissolved organic matter and (2) that algae photosynthesizing under low light conditions excrete relatively large amounts of organic matter. The unexceptional quantities found in this work would suggest either

(1) that the hypotheses are not relevant to these Arctic ice plants, or

(2) that the apparent scarcity of ice-flora in 1971 was in fact due to lesser quantities of dissolved organic carbon.

It does not appear possible to choose between these alternatives until additional measurements of organic carbon in sea ice are made for comparison.

Summary and Conclusions

The apparently very abnormal conditions of spring 1971—the poor development of ice flora in Jones Sound and along the west coast of Ellesmere Island—prevented accomplishment of the objectives of this work, or the making of useful inferences or conclusions. Sufficient material simply was not present in the ice. The reason for this dearth of ice flora is not apparent. Neither the thickness of ice nor depth of snow in any of the areas sampled—from Jones Sound to Nansen Sound—appears to be so unusual as to account for the paucity of ice flora.

Nor does it appear likely that the sampling preceded the development of the ice flora: this sampling period was comparable to those of previous years in which abundant flora had been found. Further, the flora must develop in May, prior to the melt of the snow cover in early June, because earlier work (Apollonio, 1961) showed that the ice algae disappear as the snow melts.

One can only conclude, apparently, that there are occasional years when, instead of a proliferation of the abundant ice flora thought to be typical of Arctic sea ice in the spring of the year, there is only a very poor development of the flora—for reasons unknown—and that 1971 was one of those years.

REFERENCES

ANDRIASHEV, ANATOLE P.

1968. The problem of the life community associated with the Antarctic fast ice. Pp. 147-155 *in* "Symposium on Antarctic Oceanography." Scott Polar Research Institute, Cambridge, England.

APOLLONIO, SPENCER

1961. The chlorophyll content of Arctic sea-ice. Arctic, vol. 14, pp. 197-200.

1965. Chlorophyll in Arctic sea ice. Arctic, vol. 18, pp. 118-122.

BUNT, J. S.

1963. Diatoms of Antarctic sea-ice as agents of primary production. Nature, vol. 199, pp. 1255-1257.

1967. Some characteristics of microalgae isolated from Antarctic sea ice, Pp. 1-14 *in* "Biology of the Antarctic Seas III"; George A. Llano and Waldo L. Schmitt, eds. Antarctic Res. Ser., vol. II, 261 pp., illus. American Geophysical Union, Washington.

BURKHOLDER, PAUL R., and MANDELLI, ENRIQUE F.

1965. Productivity of microalgae in Antarctic sea ice. Science, vol. 149, pp. 872-874.

BURSA, A. S.

1965. *Discoasteromonas calciferus* n. sp. an Arctic relict secreting *Discoaster* Tan Sin Hok 1927. Grana Palynologica, vol. 6, pp. 147-165.

DUURSMA, E. K.

1961. Dissolved organic carbon, nitrogen and phosphorus in the sea. Netherlands Journ. Sea Res., vol. 1, no. 1-2, pp. 1-148.

GRAN, H. H.

1904. Diatomaceae from the ice-floes and plankton of the Arctic Ocean. Pp. 1-74 *in* "The Norwegian North Polar Expedition 1893-1896: Scientific Results," vol. 4, illus., Fridtjof Nansen, ed. London.

HATTERSLEY-SMITH, G.; KEYS, J. E.; SERSON, H.; and MIELKE, JAMES E.

1970. Density stratified lakes in northern Ellesmere Island. Nature, vol. 225, pp. 55-56.

IGNATIADES, L., and FOGG, G. E.

1973. Studies on the factors affecting release of organic matter by *Skeletonema costatum* (Greville) Cleve in culture. Journ. Mar. Biol. Assoc. United Kingdom, vol. 53, pp. 937-956.

KEYS, J. E.; JOHANNESSEN, O. M.; and LONG, A.

1969. The oceanography of Disraeli Fiord, northern Ellesmere Islands. Defense Research Board, Department of National Defense, Canada. Ottawa. (Unpublished MS.)

MEGURO, HIROSHI; ITO, KUNIYUKI; and FUKUSHIMA, HIROSHI

1966. Diatoms and the ecological conditions of their growth in sea ice in the Arctic Ocean. Science, vol. 152, pp. 1089-1090.

MENZEL, DAVID W., and RYTHER, JOHN H.
1970. Distribution and cycling of organic matter in the oceans. Pp. 34-54 *in* "Organic Matter in Natural Waters," D. W. Hood, ed. Inst. Mar. Sci. Occ. Publ. 1, xiv + 625 pp. University of Alaska, College, Alaska.

MOHR, JOHN L., and TIBBS, JOHN F.
1963. Ecology of ice substrates. Pp. 245-249 *in* "Proceedings of the Arctic Basin Symposium, October 1962." Arctic Institute of North America, Washington.

SCOTT, ROBERT F.
1905. The voyage of the *Discovery,* 2 vols., 556 pp., 508 pp., illus. London.

STRICKLAND, J. D. H., and PARSONS, TIMOTHY R.
1968. A practical handbook of sea water analysis. Fish. Res. Board Canada Bull. 167, ed. 2, 311 pp.

SUTHERLAND, PETER C.
1852. Journal of a voyage in Baffin's Bay and Barrow Straits, in the years 1850-1851 . . . under the command of Mr. William Penny, in search of the missing crews of H. M. ships *Erebus* and *Terror,* 2 vols., 506 pp., 363 + ccxxxiii pp., illus. London.

YENTSCH, CHARLES S., and MENZEL, DAVID W.
1963. A method for the determination of phytoplankton chlorophyll and phaeophytin by fluorescence. Deep-Sea Res., vol. 10, pp. 221-231.

SPENCER APOLLONIO

Investigation of Submerged Beachrock Deposits off Bimini, Bahamas

Principal Investigator: Mahlon M. Ball, Rosenstiel School of Marine and Atmospheric Science, University of Miami, Miami, Florida.

Grant No. 1008: In support of a study of the late Quaternary geologic history of Bimini through identification, mapping, and analysis of offshore rock formations.

In 1970 and 1971 newspaper and magazine reports appeared concerning the discovery of megalithic "cyclopean" constructions submerged in 5-6 meters of water off the coast of North Bimini, on the northwest edge of the Great Bahama Bank (fig. 1). Variously interpreted as building foundations, roadways, or sea walls, these lines of subrectangular blocks subsequently were revealed to be natural geologic formations (Harrison, 1971), although one of the original discoverers of the blocks continued to support their human origin (Rebikoff, 1972).

It was felt that an extensive survey of the blocks was called for, with the capability of pursuing the problem toward either a geological or archeological solution. The Rosenstiel School of Marine and Atmospheric Science was well suited to undertake such an investigation; it is located just 43 miles west of Bimini, and its personnel includes both carbonate geologists and a marine archeologist.

Fieldwork was undertaken in September and October 1971. In addition to the Society's support, the School of Marine and Atmospheric Science supplied 14 days of ship time aboard RV *Calanus,* a 62-foot, shallow-draft research vessel, commanded at that time by Capt. Sidney G. Hartshorne. Miami-Dade Junior College Marine Science technicians, headed by Stephen Cawthon, assisted in the underwater operations off RV *Calanus,* while Eric Frehsee served as underwater photographer. The Lerner Marine Laboratory (American Museum of Natural History), located on North Bimini, was base of operations for the land survey of the island. Talbot Lindström of SEAS, Inc., gave greatly appreciated assistance in the island survey. Dr. John Hall, Department of Anthropology, University of Miami, provided valuable background and field information concerning the possible archeological aspects of the investigation.

The objective of the first week's fieldwork aboard RV *Calanus* was to survey the submerged blocks north of Paradise Point, North Bimini (station 1, fig. 2) for evidence of their origin. Three major linear features, trending northeast-southwest, were surveyed. The most seaward of the three was found to be the longest, extending (with gaps due to absence of blocks or sand cover) over 800 meters to the northeast. The feature is composed of tabular stone blocks of rectangular to subrectangular outline and measuring up to 3 by 4 meters in horizontal dimensions, although the average size is 2 by 3 meters and many blocks are a meter square or less. Edges of the larger adjacent blocks often show complementary outlines, suggesting that they were once part of a single stratum; the smaller blocks usually did not display complementary edges.

The middle and shoreward linear features are not as long (approximately 50 and 60 meters, respectively) and are composed of smaller blocks 1 by 2 meters across.

Part of the shoreward line of blocks is shown in a photomosaic (fig. 3), which was produced using the techniques described by Green et al. (1971). Although the blocks toward the northeast rest on a flat sand bottom, those to the southwest are buried to varying degrees in the sand. Calcareous algae, sea fans, and sponges coat the exposed surfaces of the blocks. Two distinct rows of blocks are visible in the center of the photomosaic; these merge to the northeast and to the southwest into a single row.

The middle linear feature lies approximately 25 meters northwest of and parallel to the feature shown in figure 3. It is identical in appearance to the shoreward feature.

The following observations were made during our initial field investigation:

1. The three features are unconnected at the southwest end; scattered blocks are present there but do not form a well-defined linear feature connecting the seaward, middle, and shoreward features.
2. No evidence exists anywhere over the three features of two courses of blocks, or even a single block set squarely atop another.
3. Not enough blocks lie in the vicinity of the three features to have formed a now-destroyed second course of blocks.
4. Bedrock closely underlies the entire area of the three features (fig. 5), eliminating the possibility of excavations or channels between them.
5. Indications are that the blocks of the inner and middle features have always rested on a layer of loose sand. No evidence was found of the blocks being cut into or founded on the underlying bedrock surface.

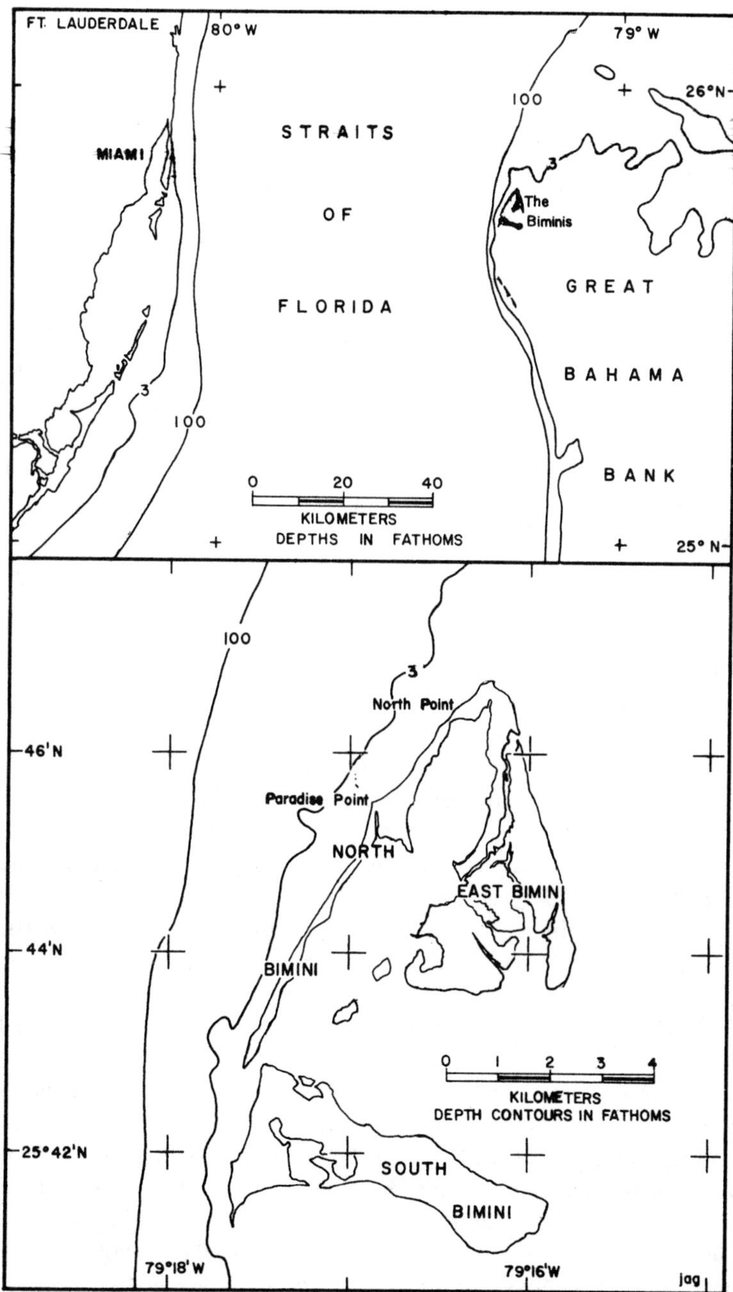

FIG. 1. Index charts of the Bimini Islands. Most of the underwater surveying was done between Paradise Point and North Point, North Bimini.

6. In areas of the seaward feature where blocks rest directly on the bedrock surface, no evidence was found of regular or symmetrical supports beneath any of the blocks.
7. We saw no evidence on any of the blocks of regular or repeated patterns of grooves or depressions that might be interpreted as tool marks.
8. The inner and middle features are continuous only over a distance of about 50 meters. Though the seaward feature extends several hundred meters farther to the northeast, it too is not well founded or continuous enough to have served as some kind of thoroughfare.

In fact, the only attributes of the three linear features that suggest a human origin are the regular shapes of some of the blocks. These are also attributes of natural beachrock deposits.

A geological survey of the island of North Bimini was made during October 1971. In addition, the position and orientation of the beachrock deposits off Paradise Point were determined by surveying from existing Bahamas Geodetic Survey benchmarks on North Bimini (BN2 and BN3, fig. 2). Lastly, a program of sampling the rock units offshore was completed, again aboard RV *Calanus*. Divers used a hydraulic-powered diamond drill to obtain core sections from the beachrock deposits (fig. 4) and from the underlying bedrock (fig. 5). Similar cores were taken at deeper stations offshore (stations 2 and 3, fig. 2).

Petrographic thin sections were made of the rock and core samples to establish the types of rock units present and their original environment of deposition. These units were placed in an absolute time framework by relation to 12 carbon-14-dated samples and one sample dated by a uranium-thorium technique (Th-230/U-234), plus other available dates from Bimini (table 1), thus giving an outline of the geologic history of North Bimini over the past 30,000 years. Specialized studies on the cements of some of the beachrock samples were undertaken by electron microprobe analysis and carbon-oxygen stable isotope ratio analysis; these results are available elsewhere (Gifford, 1973).

Geological investigations in a purely carbonate environment such as the Bahamas are affected by several unique factors. First, on a regional scale, the over-all physiography of the Bahamas: Great and Little Bahama Banks resemble vast, steep-sided plateaus, the tops of which are at present just submerged. The depth of water over the Banks averages 5 meters, which is about 1/200 the average depth of water in the Straits of Florida to the west of the Banks and about 1/1000 of the depth of water in the Blake-Bahama Basin immediately east of the Banks. A good geological description of the Bahamas is given in Newell and Rigby (1957).

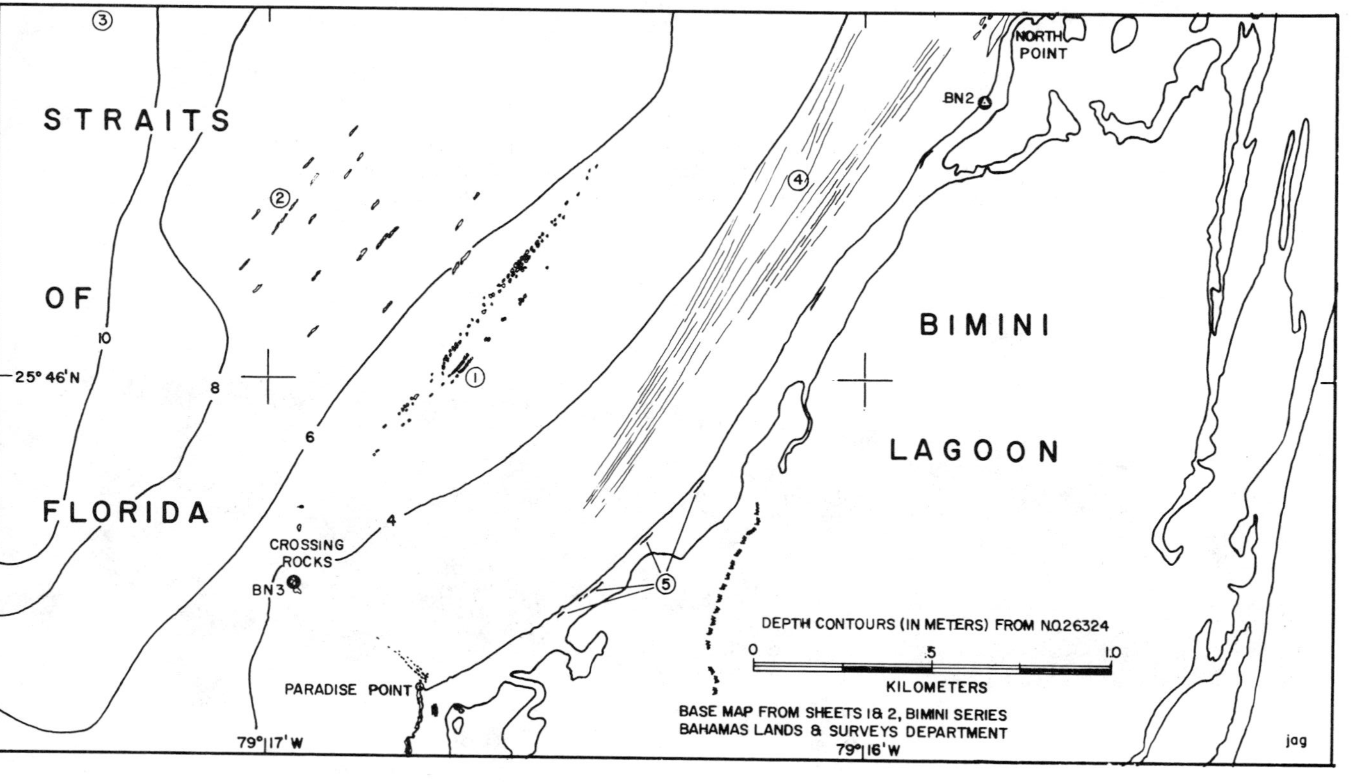

FIG. 2. Geological features off North Bimini between Paradise Point and North Point. Sampling stations (except no. 4) are described in the text.

FIG. 3. Photomosaic showing central portion of inner (shoreward) beachrock deposit located at station 1 (see fig. 2). Water depth 5 meters. The blocks shown in figure 5 are located in the upper left, below the north arrow.

This unique physiography produces unusual conditions for the deposition of sediments. Subtropical Atlantic water flowing along and over the Banks is supersaturated with calcium carbonate. This mineral is removed from the water over the Banks through organic and inorganic processes; it is the continual deposition of calcium carbonate sediment, and its cementation into rock, that account for the growth and form of the Bahama Banks themselves.

The pathway by which organic processes produce carbonate sediment begins with the uptake and inclusion of calcium and carbonate ions into the skeletal framework of corals, bryozoans, Foraminifera, pelecypods, gastropods, and marine plants, predominately species of calcareous algae. After death, the calcium carbonate framework is mechanically broken down and dispersed to form a wide variety of sediment particle sizes, the larger of which retain some attributes such as shape, internal structure, and mineralogy that are diagnostic of their particular organic origin. Since different assemblages of plants and animals living together on the banks are characteristic of different environmental conditions, these environmental differences are reflected in characteristic distributions of grain types in the sediments produced in each depositional environment (Purdy, 1963a, 1963b).

Purely inorganic deposition of calcium carbonate also will reflect environmental conditions, as the water chemistry changes that trigger this deposition usually are associated with the high turbulence and energy around the margins of the Bahama Banks. The oolitic sediment particles so produced are thus, like the organically produced sediment particles, diagnostic of their depositional environment.

On a much larger scale, carbonate sediments of both organic and inorganic origin accumulate to form sediment bodies with characteristic attributes such as location (with respect to the banks), geometry, internal structure, composition, and texture (Ball, 1967). Recognition of these types of sand bodies after they have lithified into rock units is facilitated in the Bahamas, thanks to the absence of major tectonic activity over at least the past several million years. Two of the sand-body attributes, location and geometry, may be recognized on charts and aerial photos, while others (internal structure, composition, and texture) must be studied in the field.

Because of the general physiography of the Bahama Banks, and the role of marine organic and inorganic processes in the formation of carbonate sediments thereon, one more important factor figures in the geologic history of the area. The composition of sediment in a given part of the Banks, and the type of sediment body formed, are greatly affected by the position of sea level.

If sea level were 10 meters higher, much of the area of the present Bahama Islands would be submerged and the average depth over the Banks would increase to 15 meters, greatly affecting hydrologic conditions and sediment distribution patterns. If sea level fell 10 meters, many thousands of square

FIG. 4. Station 1, looking northeast. This is the same portion of the shoreward beachrock deposit illustrated in the photomosaic. Divers are using a hydraulic-powered diamond drill to core into the blocks. Photo by J. Gifford.

kilometers of the banks would be exposed, ending the production of sediment by marine plants and animals. Loose sediment over the dry plateaus would be

FIG. 5. Station 1, looking southwestward along the shoreward beachrock deposit. Loose sand has been airlifted away, showing how the blocks are separated from the underlying bedrock by loose sand and shells. The bedrock is pocketed with solution holes (the hole at lower center is about 0.5 meter in diameter) and coated with a subaerial crust. An edge of the beachrock block at right has been removed with a carbide saw to study its structures. Photo by J. Gifford.

swept by prevailing winds into dunes, which would be themselves a characteristic type of sediment body recording subaerial, rather than submarine, conditions. With sufficient time, colonization of the exposed plateaus would produce a soil cover. This would affect the chemistry of the underlying carbonate sediment, causing it to lithify and forming a characteristic crust over the rock (Multer and Hoffmeister, 1968). A subsequent rise of sea level would reflood the platform, ending subaerial sediment processes and reinstating sediment deposition by marine organic and inorganic processes.

Worldwide oscillations of sea level with amplitudes approaching 200 meters did occur over the past several million years and they did influence the production and deposition of carbonate sediments on the Bahama Banks. Over the past 35,000 years (Milliman and Emery, 1968) sea level fell to a low at least 100 meters below its present position at about 15,000 years B.P.

With the preceding background information concerning depositional processes and environments on the Bahama Banks, we now can examine in greater detail the results of the present investigation in the Bimini area.

The oldest unit exposed in the area of North Bimini (at station 5, fig. 2) has all the characteristics of a once-submerged marine sand belt; it probably underlies the length of North Bimini and the west coast of South Bimini. A C-14 date of >29,000 years for this unit comes from the shell of a perfectly preserved horse conch (sample 7113A, table 1) that browsed on the bar some 35,000 years ago (fig. 6).

As sea level fell, between 30,000 and 35,000 years B.P. (fig. 6), the marine sand belt was exposed as a narrow sand island along the west coast of which a beach-dune complex formed (sample LL01-1, table 1). At approximately the same time a protected lagoonal environment existed east of the island, in the area of the present Bimini Lagoon and South Bimini (sample L321B, table 1).

During the period of several thousand years when sea level was at least 100 meters below its present position, dunes exposed on the outer platform to the west of the then-dry marine sand belt were cemented into rock ridges. An outcrop of this dune deposit at the south end of North Bimini has been dated to 13,200 years B.P. (sample L-321D, table 1). The deposit's distribution in the Paradise Point-North Point area is limited to Crossing Rocks, the three small islands north of Paradise Point. Soil processes over all the platform acted to partly dissolve the various rock units, producing a hard, pot-holed surface coated with a dense red-brown crust. This surface constitutes the bedrock underlying the beachrock deposits off Paradise Point (fig. 5). A uranium-thorium date for this crust is approximately 15,000 years B.P. (sample 7132-19/2, table 1).

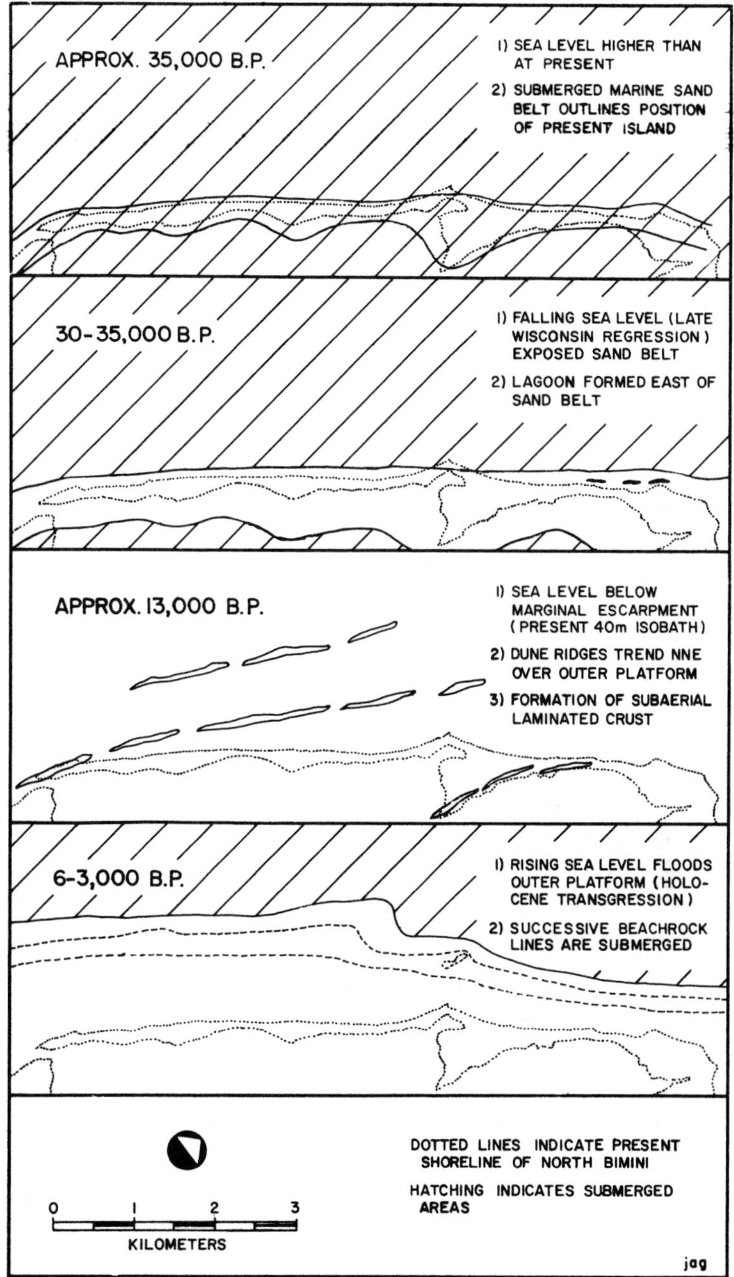

FIG. 6. A summary of the late Quaternary geologic history of North Bimini. See text for discussion.

TABLE 1. Absolute Dating of Carbonate Samples from Bimini

Sample	*Material/Preservation*	*Elevation (m ± ms1)*	*Age (Method)*[a]	*Reference*[b]
712E	Oolitic whole rock, dredged from South Bimini	–2(?)	155,000 (UTh)	LGO; Broecker and Thurber, 1965
7113A	*Fasciolaria gigantica* from intertidal marine limestone north of Paradise Point; excellent preservation	0	>29,000 (C14)	Geochron, this study
L-366H	Calcarenite whole rock, Till Hotel, North Bimini	+.5	>27,000 (C14)	LGO; Newell et al., 1959, p. 194
L-321B	*Glycimeris pectinata* from north shore of South Bimini	+1(?)	>27,000 (C14)	LGO; Newell et al., 1959, p. 194
LL01-1	Whole rock, dune ridge off North Point, North Bimini; some recrystallization	+.5	26,000±5000 (C14)	Geochron; this study
7132-19/2	Whole rock marine limestone under beachrock off Paradise Point, North Bimini; some recrystallization	–5.5	14,992±585 (UTh)	RSMAS; this study
L-321D	Oolitic eolianite, whole rock, Till Hotel, North Bimini	+2.5	13,200±400 (C14)	LGO; Newell et al., 1959, p. 194
7132-21/1	Whole rock beachrock from station no. 2, fig. 2; some recrystallization	–7	6830±250 (C14)	Geochron; this study

32-19 1/1D	Whole rock beachrock from shoreward deposit north of Paradise Point, North Bimini	–4.5	2525±160 (C14)	Geochron; this study
35-16 1/1B	Whole rock beachrock from seaward deposit north of Paradise Point, North Bimini; some recrystallization	–5	3210±150 (C14)	Geochron; this study
LL01-8	Whole rock beachrock from present intertidal zone, west coast of south Bimini; well cemented	–1.5	2290±135 (C14)	Geochron; this study
7132-19/7	*Anodontia alba* shells from fine-grained sediment under beachrock north of Paradise Point, North Bimini; excellent preservation	–5	3975±170 (C14)	Geochron; this study
L-366B	Peat sample overlying bed-rock, Lyon's channel, Bimini Lagoon	–3	4370±110 (C14)	LGO; Newell et al., 1959, p. 193
L-321A	Shell material from sea cliff along west coast of North Bimini	+2	2300±200 (C14)	LGO; Broecker and Kulp, 1957, p. 1328
"unit A"	Unidentified mollusk shells from sea cliff along west coast of North Bimini at Lerner Marine Laboratory	+1.5	1775±170 (C14)	Hannover; Müller, 1970

TABLE 1. Absolute Dating of Carbonate Samples from Bimini—Continued

Sample	*Material/Preservation*	*Elevation ($m \pm msl$)*	*Age (Method)*[a]	*Reference*[b]
"unit B"	Whole rock (calcarenite) from sea cliff along west coast of North Bimini at Lerner Marine Laboratory	+2	1818±80 (C14)	Hannover; Muller, 1970
ML573	Unidentified mollusk shells from shell bed in sea cliff along west coast of North Bimini, south of Lerner Marine Laboratory	+2	2300±90 (C14)	RSMAS; C. Neumann, unpublished
ML575	Whole rock calcarenite from sea cliff along west coast of North Bimini, south of Lerner Marine Laboratory	+2	1390±85 (C14)	RSMAS; Neumann, unpublished

[a] Geochron dates are based on the Libby half life (5,570 years) for C-14; age is referenced to the year A.D. 1950.

[b] Dating laboratories:

LGO=Lamont Geological Observatory, Palisades, New York.
Geochron=Krueger Enterprises, Inc., Cambridge, Massachusetts.
RSMAS=Rosenstiel School of Marine and Atmospheric Science, University of Miami, Florida.
Hannover=14C und 3H Laboratorium, Niedersächsisches Amt für Bodenforschung, Hannover, B.R.D.

The rise of sea level from 15,000 years B.P. to the present produced a succession of beaches that formed on the outer platform off the west coast of North Bimini as the shoreline transgressed eastward over the Great Bahama Bank. Along these transient beaches, deposits of beachrock formed and subsequently were submerged as the water over them deepened. The farthest offshore deposit located in this investigation is presently at a depth of 8 meters, 2 kilometers north-northwest of Paradise Point (station 2, fig. 2). The morphology of this deposit differs from that of the deposits farther inshore; these deeper-water deposits consist of thin ledges that overlap in shingle-fashion, suggesting that the beach at that time (sample 7132-21/1, table 1) was wide and low-angled.

Several thousand years later the shoreline migrated to a position approximately 1 kilometer north of the present Paradise Point. Here, over a period of perhaps 700 years, three successive beaches were the site of formation of three parallel, linear deposits of beachrock.

As most authoritatively defined, beachrock "refers to sediment lithified in the intertidal and sea spray zones, whether on high or low energy beaches, or even broad tidal flats and tidal channels" (Bricker, 1971, p. 1). Lithification occurs at some depth below the surface of the unconsolidated beach, which then may be eroded away by shoreline retreat or sea level rise, leaving exposed strata of beachrock in the intertidal or nearshore zones.

Beachrock is presently exposed in the modern intertidal zone along the west coast of South Bimini and of North Bimini; evidently it is forming there at a rate to be measured in decades or even years (Scoffin, 1970).

As mentioned previously, the only characteristic of the submerged blocks off Paradise Point that might continue to suggest their human origin is the shape of the blocks themselves. The modern beachrock deposit along the west coast of South Bimini illustrates the stages that lead to the formation of such regularly-shaped blocks. Part of the deposit has been cracked by a pattern of right-angle joints running parallel and perpendicular to the long axis of the deposit. At some points wave action has undercut and removed individual rectangular blocks from the jointed deposit, carrying them just offshore into 1-2 meters of water to form a jumbled pile of what appear to be quarried blocks averaging 1 by 1 by 0.5 meters. Had the joint pattern been more widely spaced, individual blocks would be comparable in size to those off Paradise Point.

Rectangular joint patterns have been described and illustrated in beachrock from Puerto Rico (Kaye, 1959) and Barbados (McLean, 1964). No single explanation for the development of these reticulate joint patterns has been accepted, but possible mechanisms (McLean, 1964, pp. 73-74) include: (1)

spalling of blocks due to thermal stresses within sun-heated beachrock coming into contact with cooler sea water on a rising tide; (2) hydraulic plucking of blocks by storm waves; (3) collapse of a slightly convex-upward stratum of beachrock by removal of unconsolidated sediment beneath it; and (4) the downward decrease in induration of beachrock strata within a single deposit may produce some anisotropic stress fabric.

The beaches that formed as sea level rose over the outer platform acted as barriers and allowed lagoonal conditions to develop between themselves and the emergent lithified sand belt underlying the present island of North Bimini. A characteristic of such back-beach lagoons is the presence of fine-grained carbonate sediment and a rich fauna of pelecypods and gastropods. As sea level continued to rise and the beach zone migrated eastward, this lagoonal sediment sometimes was buried under newly formed beachrock and thus preserved from destruction by waves and currents in the high-energy nearshore zone.

Such a relict lagoonal deposit was discovered under the blocks of the middle beachrock deposit off Paradise Point. The fauna removed from this muddy sediment correlates with pelecypods and gastropods characteristic of the present-day Bimini Lagoon (Newell et al., 1959, p. 222). Articulated shells of the pelecypod *Anodontia alba* from this sediment provided a reliable C-14 date of 3,975 years B.P. (sample 7132-19/7, table 1). Further evidence of these transitory lagoonal conditions is given by Newell's date of 4,370 years B.P. (sample L-366B, table 1) on a peat sample presently submerged at a depth of 3 meters in the boat channel just east of North Bimini.

Most recently, a well-stratified coarse carbonate sand ridge has formed along the extreme west side of North Bimini from Paradise Point to the southern tip of the island. The present beach along this stretch of coast is backed by the eroding scarp of this poorly cemented rock ridge, which varies in height above mean sea level from 2 meters at the Lerner Marine Laboratory to almost 3 meters at Paradise Point. Several C-14 dates give an age of approximately 2,000 years B.P. for this ridge.

The origin of the ridge is uncertain. It may be a very recently cemented dune that formed just before sea level reached its present position (Müller, 1970), or it may represent a beach deposit formed when sea level had reached its present position, but in an unstable period of higher nearshore energy conditions that has since ended (Neumann, unpublished).

The islands of Bimini are today far from a state of even short-term geologic equilibrium. Wave and current patterns are funneling sand from the outer platform southeastward along the east coast of the low, mangrove-covered island of East Bimini, producing an accretionary spit (Ball, 1967). The southeastward growth of this spit is constricting the wide, shallow eastern opening of Bimini Lagoon, which will affect hydrologic conditions within that body of water. Mangrove growth along the west shore of East Bimini and the north shore of South Bimini is further changing the shape of Bimini Lagoon. The west coasts of North and South Bimini, fully exposed to the winds and waves from the Straits of Florida, are undergoing rapid erosion. A break at the narrowest part of North Bimini, just south of North Point, very likely may occur in the immediate future.

Perhaps the most unique and important characteristic of the geology of Bimini (and the Bahamas in general) is its sensitivity and ability to record environmental fluctuations. Much more information concerning fluctuations of the Quaternary environment of the Bahamas is undoubtedly contained in these carbonate rocks.

REFERENCES

BALL, MAHLON M.
1967. Carbonate sand bodies of Florida and the Bahamas. Journ. Sed. Petrol., vol. 37, pp. 556-591.

BRICKER, OWEN P., editor
1971. Carbonate cements, 376 pp. Johns Hopkins Press, Baltimore.

BROECKER, WALLACE S., and KULP, J. LAURENCE
1957. Lamont natural radiocarbon measurements IV. Science, vol. 126, pp. 1324-1334.

BROECKER, WALLACE S., and THURBER, DAVID L.
1965. Uranium-series dating of corals and oolites from Bahaman and Florida Key limestones. Science, vol. 149, pp. 58-60.

GIFFORD, JOHN A.
1973. A description of the Bimini Islands, Bahamas. Unpublished doctoral thesis, University of Miami.

GREEN, JEREMY N., et al.
1971. Simple underwater photogrammetric techniques. Archaeometry, vol. 13, pp. 221-232.

HARRISON, WYMAN
1971. Atlantis undiscovered—Bimini, Bahamas. Nature, vol. 230, pp. 287-289.

KAYE, CHARLES A.
1959. Shoreline features and Quaternary shoreline changes, Puerto Rico. U. S. Geol. Surv. Prof. Pap. 317-B, pp. 49-140.

MCLEAN, ROGER F.
1964. A regional study of the distribution, forms, processes and rates of mechanical and biological erosion of a carbonate clastic rock in the littoral zone. Unpublished dissertation, McGill University.

MILLIMAN, JOHN D., and EMERY, KENNETH O.
1968. Sea levels during the past 35,000 years. Science, vol. 162, pp. 1121-1123.

MÜLLER, GERMAN

1970. Petrology of the Cliff Limestone (Holocene), North Bimini, Bahamas. Neues Jahrb. für Min., 1970, pp. 507-523.

MULTER, H. GRAY, and HOFFMEISTER, JOHN E.

1968. Subaerial laminated crusts of the Florida Keys. Bull. Geol. Soc. America, vol. 79, pp. 183-192.

NEWELL, NORMAN D., et al.

1959. Organism communities and bottom facies, Great Bahama Bank. Bull. Amer. Mus. Nat. Hist., vol. 117, pp. 177-228.

NEWELL, NORMAN D., and RIGBY, J. KEITH

1957. Geological studies on the Great Bahama Bank. Pp. 15-69 *in* "Regional Aspects of Carbonate Deposition," Soc. Econ. Pal. and Min., Spec. Publ. no. 5, 178 pp.

PURDY, EDWARD G.

1963a. Recent calcium carbonate facies of the Great Bahama Bank, I: Petrology and reaction groups. Journ. Geol., vol. 71, pp. 334-355.

1963b. Recent calcium carbonate facies of the Great Bahama Bank, II: Sediment facies. Journ. Geol., vol. 71, pp. 472-497.

REBIKOFF, DIMITRI

1972. Precision underwater photomosaic technique for archaeological mapping. Interim experiment on the Bimini "cyclopean" complex. Int. Journ. Naut. Archaeol. and Underwater Expl., vol. 1, pp. 184-186.

SCOFFIN, TERRANCE P.

1970. A conglomeratic beachrock in Bimini, Bahamas. Journ. Sed. Petrol., vol. 40, pp. 756-759.

JOHN A. GIFFORD
MAHLON M. BALL

Progress of Plant Successions on Soufrière Volcano, St. Vincent Island, West Indies, 1972

Principal Investigator: John Stanley Beard, Royal Botanic Gardens and National Herbarium, Sydney, Australia.

Grant No. 991: For a study of plant succession on the Soufrière Volcano of St. Vincent.[1]

In 1945 I published in the *Journal of Ecology* the results of observations of the vegetation of the Soufrière Volcano of the West Indian Island of St. Vincent made in 1942 (Beard, 1945). Together with a previous account by W. N. Sands (1912) of the situation during the first decade after the eruptions of 1902, a record was provided of 40 years of progress in plant succession upon the devastated area leading back to the plant cover of the mountain prior to 1902, as briefly described by Hooper in 1886. Early in 1972 I had the opportunity for another visit to study progress over a further 30 years during which the mountain had been quiescent, and these observations are now reported in the present paper (further information is contained in Beard, 1976).

The 1945 paper described the physical and climatic features of St. Vincent and its principal vegetation types, as well as giving a detailed account of the plant cover of the Soufrière mountain, so that it is unnecessary to repeat these. Additional information on the vegetation of the island is to be found in Beard (1949). From 1942 to 1971 the volcano continued to be dormant so that plant succession on the upper slopes continued unimpeded. Below about 300 meters above sea level the slopes were subject to shifting cultivation; above that level there was no human interference. Bush fires do not occur there. In October 1971, however, just as I was planning to visit the island, the volcano went into a minor state of eruption. The lake in the crater, with a water depth of 100 meters, was observed to have risen in temperature and to be giving off vapor. Later its level rose, and in November a mass of lava began to appear, forming an island in the center. By January 1972 this formed a steaming pile projecting some 60 meters above water level, which had begun to drop again. The lake water was hot, but not boiling, and was heavily

[1] Grateful acknowledgment is made to the National Geographic Society for the grant that made this study possible. I am grateful also for the assistance I received while on the island from officers of the St. Vincent Department of Agriculture, especially C. N. de Freitas, acting superintendent of agriculture.

yellow-stained by sulphur. At the time of my ascent of the mountain on January 20 the volcano was technically in eruption but nothing more drastic had occurred, and there had been no damage to vegetation except inside the crater where actually inundated by the rise of the lake. It was apparent from the smell that sulphur-dioxide fumes were being emitted, but no observable damage to vegetation had occurred. Plant succession as observed at that date, therefore, had not been affected by this latest eruptive phase.

On January 20 I ascended the mountain on the windward side, up to a height of 290 meters by Land-Rover, thereafter on foot up to the crater rim at 880 meters, traversing around the rim on the south side and descending by the path to leeward down to sea level. It will be understood that owing to the constancy of the trade wind in this latitude it is customary in the islands to speak of the east coast as being to windward and the west coast as being to leeward. Certain differences in the vegetation between windward and leeward slopes are due to aspect, the windward side being more exposed to strong winds and more cloudy, with higher rainfall and humidity and less sunshine. My observations of 1942 were based on the windward side and summit of the Soufrière, whereas Sands (1912) spoke mainly of the leeward side.

Along the track up the windward side, coconut plantations have been established up to the 300-meter contour, above which and up to 425 meters is a zone devoted to shifting cultivation. The vegetation of this is naturally very mixed and patchy with areas of secondary tree species, fruit trees, shrubs, and abandoned gardens. The matrix is a secondary forest of *Inga ingoides, Freziera hirsuta, Cecropia peltata, Ochroma pyramidale, Sapium caribaeum,* and *Ficus* spp., the last often very large and spreading. Most of the large trees of any species have *Clusia alba* established on them. Fruit trees, planted by the cultivators, include the coconut, breadfruit, avocado, and mango, some already 15 meters in height.

Above the last of the gardens the forest is unbroken and of the same composition as listed above. *Freziera hirsuta* is the dominant species, associated mainly with *Inga* and *Cecropia.* At this level there was forest of just this same composition 30 years before, and it was evident that the same individual trees were still present. Pioneer species in the Tropics are expected to be short-lived, especially *Cecropia,* yet here was evidence to the contrary. The stand appeared to have thinned itself out somewhat by death of individuals, and those that remained were little taller, somewhat stouter in girth, and more loaded with epiphytes than before. A significant change, however, could be noted in the understory, which now contains large numbers of young palms, *Prestoea montana,* in lieu of the previous tree ferns most of which have died and disappeared. In 1942 only a few of these palms were noted higher up at the 570-

meter level, whereas today they are generally abundant between the 450- and 600-meter contours, and the stage is set for the establishment of the palm-dominated community called "hurricane forest" (Beard, 1945) or "palm brake" (Beard, 1949), which is characteristic of the steeper mountain slopes elsewhere in the island. The fact that some of the larger palms are just beginning to bear fruit will no doubt further accelerate their colonization. Hitherto fruits have presumably been conveyed to the Soufrière from elsewhere on the island in the gut of birds or bats. The ripe fruit is spherical, half an inch in diameter, and has a succulent thin outer rind. No sign of the associate *Richeria grandis,* which normally accompanies *Prestoea montana* elsewhere, was detected. The tree ferns, mostly *Cyathea arborea,* which formed much of the understory in 1942, have evidently died out and disappeared. This actually is a case of a short-lived pioneer. The tree ferns often form a brief pioneer community on abandoned peasants' gardens.

In 1942 the upper limit of this community was at about 570 meters; in 1972 it had advanced to 600 meters. At this level, approximately, the dense woody growth, which has lowered progressively to some 4 meters in height, becomes confined, in general, to the ridges, the slopes and gullies being densely covered with masses of the sprawling fern *Gleichenia* (probably *G. bifida*). In 1942 these fern patches also contained considerable numbers of tree ferns, *Cyathea,* but as at other levels on the mountain the latter have declined. The woody thickets are composed of *Freziera hirsuta* and *Charianthus coccineus,* the latter a melastome with attractive red flowers. The fruit, borne in profusion, is a dark-blue succulent berry obviously very attractive to fruit-eating birds or bats, a fact that would appear to explain its rapid colonization of the upper slopes of the mountain. *Prestoea montana* is present up to the 650-meter level, above which the ground is covered in irregular patches about 50 percent by *Gleichenia* and 50 percent by *Freziera* and *Charianthus,* about 1.5 meters in height, and with associated ground-level plants including the bromeliad *Pitcairnia sulphurea,* another rosette plant *Lobelia cirsiifolia,* the so-called Soufrière grass *Lycopodium cernuum,* a true grass *Ischaemum* sp., a sedge *Claudium restioides,* very numerous fern species, especially *Lomaria procera* and *Aspidium trifoliatum,* a very few *Cyathea* tree ferns, and some woody plants including *Calolisianthus frigidus* and *Hillia parasitica.*

At 750 meters *Gleichenia* begins to yield dominance, in the open patches, to *Pitcairnia,* with *Lycopodium, Lobelia,* grass, and ferns. Patches of bush comprise *Charianthus* and *Cyathea* with several other smaller melastomes—*Sauvagesia erecta, Tibouchina cistoides*—and gesneriads, e.g., *Besleria lutea.* The *Pitcairnia* community continues right up to the crater rim at 880 meters with scattered small plants of the woody species just mentioned.

It is at this highest level that the greatest change since 1942 has occurred. At that time above 800 meters the ground cover consisted almost entirely of lichens, *Usnea* and *Cladonia,* either gray or orange, with only a few small scattered plants of *Pitcairnia* and *Lobelia.* In 1972 the lichens had been overgrown by the phanerogams, still existing in the spaces between them but dominated and no longer conspicuous. The only section where the lichens are still dominant appeared to be on a small portion of the crater rim on both the inner and outer slopes on the west side where the footpath descends to leeward.

There has also been a major change on the inside slopes of the crater. In 1942 there was a small woody shrub species, *Baccharis cotinifolia,* plus ferns and grasses. In 1972 large numbers of *Charianthus* and *Freziera* were seen to have added themselves to the assemblage, in places almost forming closed thickets. *Baccharis* is still present but is inconspicuous.

The footpath across the mountain follows the crater rim, undulating up and down with it, around the south side of the crater until on the southwest side at a height of 835 meters it follows a long bare ridge to the south and southwest and then descends. The leeward side of the mountain gives the impression of being drier than the windward side. Much of the vegetation looks drier and is more open, with succession not as far advanced, but it is possible that the substratum is at least partly responsible for this. Possibly the coarser ejecta were deposited on this side during the last eruption, as it is true that the ground seems to consist of coarse volcanic cinders and there has not been the same formation of soil as on the windward side. In 1912 Sands observed that the mountain was more completely covered with vegetation on the windward than on the leeward side.

It will make for easier comparisons if the observations made along the track to leeward are recorded from the bottom up as in Sands's account of this side and my descriptions of the windward side.

To leeward there is not the gently sloping apron running up to the 300-meter altitude that has enabled estate plantations to be re-established. The ground at the foot on the leeward side is very broken and dissected and is largely devoted to shifting cultivation up to the 450-meter level. The general condition is much as on the windward side, with patches of regrowth in all stages, fruit trees and patches of woodland in which *Inga ingoides* is dominant. Species not seen to windward include *Ormosia monosperma, Andira inermis,* and *Lonchocarpus benthamianus. Sapium caribaeum* is more common than to windward. Above the peasants' gardens there is a forest zone up to the 600-meter level, similar to that to windward, with *Freziera, Inga, Cecropia, Ficus,* and *Sapium,* but in 1972 there seemed to be virtually no invasion by *Prestoea montana,* of which very few were seen. Up to this point it is apparent that the forest has re-established itself where the recent volcanic deposits had been washed away, were only a thin veneer over old soil, or consisted of fine material.

At the 600-meter level there is a rather abrupt change to a substrate of coarse, unweathered volcanic cinders that continues to the summit. This is accompanied by a radical change in vegetation, from the *Freziera-Inga-Cecropia* forest through a narrow band of *Freziera-Charianthus* woodland to the low *Pitcairnia* community. All the ridges on the south and west side of the mountain above this level are covered with *Pitcairnia.* On exposed crests and eastward-facing slopes it has only a few herbaceous associates such as the *Lobelia, Lycopodium,* ferns, and lichens. On west-facing slopes there are in addition scattered shrubs of *Freziera* and *Charianthus* up to 2.5 meters tall, with *Baccharis, Gleichenia, Ischaemum,* and a small *Cassia, C. schwarzii,* which is rather common. The gullies are full of tree ferns.

Discussion

Rather less change in the vegetation over a time span of 30 years was observed than had been expected. Nonetheless, significant alterations have taken place. Vegetation zones have risen upward on the mountain and there is some species change in progress. The basal secondary forest of *Freziera, Inga,* and *Cecropia* has risen vertically by 30 meters and on the windward side is being invaded by *Prestoea montana,* which if there is no further destructive eruption will be dominant by the end of the century. The next succeeding zone of *Freziera* and *Charianthus* extended to windward from 570 to 720 meters in 1942 and had risen to 600-750 meters in 1972, the shrubs having become at the same time taller and spread to occupy more of the ground at the expense of patches of *Gleichenia.* The third zone, of *Pitcairnia* and its associates, has risen from 720-820 meters in 1942 to 750-880 meters plus, right to the top, with the virtual extinction of the former fourth zone of lichen, which was there above 600 meters in 1912 and above 820 meters in 1942. The *Freziera–Charianthus* community has colonized the inside walls of the crater. At first sight it may appear insignificant that a vegetation zone should have moved upward 30 meters in as many years, but the distance along the ground would be about three times as much as this and amount to 3 meters per year, which is by no means inconsiderable.

In time, if there is no destructive eruption, "palm brake" of *Prestoea montana* may be expected to occupy almost all the uncultivated mountain slopes above 450 meters with the exception of the highest ridges above 800 meters, where we may expect an "elfin woodland" to develop similar to that of the highest ridges elsewhere in the island. For this to be effected, arrival of species will be required of which so far there is little or no sign. *Charianthus coccineus* and *Freziera hirsuta* are members of the climax community, but we need in addition *Didymopanax attenuatum, Weinmannia pinnata, Ilex sideroxyloides, Rondeletia stereocarpa,* and *Graffenrieda latifolia.* In 1972 I found one plant of *Weinmannia pinnata,* small and prostrate, on the crater rim. None of the others has so far been observed on the Soufrière.

At this time, 70 years after the last major eruption, it is of interest to examine again Hooper's account of the vegetation in 1886. As that was 74 years after the eruption in 1812 it might now be expected that the condition of the plant cover of the mountain might be very similar. Hooper's description, unfortunately, was very brief, as follows:

> There remains to refer to the flora of the Main Ridge summit. This is met with above Cavaleries, on St. Andrew's mountain, and is continued for the last 500 ft. to the top. The same plants are to be found at a similar elevation on the slopes of the Soufrière and comprise comparatively few species—none of them attaining any important or useful dimensions. It will be sufficient to quote the Weinmannia, the Mountain Cabbage, Sauvagesia, Desmodium, Charianthus, Lisianthus, and a dense damp fern growth. A gregarious slender stemmed tree known as the Burnlime is found on the Soufrière below the influence of the sulphurous atmosphere, but already on a soil formed by the eruptions of the crater, higher up the vegetation is reduced to a series of woody dead stems up to 1 ft. in girth, killed some years ago by the exhalations from the mountain, and everywhere a carpet of the Weinmannia, an Iris and a few aroid growths.

The "Burnlime" tree (corruption of "bird lime") is *Sapium caribaeum,* which is sparingly present on the Soufrière today, mainly to leeward, and is certainly not gregarious. The dead vegetation at the higher levels appears to have resulted from some sort of minor eruption in the year 1880. The writer is indebted to Dr. Haraldur Sigurdsson for drawing attention to a report in Anderson and Flett (1902) which states that vegetation in and round the crater was destroyed in 1880 "it is supposed by volumes of gas, which have rolled around the crater and overlapping its edge have rolled some way down the leeward side of the mountain and there, likewise, destroyed the vegetation." Dr. Sigurdsson (pers. comm.) has advanced the alternative explanation that the crater lake boiled in 1880, perhaps spilling over the sides, scorching vegetation inside and outside the crater.

It remains difficult to reconcile the relatively large size of the dead stems reported by Hooper (up to a foot in girth) with those found on the upper levels of the Soufrière today where woody plants are no more than a few small bushes. It seems necessary to argue that the 1812 eruption was not as destructive as that of 1902 and did not leave the slopes covered with a thick layer of fresh ejecta. If so, regrowth of the elfin woodland on original soil would have been rapid and able to attain its original dimensions within a few decades. Then the disturbance of 1880 again killed the top growth, and was followed by regeneration. If *Weinmannia* was a major constitutent of the assemblage prior to 1812, it could also have been a leading coloniser after the 1812 eruption and the mortality in 1880. This seems the only way to account for Hooper's "carpet" of *Weinmannia*. Being normally a tree, this species would only form a carpet in an early stage of regeneration. The writer found only one prostrate plant of it in 1972.

Some information on the 1812 eruption is to be found in Musgrave (1891) as follows:

> So recently as 1812 the "Soufrière," a mountain at the north end of the island, 4048 feet high, broke out in eruption and overwhelmed much of the surrounding country with scoria and ashes; a deep crater was then formed, closely adjoining one of still larger dimensions, the result of an eruption at a period more remote. At the bottom of the older crater, some 1600 feet down, is a small lake about a mile in diameter. The water appears impregnated with sulphur and occasionally emits offensive though invisible fumes . . .
>
> The windward slopes of the Soufrière range are drained by a channel called the Dry River . . . Before the eruption of the Soufrière in 1812, a stream of average size filled this, now dry, watercourse, and emptied itself into the sea. During the eruption, the channel of the stream was completely filled and choked with scoria, rocks and gravel.

It is interesting to note from this that the 1812 eruption did not take place through the main crater whereas those of 1902 and 1971 did so. The 1812 crater, of which the outlines are still visible, is very much smaller than the main crater, yet close to it, almost adjacent. In spite of what is said by Musgrave about the Dry River, and the fact that the 1812 eruption caused a rain of dust in Barbados, 100 miles away, it seems impossible that the outbreak in 1812 was anything like as destructive on the mountain itself as that of 1902, or it would surely have broken out of the main crater.

It is clear that plant succession on these volcanoes following eruptions is strongly affected by the nature and quantity of ejecta deposited on the slopes. Burning of the plant growth without deposit of ejecta would have the same effect as a forest fire and would be followed by rapid regeneration through only brief successional stages to the original climax. The more the soil is disturbed either by shifting cultivators and the deposit of volcanic ash upon it, the more succession is distorted and delayed. On the Soufrière it is difficult to separate possible effects of altitude and exposure from effects of soil. Colonization and succession have been much slower on the upper part of the mountain, but then it is precisely here that the thickest deposits of new and coarse textured volcanic material were deposited. Where erosion exposed old soil, or the latter was only thinly veneered by recent ejecta, re-establishment of a forest cover has been rapid, but on thick layers of coarse cinders it is taking a long time. For 40 years after the 1902 eruption these were colonized by little more than mosses and lichens. In a further 30 years they have been covered by *Pitcairnia spicata,* a plant of wide tolerance seen on outcrops of rock at any level of altitude in the island. In sheltered places shrubs are now beginning to move in.

Colonization under these conditions is affected also by the ease of transport of propagules from elsewhere in the island, and this would be a rewarding subject for study in itself. It would require a student able to spend periods in the field at successive times of the year in order to cover the flowering and fruiting times of all species and to observe the nature of the seed and its mode of dispersal in each case. On casual observation, those species that have most quickly colonized the Soufrière have been bryophytes and ferns, whose spores are presumably disseminated by wind, and seed plants having succulent fruits and seeds attractive to fruit-eating birds and bats.

REFERENCES

ANDERSON, T. and FLETT, J. S.

1902. Preliminary report on the recent eruption of the Soufrière in St. Vincent, and on a visit to Mt. Pelee in Martinique. Proc. Roy. Soc., vol. 70, pp. 353-548.

BEARD, JOHN S.

1945. The progress of plant succession on the Soufrière of St. Vincent. Journ. Ecol., vol. 33, pp. 1-9.

1949. The natural vegetation of the Windward and Leeward Islands. Oxford Forestry Memoirs 21, 192 pp. Clarendon Press.

1976. The progress of plant succession on the Soufrière of St. Vincent: Observations in 1972. Vegetatio, vol. 31, no. 2, pp. 69-77.

HOOPER, E. D. M.

1886. Report upon the forests of St. Vincent, 13 pp. Waterlow, London.

MUSGRAVE, T. B. C.

1891. 'Sketch of the Colony of St. Vincent' quoted in Flora of St. Vincent and Adjacent Islets. Kew Bull., vol 81, pp. 231-296, 1893.

SANDS, W. N.

1912. An account of the return of vegetation and the revival of agriculture in the area devastated by the Soufrière of St. Vincent in 1902-03. West Indian Bull, vol. 12, pp. 22-33.

JOHN STANLEY BEARD

Nocturnal Orientation in the Ashy Petrel and Cassin's Auklet

Principal Investigators: Robert I. Bowman, San Francisco State University, San Francisco, California; and Bruce L. Manion, Department of Anatomy, University of Illinois Medical Center, Chicago, Illinois.[1]

Grant No.973: For study of nocturnal orientation in Leach's and ashy petrels.

Among the 12 species of marine birds breeding on Southeast Farallon Island off the central California coast, the ashy petrel *(Oceanodroma homochroa),* Leach's petrel *(O. leuchorhoa),* and Cassin's auklet *(Ptycoramphus aleutica)* share the unusual habit of arriving on and departing from the island only under cover of darkness. Diurnal occurrences of these species on the island are to be expected regularly only during the incubation period and irregularly through the nonbreeding season. At such times the birds stay well concealed in their nesting burrows. Each night upon their return to the breeding sites, they locate not only the island but also their individual nesting burrows among thousands of otherwise similar burrows and burrowlike openings. This ability is apparently not greatly diminished by weather conditions such as fog.

The purpose of the present study is to determine which sensory pathways the ashy petrels and Cassin's auklets use for orientation during their nocturnal movements. Other species of nocturnal birds, including the cave swiftlets *(Collocallia* spp.) and the oilbird *(Steatornis caripensis),* rely heavily on auditory cues and orient by using echolocation as do bats. Whereas the avian orientation signals are audible to humans and readily recorded on tape, the bat orientation signals are inaudible to humans, occurring in the ultrasonic range (Griffin, 1958; Griffin and Suthers, 1970). The barn owl *(Tyto alba)* also relies on auditory cues, but only those generated by the prey to which the bird is guided even in complete darkness (Payne, 1962; Konishi, 1973). Petrels and kiwis use olfactory cues during nocturnal activities (Grubb, 1974; Jouventin, 1977; Wenzel, 1971, 1973, 1974). All of these species, however, apparently utilize visual cues whenever there is sufficient illumination (Shallenberger, 1975). There is probably no need to postulate the existence of special senses in order to explain their nocturnal orientation abilities. The senses used by noc-

[1] Formerly of San Francisco State University, San Francisco, California.

FIG. 1. Aerial view of Southeast Farallon Island looking almost due North (photo courtesy U. S. Coast Guard, 12th District).

turnal birds often may be highly specialized for the purpose, but with the specialization being one of degree rather than of kind. It seems most probable that the answer to the question of how ashy petrels and Cassin's auklets orient at night lies in their use of one or more of the visual, auditory and olfactory pathways, and the present investigation is restricted to these sensory areas.

Southeast Farallon Island, approximately 36 hectares in area, plus several smaller islands, are located 43 kilometers west of San Francisco, California, at latitude 37° 42′ N. and longitude 123° W. The Farallones are composed of decaying granite which has left the islands strewn with jumbled rock. The topography of Southeast Farallon Island is very angular and is dominated by a large hill, rising over 100 meters above sea level, on which a lighthouse is situated (fig. 1). Most of the level area on the island is located in a large sea terrace along the southeastern edge of the island (see map in Bowman, 1961). The terrace is covered with a thin layer of rocky soil while the rest of the island (see fig. 2) is essentially bare rock (Hanna, 1951).

During the local wet season (November to April) Southeast Farallon Island has a scant covering of weedy vegetation, but by the end of June the island is essentially barren. Local weather is influenced by the ocean waters

FIG. 2. Example of the angular terrain of Southeast Farallon Island. Several ashy petrel burrows were found in the loose rocks associated with the large outcropping in the background. The mouths of several Cassin's auklet burrows can be seen in the foreground. The concrete pilings once supported watertanks.

surrounding the island, and temperatures are mild, with small variation between night and day. Heavy fog is common during much of the year, and winds can reach velocities of 55 knots.

Southeast Farallon Island has had since the late 1800's a manned aids-to-navigation station, which includes a lighthouse, a foghorn, and, more recently, a radio beacon. In 1973 the U. S. Coast Guard automated the station and withdrew all personnel from the island. During my two summers on the island, while U. S. Coast Guard personnel were still present, it was standard procedure for the lights in the powerhouse and the lamps along the walkway, which ran nearly the length of the island, to be constantly lighted. The lighthouse beacon was lighted automatically each night at dusk and was extinguished automatically each morning.

Cassin's auklet is the most abundant bird breeding on Southeast Farallon Island, with over 50,000 pairs estimated to breed each year (Manuwal, 1974). The population of the ashy petrel is estimated to be 4,000 birds, while that of the Leach's petrel is about one-third this number (Ainley and Lewis, 1974). Because of the small size of the population, Leach's petrel was not a study subject. About half the auklets and almost all the ashy petrels nest in adventitious spaces in rock piles and stone walls and under walkways (Veitch, 1970), while the remaining auklets dig their own burrows in the thin soil. The auklets tend to nest in clusters, and their burrows are easily spotted (see fig. 3). The petrel burrows are scattered, with the naturally occurring openings in the rock piles serving as entrances and exits (see fig. 4).

Both the auklets and petrels breed mainly during the months of April to September and require three and four months, respectively, to raise a single chick. Generally both auklet parents visit the burrow each night to feed the chick, whereas the petrel parents do not always visit the chick every night. Cassin's auklets and ashy petrels can be found on Southeast Farallon Island throughout the entire year, and both species may remain mated to the same individual and utilize the same burrow for two or more years.

Ashy petrels are small birds (35-50 grams) with relatively large wings, and their nocturnal flight on the island is very batlike. They are capable of hovering flight and impressive aerial acrobatics. In contrast, Cassin's auklets are heavy birds (150-200 grams) with relatively small wings, and their flight is direct with rapid wing beats. Auklets are awkward at slow flight speeds, but at high flight speeds they are capable of quick evasive movements. During the breeding season the majority of the auklets arrive on the island within two hours after dark and leave the island en masse the following morning just before dawn. The visits of petrels to their burrows may occur at any hour of the night.

FIG. 3. Five burrows excavated by Cassin's auklets on the large sea terrace. Three of the burrows are marked by wooden stakes approximately 25 centimeters long.

Methods

Field work was conducted exclusively on Southeast Farallon Island during eight weeks in 1971 (April 7–21, June 30–July 14, July 28–August 11, August 18–September 1) and six weeks in 1972 (May 24–June 7, June 14–July 12). During these periods I found and marked 24 ashy petrel burrows and 162 Cassin's auklet burrows on the terrace at the southeast end of the island. All these burrows were more or less rebuilt to allow the investigator ready access to the breeding chamber, but with the rearrangement being kept to a minimum. Only those burrows containing very young chicks were used in experiments because the parents seemed least inclined to abandon such burrows when disturbed. Adult birds captured in these burrows were marked either with waterproof paint on wing and tail feathers or small holes punched in the webbing between the toes.

AUDITORY EXPERIMENTS

To obtain evidence of echolocation in the ashy petrel and Cassin's auklet I recorded all their sounds under conditions that might reasonably be expected to present difficult orientation situations. This usually involved stationing myself at night near active burrows surrounded by various types of obstacles. My recording equipment consisted of a Nagra IIIB tape recorder and a Sennheiser ultradirectional microphone (MKH 805), which when coupled yield a "flat" frequency response from 50 Hz to 20 KHz. On one occasion I watched an ashy petrel repeat over 20 times a pattern that required dodging around several obstacles and flying parallel to a stone wall. Parts of the flight path were through some areas that to my eyes were in total darkness. The petrel successfully dodged all obstacles time after time and called only once during the entire episode.

In order to work under more controlled conditions, I captured five ashy petrels in a mist net one evening and observed their behavior when released inside a cave on the island. The cave measured approximately 6 by 6 meters and nearly 5 meters high at the center. The long narrow entrance to this room was blocked so that absolutely no stray light could enter. The captured birds were allowed to rest in this total darkness for 30 minutes. With my recording equipment turned on I released the birds one at a time. None took flight voluntarily, and each was hand launched into the air. The first bird flew strongly but collided with the opposite wall and slid to the floor. The remaining four birds merely fluttered to the ground. After several minutes of total quiet, I turned on my headlamp and found all five birds huddled on the floor of the cave. I launched two of these birds into the air in the light of my headlamp, and both birds flew about the cave with a slow hovering flight. Both birds eventually found crevices and hid themselves. A third bird was then launched into flight with the headlamp on, but it immediately collided with a wall when I turned off the lamp in midflight. Auklets were not subjected to this experiment as the dimensions of the cave did not allow these heavy-bodied birds sufficient room to become airborne. Several auklets did, however, have burrows deep inside the tunnel entrance to the cave. Except on very bright nights this tunnel is usually dark enough to preclude the use of, at least, human vision and, presumably, avian vision. On one night I sat in this tunnel and recorded all the sounds made by auklets seeking their burrows inside.

To determine the role, if any, of "auditory homing" in the nocturnal orientation of the ashy petrel and Cassin's auklet, I stationed myself at nightfall with recording equipment in a small courtyard enclosed by one wall of a building and three stone fences. The enclosed area tends to be more poorly illuminated and quieter than the surrounding open area. I had previously found and marked burrows of two ashy petrels within this enclosed area, and I also knew that several active auklet burrows were located under lumber piles. I made observations on two nights, one with a very heavy fog and a nearly full

FIG. 4. Typical ashy petrel burrow in a pile of loose rocks. The triangular opening just diagonally left of the center of the photo is one of the possible entrances.

moon, and the other without fog or moon. I was able to observe the arrivals of petrels twice at each petrel burrow and the arrivals of uncounted auklets at their many burrows during the 2-night vigil. At the beginning of the first night of observation, both petrel nests contained a chick plus a brooding adult, whereas at the beginning of the second night of observation only the chicks were present. The auklet burrows each contained only a chick at the beginning of both periods, but adults were probably present in some of the burrows later in the observation periods.

OLFACTORY EXPERIMENTS

I calculated the olfactory ratios of the ashy petrel and Cassin's auklet to establish possible anatomical evidence for a high development of the olfactory sense in these two species. According to the method devised by Cobb (1960), the measurements required are the greatest possible diameters of the olfactory bulbs and cerebral hemispheres regardless of the orientation of the axis of measurement. The measurements on the brains were taken in situ with precision dial calipers after the left half of the skull was removed. The skulls were soaked in 2 percent nitric acid until soft and neutralized in 5 percent sodium sulphate to facilitate the removal of bone.

To determine the possible role of olfactory cues in the nocturnal orientation of the ashy petrel, I tested the ability of individual petrels to find their burrows with their olfactory sense impaired. I selected 10 marked burrows containing young chicks and checked them each night by hand, once every hour from sunset to sunrise, until an adult was captured in each one. Adults were then taken inside the banding laboratory where they were marked for future identification, and their external nares were plugged with waterproof Duco cement. If, after an hour or more in captivity, these birds were alert and the cement plug was firmly in place, they were released outside in the dark away from the building. I released the petrels in this manner rather than returning them to their burrows because I discovered that when captive petrels were returned to their burrows they merely escaped out another opening, greatly agitating the chick in the process. To recapture these plugged birds, their burrows were checked by hand once every hour each subsequent night from sunset to sunrise.

Because suitable burrows were scarce, I did not have 10 separate burrows to use as controls for this experiment. Therefore, as a control for this experiment I recorded the visits to the burrows by the mates of the plugged birds. Most of these birds had been captured in the burrow at least once and handled as much as the experimental birds. I had originally planned to follow up this experiment with one in which I was to surgically transect the olfactory nerves rather than merely block the external nares. However, circumstances did not allow this and I switched my emphasis to experiments with the Cassin's auklet during the summer of 1972.

I performed nose-plugging experiments on the Cassin's auklets similar to those done on the ashy petrel. Because suitable burrows were more readily available, I was able to use 10 burrows as controls. My first attempt was unsuccessful because the cement plugs failed to stay in place. To conserve birds I recaptured as many of the above birds as possible and re-plugged the experimental birds with a plastic wood dough while the control birds, as before, were manipulated similarly except that their nostrils were not plugged.

Following this experiment I subjected a number of auklets to olfactory nerve transections to preclude the possibility that the auklets returning with plugs intact were able to smell through their internal nares, or that auklets that did not return were prevented from doing so because the plugs interfered with breathing or salt gland functioning.

In the auklet the olfactory nerves (fig. 5) run from the olfactory bulbs forward approximately 12 millimeters to the olfactory epithelium in the nasal

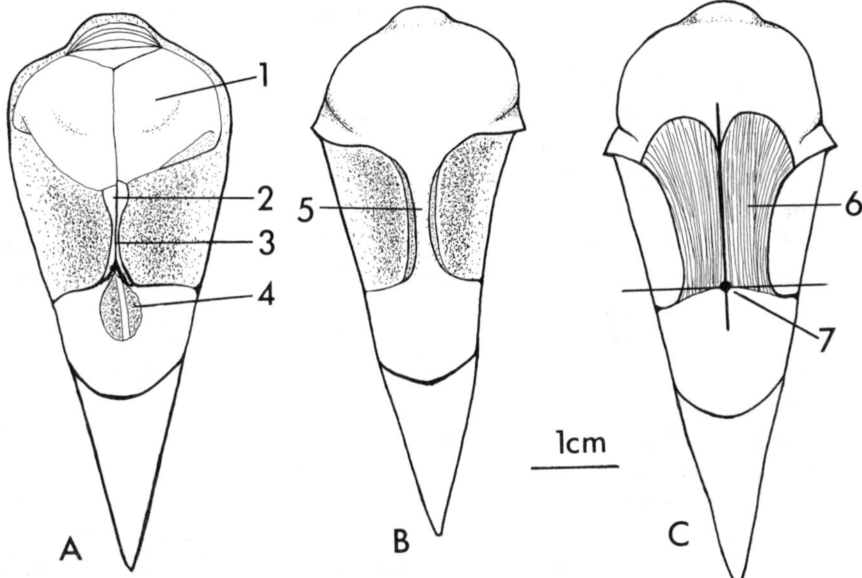

FIG. 5. Topography of the Cassin's auklet brain and skull as viewed from above. (A) 1, cerebrum; 2, olfactory bulb; 3, olfactory nerve; 4, nasal chamber lined with olfactory epithelium. (B) 5, nasal and frontal bones protecting the olfactory nerves. (C) 6, salt glands; 7, target area for insertion of drill bit. The drawings are based on three different skulls.

chambers through a blood-filled sinus roofed over by a narrow bridge of bone, which is presumably formed by the fusion of the frontal and nasal bones and serves to separate the eyes and to support the kinetic upper bill. Overlying and completely hiding this bridge are large salt glands, which abut tightly against each other along the midline of the bridge. During exploratory surgery on anesthetized auklets I found that because of severe bleeding I could not remove enough salt gland tissue to allow direct access to the skull beneath. Thus, a direct visual confirmation of a complete transection of the olfactory nerves was not possible. The method finally developed involved the use of a small high-speed electric drill to pierce both the salt glands and the skull beneath. It was assumed that the olfactory nerves were completely destroyed by the drill bit. A 2-millimeter-diameter drill bit (no. 48) was used because it was wider than the combined width of the two olfactory nerves, but not so wide as to completely sever the narrow frontal bridge of bone. The dimensions of the skull and nerves at the point of transection allowed very little room for error. The drill bit was inserted at a point defined by the intersection of the interface of the two salt glands and an imaginary line between the anterior borders of the orbits (fig. 5).

I arrived at the proper dosage of anesthetic by calculating a dosage based on the body weight of the auklet and then injecting many birds with experimental dosages near the calculated dosage until I obtained the proper level of anesthesia. I found that 0.25 cubic centimeters of "Equithesin" (a tranquilizing drug based on chloral hydrate and pentobarbital, Jensen-Salsbery Laboratories) given intraperitoneally produced anesthesia from which birds always recovered within a few hours.

The complete transection operation involved: 1, anesthetizing a newly captured auklet with an injection of "Equithesin"; 2, clipping the feathers on top of the head down to the skin; 3, incising open the skin along the midline of the skull with a scalpel; 4, drilling through the skull as described above; 5, suturing the skin after bleeding was stopped; and 6, sealing the wound with several layers of flexible collodion. During surgery the birds were securely held beneath rubber bands stretched between nails anchored to a board. On occasion some help was required in restraining larger birds under light anesthesia. All birds were then allowed to recover to complete alertness in the dark in small chambers, constructed from pasteboard boxes, in order to avoid self-inflicted damage. Other than keeping the surgical tools in 95-percent ethyl alcohol and washing my hands and the operating area, no attempt was made to obtain antiseptic conditions. No birds died during surgery, and none of the birds recovered from their burrows during the experiment showed any signs of infection.

The experiment involved taking one adult auklet from each of 45 marked burrows at night and marking the birds for future identification. Of these birds 15 were given the olfactory nerve transection operation as described, 15 others were given sham operations involving all steps except actual penetration of the skull, and the remaining birds were given anesthesia only. After being allowed to recover to full alertness, the birds were placed back into their respective burrows at least one hour before their normal departure time. The burrows were checked the next day to make sure all birds had left the island. Beginning the next night and on all subsequent nights all the experimental burrows were checked by hand several times per night in order to recapture any experimental birds that might return.

Visual Experiments

The measurement of dark adaptation in my study subjects and the histological examination of their retinas were beyond the scope of this study. I therefore approached the problem by determining how much illumination is available on the island at night under different combinations of lunar phase, cloud cover, and fog. The behavior of petrels and auklets under similar sets of conditions was noted, especially their facility in avoiding collisions with obstacles and in finding their burrows. All measurements of illumination were taken with a photographic light meter ("Gossen Luna-Pro"). This instrument is designed to measure reflected light but can be used to measure incident light by using a hemispherical light diffuser in front of the sensor. Even though this instrument is not a true foot-candle meter it gives useful approximations of illumination down to 0.016 foot-candle (0.17 lux). I make no inference that the sensitivity or functioning of this instrument is in any way similar to that of the eyes of the petrels, auklets, or humans. The illumination (incident light) from a full moon at the zenith on a clear night is approximately 0.02 foot-candle. This illumination is reduced to 0.002 foot-candle for a quarter moon while the illumination available on a clear moonless night is approximately 0.0004 foot-candle (Dice, 1945). Therefore, the lowest sensitivity of the light meter I used is at a level of illumination under which almost any species of bird could be expected to use visual cues for orientation, i.e., a clear night with a nearly full moon. At levels of illumination beyond the sensitivity of my instrument I used my own visual acumen to make a subjective analysis of the degree of visibility of burrow entrances and obstacles under given conditions. The meaurements and observations were taken at 24:00 hours near petrel and auklet burrows located in many different areas of the island. The available incident illumination was always measured with the light meter aimed at the brightest source of light whether natural or artificial.

During the summer of 1972 an advanced model of a "Starlight" scope (on loan from the U. S. Army) was available for use on the island. This instrument requires no artificial light sources, and thus there is no possibility of disturbing the study subjects. Even on the darkest nights, I could readily see anything on the island I wished except on foggy nights. With this instrument I watched several auklets arrive at their burrows in places where I could not detect them with my unaided eyes.

Results

Analysis of the tapes recorded during the auditory experiments revealed that auklets apparently do not call while flying about the island. The petrels often uttered their typical species recognition call while flying but not often enough and in the right situations to be an echolocation signal. The petrel observed performing the intricate flight pattern only called once during the entire episode. None of the auklets or petrels uttered any sounds in the cave, and there was no exchange of signals between approaching auklets or petrels and their burrows in the small courtyard.

The results of measuring the olfactory ratios are summarized in table 1. The ratios obtained for the ashy petrel (32.9 percent) and the Cassin's auklet (20.7 percent) are compared in table 2 with a series of species that have been measured by Bang (1971). The ratio for the ashy petrel is virtually the same as that of the closely related Leach's petrel, which apparently uses its olfactory sense for orientation (Grubb, 1974). The olfactory ratio of the ashy petrel compares favorably with that of the kiwi (34 percent) and the turkey vulture (28.7 percent) which are known to rely heavily on olfactory cues to find food (Wenzel, 1974; Stager, 1964). The olfactory ratio of the Cassin's auklet is

TABLE 1. Olfactory Ratio for Ashy Petrels and Cassin's Auklets

Greatest diameter			
Olfactory bulb (b)	*Cerebral hemisphere (a)*	*Olfactory ratio (%, b/a x 100)*	*Sex*
	ASHY PETRELS		
3.40	10.80	31.5	♂
3.65	11.23	32.4	♂
3.80	10.85	35.0	♀
3.99	12.16	32.8	♂
average olfactory ratio = 32.9% N = 4 S^2 = 2.21 S = 1.49			
	CASSIN'S AUKLETS		
2.83	14.30	19.8	♂
2.80	14.50	19.3	♂
2.70	13.80	19.6	♂
2.95	13.65	21.6	♂
2.85	13.95	20.4	♀
2.75	12.90	21.3	♀
2.80	12.83	21.8	♀
2.80	12.80	21.9	?
average olfactory ratio = 20.7% N = 8 S^2 = 1.13 S = 1.06			

slightly greater than that of the domestic pigeon (18 percent), a species that responds to olfactory cues in the laboratory and which may use olfactory cues in homing (Baldacinni et al., 1975; Wenzel, 1971; Walcott, 1974). The pigeon guillemot (14 percent) is a diurnal, burrow-nesting alcid which also breeds on Southeast Farallon Island.

The results of the nose plugging experiments are presented in tables 3 and 4. Consistent with the anatomical implications, the ashy petrels could not locate their burrows with their olfactory sense impaired, indicating a possible reliance on olfactory cues for orientation. Contrary to the anatomical implications some of the Cassin's auklets were able to locate their burrows with their

TABLE 2. Comparison of Olfactory Ratios for Several Species of Birds[a]

Species	*Olfactory ratio (%)*
Snow petrel *(Pagodroma nivea)*	37.0
Kiwi *(Apteryx australis)* (b)	34.0
Leach's petrel *(Oceanodroma leucorhoa)* (b)	33.0
Wilson's petrel *(Oceanites oceanicus)*	33.0
Ashy petrel *(Oceanodroma homochroa)* (c)	32.9
Wedge-tailed shearwater *(Puffinus pacificus)*	30.0
Greater shearwater *(P. gravis)*	30.0
Dove prion *(Pachyptila desolata)*	29.5
Blackfooted albatross *(Diomedea nigripes)*	29.0
California shearwater *(Puffinus opisthomelas)*	29.0
Turkey vulture *(Cathartes aura)* (b)	28.7
Cape pigeon *(Daption capensis)*	27.5
Fulmar *(Fulmaris glacialis)*	27.0
Steller's eider *(Polysticta eideri)*	23.7
Trinidad oilbird *(Steatornis caripensis)*	23.0
Pukeko *(Porhyrio poliocephalus)*	23.0
Yellow billed cuckoo *(Coccyzus americanus)*	21.0
Cassin's auklet *(Ptycoramphus aleutica)* (c)	20.7
Peregrin falcon *(Falco peregrinus)*	20.0
Diving petrel *(Pelecanoides georgicus)*	18.0
Domestic pigeon *(Columba livia)* (b)	18.0
Coucal *(Centropus sinensis)*	18.0
Wilson's snipe *(Capella gallinago)*	14.0
Pigeon guillemot *(Cepphus columba)* (c)	14.0
Roller *(Coracias benghalensis)*	14.0

[a] Reference/Bang, (1971) unless otherwise stated.
[b] Experimental evidence exists for an ability in this species to use its olfactory sense in finding food and/or in orienting.
[c] Reference this study.

olfactory sense impaired, some more than once over a number of nights. More clear cut were the results of the olfactory nerve transection experiment presented in figure 6. The number of returns was nearly identical in all three experimental classes. An autopsy of the seven birds that returned after having transection operations revealed that three had complete transections while the remaining four had at least one nerve completely cut with the other hanging together by only a few fibers.

Owing to the limitations of my light meter, I was able to obtain very little quantitative data regarding visual cues (see Manion, 1974). I did find that because of constant artificial illumination associated with Coast Guard activities some areas of the island were so well lighted that the auklet and petrel burrows located there surely could have been found by sight alone. In areas remote from the artificial illumination, the natural illumination varied, as expected, with the lunar phase and the amount of cloud cover. On one clear night with a full moon, I stood on top of Lighthouse Hill and measured the light being reflected from some guano-covered slopes below and obtained a reading equal to that of a full moon. Thus the island may at times be visible for long distances out to sea.

TABLE 3. Burrow Returns of Ashy Petrels with Plugged External Nares

Burrow no.	*Number of nights burrow monitored*[a]	*Returns by plugged birds*[b]	*Returns by mates*[b]	*Returns unrecorded*[c]
2	45	0	8[d]	3
8	11	0	2	2
12	6	0	0	0
17	5	1[e]	0	1
20	11	0	0	0
21	4	0	0	0
22	8	0	2	1
23	13	1[e]	0	3
24	8	0	0	0
25	11	0	0	0

[a] Monitoring terminated when chick disappeared or died.
[b] Based on capture of birds by hand within burrows.
[c] Based on increase in chick weight, visit could have been by either parent.
[d] Burrow monitored hourly only during first 16 days of monitoring period.
[e] Plugs missing; nostrils were re-plugged.

I found that it was never so dark on the island that I could not make out enough of the abundant topological detail to find my way about the island and find my experimental burrows without the aid of a flashlight. Nights with heavy fog were exceptions, and sometimes it was difficult to see the powerful lighthouse beacon. Light fog diffused illumination, and this tended to eliminate shadows and give an appearance of overall brightness. On such nights diffusion of light from the lighthouse beacon also contributed to the illumination. Owing to their being located in narrow ravines, some auklet and petrel burrows were nearly always in deep shadow and hard for me to find at night.

TABLE 4. Burrow Returns of Cassin's Auklets with Plugged External Nares

Burrow number	*Experimental class*	*Number of nights monitored*[a]	*Returns*[b]
PH5	Plug	9	0
PH11	"	9	1
PH13	"	7	0
PH14	"	7	3
RB5	"	9	0
CA1	"	7	2
CS1	"	3	0
CS3	"	2	1
EL3	Control	10	5
PH6	"	10	2
PH9	"	7	0
PH10	"	10	10
PH12	"	8	5
RB4	"	1	0
RB8	"	10	8
CA2	"	1	1
CA5	"	7	0
CA9	"	1	1
CS2	"	2	1
CS4	"	11	1

[a] May 31 to June 19, until adult recaptured or chick disappeared or died. Burrows were checked 4 times per night on 2 dates, 3 times per night on 4 dates, 2 times per night on 1 date and 1 time per night on 4 dates. At least 1 check of each burrow was made within 2 hours after sunset.

[b] Based on capture of bird within burrow by hand or trap.

Both the auklets and petrels visited their burrows under all conditions of illumination including the heaviest fog. In fact, overt activity of both birds is greatest on foggy nights with great numbers of petrels flying about and calling. Overt activity by these same birds is greatly subdued on bright clear nights, and the arrival of the auklets may be delayed one or more hours if a bright moon is in the sky at nightfall. During the winter the auklets may not even come onto the island under these conditions (Manuwal, 1974). This behavior may be a result of their greater visibility to predatory western gulls *(Larus occidentalis),* which nest in some of the same areas as the auklets and petrels. On bright nights it was generally a waste of effort to try to capture petrels in a mist net, and it was my impression that the petrels could see and avoid the nets.

When I viewed auklets through the "Starlight" scope, I found that they always seemed able to land close to their burrows even in the darker areas. When landing the auklets often struck weed stalks and rocks but with no apparent damage. Auklets have very compact, densely feathered bodies, and this, along with slow landing speeds, probably help prevent many injuries. Possibly over 100,000 auklets and petrels may come and go on a given night, but I found few birds that appeared to have been injured in collisions with stationary objects.

Summary and Discussion

The results of my experiments indicate that Cassin's auklets and ashy petrels on Southeast Farallon Island do not rely on auditory cues to locate their burrows. The auklet does not rely on olfactory cues to locate its burrow, whereas, in contrast, the ashy petrel may so rely. The auklet must certainly rely strongly on visual cues to locate its burrow. Until the exact role of the olfactory sense in the physiology and orientation of the ashy petrel is known, one must also assume that it also relies a great deal on visual cues anytime there is opportunity to do so.

It has been suggested that auklets and petrels may have evolved nocturnality due to feeding opportunities and predator pressure (Cody, 1973; Grubb, 1974). Indications are that the ashy petrel (Veitch, 1970) and other storm petrels (Grubb, 1974) feed to some degree at night on zooplankton on the surface of the sea. An enhanced olfactory sense could be very useful in locating this source of food. The Cassin's auklet obtains its food by diving and underwater pursuit during daylight hours (Manuwal, 1974). Both the auklets and petrels share a common predator on Southeast Farallon Island in the form

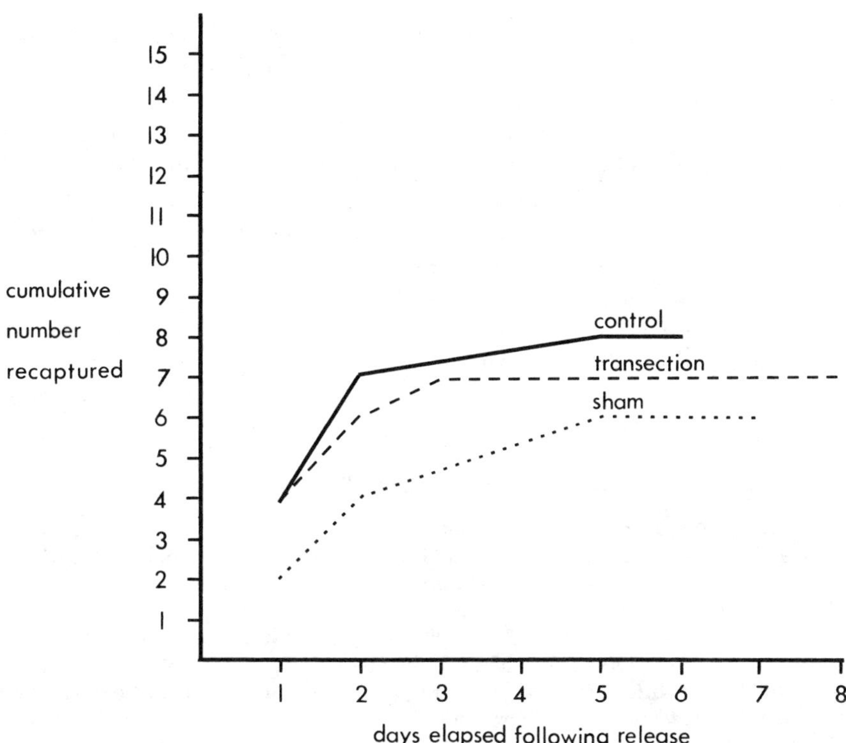

FIG. 6. Cumulative number of experimental auklets recaptured in their burrows during the olfactory nerve transection experiment. Control birds (anesthetic only) are represented by the solid line, sham-operation birds by the dotted line, and birds with transected nerves by the dashed line.

of the western gull. Remains of auklets and petrels, chicks and adults, are readily found in gull regurgitation pellets on the island. Unwary auklet chicks and incubating adults are often snatched from burrows during the day by gulls which walk about the island peering into burrow after burrow. Certainly auklet and petrel chicks could not survive on the island without the protection of the burrow. The nocturnal habits of the adults must protect them from attack to some degree and also would prevent the detection of otherwise cryptic burrow entrances. Presumably the diurnal pigeon guillemot is large enough to defend itself, while the chick requires the protection of a burrow when the parents are away obtaining food.

Acknowledgments

This paper is based on a master's thesis (Manion, 1974) completed at San Francisco State University under the guidance of Dr. Robert I. Bowman. Generous help and advice was also given by Drs. Margaret Bradbury, Jerry Gerald, Bernice Wenzel, Betsy Bang, Donald Griffin, David Manuwal, and Thomas Grubb. I also thank James Lewis, Harris Keston, John Brooke, and my wife, Cynthia, for timely help.

Financial support, in addition to this National Geographic Society grant, was obtained from the Frank M. Chapman Memorial Fund and the San Francisco State University Faculty Research Committee. Field work was conducted at the research station maintained by Point Reyes Bird Observatory on Southeast Farallon Island. Boat transportation was provided by the U. S. Coast Guard, 12th District. Recording equipment was made available through grants to Dr. Bowman from the National Science Foundation.

REFERENCES

AINLEY, DAVID G., and LEWIS, T. JAMES
1974. The history of Farallon Island marine bird populations, 1854-1972. Condor, vol. 76, pp. 432-446, map and charts.

BALDACCINI, N.E., et al.
1975. New data on the influence of olfactory deprivation on the homing behavior of pigeons. Pp. 351-353 in "Olfaction and Taste V, Proceedings of 5th International Symposium," D. A. Denton and J. P. Coghlan, eds. Academic Press, New York.

BANG, B. G.
1971. Functional anatomy of the olfactory system in 23 orders of birds. Acta Anat., vol. 79, pp. 1-76.

BOWMAN, ROBERT I.
1961. Late spring observations on birds of South Farallon Island, California. Condor, vol. 63, pp. 410-416, illus.

COBB, S.
1960. A note on the size of the avian olfactory bulb. Epilepsia, vol. 1, pp. 394-402.

CODY, M. L.
1973. Coexistence, coevolution and convergent evolution in seabird colonies. Ecology, vol. 54, pp. 31-44.

DICE, LEE R.
1945. Minimum intensities of illumination under which owls can find dead prey by sight. Amer. Nat., vol. 79, pp. 385-416.

GRIFFIN, DONALD R.
1958. Listening in the dark, 413 pp. Yale Univ. Press, New Haven.

GRIFFIN, D. R., and SUTHERS, RODERICK A.
1970. Sensitivity of echolocation in cave swiftlets. Biol. Bull., vol. 139, pp. 495-501.

GRUBB, THOMAS C., JR.
1974. Olfactory navigation to the nesting burrow in Leach's Petrel *(Oceanodroma leuchorhoa).* Anim. Behav., vol. 22, pp. 192-202.

HANNA, D. G.
1951. Geology of the Farallon Islands. California Dept. Nat. Res., Div. Mines Bull., vol. 154, pp. 301-310.

JOUVENTIN, P.
1977. Olfaction in snow petrels. Condor, vol. 79, pp. 498-499.

KONISHI, MASAKAZU
1973. How the owl tracks its prey. Amer. Sci., vol. 61, pp. 414-424.

MANION, BRUCE L.
1974. Nocturnal orientation in the ashy petrel and Cassin's auklet. M.A. Thesis, San Francisco State University, 84 pp.

MANUWAL, DAVID A.
1974. The natural history of Cassin's auklet *(Ptychoramphus aleuticus).* Condor, vol. 76, pp. 421-431.

PAYNE, R. S.
1962. How the barn owl locates prey by hearing. Living Bird, vol. 1, pp. 151-159.

SHALLENBERGER, R. J.
1975. Olfactory use in the wedge-tailed shearwater. Pp. 355-359 *in* "Olfaction and Taste V, Proceedings of 5th International Symposium," D. A. Denton and J. P. Coghlan, eds. Academic Press, New York.

STAGER, KENNETH E.
1964. The role of olfaction in food location by the Turkey Vulture. Los Angeles County Mus. Contr. Sci., vol. 81, pp. 1-63.

VEITCH, E.A.J.
1970. The Ashy petrel, *Oceanodroma homochroa,* at its breeding grounds on the Farallon Islands, California. Ph.D. Thesis, Loma Linda Univ., Univ. Microfilms, Ann Arbor. 366 pp.

WALCOTT, CLIMES
1974. The homing of pigeons. Amer. Sci., vol. 62, pp. 542-552.

WENZEL, BERNICE M.
1969. Olfaction in birds. Beidler Handbook of Sensory Physiology: Chemical Senses, vol. 4. Springer Verlag, Heidelberg.
1971. Olfaction in birds. Pp. 432-448 *in* "Olfaction, Handbook of Sensory Physiology," vol. 4 (part 1), L. M. Beidler, ed. Springer Verlag, Heidelberg.
1973. Chemoreception, Pp. 389-415 *in* "Avian Biology," vol. 3, D. S. Farner and J. R. King, eds. Academic Press, New York.
1974. The olfactory sense in the kiwi *(Apteryx).* Nat. Geogr. Soc. Res. Rpts., 1967, pp. 293-300.

BRUCE L. MANION

Behavior of Vertebrate Populations on Abandoned Strip-mine Areas

Principal Investigator: Fred J. Brenner, Grove City College, Grove City, Pennsylvania.

Grant Nos. 1029, 1158, 1345. For an ecological study of abandoned strip-mine areas in Mercer County, Pennsylvania.

Surface-mine operations during the past three decades have resulted in the alteration of large portions of wildlife habitats. Reclamation efforts have been concerned primarily with providing cover, with little regard to enhancing these areas for fish and wildlife. Unfortunately, the ecology of these areas has not been subjected to detailed studies as have other ecosystems. Similarly, these areas and their flora and fauna have been neglected by wildlife and fishery biologists. The current study was concerned with the behavior of vertebrate animals on strip-mine areas in order to evaluate their potential as a recreational resource as well as to understand these complex ecosystems.

Wildlife populations on surface mines of different ages and subjected to different reclamation practices were studied. The characteristics of the flora and fauna were determined for both terrestrial and aquatic habitats.

This study was conducted on 81 strip mines located in Mercer County, northwestern Pennsylvania. The county has an area of 435,830 acres of which 4,470 acres, or approximately 1 percent of the land area, has been strip-mined. Grice et al. (1971) classified the strip-mine spoil of the county as either gentle slope, indicating that some areas have been leveled after stripping (520 acres), or moderately steep slope, where some areas have been leveled but the majority remain as rough terrain, ranging from 10 to 100 acres in size (1,040 acres). Grice also classified a steep spoil as characterized by many short, steep slopes and some with water at the base and the acreage ranging from 10 to 200 acres in size (2,910 acres). The soil of strip-mine spoils consists of fragments of limestone, shale, impure coal, and sandstone.

Methods

Surface mines were located on aerial photographs and identified by a letter for township and number for mine operation. In addition, each permanent pool was identified by a letter. An initial survey was conducted on 81 surface mines to record the type of vegetation and state of reclamation. Water quality was determined on 132 pool areas, and detailed studies on the relationship between depth, water quality, and plankton populations were conducted on 60 mines. Age and growth and other characteristics of fish populations were studied on 8 mines. Fish were captured by hook and line, weighed to within 0.1 gram, and total length measured to within 1.0 millimeters.

Surveys were also conducted utilizing seines and trap nets, but they proved unsuccessful owing to extremely steep, high walls. Additional observations on fish populations were made with the aid of SCUBA equipment, which provides information on the species composition and pool characteristics.

Ten mines and one control area were selected as permanent study areas and their flora and vertebrate fauna studied over a four-year period. These sites were selected on the basis of their age, type of reclamation, and vegetation association. Four permanent 50-by-50-foot grids (two live traps and two snap traps) with traps set at 10-foot intervals were established on each mine. Traps were checked twice daily. Mammals captured in snap traps were frozen at -20°C until study skins were prepared. During the preparation of study skins, the adrenal weight and fat content were determined, and the eye lens was removed and saved for protein analysis. Individuals captured in live traps were marked by a toe clip and released. The place of initial capture by both live and snap trap and that of subsequent recapture were recorded for each grid. In all, 250 trap nights (5 days each grid) and an equal number of live-trap nights were conducted on each mine per year. In addition, 60 trap nights were conducted per year utilizing HAVA-HART rabbit traps. All rabbits and other larger mammals captured were weighed, tagged with ear tags, and released. Trapping was conducted also during the winter months on six mines and a control area for rabbits and other larger mammals.

The genetic structure of these small mammal populations was analyzed by the separation of eye-lens proteins. Separation of proteins by gel electrophoresis has been described in detail by Selander et al. (1971), Selander and Yang (1964), Selander and Hunt (1973), Wheeler and Selander (1972), and Selander and Johnson (1973). The techniques utilized by these authors were followed and the proteins separated in a discontinuous Plexiglas buffer reservoir connected by 12 glass gel cylinders with an inside diameter of 0.5 centimeters.

The nutritional content and the digestibility of the different types of vegetation were determined for the cottontail rabbit *(Sylvilagus floridanus).* Plants were clipped and rabbits were fed a predetermined amount of material. After 24 hours, the uneaten food and fecal material were collected, dried, and reweighed. The caloric content was determined by a plain oxygen bomb

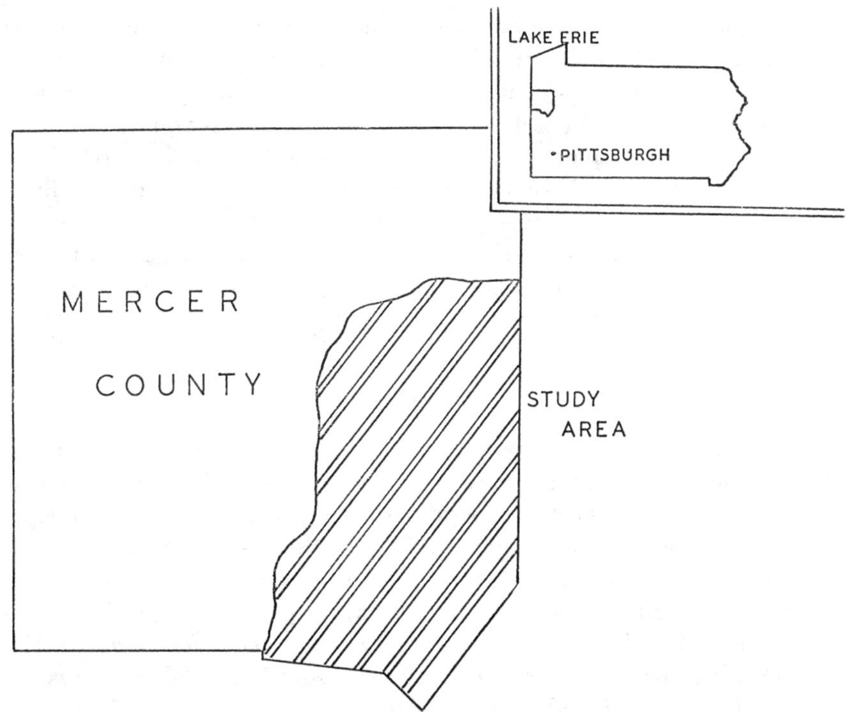

FIG. 1. Map of study area in Mercer County, Pennsylvania.

calorimeter, and the chemical analysis was conducted according to the methods described by Maynard and Loosli (1962) and Hawk et al. (1954, pp. 874-878). The amount of protein in each sample was determined by the total nitrogen as determined by micro-Kjeldahl times 6.25.

Browsing behavior of the white-tail deer *(Odocoileus virginianus)* was determined on two mine areas and on farmland abandoned to agriculture for 20 years. Four quadrants 50 by 50 feet were established on each study area, and height and amount of browse were determined for each tree within the quadrant. The amount of browsing was categorized on a scale from 0 to 100 as follows:

0 = no browse	3 = 41-60 percent twigs browsed
1 = 1-20 percent twigs browsed	4 = 61-80 percent twigs browsed
2 = 21-40 percent twigs browsed	5 = 81-100 percent twigs browsed

Samples of the terminal branches of the different species present on the quadrants were collected during November, January, and March. The moisture, nutrient, and energy content was determined according to the methods described previously. Digestibility of each species was determined by digesting twigs in a pepsin solution. A defatted sample was digested for 16 hours at 45°C under constant agitation. The insoluble residue was isolated by filtering, washed, dried, and weighed as a percent of the residue. This was examined microscopically and analyzed for protein. Pepsin digestibility was utilized as an indicator of the usability of these species as a food source for deer.

Results

The vegetation associations found on strip mines in Mercer County, Pennsylvania, have been described previously by Brenner (1973, 1974) and Brenner et al. (1975). These associations were described as conifer, deciduous, mixed conifer-deciduous, and grassland. The conifer association is found less frequently with white pine *(Pinus strobus)* as the dominant species and an even mixture of red pine *(Pinus resinosa),* Virginia pine *(Pinus virginiana),* larch *(Larix laricina),* and red and black spruce *(Picea rubens* and *Picea mariana).* The deciduous associations consisted of quaking aspen *(Populus tremuloides)* as the dominant species, with red maple *(Acer rubrum)* and black cherry *(Prunus serotina)* being of lesser importance. A mixture of the two previous associations with the addition of black locust *(Robinia pseudoacacia)* comprise the mixed conifer-deciduous association. Grassland associations are characterized by a variety of grasses and legumes with switch grass *(Panicum virgatum),* sweet-clover *(Melilotus* spp.), red clover *(Trifolium pratense),* and birdsfoot trefoil *(Lotus americanus)* as common species.

The woodland deer mouse *(Peromyscus leucopus)* was the small mammal with the widest distribution and adaptation to a variety of habitats. Short-tail shrews *(Blarina brevicauda)* were also found in the majority of the mines studied, but the common shrew *(Sorex cinereus)* appeared to be more specific in its habitat requirements. While the meadow vole *(Microtus pennsylvanicus)* was found only in the grassland association, the other three species were captured in both grasslands and woodland habitats. All species had a tendency to have a clumped distribution within the grid and did not appear to exhibit a uniform or random distribution. These populations exhibited considerable variation in numbers as well as fluctuations in population size from year to year, with figures for each mine area different. However, in general, *Microtus* populations followed the classic correlation between population size and adrenal weight as summarized by Christian (1964), whereas the reverse occurred in *Peromyscus* populations.

Protein analysis of the eye lens revealed that each mine appeared to be a separate genetic unit, and hence the independent nature of each population becomes more readily understandable. Thus, it might be possible to consider it as an island with distance and changing habitats as barriers.

Cottontail rabbits were the most common game mammal found on mine areas, remaining fairly constant between years as well as between mines. Other mammals trapped included the striped skunk *(Mephitis mephitis),* raccoon *(Procyon lotor),* red fox *(Vulpes fulva),* opossum *(Didelphis marsupialis),* and mink *(Mustela vison).* The red squirrel *(Tamiasciurus hudsonicus)* and the eastern chipmunk *(Tamias striatus)* were the only members of the Sciuridae observed or captured during this study.

Cottontail rabbits indicated a preference when fed plants common to strip-mine areas. The nutritional value of dandelion *(Taraxacum officinale)* was greater than that of all other plants analyzed. Birdsfoot trefoil, sweetclover, and aster *(Aster* spp.) had similar nutrient values, as did switch grass, red clover, and goldenrod *(Solidago* spp.). Cottontails refused to eat birdsfoot, and hence the utilization of this species under natural conditions is doubtful. The total digestible nutrients (TDN / 100 g. food intake) were greatest in dandelion, followed by red clover and sweetclover, respectively. The least amount of TDN / 100 g. food intake occurred in switch grass, whereas similar TDN values occurred in aster and goldenrod.

White-tail deer browsed primarily on quaking aspen, red maple, and hawthorn *(Crataegus* spp.). On the other hand, deer avoided black locust, bristly locust *(Robinia hispida),* and alder *(Alnus serrulata).* Browsing by deer was inversely correlated with sapling height. Hence, deer selected browse according to height with the heaviest browsing occurring on the smaller saplings. Nutrient content, moisture, and digestibility as determined by pepsin was similar among the various species that were browsed by deer compared with those that were not so utilized, the exception being the greater pepsin digestibility of white pine compared to that of the other species analyzed. Moisture may be a factor in the avoidance of black and bristly locusts, since these had the lowest moisture content of all species. Apples *(Malus* spp.) appear to be a preferred species by deer, since they were browsed extensively where they were planted during reclamation.

The avian fauna consisted of a total of 50 species representing 10 orders. Thirty-three species were members of the order Passeriformes, and of these 10 were permanent residents, the others inhabiting strip-mines only during the breeding season. The size and composition of the avian fauna did not vary over the four years of the study. Likewise, the avian fauna did not differ greatly among the various mines with the exception of the ovenbird *(Seiurus aurocapillus)* and the wood thrush *(Hylocichla mustelina),* which were found only in fairly dense woodlands. Game species consisted of the orders Anseriformes and Galliformes as well as the woodcock *(Philohela minor)* and the mourning dove *(Zenaidura macroura).* Waterfowl visited strip-mine pools during migrations but as of this date there has been no evidence of reproduction occurring. Resident populations of ruffed grouse *(Bonasa umbellus)* and ringneck pheasant *(Phasianus colchicus)* occur on strip-mine areas while the wild turkey *(Meleagris gallopavo)* has been observed occasionally, but there is no evidence of reproduction occurring in the latter species. Woodcock visit these sites during migration but similarly there has been no evidence of nesting within the study areas. Mourning doves are common inhabitants and indications are that they are nesting in the conifer and mixed conifer-deciduous associations.

A survey of 138 strip-mine pools indicated that 18 had a pH below 6.5. Thus, pH coupled with other chemical factors indicated that the majority were able to support aquatic life. *Certium* and *Dinobryon* were the phytoplankton with the widest distribution. *Nauplius, Bosnina, Limnocalanus, Anuraea,* and *Daphnia* were the zooplankton found in the majority of the pools sampled. Submergent vascular vegetation consisted of water milfoil *(Myriophyllum* spp.) and cattails *(Typha latifolia).* Alders and black willow *(Salix migra)* have become established along the edges of pools, providing cover for both fish and wildlife.

In general, strip-mine pools support approximately 9 species of fishes, the various species of Centrarachidae being the most common. Bluegills, pumpkinseeds, and large-mouth bass have the largest distribution. Samples obtained by hook and line indicate that these species have a good growth rate, and SCUBA observations indicated that they are reproducing.

Strip-mine pools are relatively deep, 6 to 8 meters, with rapid dropoffs due to the high walls, which prevent the use of conventional survey equipment (i.e., seines, trap nets, electro-fishing); hence, for this reason hook- and-line fishing and SCUBA diving were used for fish surveys.

Depth and temperature profiles of these pools indicate that they may be suitable for walleye pike *(Stizostedion vitreum)* and northern pike *(Esox lucius)* as additional predatory species. These two species were stocked on an experimental basis and observations by SCUBA indicated that they are surviving and exhibiting good growth. A limiting factor for these and other species may be the availability of shallow water and/or gravel for spawning because the only species usually found are those in and around the ramp used for the removal of coal during mining.

Summary

These studies indicate that strip-mine areas offer a tremendous potential for fish and wildlife. Studies are continuing on the feasibility of establishing artificial nesting structures for waterfowl. Studies are also being conducted on the utilization and digestibility of the different vegetations found on mine sites. The use of SCUBA has considerable potential for studying the behavior and structure of fish populations, and these investigations are continuing. Future studies on the movement and introduction of new wildlife species should include the use of telemetry equipment. This would be especially important in studying deer or other animals with a large center of activity.

REFERENCES

BRENNER, FRED J.

1973. Evaluation of abandoned strip mines as fish and wildlife habitats. Trans. N. E. Sect. Wildlife Soc., vol. 30, pp. 205-229.

1974. Ecology and productivity of strip-mine areas in Mercer County, Pennsylvania, 70 pp. Research Project Technical Completion Report, Institute of Land and Water Resources, Pennsylvania State University.

BRENNER, FRED J.; CROWLEY, R. H.; MUSAUS, M. J.; and GOTH, J. H.

1975. Evaluation and recommendations of strip mine reclamation procedures for maximum sediment-erosion control and wildlife potential. 3d Symposium, Surface Mining and Reclamation, vol. 2, pp. 2-23.

CHRISTIAN, JOHN J.

1963. Endocrine adaptive mechanism and the physiological regulation of population growth. Pp. 189-353 *in* "Physiological Mammalogy," vol. 1, W. E. Mayer and R. G. Van Gelder, eds. Academic Press, New York.

GRICE, D. G.; GRUBB, R. G.; and JAQUISH, O. U.

1971. Soil survey of Mercer County, Pennsylvania, 95 pp. U. S. Department of Agriculture.

HAWK, PHILIP B.; OSER, BERNARD L.; and SUMMERSON, WILLIAM H.

1954. Practical physiological chemistry, 1,439 pp. Blakiston Co., New York and Toronto.

MAYNARD, L. A., and LOOSLI, JOHN K.

1962. Animal nutrition, ed. 5, 533 pp. McGraw-Hill Book Co., New York.

SELANDER, ROBERT K., and HUNT, W. G.

1973. Biochemical genetics and hybridization in European house mice. Heredity, vol. 31, pp. 11-33.

SELANDER, ROBERT K., and JOHNSON, WALTER E.

1973. Genetic variation among vertebrate species. Ann. Rev. Ecol. and Syst., vol. 4, pp. 75-91.

SELANDER, ROBERT K.: SMITH, MICHAEL H.; YANG, SUH Y.; JOHNSON, WALTER E.; and GENTRY, JOHN B.

1971. Biochemical polymorphism and systematics in the genus *Peromyscus,* 1: Variation in the old-field mouse *(Peromyscus polionotus).* Studies in Genetics VI, Univ. Texas Publ. 710B, pp. 49-90.

SELANDER, ROBERT K., and YANG, SUH Y.

1969. Protein polymorphism and genetic heterozygosity in a wild population of the house mouse *(Mus musculus).* Genetics, vol. 63, pp.653-667.

WHEELER, LINDA L., and SELANDER, ROBERT K.

1972. Genetic variation in populations of the house mouse, *Mus musculus,* in the Hawaiian Islands. Studies in Genetics VII, Univ. Texas Publ. 721B, pp. 259-296.

FRED J. BRENNER

Conventionality of Territorial Leks in a Population of Uganda Kob

Principal Investigator: Helmut K. Buechner, National Zoological Park, Washington, D. C.[1]

Grant No. 1018: For a study of conventionality of territorial leks in a population of Uganda kob.[2]

This grant made it possible for me to carry out field work on the Uganda kob antelope *(Adenota kob thomasi)* from March 10 to 20, 1972, in the Toro Game Reserve in western Uganda. The main objective was to determine the present locations and status of territorial breeding grounds (TGs or leks) for comparison with locations noted in earlier periods of field work. The numbers of kob classified in different parts of the Reserve to determine the sex and age composition of the population provided a basis for estimating changes in the size of the population and for an evaluation of some of the probable effects of cropping for the market over the past decade.

Methods

The initial field work in the Toro Game Reserve started in July 1957, the objective at that time being to make 12 monthly collections as a basis for studying the annual reproductive cycle. TGs 3, 4, 5, 6, 7, 10, and 12 came into my purview gradually during this year, and in July-September 1959 I returned to survey the leks throughout the Reserve and begin studies of territorial behavior. The location and status of the TGs were observed during nearly 2 years of research on territoriality and mating behavior from July 1962 to April 1964. In March 1968 Walter Leuthold, who assisted me in 1962-64 as a predoctoral student, resurveyed the locations of the leks.

---

[1] Helmut K. Buechner died October 7, 1975, at Arlington, Virginia.

[2] I am grateful to the Uganda Government for permission to resurvey the Toro Game Reserve, and I especially appreciate the assistance of Sylvester Ruhweza, Peter S. K. B. Kyeyune, Honorat M. Nkalubo, Denisi Doktari, and other personnel of the Uganda Game Department in carrying out the field work. Robert E. Brown provided valuable assistance with photography and helped to ease the burden of field operations. Walter Leuthold made some excellent suggestions for improvements in the original draft of the report.

During the 1959 survey, the size of the central area of activity of each lek was estimated and the number of central and peripheral territories was determined by counting the males on territories. Site locations were fixed with reference to trees, clumps of shrubs, waterholes, and topography. These features are sufficiently unique at each lek to provide an accurate determination of location. Photographs of leks were taken during each period of field work to aid in detecting changes. Concrete blocks, used to mark individual territories in 1963, remained on TGs 3, 6, and 7 to 1972.

Establishment of the 1959 base line and locations of new TGs formed since then were accomplished with the help of Game Guard Denisi Doktari, a man with a lifelong familiarity of the Toro Game Reserve. Some leks can be traced through his memory to the 1920s.

Herd-composition counts involved classification by sex and age. Males older than 6 months can be distinguished from females by their horns. In terms of body proportions the young at 6-7 months are about half the size of fully grown females. Horn development begins at 5 months and starts to exceed the length of the ears at 1 year. Thus juvenile males between 7 and 12 months of age can be distinguished in the field; and since the sex ratio probably is approximately equal up to 12 months, the number of young females in the same cohort can be estimated. The method is somewhat crude in that: (1) females grow more slowly than males and are more likely to be included in the $<$ 7-month old group and (2) mortality in males, partly because many leave the mother and join bachelor herds at 6-7 months of age, very likely begins to exceed that of females during the latter half of the first year of life. Females 7-12 months old are about three-quarters grown and their body proportions blend imperceptibly into those of adult females, making this age group difficult to count in the field, and an estimate based on the number of males with horns less than ear length seems to be the best solution despite the inherent inaccuracies. The age of males can be further delineated by horn growth. As males approach 3 years their horns begin to form a lyre-shaped double curve, which appears to be fully developed by 3½ years of age. From 1 to 2½ years the horns are single-curved and greater than ear length, and at the time of change (2½-3 years) the horns can be distinguished as "approaching double curve."

Using herd-composition counts and flight distances, we made comparisons between the populations of kob in the area west and northwest of the Wasa River, where cropping took place, and the area east of the river where the animals have been protected from hunting.

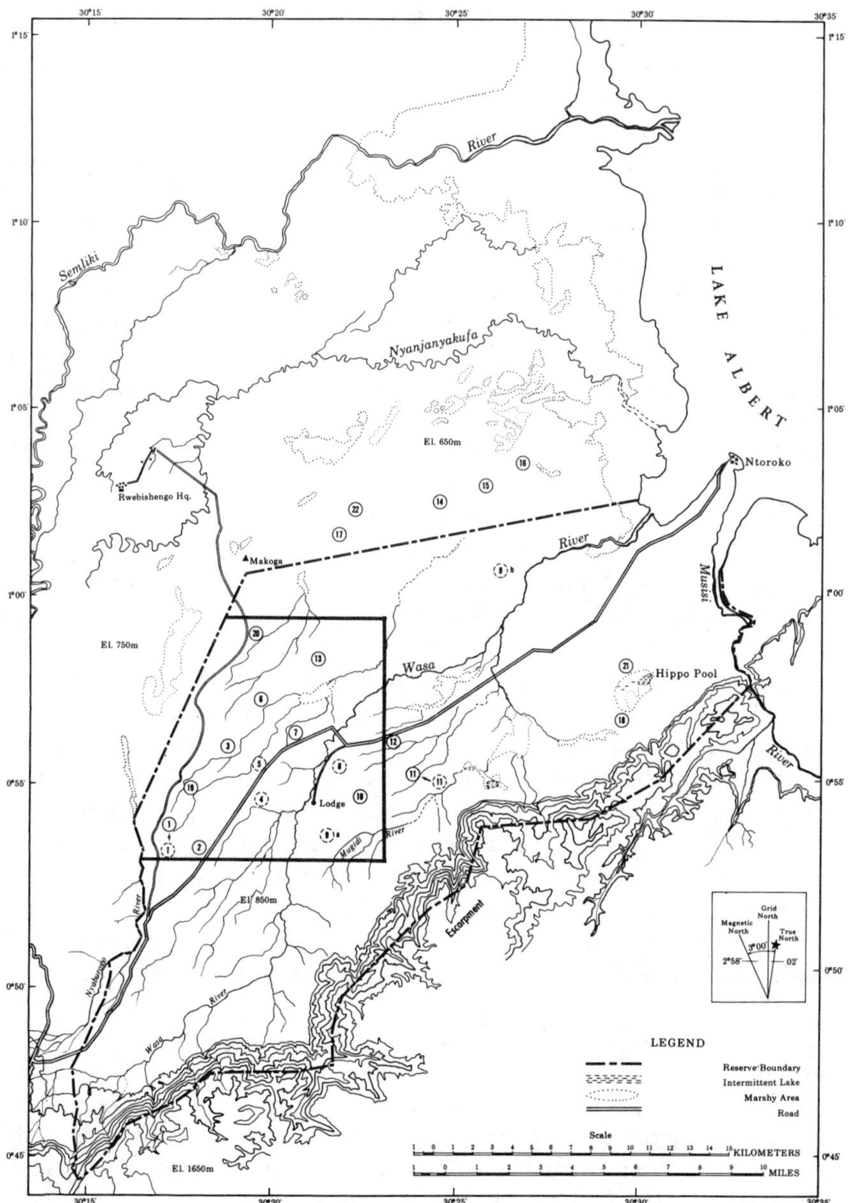

FIG. 1. Map of Toro Game Reserve; main study area 1962-64 outlined with solid line.

Conventionality of Territorial Leks

The locations of 12 leks have remained exactly the same since 1959 (tables 1 and 2, fig. 1). One lek (TG 17), which probably was established prior to 1959 and overlooked in that survey, was located by Walter Leuthold in April 1963 and apparently continues in its same location. The precise location needs further verification. Five leks have been abandoned since 1959, and five new ones have formed since 1964. One of the new grounds (TG 18) was noted by Walter Leuthold in 1968. Numbers 19, 21, and 22 are small in area and number of territories, and with low activity, giving the impression that they may be temporary breeding grounds. On the other hand, TGs 18 and 20 seem to be well established, judged by their size and activity. Thus there are now 15 major leks serving the population, 10 of which are in traditional locations that can be dated positively to 1959; 13 can be traced to the period 1962-64 and 14 to 1968. Besides the 15 well-developed leks there are 3 (TGs 19, 21, 22) small leks that are either incipient or temporary TGs. Five of the present leks were known to me in the same locations in 1957, at which time I had not surveyed the whole Reserve for the locations of TGs.

The expansion of some leks in both area and number of territories was unanticipated. TG 2 spread from its original hilltop location onto a south-facing slope, where the males on territories and the activity on the lek can be seen clearly from the main road at a distance of about half a kilometer. TG 3 increased in the number of peripheral territories, some of which were distributed southwestward among trees and clumps of shrubby vegetation, and the diameter of this lek appeared to have been extended considerably. Most of the males on peripheral territories ran off as the Land-Rover approached to within 150 meters, followed by the males on central territories, and this shyness made accurate determination of the number of territories impossible. The center of activity had shifted west and northwest, as noted by Walter Leuthold in 1968, who pointed out further that "a tendency in this direction was already evident in early 1964." The area in which concrete blocks were placed in 1963 was still occupied.

The area and number of territories at TG 10 approximately doubled, making this lek one of the largest. There were two centers of concentrated breeding activity, as in 1962-64. TG 11 was well developed and highly active 1 kilometer north of its location in 1959 where it was incipient in 1962. Against the background of the 500-meter escarpment, this lek, which is now along the tourist viewing circuit road, is one of the most attractive. TG 14 had increased in size to nearly 100 territories, becoming the largest lek both in area (estimated 500 by 1,000 meters) and number of territories. Here the

TABLE 1. Changes in Location and Size of Leks

(1968 comments from a report by Walter Leuthold to Office of Ecology, Smithsonian Institution, April 15, 1968.)

Lek TG No.	*Change for period indicated*			
	1959-1962	*1962-1964*	*1964-1968*	*1968-1972*
1	Decreased from ca. 25 territories to < 5; invaded by tall forbs.	Abandoned by Feb. 1964; new TG of 8-10 territories formed ca. 2 kilometers north.	New TG 1 still small, ca. 10 territories; same location.	New TG 1 in same location; ca. 10 territories.
2	No change; comparatively small in size; 10-15 territories.	No change.	Still relatively small, 20 territories.	Expanded, spreading from original ridgetop ca. 200 meters onto south-facing slope (can be seen from main road); ca. 40 territories.
3	Entire lek shifted 200 meters southward; ca. 40 territories.	Center of activiity moved ca. 100 meters westward.	Shifted to west and northeast (tendency already evident in 1964); older area still occupied; TG larger and more spread out; ca. 25 territories.	Expanded westward on terrace of high ground; 1962-64 center of activity now peripheral; lek increased in diameter from ca. 200 to 300 meters; slight increase in number of territories.
4	Fewer territories, declined from ca. 25 territories; reduced activity.	Continued decline in activity.	Still rather small; 13 territories.	Abandoned.
5	Small lek (ca. 15 territories) with low activity in 1959. Abandoned by 1962.	–	–	–
6	Same location; ca. 45 territories.	Began shifting center of activity to west.	Very active; shifted to west (started in 1963); "old" part still occupied.	Center of activity shifted ca. 150 meters westward; fewer territories (15-20); males shy as result of cropping.

TABLE 1. Changes in Location and Size of Leks—continued

Lek TG No.	Change for period indicated			
	1959-1962	*1962-1964*	*1964-1968*	*1968-1972*
7	Main road constructed through lek in 1958; initially active on both sides of road; 45-50 territories in 1959; east side reduced to single territories by 1962.	Smaller and less active than before 1959; occasional periods of low activity; 15-20 territories.	Perhaps smaller; 7 males on territories.	Well established and active; about same size as in 1962-64; 10-15 males on territories; exactly same location.
8	Abandoned.	–	–	–
9	Number initially assigned to a lek 2 kilometers southwest of TG 10; abandoned by 1962.	Number reassigned to new lek (in grove of Borassus palm-marginal habitat); abandoned by 1964.	–	–
10	Center of activity shifted ca. 300 meters and then west ca. 100 meters; 30-40 territories.	Two centers of activity; same location.	Perhaps slightly shifted to south; large and well used; 30 territories.	Expanded eastward and southward; lek considerably enlarged and spread out; 60-65 territories.
11	Shifted 1 kilometer north during this period; old site abandoned; ca. 10 territories on new site.	Area seldom visited during course of field work; probably no change.	Not visited.	Well established, active lek; now conspicuous along tourist viewing circuit road; 25-30 territories.
12	No change; 25-30 territories.	No change.	Well used, but rather small; 15 territories.	Exactly same location; about same size as in 1959.
13	No change; ca. 35 territories.	No change.	Ca. 28 territories; in same area.	Exactly same location and no perceptible change in size since 1959.
14	Increased from 15-20 territories to 30-40 territories.	Slight increase in size.	Still very large and spread out; appears shifted somewhat to south; ca. 50 miles.	Expanded in area and number of territories; now largest lek; ca. 500 by 100 meters with nearly 100 territories.

15	No change; ca. 30 territories.	No change.	Medium size; ca. 35 males.	No change.
16	No change; 60-70 territories.	No change; large, active; spread out.	Very large and active; shifted a bit to east-southeast.	Still large and very active.
17	Not known; probably existed.	Found by Leuthold in April 1963; no change.	15-20 males; skulls suggest TG same location for some time.	Apparently no change; location needs further verification.
18	Nonexistent.	Nonexistent.	New; fairly large and well used; much bare ground; gentle slope southwest of "Hippo Pool"; ca. 35 males; same location where a "cluster of STs" was seen on Feb. 10 and Mar. 1, 1964.	South end "Hippo Pool" on area flooded during wet season, at which time lek shifts to higher ground; 28 males on territories on Mar. 11, 1972.
19	Nonexistent.	Cluster of 8-10 territories about 2 kilometers south-southeast TG 3 noted by Leuthold on Feb. 13 and Mar. 3, 1964; possibly incipient stage of this lek.	Not visited.	Initiated in 1970, according to Doktari; small in size with 12-15 territories.
20	Nonexistent.	Nonexistent.	Nonexistent.	Began forming in 1969 after moving twice earlier, according to Doktari; ca. 25 terrtiories; well established.
21	Nonexistent.	Nonexistent.	Nonexistent.	Northwest edge of "Hippo Pool"; small, only 8-10 territories; started about 1968, according to Doktari.
22	Nonexistent.	Leuthold noted a lek as "TG 18, temporary (?)" ca. 3 kilometers northeast of TG 17 on Feb. 10, 1964; 12 males; possibly incipient stage of this lek.	Not visited.	Ca. 10 territories; location needs verification.

TABLE 2. Summary of Changes in Leks

Status of lek	*Lek in status for period indicated*			
	1959-62	*1962-64*	*1964-68*	*1968-72*
Location exactly the same:				
a. No significant change in area or number of territories.	2, 6, 12, 13, 14, 15, 16, 17?	1, 2, 6, 7, 10, 11, 12, 13, 14, 15 16, 17	1, 2, 4, 6, 7, 10, 11, 12, 13, 14, 15, 16, 17	1, 7, 12, 13, 15, 16, 17?
b. Significant decrease in size.	4, 7	4	—	—
c. Significant increase in size.	—	—	—	2, 3, 10, 11, 14
Location same but center of activity shifted 50-300 meters.	3, 10	3, 6	3, 6, 10	3, 6
Entire lek shifted 1-2 kilometers to new location; earlier site abandoned.	1, 11	—	—	—
Abandoned completely.	5, 8, 9a,	9b	—	4
New leks.	9b	—	18	19, 20, 21, 22

TABLE 3. Herd-Composition Counts of Uganda Kob in Semliki Plains

Age Class	*Number counted*							
	1972 - E. of Wasa R.		*1972 - W. of Wasa R.*		*1972 - Total*		*1963 - Average*	
	No.	*Pct.*	*No.*	*Pct.*	*No.*	*Pct.*	*No.*	*Pct.*
Males and females < 7 months	248	14.5	696	12.1	944	12.7	1,271	15.4
Males 7-12 months	63	3.7	310	5.4	373	5.0	616	7.4
Females 7-12 months	63	3.7	310	5.4	373	5.0	616	7.4
Adult females	923	53.9	2,817	49.1	3,740	50.2	3,568	43.1
Nonbreeding subadult males (1-3 years)	177	10.3	782	13.6	959	12.9	1,395	16.9
Breeding males (> 3 years)	238	13.9	823	14.4	1,061	14.2	812	9.8
Total	1,712	100.0	5,738	100.0	7,450	100.0	8,278	100.0
Sex ratio (males: 100 females)	45:100		57:100		54:100		62:100	
Age ratio (young < 1 year: 100 females)	41:100		47:100		45:100		70:100	

TABLE 4. Exploitation of Kob in Semliki Plains

Type of harvest	Year								
	1963	*1964*	*1965*	*1966*	*1967*	*1968*	*1969*	*1970*	*1971*
Cropping for market	166	600	1,197	738	648	927	1,108	1,011	569
Licensed hunting	114	94	58	91	112	74	79	43	84

territories were also considerably larger in diameter compared to those on most other leks.

One lek (TG 6) decreased significantly in area and number of territories; and the center of activity shifted westward about 150 meters, a shift Walter Leuthold saw beginning to occur in 1964. As with the males on TG 3, the flight distance was exceptionally high, and on two out of four approaches to the lek the males ran off at distances of 200-300 meters.

The significance of the changes in territorial breeding grounds over the past 13 years is not altogether clear at this time. A core of 13 TGs has persisted, and 10 of these leks may have existed in the same locations for 50 years or more. The shifts in locations of TGs 1 and 11 involve new locations that have lasted about 10 years. TG 1 moved to higher (15-20 meters) ground, but between the old and new locations of TG 11 the elevational difference was imperceptible. The reason for these translocations of leks remains obscure.

Sex and Age Composition

Significant changes in both sex and age ratios appear to have occurred between 1963 and 1972, as indicated by the data summarized in table 3. However, caution is required in interpreting the data, since the 1963 figures are averages of the four best herd-composition counts made that year, and the counts in 1972 represent only one effort during 5 days of a 10-day period of field research. Also, three of the earlier counts were made by Walter Leuthold alone, and the differences in observers may have an important effect on the results. Knowledge of the distribution of herds, patterns of daily movements, and skill in counting all improved as the 1972 field work progressed, after my long absence from field work, so that a second effort may have yielded somewhat different results.

The data do not show any significant differences in either sex or age ratios between the protected and hunted portions of the population. In fact, fewer males were recorded east of the Wasa River (45 males: 100 females) than on the west side (57:100), probably because the main bachelor herds associated with TGs 10, 11, and 12 were not encountered. The sex ratio of the total count (54:100) shows fewer males than in 1963 (62:100). This apparent decrease in males is probably not meaningful, since the combined percentages of subadult and adult males in the total count in 1963 (26.7 percent) and 1972 (27.1 percent) are nearly identical. The larger proportion of adult females in the 1972 population, which is correlated with a lower count of young < 1 year old, influences the sex ratio.

On both sides of the Wasa River the age ratio was markedly lower in 1972 (45 young < 1 year old: 100 adult females) than in 1963 (70:100). However, east of the river a high proportion of adult females was counted one evening when about 1,000 kob moved from lower to high ground immediately before a heavy thunderstorm, and west of the river the shyness of females made it impossible to count enough groups for a reliable age ratio; therefore the reduced recruitment is likely to be an artifact of the data. I had the general impression that many young were present and that reproduction was as high as during the earlier studies.

Stability of Population

No major change seems to have occurred in total numbers since 1959 when the Uganda Game Department estimated 18,000 kob. During September 15-17, 1969, a total count and estimate of slightly over 19,000 kob was made in the Reserve and adjoining areas by one biologist and one game warden with supporting personnel (Ruhweza, letter May 12, 1972). The sex-and-age composition counts of 7,450 kob in 1972 provided a modest basis for estimating the total population of kob in the Semliki. In figure 2 the areas in which counts were made on different days are shown, together with estimates of numbers and actual counts. The total estimate of 16,000 kob is conservative, and the population could be as high as 19,000. The data suggest that the population has remained approximately stable, despite harvesting for the market.

Impact of Exploitation

A program of cropping for the market and licensed hunting was initiated by the Uganda Game Department in 1963, and about 1,000 kob have been removed annually since 1965 (table 4). An important experiment has emerged from the department's policy of assiduously protecting the kob east

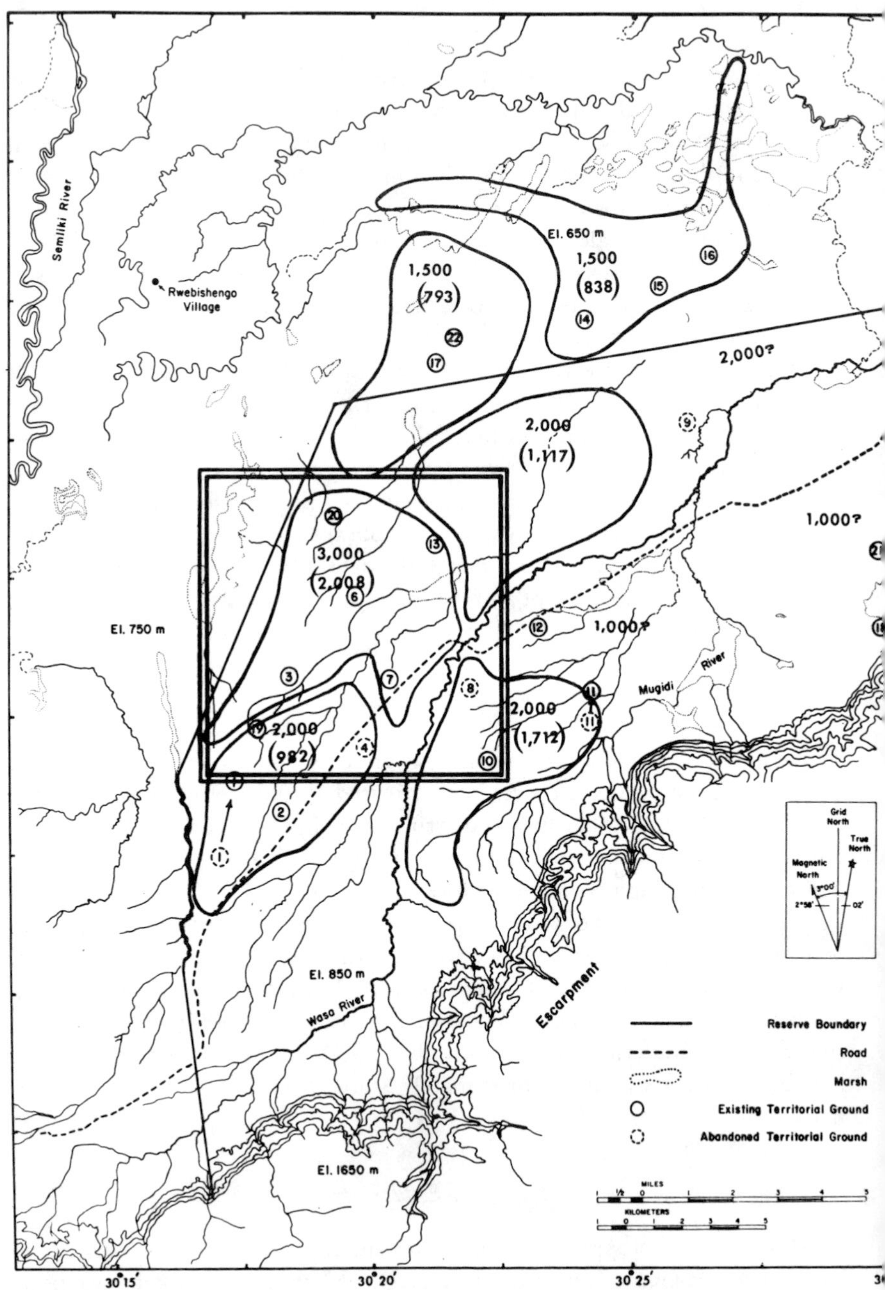

FIG. 2. Areas in which herd-composition counts were made with estimates of total numbers and actual counts (in parentheses).

of the Wasa River to assure good viewing for tourists. In the exploited area west of the river, flight distances of males on territories and of females in herds were notably greater than in the protected area (100-200 meters compared to 10-50 meters). The females were particularly shy, and in the area where research was concentrated in 1962-64 (outlined on map in figure 1) it was impossible to make a fully satisfactory herd-composition count. Efforts to approach a herd of about 50 females and their young on March 15, 1972, for example, triggered flight of the entire group at a distance of about 300 meters as the Land-Rover approached. Other herds of similar size joined the first one as the approach continued, until nearly 1,000 kob swarmed over the landscape in full flight 2-3 kilometers away from the Land-Rover. The sight was reminiscent of the behavior of the kob when pursued by wild dog *(Lycaon pictus)*. Because of easy accessibility from the Rwebishingo Road, the area in which this event occurred has been cropped more heavily than other parts of the kob's range. It should be noted, however, that such wild flight may not be due to hunting alone. In October 1964, after his absence of a month, Leuthold found, for a brief period of time, that large herds often started running at 200 meters from the Land-Rover, sometimes turning into a chase that continued for many kilometers.

Of all the males on territories, those on TG 6 were the most frightened at the approach of the Land-Rover. On two occasions these males abandoned the lek completely, starting when the vehicle was 300-400 meters distant, whereas usually one can drive to the edge of the territorial ground without stimulating departure of the occupants. The males on TG 3 held their territories more tenaciously when the Land-Rover approached, compared to those on TG 6, but their extreme wariness also reflected the behavioral impact of cropping. By way of contrast, on TG 10 where the kob were protected from hunting, only those males within 30-50 meters of the Land-Rover were disturbed—the others continued their territorial and breeding activities, despite the presence of the Land-Rover parked at the margin of the lek.

Throughout the former research area the small number of males observed on single territories (STs), which are large, widely spaced territories distributed between the leks, suggested that removal of these males by cropping may have significantly altered the social organization of the population. The effect of the seasonal period of drought may have been partly responsible for the scarcity of males on STs in the vicinity of TGs 3, 6, and 7, but the presence of many males on STs in the protected area east of the Wasa River seems to preclude this possibility.

The expected alteration of the sex ratio in favor of females under a cropping program heavily weighed toward males was not apparent in the herd-composition counts in the exploited area. The 1972 ratio was 57 males:100 females, compared with 62:100 in 1963 (table 3). All the harvesting in 1971 was in the controlled Hunting Area northwest of the Toro Game Reserve, except for one quota in the former research area in November. The 1972 sex ratio may reflect rapid recruitment of adult males from the younger age classes and cropping of females, the extent of which is not discernible from the recorded statistics.

In summary, the effects of cropping between 1963 and 1972 show up only in a minor way in the current population, both in terms of total number and sex ratio. On the other hand, the flight behavior of the kob, and possibly the social organization with respect to ST males, have been influenced considerably by hunting.

Impressions of Changes in Populations of Other Animals

The number of lions seems to have increased since hunting was stopped in 1965. Thirty lions (6 males, 6 females, and 18 cubs) were seen during the 10 days of field work, and roaring was frequent every night. Twelve young of three ages were seen with two females, 5 young of two ages were seen alone, and one cub was alone. It was a new experience to see so many lions in such a brief period of time in the Semliki, and the large number of cubs indicated a potential for rapid increase.

Viewing by tourists, and protection from hunting since 1965, seem to be responsible for the increased diurnal visibility of lions.

Jackson hartebeest *(Alcelaphus buselaphus jacksoni)* and defassa waterbuck *(Kobus defassa ugandae)* both appear to have decreased considerably in number and are probably less than half as abundant as 10 years ago. Bohor reedbuck *(Redunca redunca)* and warthog *(Phacochoerus aethiopicus)* seemed to be about as numerous as before. No gray duiker *(Sylvicapra gimmia)* were observed, but they were rarely seen a decade ago. One bushbuck *(Tragelaphus scriptus)* was reported in 1963; none was seen during the present survey. Cape buffalo *(Syncerus caffer)* seem considerably less numerous than 10-15 years ago. The general impression is that the trend is toward a continued increase in the dominance of the ungulate community by the Uganda kob.

Discussion

It is now clear, after 15 years of observations, that a spatially fixed network system of about 13 territorial breeding grounds, augmented by temporary leks lasting 1-5 years or more, is maintained by generation after generation of Uganda kob in the Toro Game Reserve. The constancy of locations of the stable leks has been remarkable, despite seemingly major disturbances to some of them by human activities along roads and through exploitation for the market. The expansion in area and number of territories on three of the conventional leks and the establishment of five new leks, three of which are large and highly active, indicate a vigorous and substantial population.

A conservative estimate of about 16,000 kob in the Reserve indicates a minor decline, if any, in total numbers since 1959. Young kob appeared to be plentiful in the current population, and the apparent decrease in recruitment compared with 10 years ago is probably a consequence of circumstances encountered during the herd-composition counts.

Except for the extreme shyness of males on TGs 3 and 6 (especially the latter) and the apparent absence of males on STs scattered between the leks, the effect of cropping on territorial behavior and the system of leks in the Reserve appears to be of relatively minor importance. However, the behavior of the kob off the TGs, especially females, was markedly altered by the hunting; and the kob were particularly shy around TGs 3, 6, and 7 where shooting has been intensive. It will be interesting to note how rapidly the kob become "tame" again in this area, if cropping remains confined to the Controlled Hunting Area outside the Reserve.

Opportunities for continued research appear to be favorable. The Uganda Government is considering conversion of the Toro Game Reserve into a national park. Park status would terminate market exploitation and improve conditions for research, although it should be emphasized that significant research can be conducted within the framework of present management of the Reserve by the Department of Game. A new lodge, with a capacity for 80 persons, attracted more tourists after completion in August 1972. The Semliki Valley is about 3 hours' drive from Ruwenzori National Park (formerly Queen Elizabeth National Park) along a scenic road at the foothills of the Ruwenzori Mountains, and it is directly accessible to Kabalega National Park (formerly Murchison Falls National Park) by way of Lake Albert. Conceivably, tourism could increase to a level at which it might interfere with research and cause environmental degradation. Such adverse effects of tourism can be minimized through appropriate planning and management practices. Territorial behavior undoubtedly functions as an important regulatory mechanism in the biology of the Uganda kob, but precisely how the lek system is maintained and how it works will require long-term research. Eventually the full significance of the kob's territoriality, in terms of numerical regulation, maintenance of genetic variability, and homeostasis of vegetational relations, should emerge from these studies.

REFERENCE

BUECHNER, HELMUT K.
1974. Implications of social behavior in the management of Uganda kob. Pp. 853-870 *in* "The Behaviour of Ungulates and Its Relation to Management," vol. 2, 941 pp., illus. Int. Union Cons. Nature Publ. no. 24. Morges, Switzerland.

HELMUT K. BUECHNER

Distribution, Mobility, and Behavior of the Red Sea Garden Eel

Principal Investigator: Eugenie Clark, University of Maryland, College Park, Maryland.

Grant No. 961: In support of studies on the behavior of the Red Sea garden eel, *Gorgasia sillneri* Klausewitz, in the Gulf of Aqaba.

Garden eels (subfamily Heterocongrinae) consist of over a dozen species living in tropical seas at the sandy bottom in depths from 2 to at least 50 meters. Divers have been fascinated by their unique, sedentary habit of living in large colonies first described by Beebe (1938) as a "garden" of eels. From a distance they resemble a bed of plants. They live in mucus-lined burrows they

FIG. 1. A round blind made up of a metal pipe frame (1.7 meters in diameter; 1.5 meters high) located in eel colony 2. A 25-square-meter grid is laid on the sand to the left, a portable 1-square-meter frame is in center. As a diver approaches the blind all the eels retreat into their burrows.

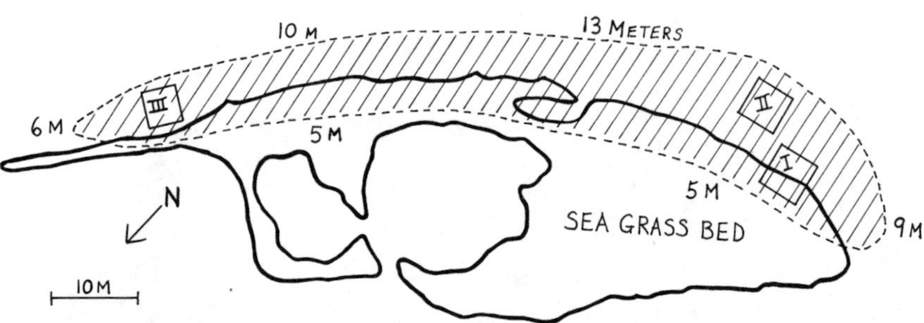

FIG. 2. Garden eel colony 1. Aerial photo (top; taken by David Darom, 1970) shows sea grass bed (upper center) along outer side of which eel colony is located. Caravan Hotel is in foreground, Aquasport diving center is large building near shore in center. Diagrammatic view of colony in relation to sea-grass bed (below) shows locations of three 25-square-meter grids. Right (top): Grid I, located partly in sea-grass bed in the area of most current and highest population density of eels (figures at corners, water depth in meters). Below: Grid III located in open sand in the area with least current and low eel density (black dot, burrow opening of female or immature eels; ♂, burrow opening of male; burrow openings of known pairs of eels are encircled).

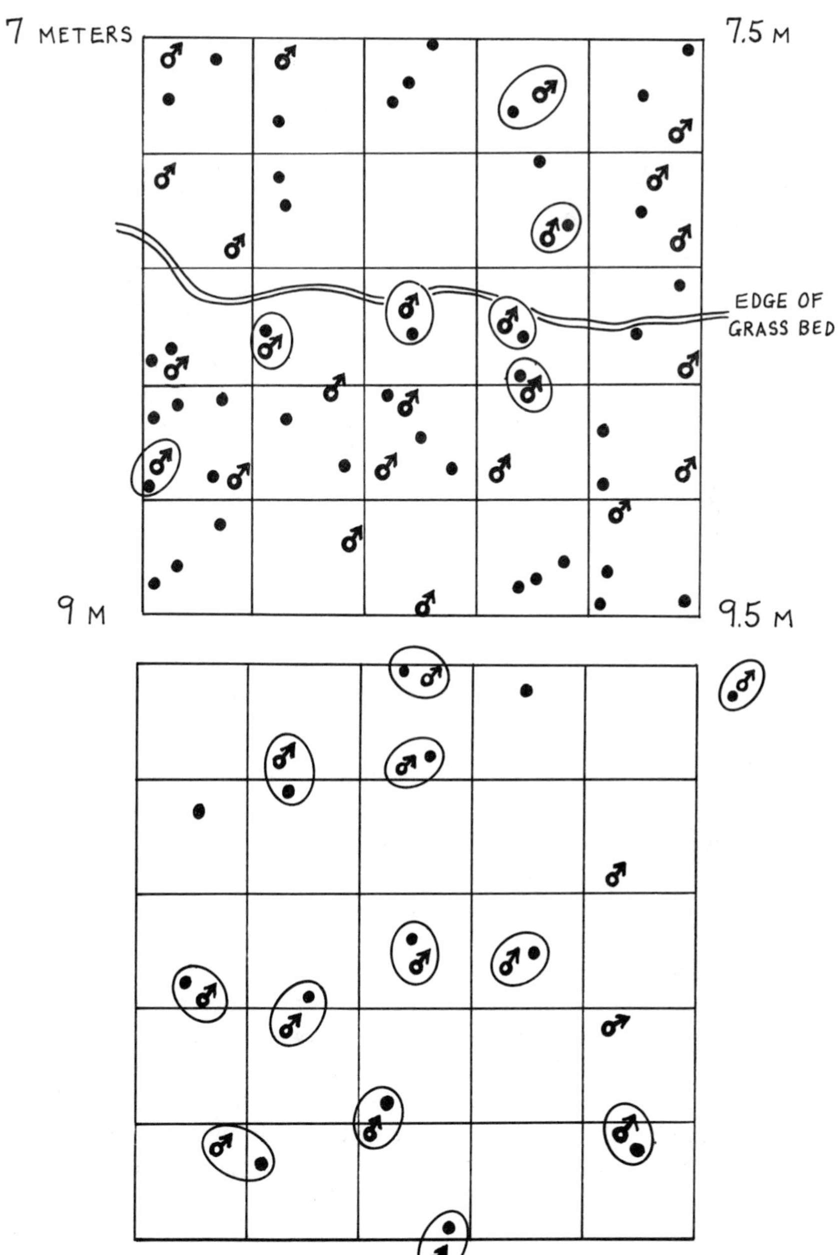
7 METERS
7.5 M
EDGE OF
GRASS BED
9 M
9.5 M

FIG. 3. A cluster of 60 immature eels (each about 20 centimeters long) occupied an area of about 4 square meters in colony 2. Adult eels are seen in background. (Photo by J. Wilkenfeld.)

make in the sand. Their swaying bodies protrude vertically bending near the top so that the head is held horizontally facing into the current. When approached by a diver from a distance of about 6 meters, the eels sink slowly into the sand until only the head protrudes and that too disappears if approached more closely. Herre (1930) first reported eels living in a "vast colony" at Dumaguete in the Philippines. Wading out from shore at low tide, he noted that the eels were living in pairs.

In the Red Sea only one species, the endemic *Gorgasia sillneri,* is known. Klausewitz (1962b) named it after the diver Ludwig Sillner who discovered it at Aqaba (Klausewitz, 1962a). Its ecology and behavior have been studied by Clark (1969, 1971a, 1971b, 1972, 1974), Clark and von Schmidt (1966), and by Fricke (1970) who compared this species with another in Madagascar.

This report is based on observations I made during periods of 2 to 8 weeks during the summers of 1964, 1966, and 1968 with more intensive studies during 1969, 1970, 1971, and 1972 with support from the National Geographic Society, the National Science Foundation, the Smithsonian Institution, the University of Maryland, and Hebrew University. Laboratory studies

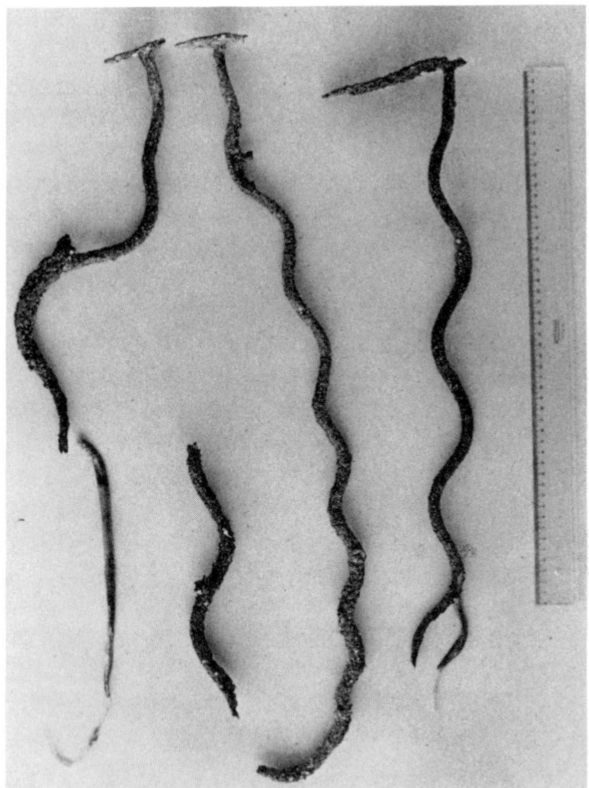

FIG. 4. Molds of eel burrows made by pouring epoxy paint down burrows (ruler is 50 centimeters). "Caps" on top of molds are overflows of paint, showing downslope orientation (left). Mold on left is broken in two pieces and its occupant (decomposed) is at lower left. (Strong horizontal flexure of this mold may indicate that upper part of the burrow leads to a secondary opening.) Mold on right has part of eel's tail protruding below deep end of burrow. Molds are thicker than actual burrows as they have a coating of sand adhering to the dried paint. (Photo by J. Wilkenfeld.)

and headquarters for field studies were made at Hebrew University's Heinz Steinitz Marine Biology Laboratory in Elat, Israel. Teams of divers, including many divers from the University of Maryland and Hebrew University, helped in underwater observations and experiments (1969-1972). Phyllis Anastos-Reidy, David Fridman, and Joshua Wilkenfeld were the main diving assistants. David Doubilet, Igor Klatzo, and James Stanfield contributed valuable photographic documentation.

The purpose of these studies was to learn more about the distribution and behavior of the Red Sea garden eel, using special underwater techniques for close-up observations and experiments within the colonies.

FIG. 5. A male garden eel cleaning sand out of its burrow (center). Female in his territory is to right. Grid lines are in background. (Photo by J. Stanfield.)

The areas we searched for eel colonies were along the east coast of the Sinai Peninsula and at Massawa in the south Red Sea, especially in the area of Green Island, where a diver reported a possible eel colony. We obtained most of our data on behavior in two large colonies near the Steinitz Laboratory (34°56′ E. 29°30′ N.). The methods we used involved: (1) Mapping colonies and counting individual eels in aliquot samples of areas of various population densities; (2) laying 4- and 25-square-meter grids on the sand, mapping locations of burrow openings within each square meter and measuring the diameter of the openings to keep track of individual eels and remapping at intervals of 1 to 3 days; (3) setting up "blinds" (fig. 1) within a colony for close-up observations and photography; (4) using time-lapse photography, mostly at 1-hour intervals, to record changes over 24-hour cycles; and (5) anesthetizing and capturing eels for anatomical and behavioral studies, such as replacing them within the colony and testing them in laboratory aquaria with deep sand floors.

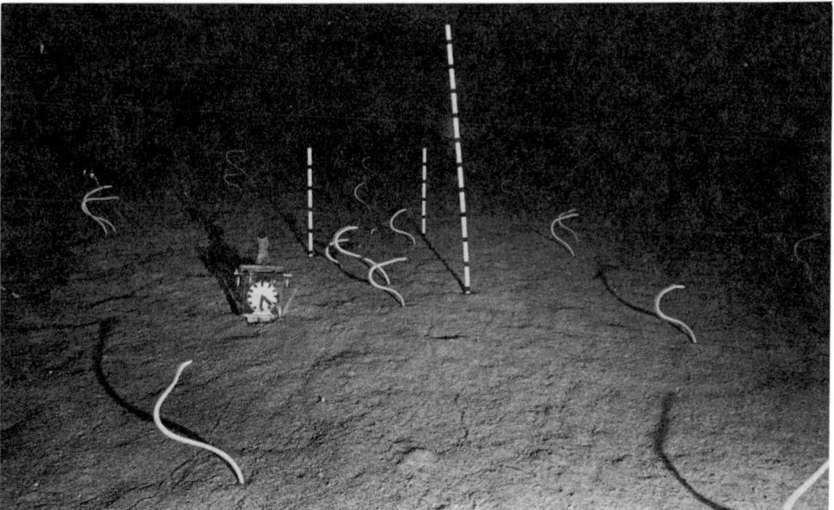

FIG. 6. Time-lapse photos show (top) a male on right side of center 50-centimeter pole, where he is in a more advantageous feeding position, that has moved (center) to a position at the left of the pole where he can mate with the female in his territory but where his feeding hemisphere will overlap hers considerably; and (bottom) eels out of their burrows and feeding at 4:31 a.m., with a strong current coming from the right (one pair, left center, is copulating). (Photo by J. Wilkenfeld.)

We observed 19 colonies of garden eels along the east coast of the Sinai from Elat south to Sharm el Sheikh. We found none in the south Red Sea. Small colonies (41 to several hundred eels) were ovoid or roundish and occupied an area of about 22 to 170 square meters on the sand bottom. Large colonies (about 400 to over 1,800 eels) were elongated ovals, irregular in outline, with a long axis 3 to 5 times the length of the short axis and covered areas of over 700 square meters. Colonies, their long axes usually roughly parallel to the shoreline, start about 25 to 90 meters from shore, at a point where the narrow continental shelf starts to drop into deep water and where complex and reversing bottom currents bring the eels their planktonic food. The density of eels is highest in the area of the colony with the most current.

The largest colony we found was located offshore from the oasis in northern Dahab and farthest out from shore, in the deepest water of any colony. The most northern colony we saw was near the oil jetty in Elat: it was destroyed by an explosion on July 9, 1969. Most of our behavioral information is from (1) a colony of about 1,600 eels located 1.6 kilometers N.NE. of the Steinitz Laboratory, offshore from Aquasport diving center at Coral Beach, in water 5 to 13 meters deep, and with the long axis of the colony 98 meters (fig. 2); and (2) a colony of about 850 eels within 0.4 kilometer S.SW. of the Laboratory, offshore from the lighthouse at northern Taba in water 6 to 12 meters deep, and with the long axis of the colony 84 meters. The general shape and the number of eels of large colonies appear the same year after year but our detailed studies of the two colonies showed many changes taking place in the distribution of the individual eels. Colony 2 shifted 12 meters N.NE. and a small group of 41 eels formed 18 meters from the new south end of the large colony between the summers of 1970 and 1971. Small colonies are unstable. At least four have disappeared for no apparent reason during these studies. Young eels, 20 to 40 centimeters long, are found scattered singly or in groups within large colonies. We found one cluster of 60 eels, each about 20 centimeters long, in a 4-square-meter area within the Taba colony (fig. 2).

Lengths of eels with mature gonads measured 76.7 to 95.7 centimeters (N 12, $\bar{x}$ 88.2) for males and 55.6 to 77.3 centimeters (N 14, $\bar{x}$ 63.5) for females. Although there is an overlap in sizes of the sexes we could usually tell by the diameter of a burrow opening whether it was inhabited by a male or female especially when they were paired (fig. 2, right).

Diameters of burrow openings in paired eels measured 8 to 11 millimeters for males and 6 to 9 millimeters for females. In addition to a sexual difference in length and overall diameter, the male has a dorsal swollen area between the eyes and pectoral fins.

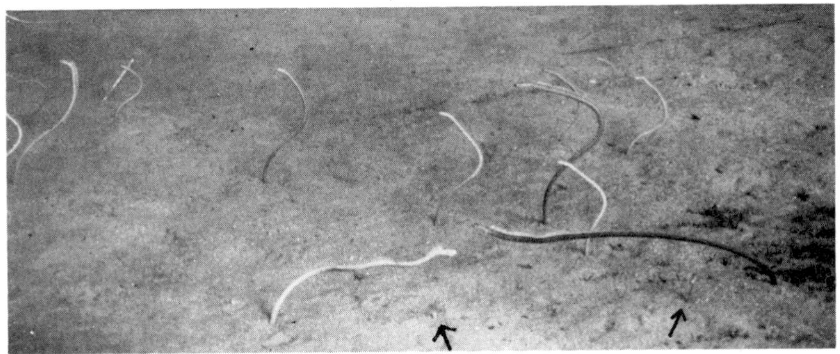

FIG. 7. Two male eels (foreground) in adjacent territories, showing agonistic behavior at their territorial boundary. Larger, darker, and more dominant male on right has a larger territory. Each male has a female within his territory that is almost completely withdrawn into the sand. Arrows point to the heads of these females. Other eels, facing into the current coming from the left, are feeding on plankton. (Photo by I. Klatzo.)

We placed three 25-square-meter grids in areas of different population densities in colony 1 (fig. 2). The highest numbers of eels (indicated by burrow openings kept smooth with mucus) were 68 eels or 2.7 eels per square meter, for Grid I; 59, or 2.4 per square meter, for Grid II; and 25, or 1.0 per square meter, for Grid III. Repeated mappings of Grids I and II within 1- to 3-day intervals (Grid I was remapped also after one year) showed that eels frequently abandoned their burrow openings and made new openings. New openings were usually made within a radius of one meter from the old opening (usually still visible after 2 days even though collapsing from sand), and conceivably an eel might retain the lower part of its old burrow by withdrawing into the sand and coming up in a new spot. Some of the molds of burrows showing a sharp horizontal curve support this possibility (fig. 4). In hundreds of hours of observing hundreds of eels at a time, we have never seen an eel leave its burrow and move its tail even a slight distance across the sand except possibly when cleaning its burrow (fig. 5). When captured by an anesthetic and then released above the sand, the eel will burrow down tail first, making a new burrow.

Eight mappings of Grid I in 11 days showed that 74 percent of the eels moved their burrow openings at least once: 65 percent of the males moved, 91 percent of the females, 79 percent of the adults of unknown sex, and 100 percent of the immature eels. As eels, especially around the periphery, moved in

FIG. 8. Mating behavior of eels photographed from a blind in colony 2: A, female (foreground) is low in her burrow with her genital opening below sand level; B, male touching along ventral surface of female, turgid from ovulated eggs in the lumen of an elongated ovary beneath the skin of this region; C and D, male looping around female; E, and F, male looping under female and pushing her upwards out of her burrow; G, H, and I, female initiating copulatory loop around male and sliding out of her burrow higher onto male's body. (Photo by J. Stanfield.)

---

and out of the grid the number of burrow openings in the grid changed from day to day. Remappings of Grids I and II showed that on the average 18.6 percent of the eels moved their burrow openings in 1-day and 29.4 percent in 2-day periods. Eels in less dense areas may not move as much.

Moves of eels were also recorded on time-lapse photographs (fig. 6). Studies of their diel cycles, by means of series of time-lapse photographs and teams of divers, showed that eels in colonies 1 and 2 retired into their burrows during the night from about 8 p.m. until 4 a.m., depending on the time of sunset and sunrise, and were out of their burrows feeding during most of the daylight hours. There are also periods of "siestas" during daylight from 10 a.m. to 3 p.m. when, for no apparent reason such as current velocity, the entire colony may withdraw into the sand for one to two hours. These daytime "siestas" are irregular from colony to colony. Synchronized dives (every hour) throughout the day on five different colonies on July 28, 1971, showed a different "siesta" pattern for each colony.

Details of the above studies and studies of territoriality (fig. 7), mating behavior (fig. 8), experiments on eel movements, ecological relationships of these eels to other fishes feeding in the colonies, and taxonomic studies (vertebral counts 172-182) will be reported in another publication.

REFERENCES

BEEBE, CHARLES WILLIAM

1938. Zaca venture. xiv + 308 pp. illus. Harcourt Brace and Co., New York.

CLARK, EUGENIE

1969. The lady and the sharks. xi + 269 pp. illus. Harper and Row, New York. [See pp. 205-208.]

1971a. Observations on a garden eel colony at Elat. Sci. Newsletter, Mar. Biol. Lab. Elat., vol. 1, no. 1, p. 5.

1971b. The Red Sea garden eel. Bull. Amer. Littoral Soc., vol. 7, no. 1, pp. 4-10.

1972. The Red Sea's gardens of eels. Nat. Geogr., vol. 142, no. 5, pp. 724-735.

B
C
E
F
H
I

CLARK, EUGENIE—Continued

1974. Houdinis of the Red Sea. Internat. Wildlife, vol. 4, no. 6, pp. 13-17.

CLARK, EUGENIE, and VON SCHMIDT, KAY

1966. A new species of *Trichonotus* (Pisces, Trichonotidae) from the Red Sea. Bull. Sea Fisher. Res. Station Haifa, no. 34, pp. 29-36.

FRICKE, HANS W.

1970. Ökologische und verhaltensbiologische Beobachtungen an den Röhrenaalen *Gorgasia sillneri* und *Taenioconger hassi.* Zeitchr. Tierpsych., vol. 27, no. 9, pp. 1076-1099.

HERRE, ALBERT W.

1930. *Heteroconger polyzona* in the Philippines. Copeia, no. 3, pp. 75-76.

KLAUSEWITZ, WOLFGANG

1962a. Röhrenaale im Roten Meer. Natur und Museum, vol. 92, no. 3, pp. 95-98.

1962b. *Gorgasia sillneri,* ein neuer Röhrenaal aus dem Roten Meer. Senck. Biol., vol. 43, no. 6, pp. 433-435.

EUGENIE CLARK

Three Surging Glaciers, St. Elias Mountains, Canada

Principal Investigator: Sam G. Collins, Council Bluffs, Iowa.

Grant No. 971: To study presurge glacier dynamics of Rusty, Backe, and Trapridge Glaciers, Yukon Territory.

This research program was initiated with the goal of providing data helpful in developing a clearer theoretical understanding of the phenomenon of glacier surge, or rapid flow and advance of the lower glacier following a long period of very slow flow, stagnation, and wastage (Meier and Post, 1969). A large body of data is available respecting the behavior of glaciers during and immediately after the period of rapid advance in the surge cycle, but much less is known about the conditions and changes in the glaciers immediately preceding surge, which may be parameters of an explanatory or predictive theoretical model. Thorough study of a surging glacier prior to an active surge was believed necessary to provide data in this part of the cycle.

Rusty Glacier, then unofficially named "Fox" Glacier (Clarke and Crossley, 1972), was chosen for investigation because it is known to have exhibited surge behavior in the past and its features were interpreted to indicate that it is about to begin a new surge (Arctic Institute of North America, 1967). Backe and Trapridge Glaciers, then unofficially named "Jackal" and "Hyena" glaciers, were included in the study later, because they are in adjacent valleys, easily accessible from Rusty Glacier, and because they too are known surgers, but in different phases of the surge cycle; Rusty and Backe Glaciers probably surged simultaneously in the early decades of this century, Trapridge surged in the early 1940's, and Backe surged again, beginning about 1963 and ending about 1971 (Collins, 1972).

This is a continuing study, in keeping with the goal of observing the glacier as surge flow develops from the quiescent "between surge" pattern. Surveying has been repeated at intervals from 1967 through 1974 to maintain surveillance and detect early indications of possible surge flow. A summary report has been published (Collins, 1972) covering results obtained through 1970. A number of related investigations have been undertaken by others relying in one way or another upon the survey data; these are referred to both in the text following and in the list of references at the end of the article.

Financial support from the National Geographic Society in 1971 is gratefully acknowledged, as is support that has come in other years from the Na-

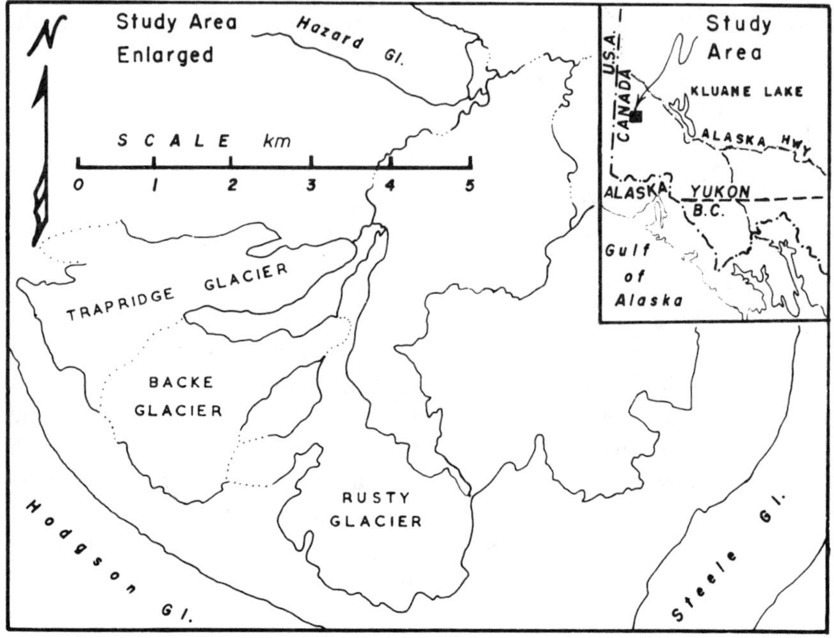

FIG. 1. Location of the study area and the relationship of Rusty Glacier to major nearby features.

tional Science Foundation, the Explorers Club of New York, the American Geographical Society, the Canadian Department of Energy, Mines and Resources, the University of British Columbia, and from private funds. The Arctic Institute of North America has continued throughout the study to provide logistic support through the field facilities of its Icefield Ranges Research Project, under whose aegis the program was begun.

Location and General Description of Study Area

The three glaciers are about 73 kilometers west-southwest of Burwash Landing, the nearest settlement. They lie on the eastern flank of Mount Wood, on the northeastern (interior) slope of the St. Elias Range in the watershed of Steele Creek, tributary via Donjek and White Rivers to the Yukon. Their Canadian Glacier Inventory catalogue numbers and geographical locations are listed below; their general location, orientation, and relationships to each other can be seen in figure 1.

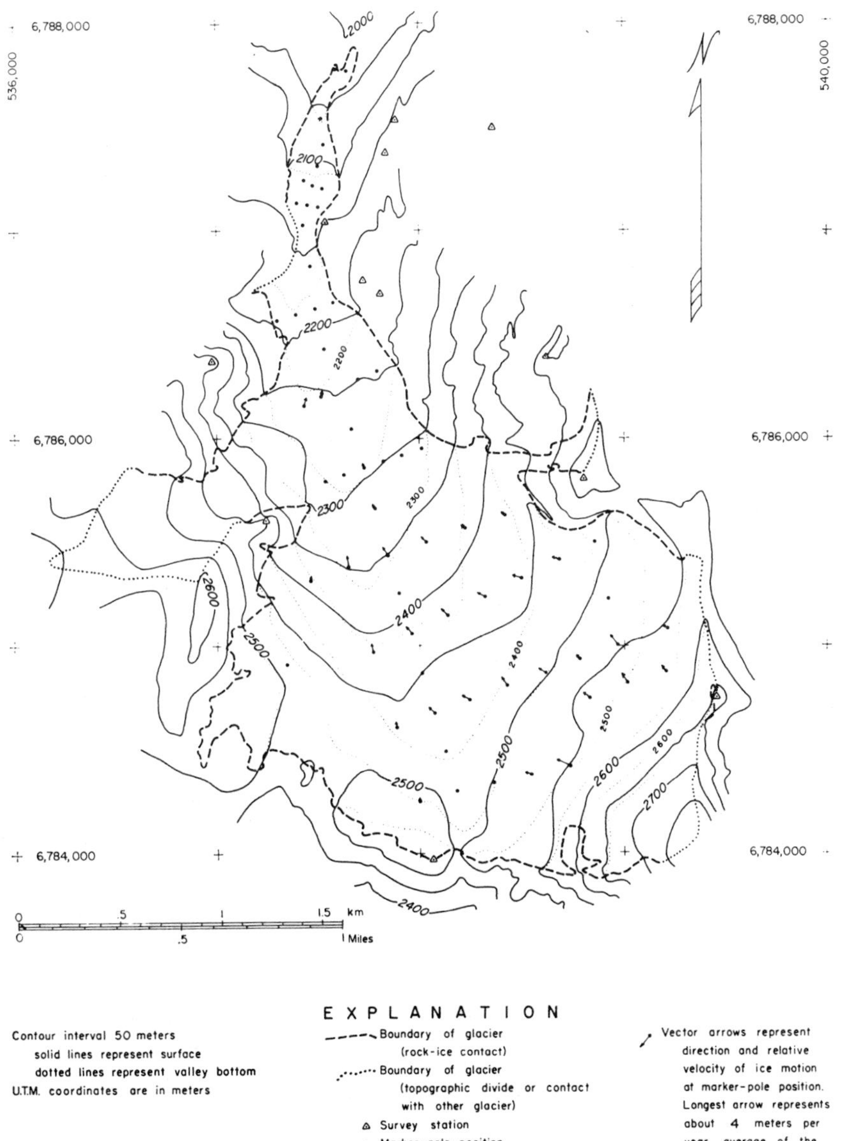

FIG. 2. Map of Rusty Glacier, showing surface and bedrock topography, positions of survey stations and marker poles, and direction and relative amount of motion in all cases where pole was observed to move more than 0.3 mile per year. (After Crossley and Clarke, 1970; Canada Dept. Energy, Mines, Resources, Surveys and Mapping Branch, 1968; Crossley, 1970.)

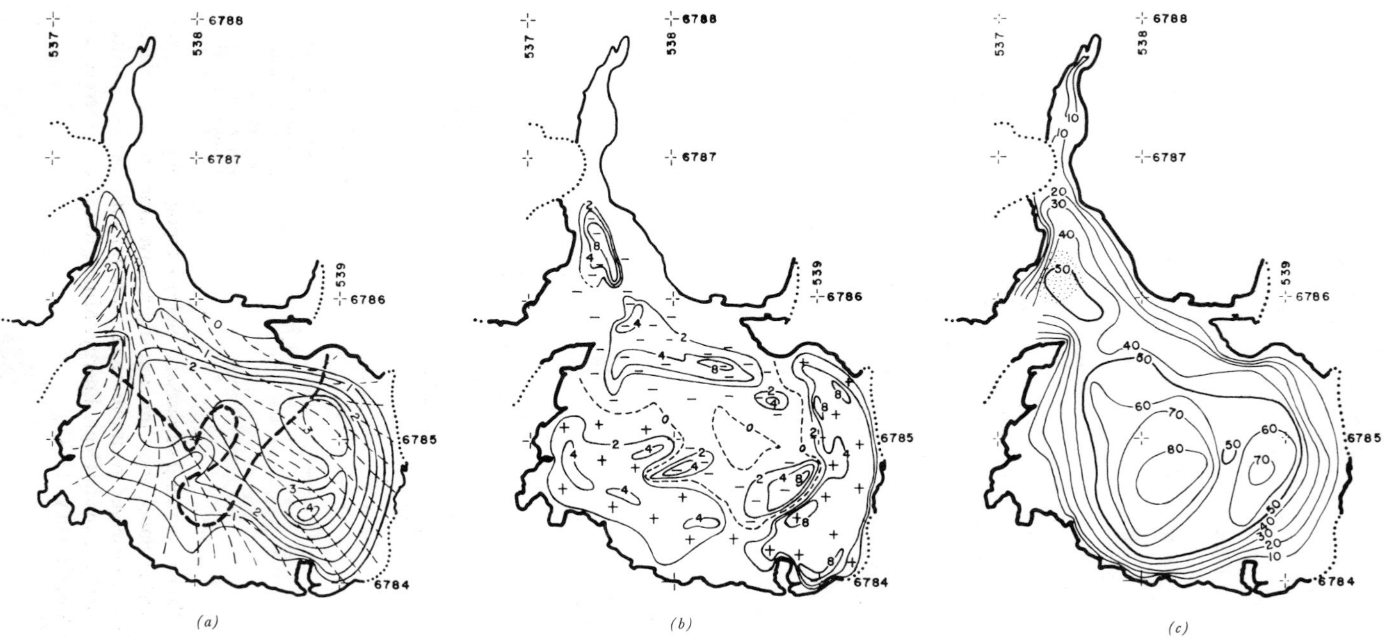

FIG. 3. *a,* Horizontal flow lines and contours of average annual movement, contour increment 0.5 m.yr.$^{-1}$; heavy dashed line represents zone of zero emergence or "equilibrium line" where flow lines parallel the glacier surface, emergence is negative south of the line and positive to the north. *b,* Distribution of longitudinal strain-rates; negative values indicate compression, positive, extension; contour units are 10^{-3} yr^{-1}. *c,* Ice thickness and bottom "hot spot"; isopachous contours are in meters; stippling represents area in which a layer of ice near the glacier bottom is at the pressure-melting point. (After Classen and Clarke, 1971.)

Name	*Inventory No.*	*Latitude*	*Longtitude*
Rusty	*4*9CAS091	61° 12.4′N.	140° 17.0′W.
Backe	*4*9CAS092	61° 12.8′N.	140° 19.3′W.
Trapridge	*4*9CAS093	61° 13.6′N.	140° 20.0′W.

The glaciers lie between 2,000 and 3,050 meters above sea level. Average firnline altitude is about 2,450 meters on Rusty Glacier, somewhat lower on Backe, and somewhat higher on Trapridge; the variation reflects differences in topography and orientation that affect snowfall and ablation rates. Nearby valleys are about 1,600 meters; the entire study area is well above general tree-line (about 1,300 meters in the lower Steele Creek Valley) and above the local limit of continuous vegetative cover as well, although scattered clumps of alpine flora occur except at the very highest levels.

Summary of Survey Program

Ground-control surveying and photogrammetric mapping of Rusty Glacier began the research program in 1967. A topographic map of the area at 1/10,000 scale and contour interval 10 meters (Canada Department of Energy, Mines, Resources, Surveys and Mapping Branch, 1968) provided an excellent base map for subsequent work. An array of 70 marker stakes was set on the glacier surface in the same year for accumulation-ablation measurements, ice-movement monitoring, and as geographic references for other investigations. This stake array has been maintained with few changes, except for lost stakes in the lower glacier, and was resurveyed in 1968, 1969, 1970, 1971, and 1974.

Trapridge Glacier was instrumented in 1969 with an array of 26 marker stakes, set mostly along the glacier midline. These were surveyed in 1969, 1970, 1971, 1972, and 1974. Six additional marker stakes were set in 1972 and observed in 1972 and 1974 surveys.

On Backe Glacier no marker stakes have been maintained for more than two consecutive seasons; consequently, such measurements of its movements as have been made are nonsystematic and of limited usefulness for interpretation.

The accuracy of the survey was sufficient to detect reliably annual marker stake motions in excess of about 0.2 meter and to determine absolute stake positions within about 0.4 meter. A detailed discussion of surveying procedures and other field methods employed is given in the writer's 1972 report.

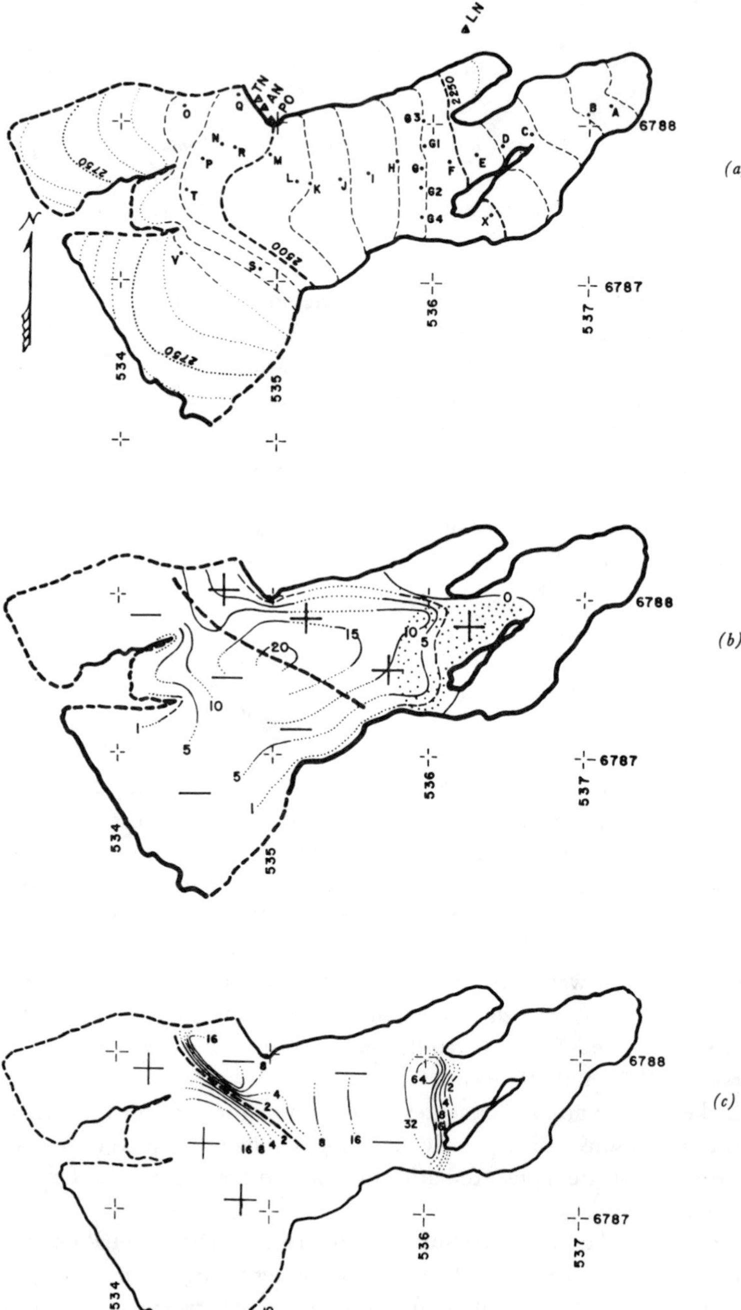

(a)
(b)
(c)
LN
TN
AN
PO
2250
2500
2750
6788
6787
534
535
536
537
A
B
C
D
E
F
G
G1
G2
G3
G4
H
I
J
K
L
M
N
O
P
Q
R
S
T
V
X
0
1
5
10
15
20
2
4
8
16
32
64

Analysis of Results

The map, figure 2, summarizes the gross information retrieved by the survey and allied investigations of ice thickness: glacier outline and topography, valley-bottom topography, layout of survey stations and marker stake array, and direction and annual velocity of ice flow.

Computed from map and source materials, the general geometric parameters of the glacier are: length, 4.5 kilometers; area, 4.97 square kilometers; maximum ice thickness, 88 meters; average ice thickness, 36 meters; volume, 0.178 cubic kilometers; lowest altitude, 2,010 meters; highest altitude, 2,770 meters; average slope, 0.169.

Flow pattern of the glacier ice is shown in figure 3*a*. Horizontal flow paths are represented by dashed lines; solid contours represent horizontal velocities in units of m. year^{-1}.

Vertical-flow rates were difficult to establish because the very small values are near the limits of surveying accuracy, but the general pattern of emergence is clear: the heavy dotted line across the glacier in figure 3*a* represents the equilibrium zone where vertical flow is parallel to surface slope. Flow lines in areas lower on the glacier diverge upward from the sloping surface plane (emergence), and in areas higher on the glacier flow lines diverge downward from surface slope (negative emergence).

The pattern of flow seems usual for small, thin glaciers, except that an area was found in the upper tongue in which emergence lines diverge upward very strongly, rising above the horizontal; this suggests a condition possibly characteristic in surge-type glaciers, in which the lower tongue becomes stagnant and acts as an immobile "dam" forcing flow upward (Nielsen, 1969).

Figure 3*b* shows the general pattern of longitudinal strain-rate across the glacier in units of 10^{-3} year^{-1}; positive sign indicates compression and negative extension. Strain-rates are all small, near the lower limits at which crevasses could be expected to form. That numerous crevasses are known to exist in the areas of extending strain-rates confirms nontemperate ice-temperature conditions found in deep bore holes elsewhere on the glacier by Classen

---

FIG. 4. *a,* Trapridge Glacier; approximate topography and location of surveyed points. *b,* Horizontal motion and pattern of emergence; contours (dotted where estimated) represent amount of horizontal annual motion in meters; heavy dashed line represents zone of zero emergence; areas of negative and positive emergence are designated and stippling shows the area where flow lines diverge upward from the horizontal. *c,* Distribution of longitudinal strain-rates; heavy dashed line represents zone of zero strain; negative values indicate compression, positive, extension; contour units are 10^{-3} yr.$^{-1}$.

TABLE 1. UTM Coordinates and Average Annual Motion Data for Marker Poles

E_{74}, N_{74}, and A_{74} are Universal Transverse Mercator easting, northing, and altitude, respectively. $\bar{V}_h$ and $\bar{V}_z$ are average annual motion in the horizontal and vertical direction, respectively, in meters. Dir. is the map direction of the horizontal motion, in degrees clockwise from north. E is the angle of emergence (angle between flow line and glacier surface) in degrees.

MP. No.	E_{74}	N_{74}	A_{74}	$\bar{V}_h$	*Dir.*	$\bar{V}_z$	*E*
10	537482.60	6786798.97	2165.02	2.50	081	+2.18	+048
12W1	537398.11	6786600.39	2176.98	0.60	035	+0.20	+025
14	537535.24	6786434.85	2215.08	N/S	–	N/S	000
16E2	537795.31	6786330.54	2243.92	N/S	–	N/S	000
16	537616.29	6786248.06	2243.58	N/S	–	N/S	000
16W1	537528.99	6786211.95	2252.22	1.65	019	+0.19	+016
20E2	537918.48	6785919.78	2305.32	0.23	000	N/S	+009
20E1	537825.05	6785891.90	2297.02	N/S	–	N/S	000
20	537730.50	6785861.47	2291.48	0.66	346	+0.11	+015
20W1	537636.40	6785831.29	2287.94	0.52	333	+0.17	+024
20W2	537541.63	6785803.10	2286.26	1.06	354	+0.17	+013
22W11	536732.68	6785638.04	2503.02	5.34	081	–0.97	000
24E6	538422.55	6785633.72	2418.34	0.20	303	N/S	+010
24E4	538222.47	6785571.35	2391.80	0.53	323	N/S	+011
24E2	538026.92	6785515.81	2373.73	1.96	319	–0.10	+004
24W2	537650.67	6785401.01	2352.09	2.30	343	N/S	+011
26	537893.84	6785268.98	2381.34	2.10	325	+0.30	+005
26W6	537346.00	6784921.62	2485.99	1.52	048	–0.88	–017
28E10	538856.43	6785504.88	2495.42	N/S	–	N/S	000
28E6	538487.47	6785333.13	2441.51	2.27	292	–0.03	+010
28E4	538301.97	6785249.81	2425.59	2.47	308	0.00	+007
28E2	538120.89	6785164.62	2421.24	2.47	319	–0.53	–003
28	537947.10	6785077.86	2422.34	2.13	328	–0.14	+005
28W2	537767.01	6784988.86	2418.41	2.30	348	+0.60	–001
28W4	537600.59	6784896.25	2444.94	1.61	036	–0.17	+005

30E10	538898.17	6785235.65	2510.29	3.10	287	–0.60	–004
30	538002.36	6784885.26	2449.97	1.74	320	–0.62	–013
32E12	539210.15	6785090.71	2553.04	1.20	306	–0.80	–028
32E10	538952.20	6785019.32	2546.31	3.20	326	–0.73	–001
32E8	538764.61	6784946.10	2524.64	2.66	307	–0.80	–007
32E6	538596.18	6784881.16	2493.15	1.98	304	–0.67	–009
32E4	538414.80	6784821.61	2487.91	2.67	292	–0.28	000
32	538058.79	6784698.51	2462.98	1.97	320	+0.12	+011
32W2	537882.39	6784617.80	2467.81	1.06	356	–0.13	000
32W4	537696.67	6784543.73	2486.73	0.43	017	–0.17	–013
34E10	539009.10	6784842.90	2566.09	2.78	329	–0.16	–014
34E8	538819.98	6784765.32	2561.74	2.28	303	–0.07	+001
34	538120.69	6784497.39	2475.37	0.83	328	0.00	+004
36E6	538715.78	6784436.62	2549.18	4.00	292	–1.16	–004
36E4	538538.90	6784389.53	2522.79	1.98	288	–0.30	–002
36E2	538364.72	6784345.48	2501.98	0.49	291	–0.34	–027
36W2	537995.81	6784262.10	2510.99	0.75	358	–0.42	–022
E	536279.34	6787817.37	2226.85	0.36	112	+0.30	+053
F	536110.74	6787762.36	2271.18	0.51	005	+0.17	+032
G1	535956.42	6787863.72	2303.84	14.3	102	+0.28	+014
G3	535937.01	6788015.10	2300.62	N/S	–	–0.84	–090
H	535817.84	6787713.04	2353.07	11.77	070	–0.17	+006
I	535648.23	6787703.60	2379.42	14.81	072	–0.92	+008
K	535297.21	6787644.77	2434.22	19.63	077	–4.34	000
L	535212.71	6787652.25	2460.80	20.54	089	–2.10	+003
M	535026.78	6787814.85	2488.95	16.92	087	–1.20	+001
O	534460.11	6788100.17	2575.76	11.22	103	–1.24	+002
P	534573.16	6787778.99	2531.12	12.99	090	–3.88	–005
R	534778.56	6787838.89	2514.38	11.95	076	–0.05	+003
S	534858.07	6787100.32	2584.28	6.47	090	–1.28	–006
T	534452.45	6787575.63	2253.69	9.72	090	–0.97	–015
V	534397.77	6787189.93	2687.41	3.22	046	–0.68	–007
X	536379.43	6787433.64	2230.72	N/S	–	N/S	000

(1970); also Classen and Clarke (1971). Crevasses are mostly covered by firn except during seasons of unusually high ablation, indicating that they must open very slowly.

Mass-balance measurements (Brewer, 1969) show the glacier as a whole to be nearly in equilibrium. The lower tongue, however, because ice flow does not replace ablation losses, is rapidly wasting away. At the beginning of this study in 1967 it was clear from earlier photographs (Wood, 1939; Sharp, 1947) and geologic evidence that the tongue has experienced recession for several decades from a formerly much extended position. By 1974 most of the ice below the confluence with Backe Glacier was gone and the little remaining had been cut through to the valley floor by meltwater streams. Only if the glacier surges again will the tongue become re-extended.

Figure 3*c* shows ice thickness in meters. The information is a summary of results obtained from deep drilling (Classen and Clarke, 1971) and gravimetric measurements (Crossley, 1970). Seismic measurements were also attempted without acceptable results, and radio echo soundings have been made (Goodman et al., 1975). The stippled area indicates basal ice temperature at or near the pressure-melting point reported by Classen and Clarke (1971).

Trapridge Glacier has been studied in less detail and found to be similar to Rusty in most respects. Figure 4*a* shows surface topography; *b,* horizontal motion and emergence patterns; and *c,* distribution of strain-rates.

Surveillance of Rusty and Trapridge Glaciers since 1970 has added little to the general pattern of behavior reported earlier (Collins, 1972), and readers are referred to the earlier report for greater detail. Later measurements have confirmed the earlier ones and shown no evidence of changing flow velocities. Surveys will be repeated in the future in hopes of detecting early the onset of surge activity in one glacier or the other. No surge has so far been reported in a glacier for which pre-surge details are available; precise information respecting changes in motion and flow patterns at the very onset of a surge would be helpful in establishing a reliable theoretical model of glacier surge.

Related Research

A number of research efforts have been undertaken relying upon the data base provided by the series of surveys of Rusty and Trapridge glaciers. Some could have been done even without the author's prior work, but not so directly; some could not have been undertaken at all without it. The list of references includes both reports cited in the text and other reports (marked with asterisks) relying to some degree upon the data provided by the author's surveys. Table 1 gives the 1974 positions of all markers surviving at that time, their horizontal and vertical velocities, and emergence rates.

REFERENCES

(Asterisk indicates publications relying to some degree on data provided by these surveys.)

AMERICAN GEOGRAPHICAL SOCIETY

1970. Field research, Fox Glacier, summer 1970. Ubique, winter issue 1970-71, p. 1.

ARCTIC INSTITUTE OF NORTH AMERICA

1967. Investigation of a small glacier in the St. Elias Mountains, Yukon Territory, Canada, prior to predicted surge. Unpublished proposal (GA-1080) to National Science Foundation.

*BREWER, T.

1969. A mass-balance study of "Fox Glacier," Yukon Territory, Canada, 43 pp. Unpublished M.A. thesis, Boston University.

1972. A two-year mass-balance study of the Rusty Glacier 1968-1969. Icefield Ranges Res. Proj., Sci. Results, vol. 3, pp. 75-82. American Geographical Society and Arctic Institute of North America.

*CANADA DEPARTMENT OF ENERGY, MINES, RESOURCES, SURVEYS AND MAPPING BRANCH

1968. Fox Glacier: Map, 1:10,000, 1967 aerial photography, Topographic Survey Division. Unpublished.

*CLARKE, GARRY K.C.

1971. Temperature measurements in Fox Glacier, Yukon Territory. Pp. 47-48 *in* "Glaciers," J. Demers, ed. Proceedings of Workshop Seminar sponsored by Canadian National Committee for the International Hydrological Decade.

1972. Glacier! A 22-minute color documentary film, 16 millimeters, with sound track and animations.

1976. Thermal regulation of glacier surging. Journ. Glaciol., vol. 16, no. 74, pp. 231-250.

*CLARKE, GARRY K.C., and CLASSEN, DAVID F.

1970. The Fox Glacier project. Can. Geogr. Journ., vol. 81, pp. 26-29, illus.

*CLARKE, GARRY K.C., and CROSSLEY, D.J.

1972. The Fox Glacier in Yukon Territory is now the Rusty Glacier. Journ. Glaciol., vol. 11, no. 63, pp. 456-457.

*CLARKE, GARRY K.C., and GOODMAN, R.H.

1975. Radio echo soundings and ice temperature measurements in a surge-type glacier. Journ. Glaciol., vol. 14, no. 70, pp. 71-78.

*CLASSEN, DAVID F.

1970. Thermal drilling and deep ice-temperature measurements on the Fox Glacier, Yukon, 66 pp. M. Sc. thesis, University of British Columbia.

*CLASSEN, DAVID F., and CLARKE, GARRY K.C.

1971. Basal hot spot on a surge type glacier. Nature, vol. 229, no. 5285, pp. 481-483.

1972. Thermal drilling and ice-temperature measurements in the Rusty Glacier. Icefield Ranges Res. Proj., Sci. Results, vol. 3, pp. 103-116. American Geographical Society and Arctic Institute of North America.

COLLINS, SAM G.

*1971. Exploration on a surging glacier. Explorers Journ., vol. 49, no. 2, pp. 124-129, illus.

1972. Survey of the Rusty Glacier area, Yukon Territory, Canada, 1967-1970. Journ. Glaciol., vol. 11, no. 62, pp. 235-253, illus. (Republished, 1974, *in* Icefield Ranges Res. Proj., Sci. Results, vol. 4, pp. 259-272.)

*CROSSLEY, D.J., and CLARKE, GARRY K.C.

1970. Gravity measurements on "Fox Glacier," Yukon Territory, Canada. Journ. Glaciol., vol. 9, no. 57, pp. 363-374.

1972. Gravity and shallow ice-temperature measurements on Rusty Glacier. Icefield Ranges Res. Proj., Sci. Results, vol. 3, pp. 93-101. American Geographic Society and Arctic Institute of North America.

*FABER, TH.

1972. Hydrological study of the Rusty Glacier. Icefield Ranges Res. Proj., Sci. Results, vol. 3, pp. 83-92. American Geographical Society and Arctic Institute of North America.

1973. Rusty Glacier Basin, Yukon Territory, Canada. Results of the 1968 hydrological field work. I.A.S.H. Publ, no. 95, Symposium on the Hydrology of Glaciers, I.U.G.G., p. 197 (abstract).

*GOODMAN, R.H.; CLARKE, GARRY K.C.; JARVIS, G.T.; and COLLINS, SAM G.

1975. Radio echo soundings on Trapridge Glacier, Yukon Territory. Journ. Glaciol., vol. 14, no. 70, pp. 79-84.

*JARVIS, G.T.

1973. Thermal studies related to surging glacier, 194 pp. Unpublished M. Sc. thesis, University of British Columbia.

*JARVIS, G.T., and CLARKE, GARRY K.C.

1975. The thermal regime of Trapridge Glacier and its relevance to glacier surging. Journ. Glaciol., vol. 14, no. 71, pp. 235-250.

MEIER, MARK F., and POST, A.S.

1969. What are glacier surges? Can. Journ. Earth Sci., vol. 6, pp. 807-817.

*NAROD, B.B.

1975. Ultra high frequency radio echo soundings of glaciers. vii + 69 pp. Unpublished M. Sc. thesis, University of British Columbia.

NAROD, B.B. and CLARKE, G.K.C.

——. Airborne UHF radar surveys of three Yukon glaciers. Journal of Glaciology (in press).

NIELSEN, LAWRENCE E.

1969. The ice-dam, powder-flow theory of glacier surges. Can. Journ. Earth Sci., vol. 6, pp. 955-961.

SHARP, ROBERT P.
1947. The Wolf Creek glaciers, St. Elias Range, Yukon Territory. Geogr. Rev., vol. 37, pp. 26-52, illus.

*WEST, K.E.
1972. H_2O^{18}/H_2O^{16} variations in ice and snow of mountainous regions of Canada, 123 pp. Ph.D. thesis, University of Alberta.

WOOD, WALTER A.
1939. Expedition photographs of Rusty and Trapridge Glaciers (in author's collection).

SAM G. COLLINS

Spectroscopy of Volcanic Flames and Fume

Principal Investigators: Dale P. Cruikshank and David Morrison, Institute for Astronomy, University of Hawaii at Manoa, Honolulu, Hawaii.

Grant No. 983: To study by spectroscopy the chemistry of flames and fumes from Kilauea Volcano, Hawaii.

Since the earliest days of European man in the Hawaiian Islands, visitors to Kilauea Volcano have been fascinated by the bright and multicolored flames that are seen to emanate occasionally for brief periods from vents in active areas at the summit or on the flanks of the mountain. With colors ranging from intense orange to pale blue, the flames sometimes roar with great fury from a constricted vent and at other times lazily lap at the dark sky from a gaping crack on the barren floor of the great Kilauea caldera. Smaller and much shorter-lived flames of pale blue or green are occasionally seen bursting from cracks in the slaggy crust on the surfaces of lava lakes on Kilauea Volcano. They are common on the lake surface in Halemaumau, which was active continuously from the latter 19th century until 1924, and intermittently since then, and on the new lava lakes at Mauna Ulu and the Alae shield some 10 kilometers from Kilauea's summit.

The flames seen at Kilauea and at other volcanoes around the world (in the Congo, on Kamchatka, and elsewhere) have attracted somewhat less attention than the more spectacular lava fountains, lava flows, and other more violent aspects of volcanic eruptions. Nonetheless, flames from combusting volcanic gas may hold important clues to the origin and nature of the gases inside the earth, from which is derived the atmosphere that we breathe. Geochemists have long recognized the important role of gases in the eruptive process of volcanoes. Because the prediction of volcanic activity is one of the main goals of contemporary volcanology, a full understanding of the chemistry and physics of gases in subterranean magma chambers and in lava lakes and flows on the earth's surface is crucial.

Volcanic gases are normally analyzed from samples collected at fuming vents, but contamination of samples by ordinary air is difficult to avoid and a large number of samples must be studied for any complete picture of the composition of the gas at any particular vent. While great volumes of gas pour forth at nearly all volcanic vents, combustion to form flames occurs relatively rarely. In those cases when flames are present and conditions of access are favorable, the technique of spectroscopy can be applied to the analysis of the gas composition as well as the identification of the chemical processes occurring as combustion takes place in the ambient atmosphere.

The application of spectroscopy to the study of volcanic flames came late in field studies of eruptions for three reasons: (1) Volcanic eruptions frequently occur in geographical locations where access is impeded by snow, high elevation, or jungle, and spectrographic equipment is usually bulky and not easily handled in the field; (2) the principal optical emission from incandescent lava, an intense continuum characteristic of a black body at temperature 1,000° to 1,100°C. (with peak intensity of emission at about 2.8 microns), has few diagnostic spectral features; and (3) flames with diagnostic spectra are uncommon and when present are often faint, far too distant to observe easily, and always short-lived. The fact that flames are relatively less uncommon at Kilauea Volcano and because access to the volcano was easy (only 400 kilometers and 2 hours away by plane and car) encouraged us to undertake spectroscopic studies aimed at clarification of the composition of the gases as well as the identification of the combustion process giving rise to flames.

Our interest in terrestrial volcanic flames was in large measure inspired by reports in recent years of spectroscopic evidence for volcanic activity on the moon. Soviet astronomer N. A. Kozyrev, observing at the Crimean Astrophysical Observatory in 1958, obtained the first evidence for active volcanism on another planet. His spectrum of a glowing red spot in the lunar crater Alphonsus has been interpreted as evidence for fluorescence (excited by the sun) of gas given off by a volcanic eruption in the central peak on the crater floor. Kozyrev observed another red spot in the crater Aristarchus in 1969, but the spectra are of lesser quality. Kozyrev himself studied volcanic flames by spectroscopy on Kamchatka. His account of the 12-hour plane flight from Leningrad to Petropavlovsk-Kamchatskii, followed by a 3-day ride on horseback through the high-altitude snowfields to get to the volcano, makes us feel a bit guilty working in the relative comfort of Kilauea, where the vents are commonly within a short drive and half-hour hike from a comfortable hotel in the lush Hawaiian rainforest. The establishment of spectroscopic criteria for the identification of volcanism on the moon or other planets has been an important goal of the research undertaken at Kilauea under the Society's sponsorship and also in the preliminary work done there in 1967-1969 by Cruikshank.

The main source of activity at Kilauea from 1969 to the present has been the almost continuous flank eruptions along the east rift zone of the volcano, and it is here that we began our spectrographic studies of volcanic flames. During the first year of this eruptive series, alternating high lava fountains and surface flows in the region between the former large pit craters Alae and

Aloi, on the Chain of Craters Road about 10 kilometers from the summit of Kilauea, completely filled in the pit craters and built a low dome, forming a small but typical Hawaiian shield volcano. This feature was named Mauna Ulu, which means "growing mountain" in Hawaiian. Most of the activity centered in the fissure at the summit of the dome, which transformed itself during 1970 into a permanent lava lake about 100 by 60 meters in size. From time to time lava overflowed from the summit lake or from subsidiary pit craters and vents on the slope of the shield. Within the summit lake, the lava circulated from east to west, and frequently the release of gas from beneath the partially congealed surface generated fountains of incandescent lava and gas up to 20 meters high along the edges of the lake. Occasionally, these fountains also produced flames, which rose in flickering yellow streamers far above the spattering lava, sometimes shooting up as far as 40 meters above the lava lake.

On three evenings during the winter and spring of 1971 we hiked the 2 kilometers to the summit of Mauna Ulu from the place where earlier lava flows had inundated the road; there we set up our spectrograph to record these flames. Only the largest flames could be studied, since it was necessary to photograph them against the black sky in order to avoid overexposure from the continuous thermal spectrum of the fountaining lava. During this period the lava lake was gradually enlarging itself through collapse of its 30-meter-high walls, and on more than one occasion we learned that the area of the rim from which we made our observations collapsed into the crater within a few days of our visit.

The spectra we obtained at Mauna Ulu were dominated by the emission of the D lines of sodium, and indeed this emission provides the explanation for their brilliant yellow color. However, we believe that sodium is only a small constituent of the burning gas, and these spectra gave us no information on the gas that was actually involved in the combustion process. Another disadvantage of studying flames from a stable lava lake is that the gases released are not necessarily representative of the materials, coming from deep within the earth, that are of most interest to us.

Of more interest was the study of flames associated with new vents, but we had to wait until the summer of 1971 for the desired opportunity. Hawaiian volcanoes are known for their formation of kilometer-long cracks from which lava and cinder fountains spray in a "curtain of fire" that sometimes reaches 100-150 meters in height. The fissures open in the course of a few tens of minutes and the uniform lava fountains frequently play for 10 or 20 hours, after which the fountaining is normally concentrated in one small reach of the crack and the spray may reach higher than 300 meters. More often, however, the fountaining subsides completely all along the fissure. For the several hours following the subsidence of fountaining, characteristic yellow and blue flames lick out in incandescent tongues 10 or 20 meters in length. Gradually, in the course of a few hours they die out, leaving only the hot, steaming cracks surrounded by fresh lava and pumice.

Such was the case on August 14, 1971, when an 11-hour episode of lava fountaining began at 8:55 a.m. on the floor of the Kilauea caldera, just a few meters from the road traversed by thousands of visitors each year. Large portions of the caldera floor were covered by new lava from *en echellon* lines of vents, the first new lava on the caldera since a brief eruption in 1954. We were summoned to the volcano by the scientist-in-charge of the Hawaiian Volcano Observatory, Dr. Donald W. Peterson, who cooperated with our spectroscopic program in every way. We arrived at sunset with our equipment, just in time to see the last major fountain die away. Having prepared the spectrograph and cameras, we proceeded to the southwestern extremity of the fissure system. The sky was illuminated by the glowing red lava covering a few hundred acres of the caldera floor and by large luminous flames surging from the cracks that had spewed forth thousands of tons of liquid lava in the preceding few hours. Our observing party approached to within 25 meters of a line of flaming vents and at the edge of a fresh lava flow set up the spectrograph. This section of the line of vents was 30 meters long and consisted of six separate flaming orifices. Flames at one end were greenish blue and those at the other end intense yellow-orange, with intermediate colors between. Larger flames issued from other sections of the new rifts, but the voluminous new lava flows made them inaccessible. We made hour-long exposures with the spectrograph until after midnight, by which time the flames had diminished considerably in size and intensity.

The spectra we obtained that night revealed hitherto unobserved lines of water vapor in emission. Water vapor is the most common volcanic gas, and at first thought the detection of excited water molecules may not seem significant. The lines we found are not due to "hot steam," however. These same lines were discovered in the laboratory in the 1930s by the Japanese chemist T. Kitagawa when he burned hydrogen gas at high temperature in oxygen. He showed that the lines occur as a result of the highly excited water molecules *created* by the combustion of hydrogen and oxygen. Thus it was clear at once that we had found the main cause of the flames at Kilauea—hydrogen in the volcanic gas bursts into flames as it comes out of the hot vents that have earlier been opened by the lava and gas from below. Among the questions remaining were: Why do the flames appear irregularly, and not at all gas vents; what produces the colors of the flames; what is the exact nature of the combustion reaction by which hydrogen burns in air; and, most important, what is the *source* of the hydrogen?

Our spectra showed, in addition to the water-vapor lines, very strong sodium-emission lines, such as those seen earlier at Mauna Ulu. Hawaiian lavas have sufficient sodium in them to easily account for the presence of this emission feature in our records. The variability of colors in the line of flames we observed in August arises from different abundances of sodium as evidenced by the different strength of the spectral emission lines from the greenish-blue to the orange flames. We do not understand, however, why flames 10 meters apart, both deriving from the same vent system, can show a marked difference in sodium abundance.

In an effort to understand the chemistry of the combustion of hydrogen in volcanic flames, we began a spectroscopic search for a family of lines that occurs in nearly all combustion chain reactions involving hydrogen and oxygen, and it should be said that there are many hundreds of these reaction chains. The family of lines is produced by the OH radical, which is formed as an intermediary compound when hydrogen burns. Its lines lie in the ultraviolet part of the spectrum, whereas the H_2O lines were found in the red end of the spectrum. We made some modifications to our spectrograph to make it sensitive to the ultraviolet and awaited the next flames at Kilauea.

Our wait was not long. In September 1971 a new eruption began in the Kilauea caldera and quickly spread to the volcano's southwest rift zone. This rift is much less active than the east rift where most flank eruptions occur, and the last activity in the arid Ka'u desert through which the southwest rift runs ceased in 1920. On the second day after the eruption began, we watched from the Hawaiian Volcano Observatory, perched at the highest point on the Kilauea caldera rim, as a line of fuming vents rapidly opened up along the rift. The pressure of the migrating lava below cracked the ground along ancient fractures in the mountain slopes. The first sign was white clouds of volcanic fume, followed shortly by highly gas-charged lava sputtering up in fountains a few tens of meters high. The lava fountains grew as the cracks progressed seaward at about the speed a man could comfortably run. Within an hour or two, the main system of cracks was more than a kilometer long, and the lava fountains were producing large flows of pahoehoe and aa, which quickly moved downslope incinerating all the trees and underbrush in their paths. At their maximum activity the central fountains reached 50 meters in height.

New lines of fountains opened during the day, but by dusk the original fountains had vanished, leaving only a long line of fuming and flaming vents, and hundred of acres of new lava flows. At sunset we hiked 3 kilometers from the road to the fresh flaming vents. The trail, which leads past the footprints of ancient Hawaiian warriors preserved in a layer of welded volcanic ash, was brilliantly illuminated by the glow from 100-meter lava fountains more than 3 kilometers distant.

Sulphur fume and steam poured from the vents that had just a few hours earlier spouted enormous lava fountains. Flames 10 meters high surged from glowing cracks surrounded by the fresh lava. To gain access to the most suitable flames, we traversed a 15-meter span of the new lava, dark and solidified on top, but hot and plastic below, with incandescent lava showing through cracks in the surface. After a few minutes walking on it we could smell the soles of our boots smoldering. Having set up the spectrograph on the fresh hot lava, we began a long exposure and retreated to the relative comfort of the old desert surface. Through the early part of the evening the flames gradually diminished and the sulphur fume got progressively worse, ultimately driving us out of the area.

The ultraviolet spectra of the September flames showed no emission from the expected OH bands. We had a further opportunity to search for these bands on December 13, 1972, when we observed an intense yellow flame from a lava cone near the Alae lava lake adjacent to Mauna Ulu on Kilauea's east rift. Again, no evidence for the OH bands was detected.

Thus we return to the original proposal by Kitagawa that the water vapor bands are produced by the reaction $2H_2 + O_2 = 2H_2O + 114$ kcal, wherein the 114 kilocalories of heat energy excite the water vapor molecules to yield the observed spectral features. The formation of H_2O from H and O without the intermediate formation of OH is rare in nature.

In an effort to understand the origin of the hydrogen, we enlisted the help of geochemist Kenneth Lennon. Dr. Lennon showed that the concentration of hydrogen in volcanic gas can be understood in terms of its equilibrium with oxygen. The oxygen abundance (in the gaseous state) is in turn established by the oxidation states of the iron-bearing minerals in the lava. Geochemists have studied volcanic rocks at the melting temperature (about 1,100°K.) and are able to predict the abundance of oxygen based on the mineralogy of the lava. Then the abundance of hydrogen, relative to its reaction product, water, can be calculated for lava of a given composition. Once the fractional abundance of water vapor in volcanic gas has been determined, the hydrogen abundance is immediately found.

Hawaiian volcanic gas appears to be about 95 percent water, judged from infrared studies made in 1967 by J. Naughton. Thus the amount of free hydrogen in Kilauea's gas at the high temperature of the vent is on the order of 1.8 volume (mole) percent. This relatively low abundance is near the limit for spontaneous ignition in air, but with sufficiently high vent wall temperatures hydrogen mixtures as lean as one-half mole percent can ignite, according to Naughton. It therefore appears probable that the appearance and disappearance of flames at prolific fume vents depend more on the orifice temperature than on variable amounts of hydrogen in the gas; high temperatures ignite the hydrogen and air mixture, while cool vents cannot.

We have answered most of our questions about the common type of volcanic flames seen at Kilauea, but other flamelike events occur in special cases, and the clarification of their physical nature may be provided by spectroscopic investigation. The most important is probably the role of gas in the chemical and "mechanical" evolution of the great lava lakes that occur on Kilauea and other volcanoes. The gray, slaggy surfaces of the Halemaumau, Mauna Ulu, and Alae lava lakes are normally disturbed in one or more regions by lava fountains apparently induced by gas building up below the surface. From the tops of these lava sprays are often seen luminous tongues of yellow flame. Whether these are truly flames in the sense of burning gas or instead clouds of incandescent fume particles is not known. The understanding of these plumes may help clarify the gas differentiation mechanism that presumably occurs during some phases of lake activity and gives rise to variations in lake level over small time intervals. It is, however, quite clear that the main type of flames is explained by the combustion of hydrogen. Other problems await future studies of the remarkable phenomena of burning gas from the earth's interior.

REFERENCES

CRUIKSHANK, DALE P.; HARTMANN, WILLIAM K.; and WOOD, C. A.
1973. Moon: "Ghost" craters formed during Mare filling. The Moon, vol. 7, pp. 440-452.

CRUIKSHANK, DALE P.; MORRISON, DAVID; and LENNON, KENNETH
1973. Volcania gases: Hydrogen burning at Kilauea Volcano, Hawaii. Science, vol. 182, pp. 277-279.

DALE P. CRUIKSHANK
DAVID MORRISON

A Study of Fossil Old World Monkeys of the Circum-Mediterranean Region

Principal Investigator: Eric Delson, Herbert H. Lehman College, City University of New York, Bronx, New York; and American Museum of Natural History, New York City.

Grant No. 944: In support of research on fossil Cercopithecoidea (Old World monkeys) of the circum-Mediterranean region.

This grant was awarded in 1971 to permit continuation of studies of fossil monkeys from Europe begun in 1969-70. At the time of application, it was planned to work in both western and eastern European museums during the summer of 1971, but satisfactory arrangements could not be made with eastern European colleagues at that time, and so only a short trip was made in 1971. In the summer of 1973 it was possible to arrange mutually convenient schedules with these colleagues, and a second trip was then made. The results of this research have not yet been fully published as the work is still ongoing, at least in certain aspects, but a number of publications have drawn upon it and other preliminary indications can be made here.

I spent four weeks in Switzerland and France in 1971 in order to examine fossils and present a preliminary report at an international conference. In Basel, I studied specimens of *Macaca majori* at the Naturhistorisches Museum. This monkey, from cave breccia in northern Sardinia, is of uncertain age but may be some three million years old (Engesser, 1976). It is a rather small form of macaque, originally described (Azzaroli, 1946) as a "dwarf" and therefore of particular evolutionary interest. Similar monkeys inhabited both Europe and northern Africa over the past 6 million years and may be found today in Algeria and (introduced) on Gibraltar. The large Basel collection includes remains of almost 200 individuals, ranging from single teeth to partial skulls, and thus is very favorable for statistical analysis. Preliminary work has shown that *M. majori* is only slightly smaller than the living (and other fossil) forms but that some differences in morphology do suggest separate species status. Work is continuing on this and other European and North African fossil macaques with additional support from the Faculty Research Award Program of the City University of New York (CUNY–FRAP).

While in Basel, and later in Paris, I studied other fossils of *Macaca* and *Mesopithecus,* as well as some modern macaques for comparative purposes. One interesting find was the "excavation" in a collection drawer of the Institut de

Paléontologie in Paris (Muséum National d'Histoire Naturelle) of a partial humerus (elbow bone) of a fossil macaque from Tunisia, which has been previously misidentified as that of a doglike animal. This bone adds another element to the faunal list for the Garaet Ichkeul locality (about 4-5 million years old), as well as one more to the small list of northern African fossil monkeys. In Lyon, fossils of both *Dolichopithecus ruscinensis* and *Paradolichopithecus arvernensis* were studied briefly. The main purpose of the visit to Lyon was to attend the fifth meeting of the Committee on Mediterranean Neogene Stratigraphy, in order to discuss problems of relative age of fossiliferous localities with colleagues. Although not on the program, I was invited to present a summary of my finding on the distribution of fossil monkeys around the Mediterranean, which included the results of the 1971 research (Delson, 1974). Additional such results were included in my doctoral dissertation (Delson, 1973), which concentrated on the fossil colobines *Mesopithecus* and *Dolichopithecus* studied in 1969-70.

During the summer of 1973 I spent another 6 weeks in Europe to continue this work. In Paris I attended the international colloquium on problems of vertebrate evolution, sponsored by the Centre National de la Recherche Scientifique and the Muséum National d'Histoire Naturelle, where I presented a paper on the origin of Old World monkeys (Delson, 1975c). In this work the parapithecids of the Egyptian Oligocene, among the oldest known anthropoid fossils, were shown not to share any specialized or derived characters with later monkeys. Parapithecids are thus probably not ancestral or even closely related to cercopithecoids although this phylogeny has been suggested by various authors (e.g., Simons, 1972) and widely accepted. Specimens of fossil monkeys and apes were studied in Paris, Lyon, Frankfurt, and especially in Perpignan, southern France, where previously unseen specimens of *Dolichopithecus* were finally located. Fossils of *Mesopithecus pentelici* were studied in Athens, Sofia, and Belgrade, in order to complete the survey of this species begun in the dissertation. No significant differences could be seen between specimens from the type locality of Pikermi and those from Macedonian localities farther north (in Greece, Yugoslavia, and Bulgaria)—no previous study had compared these remains directly. These new specimens will be described in the published version of the "systematic paleontology" section of my thesis.

The most important aspect of this trip was a stay of 10 days in Bucharest, Romania, where it was possible to study remains of *Paradolichopithecus arvernensis* from Graunceanu. One specimen of this species had been described as *P. geticus* by Necrasov, Samson, and Radulesco (1961), and I had studied that fossil in 1970, but the new material was still undescribed. Through the generosity of Dr. Dardu Nicolaescu-Plopsor of the Center for Anthropological Research, I arranged to borrow a number of specimens of this animal in order to thoroughly clean, reconstruct, and describe them in New York. Joint field researches were also discussed but unfortunately have not yet been undertaken.

A preliminary report on these remains (Delson and Nicolaescu-Plopsor, 1975) indicated that the fossils from Romania and France are indeed the same species, despite previous uncertainty. *P. arvernensis* occurs only at the very beginning of the Pleistocene, but other specimens referable to this genus are known from France, Spain, and Romania in the later Pliocene. The presence of this form in a fossil locality, therefore, gives some indication of its age. Reconstruction work on these fossils is proceeding, and a detailed morphological-taxonomic study is planned, with the additional assistance of CUNY–FRAP. At present, it is possible to indicate that *Paradolichopithecus* was a large, highly terrestrial monkey adapted to open-country conditions in southern Europe some 2 million years ago. It is baboonlike in adaptation, but phyletically more closely related to the Eurasian macaques. It may be related also to similar-sized species of *Procynocephalus* from China and India, whose remains are as yet too incomplete for full comparison, as well as to an incompletely published population from Soviet Central Asia.

The general results of studies made on these two trips were also included in several papers considering Old World monkey evolution. Delson (1975a) detailed the history of cercopithecid evolution, discussing the major fossil genera in terms of morphology and evolutionary relationships; Delson and Andrews (1975) related this pattern to that of other catarrhines (Old World higher primates). Delson (1975b), on the other hand, concentrated on zoogeography and dispersal patterns, as well as placing the many localities in a temporal and environmental framework. This last paper suggested that the first major split among cercopithecids was the separation of the two subfamilies (Cercopithecinae and Colobinae) some 15 million years ago, followed by the split between *Cercopithecus* (and relatives) and the macaque-baboon group, or tribe Papionini. Judged from the scanty fossil evidence, there may have been one or more species of early Papionini extending across Africa in the Late Miocene, some 7-10 million years ago. After this time it would appear that the Sahara desert became a barrier to animal migration, as a result of Africa's tectonic collision with Europe and the resultant desiccation of the Mediterranean basin, which aggravated a previous drying trend in southern Europe. This barrier may have isolated populations that eventually evolved into macaques in northern Africa and into baboons farther south (each first known about 5-6 million years ago). Terrestrial adaptations occurred several times in parallel during the Pliocene, among such diverse groups as Cercopithecini (*Erythrocebus*), Papionini (*Theropithecus, Papio, Paradolichopithecus*, and *Procyno-*

cephalus and perhaps *Dinopithecus* and *Gorgopithecus* of southern Africa), and Colobinae *(Dolichopithecus)*.

REFERENCES

AZZAROLI, AUGUSTO

1946. La scimmia fossile della Sardegna. Rev. Sci. Preist., vol. 1, pp. 168-176.

DELSON, ERIC

1973. Fossil colobine monkeys of the circum-Mediterranean region and the evolutionary history of the Cercopithecidae (Primates: Mammalia), 856 pp. University Microfilms, Ann Arbor, Michigan.

1974. Preliminary review of cercopithecid distribution in the circum-Mediterranean region. Mem. Bur. Rech. Géol. et Min. de France, no. 78, pp. 131-135.

1975a. Evolutionary history of the Cercopithecidae. Contr. Primat., vol. 5, pp. 167-217.

1975b. Paleoecology and zoogeography of the Old World monkeys. Pp. 37-64 *in* "Primate Functional Morphology and Evolution," Russell H. Tuttle, ed. Mouton Publishers, The Hague and Paris.

1975c. Toward the origin of Old World monkeys. Pp. 839-850 *in* "Problèmes Actuels de Paléontologie (Évolution des Vertébrés)." Coll. Int. Centre Nat. Rech. Sci. no. 218. Paris.

DELSON, ERIC, and ANDREWS, P.

1976. Evolution and interrelationships of the catarrhine primates. Pp. 405-446 *in* "Phylogeny of the Primates," W. P. Luckett and F. S. Szalay, eds. Plenum Publishing Corp., New York.

DELSON, ERIC, and NICOLAESCU-PLOPSOR, DARDU

1975. *Paradolichopithecus,* a large terrestrial monkey (Cercopithecidae, Primates) from the Plio-Pleistocene of southern Europe and its importance for mammalian biochronology. Proc. 6th Reg. Comm. Medit. Neogene Stratigraphy, pp. 91-96. Bratislava.

ENGESSER, B.

1976. *Tyrrhenoglis majori,* ein neuer fossiler Gliride (Rodentia, Mammalia) aus Sardinien. Eclogae Geol. Helvetiae, vol. 69, pp. 783-793.

NECRASOV, O.; SAMSON, P.; and RADULESCO, C.

1961. Sur un nouveau singe catarrhinien, découvert dans un nid fossilifère d'Oltenie (R.P.R.). Anal. Stiint. Univ. "Al. I. Cuzá," Iasi, ser. nov., sect. 2, no. 7, pp. 401-416.

SIMONS, ELWYN L.

1972. Primate evolution: An introduction to man's place in nature, 322 pp. Macmillan Co., New York.

ERIC DELSON

Excavations at Tell Keisan (Israel)

Principal Investigator: Father Roland deVaux, O.P., École Biblique et Archéologique Française, Jerusalem, Israel.[1]

Grant No. 956: In support of archeological excavations at Tell Keisan, Israel.

Between July 4 and September 3, 1971, the École Biblique et Archéologique Française of Jerusalem began the first stage of excavations at Tell Keisan (coordinates 165.5 – 253.2), a hill less than 10 kilometers east of Akko. The work was directed by Father de Vaux, with the help of Reverend Prignaud as assistant director. The team was made up of D. Auscher, J. Briend, A. Chambon, A. Lemaire (archeologists), A. Spycket and M. Join-Lambert (recording), E. Godet (topographer), J.-B. Humbert (draftsman), J. Barrios Delgado (photographer), and J. Landgraf (ceramist). Funds for the archeological mission were provided by grants from the Ministry of Foreign Affairs and the National Geographic Society. Two private gifts covering rental of the excavation area made unnecessary a reduction in the budget for the first excavations.

Before presenting a survey of the results, it is necessary to set forth the importance of the site and its archeological interest. Tell Keisan, with an area of 6 hectares, rises 28 meters above the surrounding plain. The excavation aimed at reaching the levels of Late Bronze and Iron I in order to study the transition between these two archeological periods; more broadly, it aimed to study the commercial relationships between the site and the Eastern Mediterranean. The goal of this program was based on the results obtained in 1935 and 1936 by A. Rowe, who made a stratigraphic probe into the southeast corner of the tell (anonymous, 1936, p. 208). It is due to this probe that the outline of the occupation sequence from Early Bronze to Early Hellenistic is known. In this succession, three levels (XIII to XI) belong to Late Bronze and four levels (X to VII) are known as "Late Bronze-Iron I." The conditions thus seemed favorable to achievement of the desired goal.

As for the choice of an excavation site, this was made after an examination of the tell. An overall view of the hill (see fig. 1) reveals that it is formed of two parts separated by a depression. The western part of the tell rises to a summit from which the lines of a large number of walls project. The eastern part is a large flat area, slightly and regularly inclined toward the west. In order to

[1] Father deVaux died September 10, 1971.

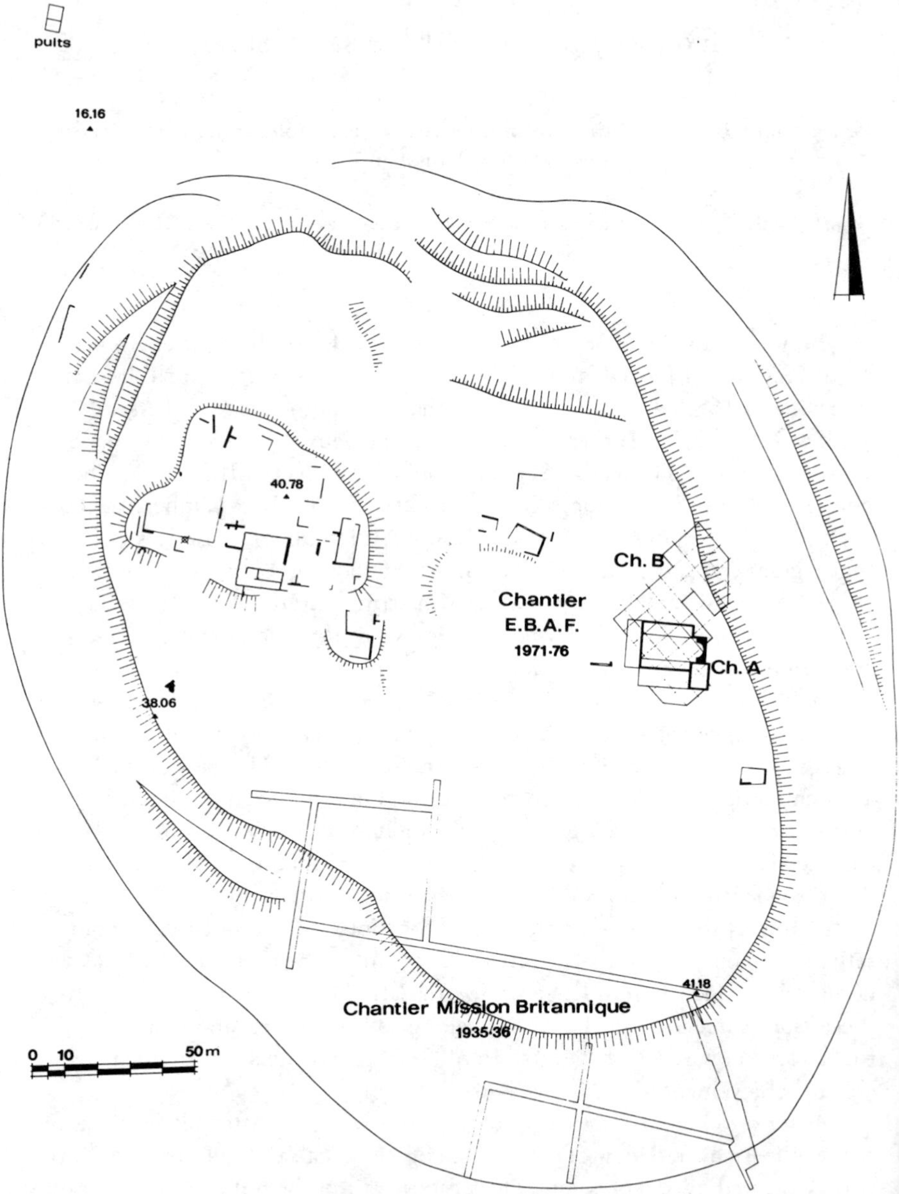

16.16

40.78

38.06

Ch. B

Chantier
E.B.A.F.
1971-76

Ch. A

41.18

Chantier Mission Britannique
1935-36

0 10 50 m

FIG. 1. Tell Keisan, showing location of excavation.

FIG. 2 (facing page). Plan of Byzantine Church (note area and foundation numbers).

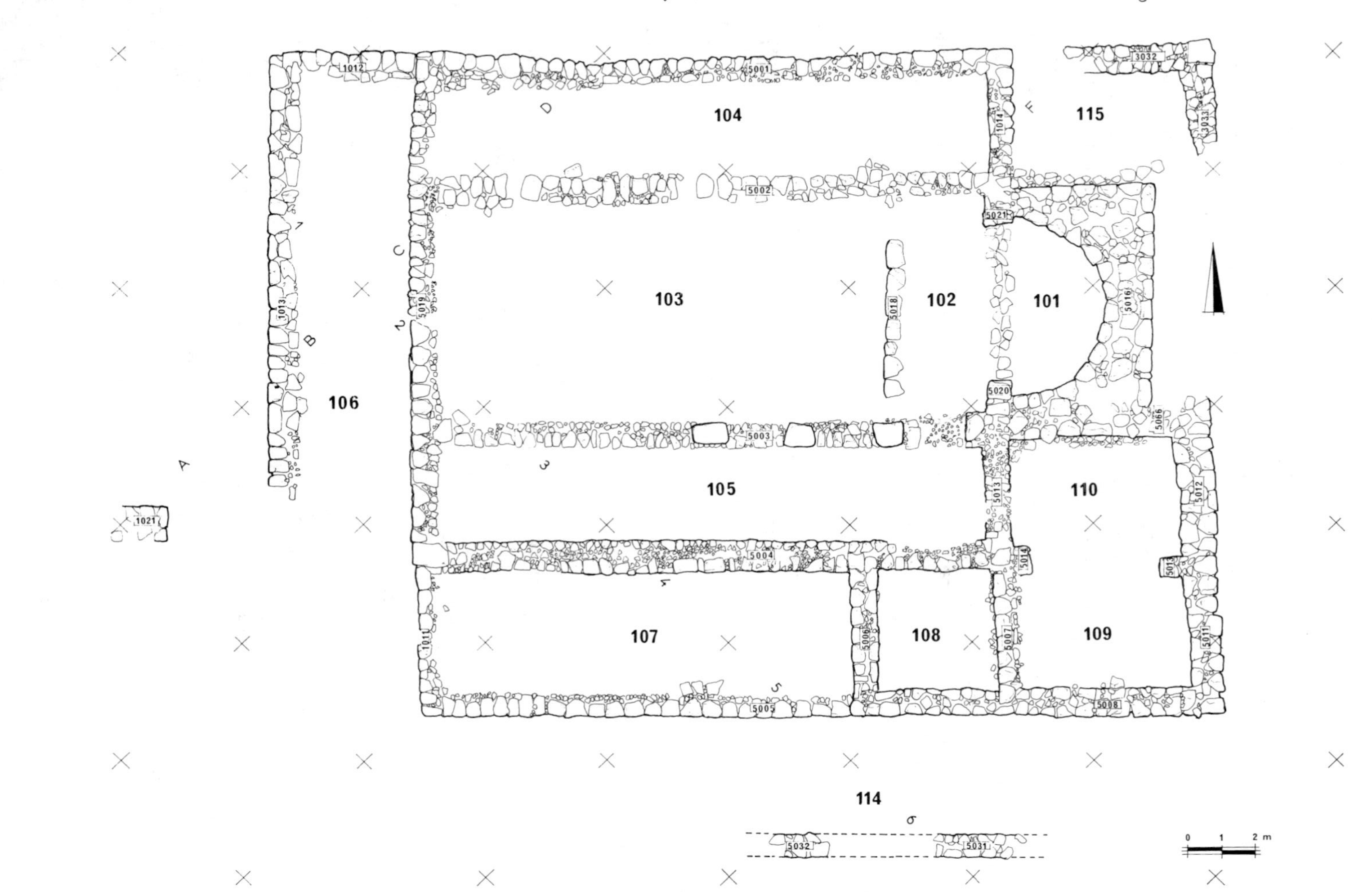

104
115
103
102
101
106
105
110
107
108
109
114
1012
5001
3032
3033
1014
5002
5021
5018
5016
1013
5019
5020
5066
5003
5013
5012
1021
5004
5014
5013
1011
5006
5007
5011
5005
5008
5032
5031
0 1 2 m

avoid the most recent levels that must exist in the western part, Father de Vaux decided to open site A (Ch. A, fig. 1) on the western part, where several lines of foundation stone were apparent on the surface. In the area, 25 squares, each 5 meters square, were opened. At the end of the work, two squares were extended to the east of site A in order to begin a new site (Ch. B). In this area, one can only say that potsherds from Iron II were very abundant. It can therefore be hoped that the levels of Iron which were sought could quickly be found here. Yet it is in Site A that the clearest results were found.

After two weeks of excavation, it became evident that the surface walls uncovered in site A outlined a church from the Byzantine period, and this was confirmed by the discovery of the apse (see figs. 2 and 3). This Byzantine level (level 1) was a bit strange, however, because nowhere inside the walls making up the outline of the building could be found a floor level attributable to the period during which the building was used. All that was found was the foundation level, but as indicated by the many scattered tesserae on the surface of the site, the floor of the church was entirely or partly covered with mosaics long ago destroyed. The following description is therefore limited to observations based on study of the foundations, and this is very important to evaluation of the conclusions reached concerning both the Byzantine level and the lower levels which, over the entire area, were disturbed by the very deep foundations of the church.

The Church

The church (figs. 3 and 5) has a basilical structure: a central nave, closed on the east by an apse, is flanked on the north and the south by aisles. On the west, the church opens to a narthex and on the south, annexes make the entire structure look like a huge, fairly regular quadrilateral building with sides approximately 25 by 20 meters.

The apse (area 101, fig. 2, and fig. 4), in the interior of the church is a semicircle with a radius of 3 meters. If extended to the west, the resulting circle would be tangent to the eastern face of stone steps (5018, fig. 2) which define the bema. Actually, the semicircle of the apse is marked on the west by a slight projection of the apse wall to the north (5021) and south (5020). Between these two projections is a foundation wall, the purpose of which was to support the thrust of the apse and thus ensure the stability of the entire structure.

The steps that separate the bema from the rest of the central nave are made up of a single footing of seven large rectangular stones, the western and upper sides of which are carefully trimmed, upon which, it can be hypothesized, the

FIG. 3. Basilica of the church, looking toward the east.

chancel rested. In this respect, it can be noted that this footing does not take up the entire width of the central nave, a significant indication of the primitive form of the chancel.

The central nave (area 103, fig. 2) was separated from the aisles by two rows of columns of which only the subfoundations remain. At the south, in foundation wall 5003, three such bases, each a large rectangular stone, can be easily identified. At the north, in foundation wall 5002, such stones no longer exist, but their placement can be found by observing two stones, placed like headers, or bondstones, which must have served as supports for such subfoundations. Indeed, foundation wall 5002 is preserved at a lower footing than that of the parallel wall 5003, and it is probable that the paired stones supported a block of stone similar to those remaining in wall 5003. Moreover, these bondstones in wall 5002 lie opposite the large rectangular blocks in wall 5003. If this data is kept in mind, and particularly the spacing between each column, one can envision on each side five columns separating the central nave from the aisle. The spacing between the columns is only 2.6 meters between centers (Ovadiah, 1970, p. 20, notes that the average maximum distance between columns in Palestinian churches is around 4 meters from center to center). These columns were to support an architrave and to bear the weight of a heavy roof covered with flat tiles, as suggested by many fragments found on the ground.

Although the floor level of the church was not preserved at all, it is possible to reconstruct it with fair precision. The top of the large stone steps (5018) is at the height of 42.52 meters (see fig. 1) and must be, to within a few centimeters, at the level of the bema. The floor of the nave could lie only slightly above the bases of the stone steps which are at a height of 42.05 meters. Furthermore, the floor level of the church must be slightly higher than the base of the blocks (height, 42.32 meters) supporting the columns. One could not be far off by proposing that the floor level of the church was 42.40 meters.

The threshold of the church must have been in foundation wall 5019. Its location in the center, between walls 5002 and 5003, can only be conjectured.

The aisles can be easily located owing to the fact that foundation wall 5004 in the southern aisle is better preserved than the northern one, so that the presence of beautiful angle stones can be noted at its extremities.

The narthex (area 106, fig. 2) can be easily reconstructed, even though wall 1013 disappears toward the south, well before the return which one would suppose should meet wall 5004. Actually, the fact that there remains only one narthex foundation in the southern part, while in the northern part two footings can be observed, can be accounted for by the downward slope of the land, which is greater to the north of the church. The foundation of the

FIG. 4. Apse, showing the line of stones defining western edge of the bema.

narthex is rather modest and leads one to think of a covered structure, the weight of which did not necessitate deep foundations.

Some data could be gathered about the decoration of the church. The ground was covered with mosaics and the flooring was made up of tesserae in which three colors dominated—white, dark red, and bluish gray—but not one fragment of noteworthy size was found, hence a density analysis cannot be made. The discovery of two incomplete capitals provides an idea of the decoration of the interior (see fig. 6). One is sculptured with a rather worn cross; its base is clearly rounded, forming an open arch, leading one to think that it topped a column. For this reason we hypothesized the existence of columns and not pillars between the central nave and the aisles, even though no tambour has yet been found in the tell. The other capital, also fragmentary, is like a large square block with a marked face having, in the center, a flattened area with a cross. This block must have topped an engaged pillar such as would be necessary on both sides of the apse or at the western ends of walls 5003 and 5002.

The Annexes

The rooms that adjoin the church, on the south and east, were only found at the foundation level. This allows one to make a plan, but not to determine their function. Though it is not possible to conclude that they belong to a later phase of the church, it can be emphasized that all the foundations rest against the walls of the sanctuary, a sign that the church was built first.

Area 108, at the south of the church, seems to be a small square room whose walls rested on solid foundations made up of two footings of large stones. Above these two footings and driven into the ground was a superior footing made of a double row of stones set on edge which could not from the beginning have supported a very high wall. Furthermore, this superior footing was drawn out to the south and to the east of the line of foundation walls 5008 and 5007. It must be concluded that this superior footing dates back to a construction subsequent to the Byzantine period. The area therefore had two states. In its first state, area 108 must have had an opening set in wall 5004 which communicated with the church; it could have also communicated with area 109.

Areas 109 and 110 form, in the southern part of the apse, a large rectangular room. The presence of two bases of pillars 5014 and 5015 which stand out in relation to the foundation walls makes it possible to distinguish only two parts, the north and the south. What is strange is that these bases of the pillars are not exactly opposite each other, but they were supposed to support a roof. Actually, the foundations of the walls were sufficiently deep to support high walls and the rectangular room must have been covered. Nothing specific was discovered which would have helped determine the function of this room.

Area 110 adjoins the southern wall of the apse and wall 5012 in the east stops immediately adjacent to it, leaving only a narrow passage where it is difficult to imagine an access such as a door. The state of the remains, considering that this is the foundation level, is such that one can only hypothesize that areas 108, 109, and 110 formed a roof-covered annex to the church, most probably lower than the roof of the church.

To the west of area 108 is area 107, which has its own characteristics. Wall 5011 begins in the southwest angle of the church, but has a slight recess, and it is made up of only one footing. Wall 5005 shares the same characteristic, a single footing lying directly on the ground. The external and upper faces of the stones of these two walls are carefully trimmed. The lack of a deep foundation and the bonding of the stones, which have perhaps been reused,

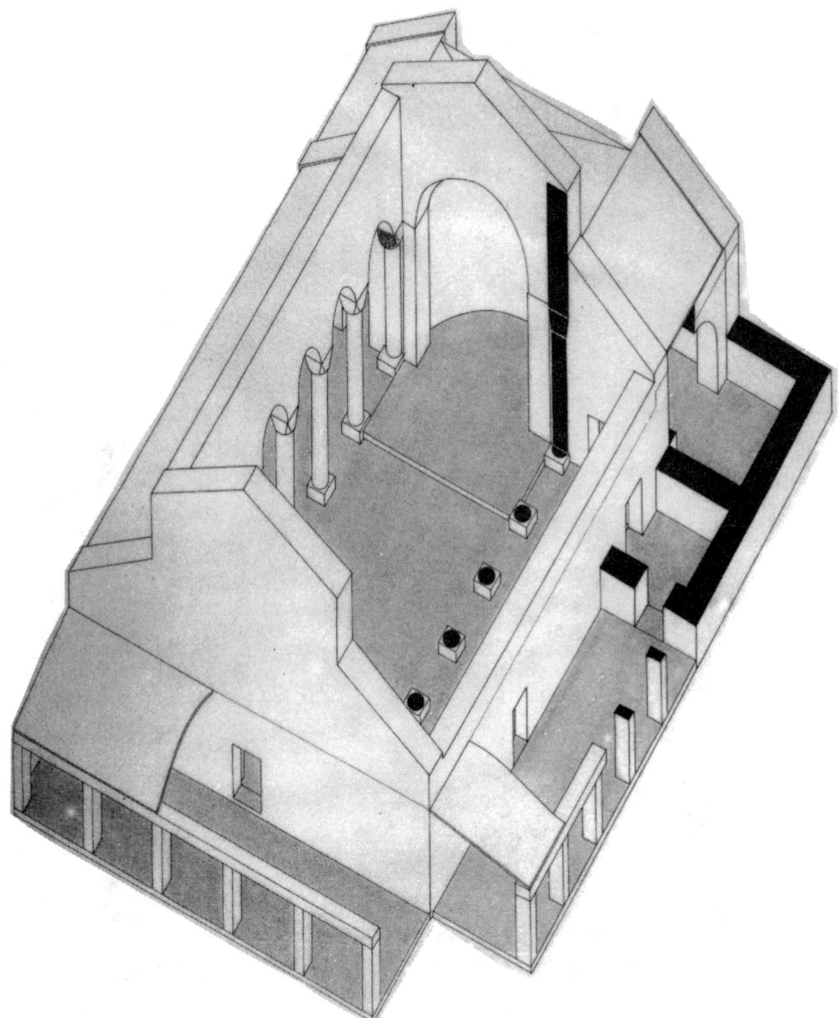

FIG. 5. Axonometric reconstruction of Byzantine Church (scale 1/200).

FIG. 6. Two capitals found in the basilica.

leads one to think that area 107 was not closed off by walls to the west and the south. It seems to have been a covered space with direct access to the church through a door in wall 5004. It is possible that area 107 was added to the construction of the church at a later date, but this remains a hypothesis.

Area 115, located in the northeast of the church, is also an annex. Foundation walls 3032 and 3033, lying at right angles, are made of smaller stones than those which can be found in the foundation walls of areas 108, 109, and 110. Though these walls are sufficiently large, they are not deeply laid and they rest on a layer of black soil containing flat potsherds. These walls do not meet, either in the west or the south, the walls of the church, but that this construction originates in the Byzantine period cannot be doubted. This area is almost undoubtedly an addition which is not contemporary with the construction of the church.

The Architecture and its Dating

Taking into account the poor state of preservation of the Tell Keisan church, one can nevertheless attempt to place the date of this construction in relation to what we know today about the construction of churches in Palestine during the Byzantine period.

The plan of the church, with its central nave and its two aisles, is basilical. This type is very common during the entire Byzantine period and is not a criterion for dating. It can only be noted that the construction of the churches in Palestine reaches its peak in the sixth century; after this date, there is an obvious decline both in the number and the quality of the constructions (Ovadiah, 1970, p. 193, gives the following statistics on the number of churches in Palestine: 45 in the fifth century, 14 in the fifth-sixth centuries, 56 in the sixth century, 15 in the seventh century, 3 in the eighth century). The increase in the number of churches in Palestine in the sixth century can be explained by the economic prosperity of the country, which existed because of the stable political situation during the long reign of Justinian I (527-565).

The apse is external and rectangular. Due to the absence of other criteria, the chronology statistics set forth by Ovadiah (1970, table 2, following p. 184) can be used to date approximately this type of construction, which is very rare in the fifth century, but of which a dozen or so examples are known in the sixth century. Moreover, though very rare in the north of Palestine, this type occurs frequently in Judea in the sixth century. One is thus led to conclude that the sixth century is the construction date for the church of Tell Keisan. Yet, although the use of such a plan for the apse raises the question of the influences which could be felt during construction, any conclusions in this realm would be dangerous.

The existence of a narthex also favors a relatively late dating, since this architectural element does not appear in Palestine before the fifth century. But if the narthex is contemporary to the church, which no fact disproves, yet the presence of this element does not allow one to set the construction of the church at a very late date.

The question of the chancel in the church at Tell Keisan now remains. On the basis of the steps (5018, fig. 2) which separates the bema from the central nave, one can conclude that the chancel was limited to the central nave and was U-shaped, the lateral branches being parallel to the foundation walls of the central nave. From a strictly archeological point of view, it is not possible to hypothesize a transversal chancel cutting across the entire church. This type of chancel appeared in the second half of the sixth century, probably following the changes in the liturgy during the reign of Justin II (565-578) (on this question, see Crowfoot, 1941, p. 55; Ovadiah, 1970, pp. 195-197). One therefore has good reason to conclude that the church of Tell Keisan was built prior to these changes, in spite of the poor state of the remains.

The excavation did not reveal the site of the baptistry. The placement of this element does not follow a fixed rule; it can be found just as easily in the north as in the south of the church. If a baptistry existed at Tell Keisan, which is very possible, it must have been in the southern part of the church since in the north, no remains from the Byzantine period were discovered.

In spite of the remaining uncertainties, the church of Tell Keisan must have been built in the first half of the sixth century, if the form of the chancel is considered.

Pottery and Coins

An examination of the architecture of the church can only provide a very approximate date of its construction. To arrive at a more precise date, one must refer to the pottery and the coins.

Though not very abundant, the pottery gathered during the excavation provides some interesting data on the time span of level 1. The study of the pottery from the Byzantine era was undertaken by J. Landgraf, but it has not yet been completed, though it is already possible to set forth the main conclusions. Examination of the "Roman Red Ware" indicates that the Byzantine occupation on the eastern side of the tell was important between 500 and 540 and that it continued until A.D. 640.

The Byzantine coins found in the tell or on the site provide the same indications as the pottery. The oldest Byzantine coins date back to the reign of Anastasius I (491-598) and the most recent ones date to the reign (641-668) of Constans II (see Fulco, 1975, p. 238).

On the basis of these facts, the date of the construction can be set at about A.D. 520. To specify the date of the destruction of the church, one can only refer back to the history of the Akko region. It is often believed that most of the churches of Palestine were destroyed by Chosroès II with the Persian invasion of 614, but this is not the case for all of Palestine, particularly for the northern part. The destruction of the Tell Keisan church must rather be seen in relation to the Arab invasion of 636 when Emir Schourahbîl conquered Tibériade, Akko, Tyr, and Sepphoris (Abel, 1952, p. 398). After this date, the population occupying Tell Keisan must have been rather insignificant. Several post-Byzantine constructions exist above the level of destruction; they can be understood in light of either the control of the tell by the Crusaders, or the passing presence of Saladin when his army used Tell Keisan in 1189 and 1190 as an observation post and a site to regroup his troops during the siege of Akko.

Identification of the Byzantine Church

Built around A.D. 520, the church of Tell Keisan, based on the general plan of buildings, seems to have been a parish church. It could not have been an episcopal church, since from the ecclesiastical point of view, the Byzantine village established on the tell depended on the nearby diocese of Akko. Nor is it a monastic church, for the buildings which surround the church could not have sheltered a community of monks, even a small one. The location of the church on the eastern tell, near the slope, suggests that the construction of the church could have taken place at the time when a village community already existed on the site for some time. The chosen location could be explained by the fact that this area was not occupied.

Two hypotheses have been proposed for the identification of the church of Tell Keisan, one by Father Bagatti, the other by A. Lemaire.

Father Bagatti (1971, pp. 170-171), who presents his suggestions in the form of a hypothesis, compares the church of Tell Keisan with a monastic church discovered near Teqoa, but this comparison is not convincing. Neither the rectangular apse, nor the three naves, nor the narthex of the church of Tell Keisan can be found in the construction used as a comparison. The plan of the two churches is too different. The reference to a passage by Jean Rufus, who believes that Claudian was the abbot of a monastery located in a village near Akko, is not sufficient to identify this with the church of Tell Keisan. Rufus's information is very vague and can apply to any site near Akko. Finally, it has not yet been proven that the church of Tell Keisan was a monastic church.

In 1972, A. Lemaire (pp. 247-250) proposed to identify the site of Tell Keisan with Porphyreon II, which, according to the younger Simeon Stylites, would have contained a church constructed by order of the emperor Justin II (565-578). Without reviewing here the evidence relating to the two Porphyreons, one must admit that this localization is not possible for several reasons. First of all, on a papyrus from Egypt dating back to the sixth century A.D. (Nordegraaf, 1939, pp. 273-310), Porphyreon II is cited in a list between Dor and Ptolemais (Akko); the city must therefore have been located somewhere close to Haifa. In the Middle Ages, the Crusaders still called Haifa Porphyreon. In the second place, Porphyreon I, situated at Khan Nebi Yunus in Lebanon, was not abandoned in the fifth and sixth centuries A.D., as is widely believed; it was, on the contrary, a very important Christian center in the sixth century, as has been shown by the 1975 excavations on the site by R. Saidah (1977, pp. 38-43). Under these conditions, it is not always possible to discern in the text which Porphyreon is being referred to. Finally, the date which A. Lemaire proposes for the church of Tell Keisan is too late, considering all the data we now have.

Thus, the identification of Tell Keisan within the Byzantine period is not possible, and we cannot propose a plausible hypothesis at this time.

The 1971 dig shed light on the Byzantine occupation of Tell Keisan (level 1), but below this occupation, we were able to find remains of a hellenistic occupation and even one from the Persian era. The excavation of these levels will take place in later digs.

REFERENCES

ABEL, FÉLIX M.

1952. Histoire de la Palestine depuis la conquête d'Alexandre jusqu'à l'invasion arabe, vol. 2, 400 pp. Gabalda, Paris.

ANONYMOUS

1936. Tell Keisan. The Quarterly of the Department of Antiquities in Palestine, vol. 5, pp. 207-209.

BAGATTI, BELLARMINO

1971. Antichi villagi cristiani di Galilea, 333 pp., illus. Tipografia dei PP. Francescani, Jerusalem.

BENOIT, PIERRE

1977. Keisan (Tell). Encyclopedia of Archaeological Excavations in the Holy Land, vol. 3, pp. 711-713. Massada Press, Jerusalem.

BRIEND, JACQUES
1972. Akshaph et sa localisation à Tell Keisan. Revue Biblique, vol. 79, pp. 239-246.
1976. Tell Keisan. Une église byzantine. Bible et Terre Sainte, no. 181, pp. 14-17.
CROWFOOT, JOHN W.
1941. Early Churches in Palestine, Schweich Lectures 1937, 166 pp., illus. Oxford University Press, London.
FULCO, WILLIAM J.
1975. Monnaies de Tell Keisan, 1971-1974. Revue Biblique, vol. 82, pp. 234-239.
JOIN-LAMBERT, MICHEL
1972. Anses de jarre à estampilles grecques. Revue Biblique, vol. 79, pp. 255-262.
LEMAIRE, ANDRÉ
1972. Porphyreon, Halzon, Tell Keisan? Revue Biblique, vol. 79, pp. 247-250.
1972. Deux épigraphes sémitiques. Revue Biblique, vol. 79, pp. 251-254.
NORDEGRAAF, CORNELIA A.
1938. A geographical papyrus. Mnemosyné, vol. 6, pp. 273-310.
OVADIAH, ASHER
1970. Corpus of the Byzantine churches in the Holy Land. Theophaneia 22, 218 pp., 74 plates. P. Hanstein Verlag, Bonn.
PRIGNAUD, JEAN
1972. Première campagne de fouilles à Tell Keisan (Israël). Revue Biblique, vol. 79, pp. 227-238.
SAIDAH, ROGER
1977. Porphyreon du Liban. Archaeologia, no. 104, pp. 38-43.
SPYCKET, AGNÈS
1972. Figurines et fibules trouvées à Tell Keisan. Revue Biblique, vol. 79, pp. 263-274.

JACQUES BRIEND

Photographic Record in Color of Live Deep-sea Cephalopods

Principal Investigator: P. Noel Dilly, Department of Structural Biology, St. George's Hospital Medical School, London, England.

Grant Nos. 939, 1241: Color photographic record of live deep-sea cephalopods.

The aim of this project was to provide a color and black-and-white reference collection of photographs of cephalopods. The colors of preserved cephalopods fade on fixation and show considerable post-mortem changes; so an accurate, lifelike photo record is essential. Eventually I hope to be able to publish, together with Professor J. Z. Young, FRS, and Dr. Marion Nixon, a book, based on this collection, surveying the behaviour and structure of as many deep-sea squids as we can acquire. The collection is expanding slowly but surely, several of the chapters have already been written, and two have been published as separate papers (Dilly and Nixon, 1976; Dilly et al., 1977).

The technique used has been to trap the animal between two sheets of clear glass in an aquarium and to photograph it, using side flash and a mirror to achieve total internal reflection that ensures good all-round lighting.

The first major paper using the results of our collection was published in the Journal of Zoology (Dilly and Nixon, 1976), and it establishes for the first time much of the detailed biology of the squid *Taonius megalops*.

In April 1975, together with Dr. Marion Nixon, I presented to the Cephalopod Symposium in honor of Professor J. Z. Young a survey of the sucker structure in cephalopods. Most of the illustrations used were produced by means of the Society's apparatus (Dilly and Nixon, 1977).

Light emission by biological systems is a fascinating study, and I have been interested in the reflector layers that back up some light organs. At the moment I am trying to construct a pinpoint parallel-ray flash source so that we can begin to discover the range of reflection from the reflector layer. Similarly, we have been introducing light probes to light organs to see if we can simulate the natural distribution of light with an artificial source. The results, being recorded photographically, are encouraging. Our preliminary results, using fibre optic bundles, suggest that the light in fact is not emitted as a beam, but more or less as an overall glow. This seems to contrast with the observations of the living animals by Young (1977), who has shown that the natural distribution of light is such as to produce very effective ventral countershading. We are now working on an apparatus that will enable us to measure the amount of light emitted from different sectors of the light organ. Use of the photographic record to measure the intensity of light seems to be the most effective way of doing this. Our initial experiments with photomultiplier tubes have not been very successful.

Meanwhile we are continuing to study the shape and structure of light organs, the equipment provided by the Society being used in making the photographic survey, and several of our results have been published (Dilly and Herring, 1974 and 1978).

Some bacteria emit light, and such bacteria are found in the light organs of some deep-sea cephalopods. I have been culturing the bacteria. We found that after a time some of the bacteria ceased to emit light. When a culture plate of luminous bacteria, that have all been grown from a single spread of bacteria, is examined and compared with the photographic record of the light emission, some of the circular patches of bacteria are found not to emit light, in contrast to other bacteria, apparently from the same parent source, that are emitting light. We have been trying to discover if the bacteria have the potential for emitting light transiently or if once they have lost their ability to emit light, they have lost it forever. It is easy to find the non-light-emitting colonies by comparing a time-exposure photograph taken in the dark with a daylight photograph of the whole culture.

We are proposing the hypothesis that the ability to emit light may be conveyed by a luminescent plasmid. So we are trying to reinfect the nonluminous bacteria and make them emit light again. The basic technique is to find an antibiotic which kills all the bacteria; make the nonluminous bacteria resistant to it; mix luminous and nonluminous bacteria; wait for a while, then treat with antibiotic: if any continue to glow, then something must have been transferred to the resistant previously nonluminescent bacteria. It is proving exciting.

With Butcher and Herring I am completing a survey of the differing light organs of *Pyroteuthis* that we expect to see published in 1979, and my coworker Dr. Nixon will be using the equipment provided by the Society while investigating *Nautilus* during a 1979 cruise of the *Alpha Helix*.

REFERENCES

DILLY, P. NOEL

1972. *Taonius megalops,* a squid that rolls up into a ball. Nature, vol. 237, no. 5355 (June 16), pp. 403-404, illus.

1973. The enigma of colouration and light emission in deep-sea animals. Endeavour, vol. 32, no. 115, pp. 25-29, illus. (color).

DILLY, P. NOEL, and HERRING, P. J.
1974. The ocular light organ of *Bathothauma lyroma* (Mollusca: Cephalopoda). Journ. Zool. (London), vol. 172, pp. 81-100.
1978. The light organ and ink sac of *Heteroteuthis dispar* (Mollusca: Cephalopoda). Journ. Zool. (London), vol. 186, pp. 47-59.
DILLY, P. NOEL, and NIXON, MARION N.
1976. Growth and development of *Taonius megalops* (Mollusca: Cephalopoda), and some phases of its life cycle. Journ. Zool. (London), vol. 179, pp. 19-83, illus.
1977. Sucker surfaces and prey capture. Symp. Zool. Soc. London, vol. 38, pp. 447-511.
DILLY, P. NOEL; NIXON, MARION N.; and YOUNG, J. Z.
1977. *Mastigoteuthis.* The whip-lash squid. Journ. Zool., vol. 181, pp. 527-559.
DILLY, P. NOEL, and WOLKEN, J. J.
1973. Studies on the receptors in *Ciona intestinalis;* IV, The ocellus of the adult. Micron, vol. 4, pp. 11-29.
STEBBING, A. R. D., and DILLY, P. NOEL
1972. Some observations on living *Rhabdopleura compacta* (Hemichordata). Journ. Mar. Biol. Assoc. United Kingdom, vol. 52, pp. 443-448, illus.
YOUNG, R. E.
1977. Ventral bioluminescent countershading in midwater cephalopods. Symp. Zool. Soc. London, vol. 38, pp. 161-190.

P. NOEL DILLY

Postfledgling Activities of Juvenile Bald Eagles as Determined by Radio Telemetry

Principal Investigator: Thomas C. Dunstan, Western Illinois University, Macomb, Illinois.

Grant No. 992: In support of a study of postfledgling activities of juvenile bald eagles.

This research project, conducted during the summers of 1971 and 1972, was a separate aspect of a 5-year program to study the biology of breeding bald eagles in north-central Minnesota begun in 1968. Prior to 1971 emphasis was placed on nesting ecology, food habits, pesticide content of nestlings, reproductive success, and local movements of banded and color-marked fledglings. Funding for this study enabled me to apply previously developed radiotracking techniques to the problem of determining the activities of fledgling eagles that travel over large areas around the nesting sites and are not easily located and identified by more conventional means. James F. Harper, graduate student and research cooperator, conducted thesis research during the summer of 1972 and provided portions of data contained in this report.

Bald eagle *(Haliaeetus leucocephalus)* breeding biology is well documented (Broley, 1947; Herrick, 1924a, 1924b, 1934), as are some aspects of the winter biology (Musselman, 1942; Southern, 1963, 1964). However, the behavior of fledgling bald eagles is poorly documented.

The objectives of this study during the breeding seasons of 1971 and 1972 were to provide basic information on (1) daily activities, (2) parent-young relationships, (3) habitat use, (4) home-range and dispersal movements of fledgling bald eagles, and (5) food habits.

The study area was within the peripheral boundaries of the Chippewa National Forest in north-central Minnesota. At least 10 major timber types exist throughout the study area. The dominant upland species common near bald eagle nests are *Pinus strobus, Pinus resinosa,* and *Pinus banksiana,* intermixed with *Populus* spp. and other deciduous trees. The dominant lowland boreal forest species are *Picea marina, Larix laricina,* and *Abies balsamea.* There are 1,217 lakes and 155 named streams totaling over 134,800 hectares of water in the Chippewa Forest (Mathisen, 1968).

Materials and Methods

Five fledglings on two home ranges were studied, two young at one nest in 1971 and three young at two nests in 1972. Fledglings were banded as nestlings in June of each year with U. S. Fish and Wildlife Service lock-on leg bands and were also affixed with radio transmitters weighing from 26 to 124 grams; the transmitters were placed either on the bird's back or on the two central tail feathers (Dunstan, 1972a, 1973a). Movements and activities of the marked birds were recorded from the date of fledging through dispersal. Ages, weights, and marking data are as follows:

Date banded	*Band number*	*Loca-tion*	*Wt.(g.) radio pkg.*	*Age*	*Weight (kilograms) of eagle*
12 June '71	599-01905	Trout L.	72	8	3.3
12 June '71	599-01907	Trout L.	124	8	4.4
8 June '71	599-01908	Trout L.	26	8	4.6
25 June '71	599-03377	Kitchi L.	26	9	4.3
25 June '71	599-03378	Kitchi L.	26	9	4.6

A Model LA 12 telemetry receiver (AVM Instrument Co.) equipped with 8-ohm headphones and matched with a Model 23 3-element or a Model 28 8-element yagi antenna (HyGain) was used in the field and at the base stations. Radio transmitters were self-pulsed, crystal-controlled transistor oscillators with whip antennas and functioned at a frequency range of 220 to 222 MHz. Circuitry was modified after that of Cochran (1967). Birds with radio transmitters were monitored from receiver-equipped base stations, automobiles, watercraft, and airplanes (Dunstan, 1972b). Signal range was up to 57 kilometers, although the working range was usually 2-13 kilometers.

Results and Discussion

The chronology of Minnesota bald-eagle activities was as follows:

Event	*Dates*
Spring arrival	Mar. 1-20
Nest building and repair	Mar. 8-28
Eggs laid	Mar 16 to Apr. 3
Eggs hatched	Apr. 22 to May 10
Nestlings fledged	July 21 to Aug. 12
Fledglings dispersed	Sept. 8 to Oct. 23
Adults dispersed	Nov. 16 to Dec. 19

Nestlings fledged (self-sustained flight from the nest) about July 21 to August 12. Flights were usually to nearby branches of trees often used by parents during the nestling stage of development. The initial fledgling flights were "target oriented"; however, the landings were usually clumsy, and on several occasions fledglings fell short distances before grasping any nearby tree limb for support or fell to the ground. Fledglings usually climbed back up with feet and beak aided by wing flapping. Three birds on the ground eventually walked to an opening and attempted to attain a perch by jumping and flapping. On July 22, 1972, at one nest (the Kitchi nest) a 10-week-old nestling was prematurely dislodged from the nest and blown away but was found again below the nest after 5 days; it weighed 3.8 kilograms, 7 percent less than when weighed 5 weeks earlier. This bird was close enough to the nest to hear the calling of the other sibling and was observed responding to both the sibling and the adult calls. The bird walked back to the base of the tree supporting the nest. On July 25 the other sibling flew about 1,200 meters and landed in underbrush below tall trees. Two days later it was seen 1,000 meters from the nest on top of a 7-meter dead tree, and on August 2, 7 days after fledging, this bird was back in the nest. Data suggest that young that have developed leg and wing muscles and wing feathers can survive landings on the ground if they can get to an opening or up onto a perch where they can be tended by the parents. It is unlikely that young prematurely dislodged nestlings will survive unless they are found and fed by the parents because at an early preflight stage (4 to 9 weeks of age) nestlings walk poorly, have poorly developed defense behavior, and their wings do not aid in climbing.

EARLY FLEDGING PERIOD

Fledglings were classed as "young" or "old" based on age and behavior, and on development of flight, as tabulated here:

Young	*Old*
Dates: July 21 to Aug. 27	Aug. 28 to Sept. 28
Age: 12 to 16 weeks	17 to 20 weeks
Days after fledging: 1 to 18	19 to 44
Short flights (3 to 100 meters)	Short and long flights (10 to 2,000 meters)
Flight and landings poorly controlled	Flight and landings controlled
Do not follow parents	At times follow parents
Little or no soaring	Much soaring (often and sustained)
Utilize both lower and upper canopy and emergents	Utilize upper canopy and emergents

Daily movements of young fledglings, 12 to 16 weeks of age, were 3 to 100 meters and limited to specific emergent trees often used by the parents and

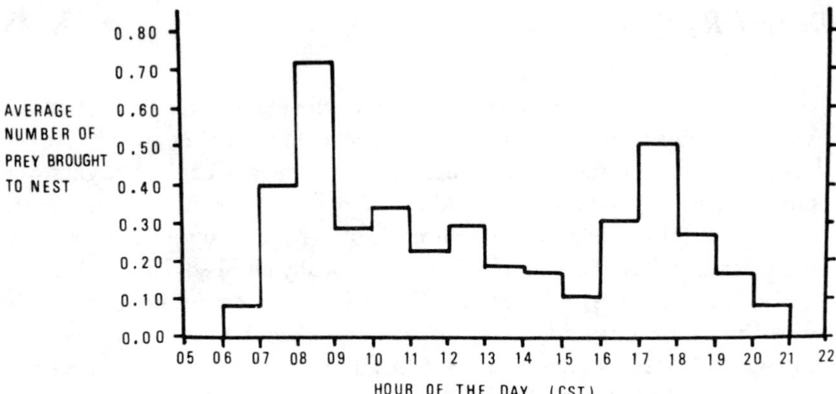

FIG. 1. Average number of prey brought to the Kitchi nest per hour of the day. (From Harper, 1974.)

located close to nests. Preferred emergents were *Pinus strobus, Pinus resinosa, Picea glauca, Populus grandidentata, Populus tremuloides,* and *Betula papyrifera.* Sibling movements were closely associated, and the larger siblings (usually two per nest) dominated perch selection and made longer flights at an earlier age.

Young fledglings gave calls often and remained perched on night roosts usually away from the shore until after sunrise, when they flew to trees along lake shores or to the nests. They fed on the nest platform and either were already present or returned to the nest when parents brought food. An average of four fish per day were brought to the nest from about 14 minutes before sunrise until sunset and two peaks of activity were noted, the more pronounced in the morning and the other in the afternoon (fig. 1). The average number of fish brought to the nest per day and the bimodal peaks of feeding activity found for the Minnesota eagles are similar to data of other interior breeding eagles near Vermillion, Ohio (Herrick, 1924b). Additional comments on food habits of our study birds are presented in two papers (Dunstan and Harper, 1975; and Harper, 1974).

The home-range areas used by five young fledglings (three broods) from two home ranges varied from 18 to 25 hectares, as follows:

Year	*Location*	*Younger fledglings*	*Older fledglings*
1971	Trout L.	20*	83*
1972	Trout L.	18	80
	Kitchi L.	25*	110*

*Range size for siblings considered the same because of the duplicate use of favored perch sites.

The movements of the young birds were within relatively short distances of the nests. The young fledglings did not go far out over the water and often roosted close to one another during the day and night and flew to night roosts together about sunset. Movements of the radio-marked birds upon the perches or nests were detected as late as 132 minutes after sunset. In 1972 at the Kitchi nest two young that had fledged four weeks prior flew about an area of 25 hectares and most of the flights were from 200 meters north to 500 meters south of the nest (fig. 2). In 1971 and 1972 at the Trout Lake nesting site three young that had fledged four weeks prior flew about an area of 18 hectares and most flights were from 100 meters south of the nest to 600 meters north (fig. 3). Fledglings at the Trout Lake site used the same emergent trees during

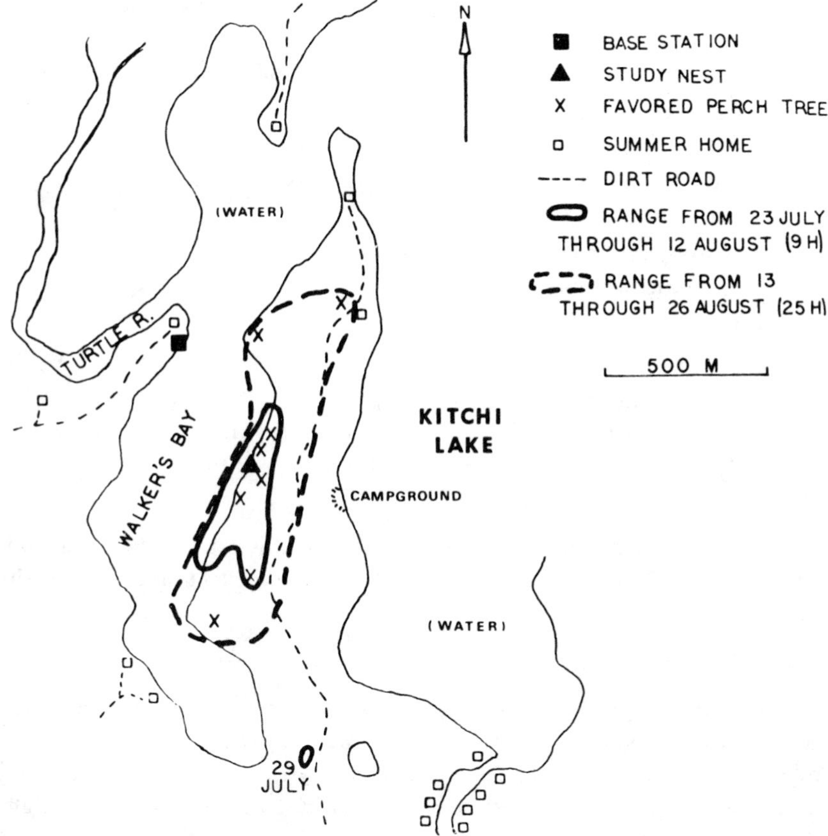

FIG. 2. Areas of home range used by two young fledglings at Kitchi Lake in 1972. Note increase in area used with age. (From Harper, 1974.)

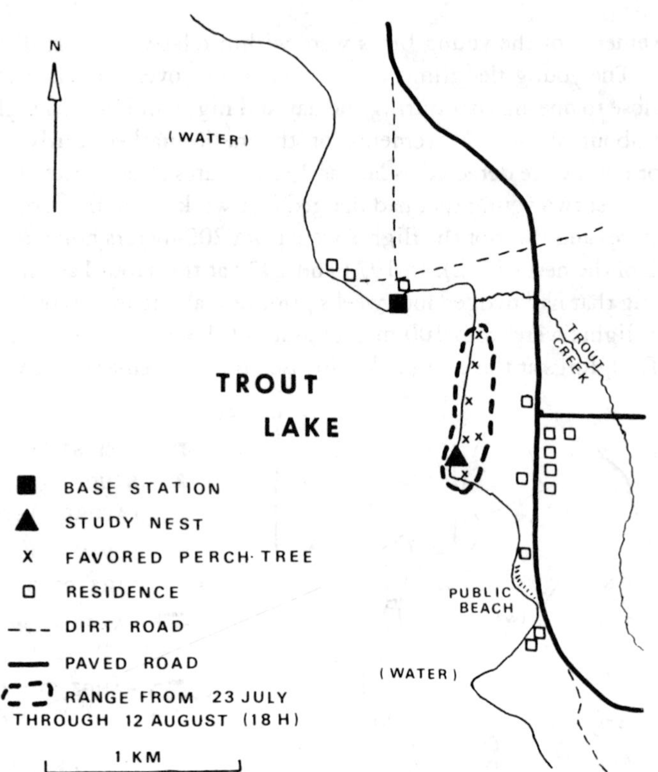

FIG. 3. Area of home range used by three young in 1971 and 1972 at the Trout Lake nest. Figure shows the area actually used in 1972 by one young, which was the same area used in 1971 by two young. (From Harper, 1974.)

both years and therefore used areas of similar size (see tabulations, above). In both years the trees used by the young were also the perch trees used by the parent birds.

LATE FLEDGING PERIOD

Older fledglings, 17 to 20 weeks of age, made daily flights of 3 to 2,000 meters across lakes, along shores, and to distant trees often used by parents and easily seen from the nest. Older fledglings used emergent trees inland and those along edges; they seldom used low deciduous trees except for night roosting on windy or rainy nights. Adults used low perches on windy and rainy nights. Older fledglings were less closely associated in their direction and distance of flights but siblings were often airborne at the same times.

Older fledglings soared more often than younger fledglings and for longer periods (1 to 45 minutes) along shores and over forested areas adjacent to lakes and occasionally in the company of the parent birds (fig. 4). Neither younger nor older fledglings soared far out over open water and were usually close to shores, while adults often soared over both land and open water.

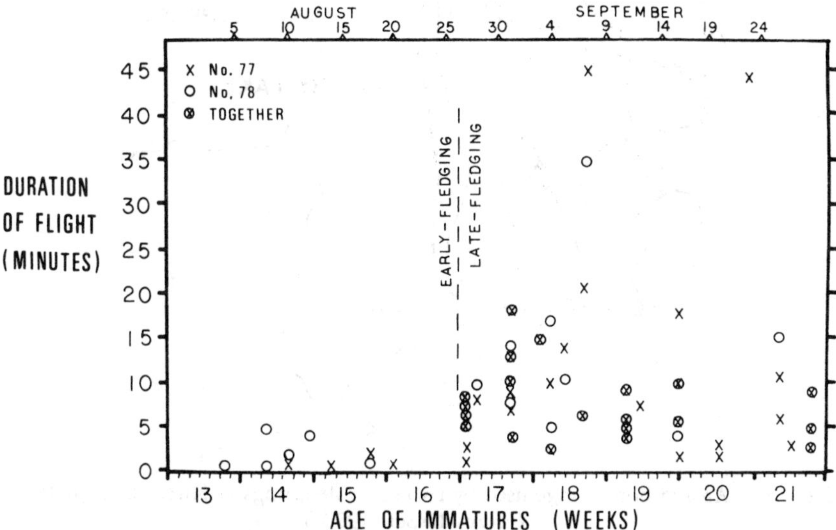

FIG. 4. Duration of flight in relation to age of fledglings at the Kitchi nest in 1972. (From Harper, 1974.)

Older fledglings often followed parents and begged food all day. Fish were still brought to the nest or to feeding perches during the morning and late afternoon. Older fledglings soared along shores on windy days, and on calm days (less than 3 km ph) they made flapping flights between feeding perches. On very warm or rainy days they perched among the branches of tall trees. Parents fed young for 6 to 8 weeks after fledging until dispersal and older fledglings did not pick up dead prey often and did not attack breeding waterfowl.

Older fledglings selected perch trees along shores of lakes on calm nights or back away from the shores on windy nights regardless of whether they were on the leeward or windward shores. In the morning fledglings remained perched until light and then flew to exposed sites and sunbathed before flying to feeding perches or to perched adults. Favored night roosts were often those used by the parents.

The portions of the parental home ranges used by older fledglings were of various sizes, depending on the location of favored feeding and roosting

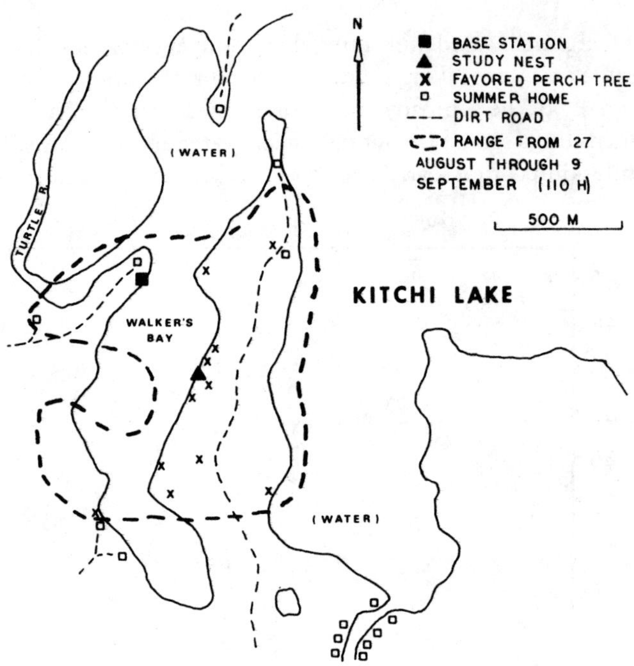

FIG. 5. Area of home range used by two older fledglings at Kitchi Lake in 1972. (From Harper, 1974.)

perches near lakes. The total area used was much larger than the areas used intensively by younger fledglings, partly because of the translake flights. In 1972 older fledglings at the Kitchi nest used an area of 110 hectares (fig. 5). In 1971 and 1972 the older fledglings at the Trout Lake site used a maximum area of about 350 hectares (fig. 6) but used an 80-hectare area more intensely.

DISPERSAL AND MIGRATION

Fledglings dispersed from the parental home range from September 7 to 30 as follows:

Year	*Band number*	*Date fledged*	*Date dispersed*	*Location*
1971	599-01905	Aug. 1	Sept. 28	Trout L.
"	599-01907	Aug. 1	Sept. 25	Trout L.
1972	599-01908	Aug. 1	Sept. 7	Trout L.
"	599-03377	July 21	Sept. 30	Kitchi L.
"	599-03378	July 26	Sept. 13*	Kitchi L.

*Bird seen on September 9 but absent on September 13.

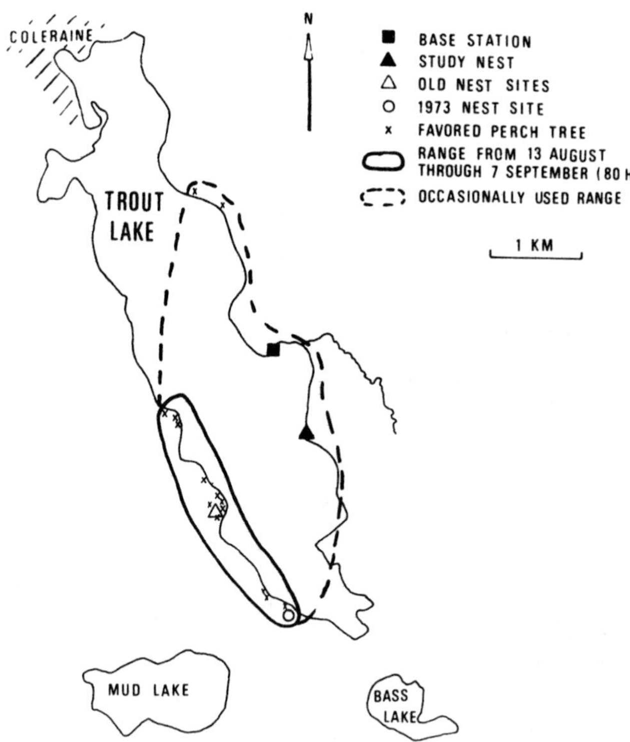

FIG. 6. Area of home range used by three young in 1971 and 1972 at the Trout Lake nest. Figure shows the area actually used in 1972 by one older fledgling, which is the same area used by two older fledglings in 1971. (From Harper, 1974.)

Dispersal movements from home ranges were in various directions, and siblings moved independently of one another and often gathered with other immature eagles along lake shores and rivers. Persons harvesting wild rice (*Zizania* sp.) or hunting ducks flushed eagles, but the birds returned and fed on crippled or dead ducks and fish. The radio-tagged fledglings were tracked on 18- to 70-kilometer flights throughout the study area and these birds frequented open water areas also used by migrating waterfowl. Ice formed on shallow lakes and along lake shores in late October and November and immature eagles left the area during this period.

Fledglings migrated from the study area beginning in October, and our data from related studies showed that one nestling banded in June 1968 was found dead in Texas by October 10, 1968 (Dunstan, 1969) and another nestling banded in June 1971 was found dead in Alabama by February the following year (J. E. Mathisen, personal communication). Nestling no. 599-01907,

TABLE 1. Prey Remains Found in or below Six Bald Eagle Nests in North-central Minnesota from 1967 to 1972

Prey	*Individuals (minimum number)*	*Fish (pct. total)*	*Prey remains (pct. total)*
Fishes			
Bullheads	106	39.0	35.1
Suckers	88	32.4	29.1
Northern pike (under 1,400 grams)	42	15.4	13.9
Largemouth bass	15	5.5	5.0
Rock bass	12	4.4	4.0
Others (5 species plus 1 unidentified centrarchid)	9	3.3	3.0
Subtotal	272	100.0	90.1
Birds			
Ducks	14		4.6
Gulls	6		2.0
Unidentified species	4		1.3
Subtotal	24		7.9
Mammal			
Muskrat	4		1.3
Subtotal	4		1.3
Invertebrates			
Crayfish	1		0.3
Clam	1		0.3
Subtotal	2		0.6
TOTAL	302		99.9

banded in June 1971 (see p. 150), was caught in a coyote trap near Matador, Texas, on January 5, 1973, and released alive (Dunstan, 1973b).

Parent eagles remained on the home ranges into December along open water and were usually absent during January and February. A few adult eagles were observed in the study area along open water during January and February, but whether these were local birds was not determined. Bald eagles migrate down the Mississippi River in large numbers in late November, and therefore birds from other areas may also be present within the study area (Harper, 1974; Reese, 1973).

FOOD HABITS

Prey remains collected from within and below the study nests during the 1971 and 1972 field season were combined with a few samples from the study nests collected previously from 1967 to 1970. The results of the prey item analysis are presented in table 1. The primary prey was fish, with bullheads (*Ictalurus* sp.) appearing most frequently followed by suckers (*Catostomus* and *Moxostoma* spp.) and northern pike (*Esox lucius*). Fish totaled 90.1 percent of total prey, birds 7.9 percent, mammals 1.3 percent, and invertebrates 0.6 percent. A more detailed discussion of the food habits was published by Dunstan and Harper (1975).

REFERENCES

BROLEY, CHARLES L.
1947. Migration and nesting of Florida bald eagles. Wilson Bull., vol. 59, no. 1, pp. 3-20.
COCHRAN, W. W.
1967. A 145-160 MHz beacon (tag) transmitter for small animals, 12 pp. BIAC Information Module, Washington, D. C.
DUNSTAN, THOMAS C.
1969. First recovery of a bald eagle banded in Minnesota. Loon, vol. 41, p. 92.
1972a. A harness for radio-tagging raptorial birds. Inland Bird Banding News, vol. 44, no. 1, pp. 4-8.
1972b. Radio-tagging falconiform and strigiform birds. Raptor Res., vol. 6, no. 3, pp. 92-102.
1973a. A tail feather package for radio-tagging raptorial birds. Inland Bird Banding News, vol. 45, no. 1, pp. 6-9.
1973b. Bald eagle from Minnesota recovered in Texas. Loon, vol. 45, no. 4, p. 132.
DUNSTAN, THOMAS C., and HARPER, JAMES F.
1975. Food habits of bald eagles in north-central Minnesota. Journ. Wildl. Man., vol. 39, no. 1, pp. 140-143.
HARPER, JAMES F.
1974. Activity of fledgling bald eagles in north-central Minnesota, 68 pp. M. S. thesis, Western Illinois University.
HERRICK, FRANCIS H.
1924a. Nests and nesting habits of the American eagle. Auk, vol. 41, no. 2, pp. 213-232.
1924b. The daily life of the American eagle: Late phase. Auk, vol. 41, no. 3, pp. 389-422.
1934. The American eagle, 267 pp. D. Appleton-Century, New York.
MATHISEN, J. E.
1968. Effects of human disturbance on nesting of bald eagles. Journ. Wildl. Man., vol. 32, pp. 1-6.

MUSSELMAN, T. E.
1942. Eagles of western Illinois. Auk, vol. 59, no. 1, pp. 105-107.
REESE, J. G.
1973. Bald eagle migration along the Mississippi River in Minnesota. Loon, vol. 45, no. 1, pp. 22-23.
SOUTHERN, WILLIAM E.
1963. Winter populations, behavior, and seasonal dispersal of bald eagles in northwestern Illinois. Wilson Bull., vol. 75, no. 1, pp. 42-55.
1964. Additional observations on winter bald eagle populations: including remarks on biotelemetry techniques and immature plumages. Wilson Bull., vol. 76, no. 2, pp. 121-137.

THOMAS C. DUNSTAN

The Battle of Lepanto Search and Survey Mission, Greece, 1971-1972[1]

Principal Investigators: Harold E. Edgerton, Massachusetts Institute of Technology, Cambridge, Massachusetts; Peter Throckmorton, Newcastle, Maine[2]; and Eletherios Yalouris, Harvard University, Cambridge, Massachusetts.

Grant No. 980: In support of sonar and diving search for wrecks of the Battle of Lepanto, August 1571.

This search for the site of the Battle of Lepanto started in the summer of 1971, 400 years after the battle, at the request of Prof. Spiridon Marinatos, late Director of Antiquities, Athens, Greece. Preliminary expeditions to the vicinity of the battle site (Bay of Patras, west of Mesolonghi and east of Oxia Island) showed the vastness of the area to be surveyed and the difficulties involved in ultimately pinpointing the wreck site. Five trips were made to the area, four in 1971 (June, July, September, and November) and one in 1972 (May 18-June 17) (fig. 1).

The battle took place on October 7, 1571, in the Bay of Patras, south of the mouth of the Acheloos River and the Koutsilaris Islands, between the Christian fleet, under the command of Don Juan of Austria, approaching from the west, and the Turkish fleet, led by Ali Pasha, coming from the east. That afternoon saw the greatest defeat, on land or sea, suffered by the Turks up to that time. The battle is well described by Lesure (1972) and Marx (1966).[3]

---

[1] This report is substantially a reprint of an article by the same authors published in the *International Journal of Nautical Archaeology and Underwater Exploration,* vol. 2, no. 1, pp. 121-130, 1971.

[2] Grateful acknowledgment is made to the following individuals for substantial contributions in carrying out this mission: Dr. Donald Frey (magnetometer operator), Fred Feyling (charts and navigation), Derek Whitmore (shipwork and navigation), Bob Sadock (sonar operator), Tom Hopkins (geologist and sonar operator), Joan Throckmorton and Pat Whitmore (many ship tasks), Tim Green (sailor), as well as many others who contributed. The interest and cooperation of representatives of the Greek Archaeological Service, Harry Kritsas and John Papapostalou, are also much appreciated.

[3] Lesure, Michel, *Lepante: La crise de l'empire ottoman,* Paris, 1972. Marx, Robert, *The Battle of Lepanto, 1571,* Cleveland, 1966.

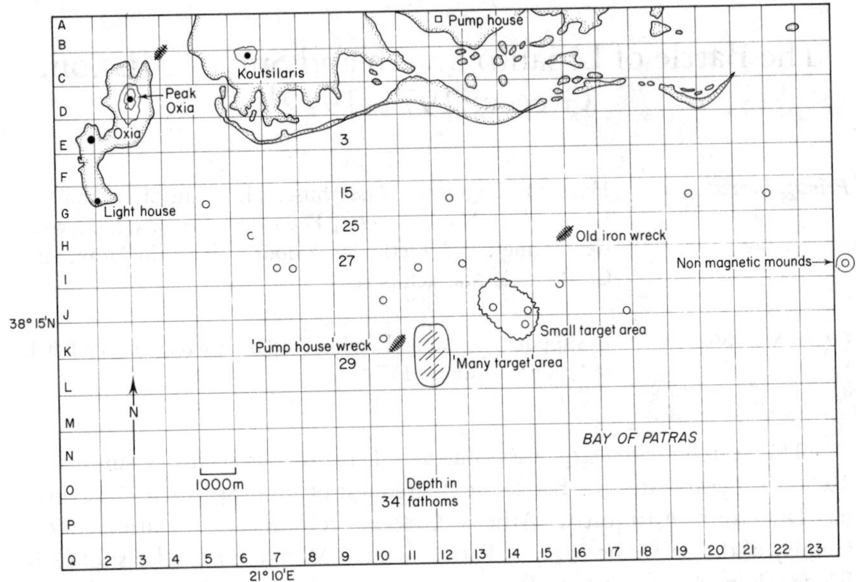

FIG. 1. Map of the suspected site of the Battle of Lepanto, showing some of the many targets plotted with side-scan sonar. From U. S. Naval Oceanographic chart no. 3962.

The exact size of each fleet is uncertain, but the best sources say that the Turkish navy had over 300 galleys and 80-90 auxiliary vessels with over 100,000 men; and the Christian fleet had some 300 ships and over 60,000 men.

Soon after the battle had begun, the Turkish right wing began to break, and eventually about 30 ships were driven into shallow water and ran aground. They were later plundered and burned by the Christians. The heaviest fighting took place in the center, where the Christians lost about 12 galleys. The exact number of ships sunk in the battle is uncertain, but it is said that the Turks lost about 80 vessels, most of which were burned.

Almost all the ships that went down were rowed galleys, of a design that had changed very little for over 2,000 years.[4] They were long and narrow, usually about 120-160 feet (36-48 meters) in length and 15-20 feet (4-6

[4] For a description of the galleys of the period, see Landström, B., *The ship,* pp. 127-141, London, 1961. For further details of construction, ironwork, etc., see Lane, Carl D., *Venetian ships and shipbuilders of the Renaissance,* Baltimore, 1934.

FIG. 2. Chart of 1598 from the Gennadeion Library, Athens.

meters) in width, averaging 100 to 200 tons. They could carry a limited number (up to five in the bigger galleys) of carriage guns in the bows and a few pieces of light artillery in the stern-castles. Most of the ships that were destroyed were either burned or shattered from collision. Because they had very little ballast, it would be unrealistic (although by no means out of the question) to expect these ships to sink to the bottom intact, although it is not impossible that considerable parts of the wooden structures could be found preserved in the mud. Various metal objects, including light artillery, weapons, armor, chains, anchors, grappling hooks, and possibly some treasure, might be expected. The best area in which to look (see below) would be in depths of 150-200 feet (45-60 meters), where a muddy bottom would help to preserve those remains not completely covered by the heavy silting from the Acheloos River.

One of the important problems that faced the Lepanto search and survey team was to determine how much the coastline of 1571 differed from that of

FIG. 3. Chart of 1702 from the Gennadeion Library, Athens.

the present. In view of the fact that the battle took place outside the mouth of Greece's largest river, the Acheloos, notorious for its silting, it would be quite reasonable to suspect considerable change in the geomorphology of the region over a period of 400 years. Thucydides (ii: 102) describes clearly this silting.

Careful inspection of a series of maps, dating from 1598 to the present, found in the Gennadeion Library of the American School of Classical Studies in Athens, showed considerable changes in the shape or extent of the land over a 400-year period.[5] Several of these maps are reproduced for this report (figs.

[5] The following is a brief list of maps in the extensive collection of the Gennadeion Library (in each entry the catalogue number is given first; the kind assistance of Francis R. Walton, the librarian, is gratefully acknowledged): GT 173. 2q. Muenster (a collection, c. 1598-1628). GT 230. *Maps of Greece* (a collection from 1700-19th century). GT 328. *The English Pilot: Pt. III, the Mediterranean Sea,* 1771. GT 225.6. Stieler, *Hand Atlas,* 1831. GT 271.9. Hellert (a collection), London, 1844. GT 220.1. Kiepert, *Atlas Antique,* 1882. Research in this collection was undertaken by Dr. Yalouris.

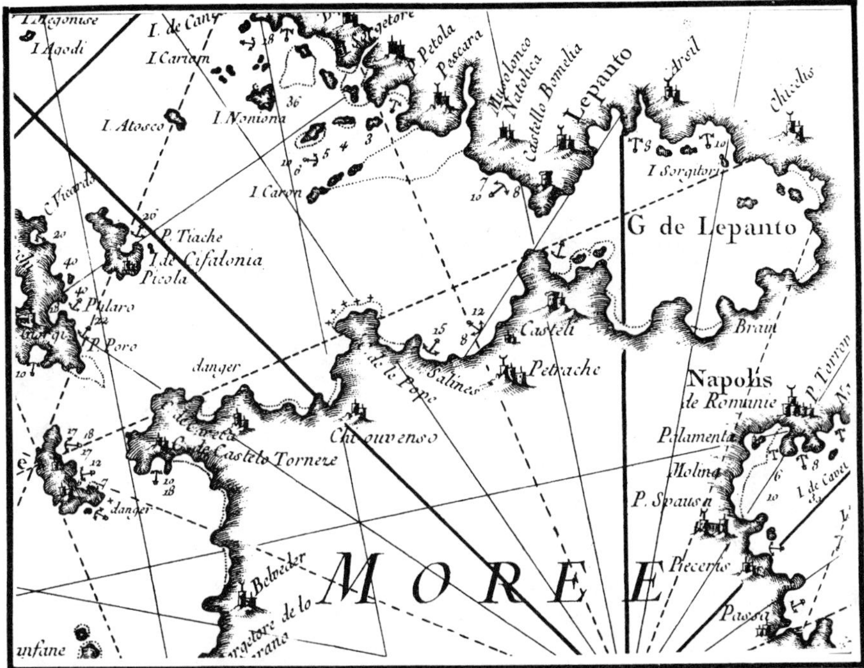

FIG. 4. Chart of 1700 from the Gennadeion Library, Athens.

2, 3, 4). The inaccuracies of 16th- to 18th-century cartographers can readily be appreciated, and the maps must be examined with considerable reservation. A number of points, however, must be considered more seriously. In most 18th-century maps, for example, the island of Oxia is either clearly marked or can be singled out among the clusters of small islands to the east and north of it (often called Curzolari Insulae, as in figs. 2 and 3). The islands that appear on these maps to the east are not shown as islands in any 20th-century map (see fig. 1). They are mountains (Koutsilaris, Scoupas, etc.). Ancient mariners and cartographers could be expected to make sizable errors in outlining the coastline of an area (especially if it was foreign to them), but islands would appear as islands on their maps. Prescott[6] describes the Christian armada as it approaches the battle site: "By sunrise they were abreast of the Curzolari, a cluster of huge rocks, or rocky islets, which in the north

[6] Prescott, William H., *History of the reign of Philip II,* vol. 3, p. 884, London, 1881.

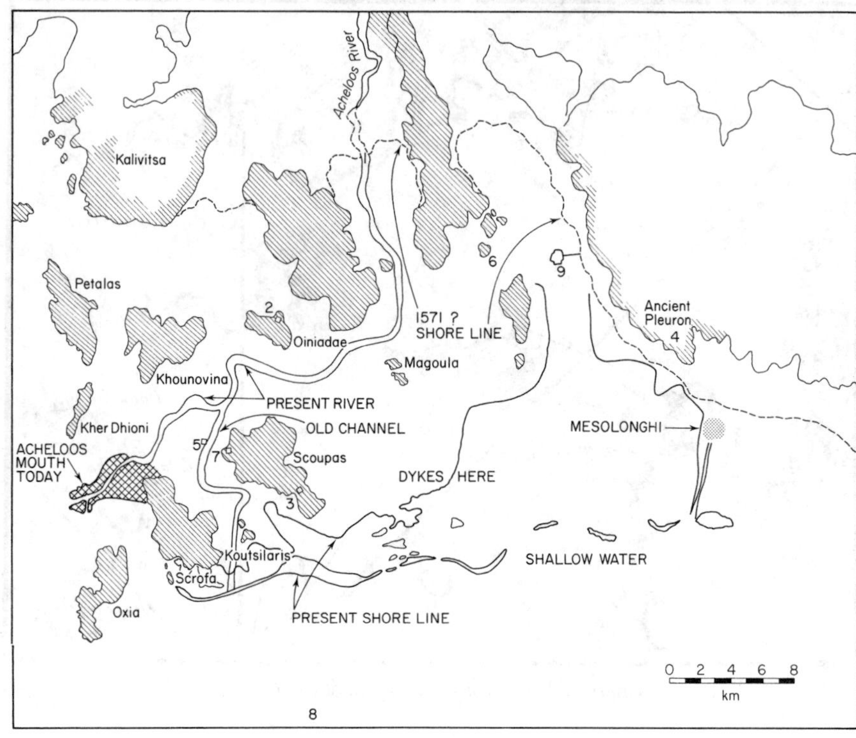

FIG. 5. Map of Lepanto battle site with possible coastline of 1571 and present beach shoreline.

defends the entrance to the Gulf of Lepanto."[7] It is also obvious that the position of the mouth of the Acheloos River changed many times. Topographical and geological surveys carried out by engineers from Edok Eter, the company hired by the Greek Government to run the giant reclamation project in the area, confirm this and the fact that the shoreline was once much farther north than it is now.

Further evidence for pushing the 1571 coastline back several miles is shown on figure 5, which can be compared with a modern chart of the same region (fig. 1). What follows is an explanation of figure 5:

1. Possible vicinity of the mouth of the Acheloos River in 1571. Core

[7] The "many target" area (fig. 5, no. 8). This is right in the area where it was suggested that the heaviest fighting took place, and the indications, many of which are undoubtedly wrecks, may be thought of as the 'dregs' of the battle.

samples taken recently by Edok Eter engineers confirm that there was once sea in this area.

2. Ancient classical city and harbor of Oiniadae. Remains of the ancient harbor, including slips for the ships, can still be seen in the north of the island, now a mountain. It was said that the land to the north of it had been swampy in Classical times and that heavy silting from the Acheloos was occurring even then. (See Bury, 1927.[8])

3. Taxiarkhai. Remains of a Byzantine monastery nestled between the two southeast ridges of Scoupas (now a mountain).

4. Ancient Pleuron. A city famous in Mycenaean times, referred to by Homer (*Iliad,* 14.116., 9.529ff.) as "Pleuron by the Sea." Also active down to Hellenistic times.

5. Samples of seashells found (May 1972) in this area, in irrigation trenches dug by Edok Eter.

6. Reconnaissance by hydraulic engineers showed that the mouth of the Acheloos was once here.

7. Old customs house. Probably used in the 19th century for ships coming into the mouth of the Acheloos when it was there.

8. Sonar and magnetometer search in this "many target" area has shown a cluster of small deposits (could be cannon, cannon balls, etc.) in about 180 feet (55 meters) of water. This is the most promising of the sites (see below), and is the prime target for future investigation.

9. Modern town of Aetoliken. Figured in Byzantine times as an important center of coastal trade.

This map, the result of preliminary, and necessarily incomplete, research, does not pretend to be totally accurate. It intends to show only that the coastline of 1571 was considerably north of where it is today. Only further research and careful geological investigation can produce a more accurate map. This was not necessary for the purposes of our search and survey work for the site of the Battle of Lepanto.

Because evidence suggests that the coastline of 1571 could have been as much as 6 miles north of its present location, it was pointless for our survey team to look for the remains of the 30 or so Turkish galleys that were allegedly forced aground by the left flank of the Christian armada and then burned. Although the beach on which they grounded could have been in any of several possible places, one thing certain is that it was not on what is now known as the Louri, a strip of sandy beach to the south of Koutsilaris (fig. 1). This beach, the present southernmost shore of the land mass in question, did not

[8] Bury, John B., *A history of Greece,* ed. 2, p. 419, London, 1927.

exist in 1571. Our attention thus turned to deeper waters, where the heavy silting from the Acheloos did not have to be dealt with.

Search and Survey

An extensive area sprinkled with small targets that could be remnants of wrecks from the Battle of Lepanto has now been identified in the area southeast of Mount Koutsilaris, in about 180 feet (55 meters) of water (fig. 5, no. 8; figs. 1, 2). Numerous other modern wrecks and other interesting "targets" were also located. The latter could be ancient wrecks, as they appear on the sonar pictures as shallow mounds. These mounds, of course, could also be of geological origin. No dives in the suspected area of the battle were made, primarily because of the depth and lack of proper diving facilities.

The survey work was conducted aboard the ship RV *Stormie Seas,* with an EG & G side-scan sonar, an EG & G 5 kHz penetrating pinger with recorder (Model 254), and an ELSEC Proton Magnetometer (Type 592) as the basic search tools. The side-scan sonar covers a 500-foot (150-meter) field to the port side only. At 8 knots, the ship's top speed, an area of about 1 square mile could be explored in about an hour. However, most of the exploration was done at 4 knots in order to get records of better quality. The track of the ship had to be controlled so that nothing was missed and to prevent duplicate coverage of an area. Several methods for navigation were used. These included the use of hand-bearing compasses and the ship's compass coordinated with a pelorus; they were used from the deck of the ship to get position lines that then could be laid out on an enlarged nautical chart. It would have been more accurate to use shore stations with the transits, but haze, lack of sufficient personnel, and the distance from the shore made it impossible to do. A shore party had been sent to the area a week ahead to make a general reconnaissance and verify the exact bearings of the several points of reference (Oxia, Koutsilaris, pump house, etc.) to be used for getting the ship's bearings.

The accuracy of the navigation was found to be influenced not only by the reading of the hand compasses but also by the heading of the ship and the position of the compass on the ship. A few experiments indicated that our position, at the farthest range in the worst case, could be ± 400 meters. This fact should be kept in mind when the charts are to be used to refind the targets, especially the weaker targets that need to be relocated and investigated. This problem is known to exist, since it was very difficult to refind several weak tartets, in particular, the one due west of the pump-house wreck. It is probable that there are other important targets that were missed owing to navigational errors or equipment. These will show up when the critical areas are

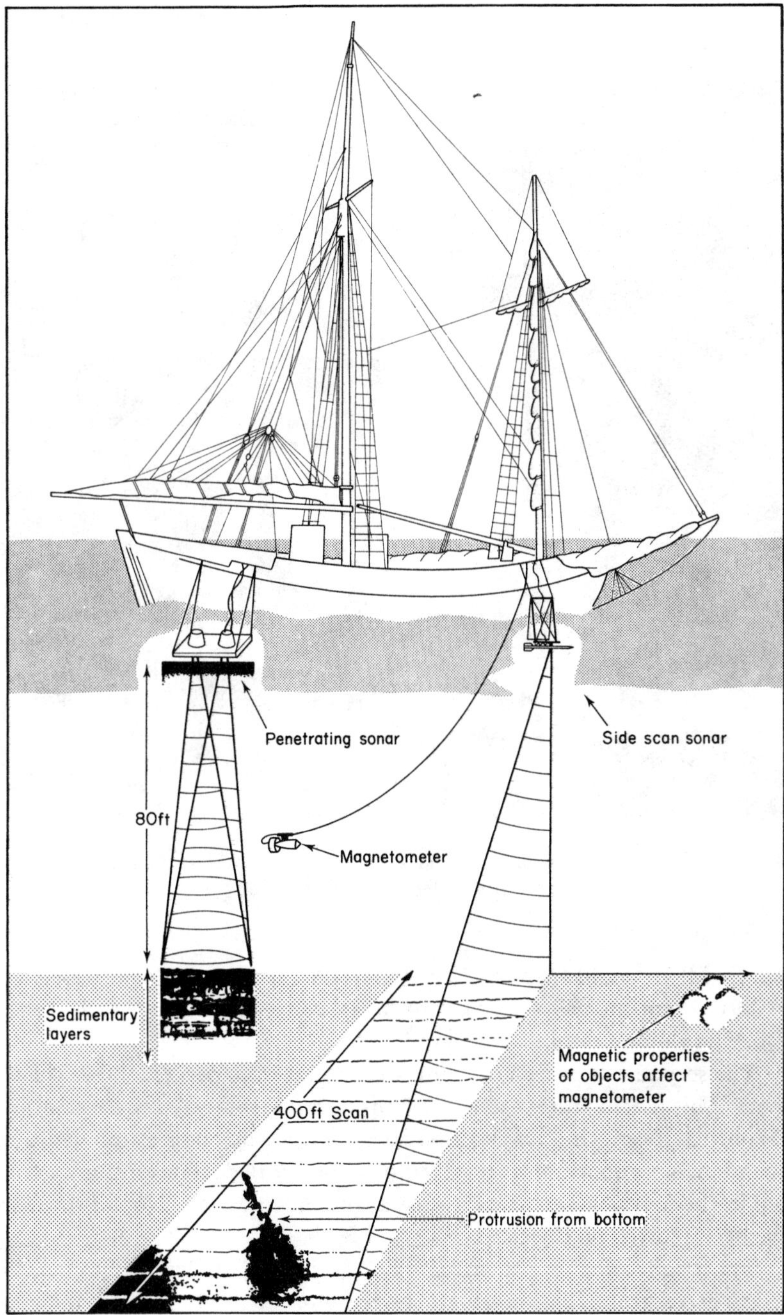

FIG. 6. Diagram showing the equipment used on RV *Stormie Seas*.

FIG. 7. The magnetometer chart on the ship's deck showing an anomaly picked up by the detector in the water.

resurveyed. It would then be most important that the ship's position should be plotted continuously on a chart to ensure complete coverage and all the information would be continually available.

The second acoustic equipment was employed to penetrate into the sediments. This used a pulse of about 0.5 ms duration with a basic frequency of 5 kHz. Much interesting information about the geology of the area was recorded, and many subbottom target features were revealed, though many were too deep in the sediments to be excavated at the present time. Not all the targets have been plotted on the chart.

The magnetometer, provided by Dr. E. T. Hall of Oxford, England, was used to detect iron. This measurement is important, since many of the targets found by the acoustic equipment are of geological origin and of no interest to the project. The magnetometer makes it possible to reject these.

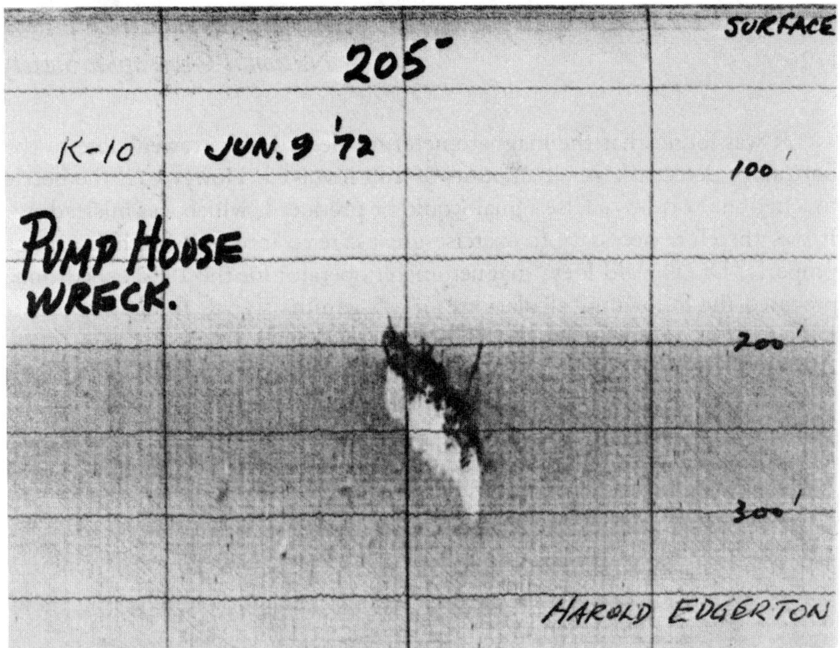

FIG 8. A side-scan sonar record of a modern wreck, directly south of the pump house. This wreck is thought to be a German escort vessel. Holes to left could be bomb craters.

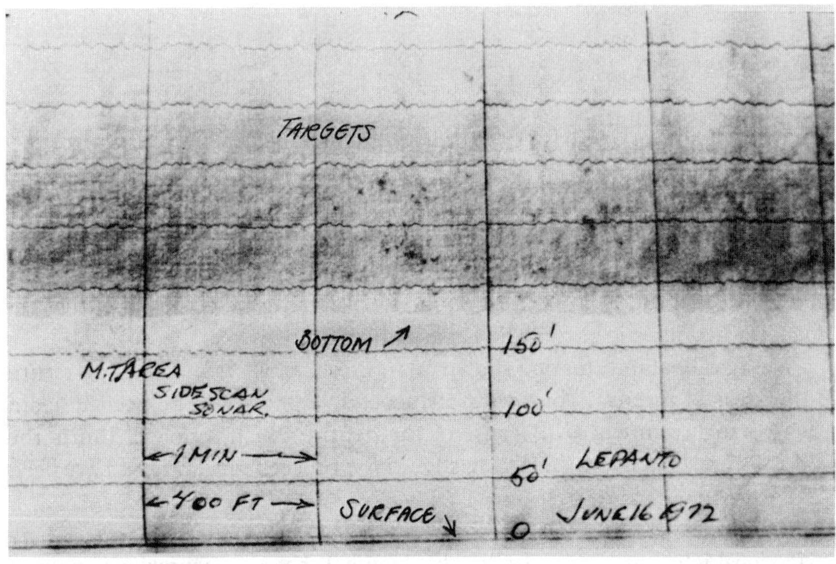

FIG. 9. A side-scan sonar record of part of the "many target" area, which could be the site of the Lepanto battle.

It was found that the magnetometer bottle had to be towed close to the bottom to detect the small amounts of iron involved. However, if the bottle touched the bottom, a false signal would be produced, which was misleading. It was therefore necessary to exercise great care in interpreting the readings properly. Dr. Donald Frey, magnetometer operator for the 1972 expedition, prepared the following calculations for a 5-gamma signal, from an approximate equation furnished by Dr. Hall:

Distance from the magnetometer bottle to the target (m)	*Tons of iron in the target*
10	0.1
15	0.33
20	0.80
25	1.6
30	2.7
40	6.4
50	12.5
60	21.6
70	34.3
80	51.2
90	72.9
100	100

If a galley contained 1.5 tons of iron, the magnetometer must be 25 meters from it for a minimum signal of 5 gammas. This calls for the magnetometer to be close to the bottom for small target detection, and a distance of 3 meters was achieved by allowing the ship to drift. Two runs over the center of the "many target" area produced significant signals, which Frey interprets to indicate iron in the appropriate amounts. This strengthens the belief that the "many target" area is part of the Lepanto battle site.

Navigational information shown on figures 1 and 9 would enable a return to the areas of interest,[9] but certainly acoustic devices will be needed again when diving commences. Because of the depth, which seriously limits the working time of a diver, the diving should not proceed until targets have been

[9] Figure 1 is a chart of the Bay of Patras, showing the modern targets found and navigational information from landmarks. Figure 9 shows the approximate position of numerous targets, some very small and weak, that should be investigated.

accurately buoyed. The diver should not be used as a search device, since his bottom time is so limited.

Modern developments have made diving at depths of 150-200 feet (45-60 meters) a practical possibility. This is the maximum practical diving depth for work with compressed air, and well across the threshold of mixed gas diving. Taken as a mixed gas diving project, the area is not excessively deep, but a serious diving project such as this, both time-consuming and costly, should not be undertaken before a preliminary investigation is launched to determine the exact nature of the contents of the target area. This can be done in any one of several ways: bounce dives with compressed air; use of a small research submarine (such as *Asherah*), with underwater television as an aid to the surface crew; bounce dives with mixed gases. Ideally, it would be best to use the submarine and the underwater TV with divers ready to make bounce dives on a site once it is pinpointed.

Conclusion

The purpose of the Lepanto search and survey project was to conduct a surface reconnaissance to locate the site of the Battle of Lepanto, with the use of acoustic and magnetometer equipment. A map of "targets" was produced that showed promise as possible sites of wrecks from the battle. The next step is to go down to the bottom and investigate the cause of the signals.

PETER THROCKMORTON
HAROLD E. EDGERTON
ELETHERIOS YALOURIS

Petrology and Origin of the Mount Stuart Batholith, Cascade Mountains, Washington[1]

Principal Investigator: Erik H. Erikson, Jr., Eastern Washington State College, Cheney, Washington.

Grant Nos. 1034, 1133, 1292. In support of a petrological and geochemical study of the Mount Stuart batholith, central Cascade Mountains, Washington, 1972-1974.

Large bodies of igneous rocks (batholiths) are exposed in the Cascade Mountains as a combined result of uplift and erosion (fig. 1). Here, as elsewhere, these batholiths consist of a variety of rock types whose characteristics and origin are studied by petrologists. In the Mount Stuart batholith detailed field study, sampling of the rocks, and subsequent laboratory analysis and computer simulation of geologic models have revealed why these rock types are associated and how the rocks originated. A model is presented whereby the Mount Stuart batholith evolved from a basaltic magma which rose from the upper mantle, invaded the overlying rocks of the crust, and progressively changed its composition during crystallization. The exposed batholith represents the solidified remnants of several related magma chambers. Periodically lava erupted onto the surface about 90 million years ago. By 55 million years ago the segment of crust containing the batholith had risen at least 5 kilometers, and erosion progressively exposed these rocks.

Geologic Setting

Calc-alkaline igneous intrusions in Washington State are exposed along the north-south axis of the Cascade Range and in north-central Washington

---

[1] The complete results of this study are published in Erikson, 1977. The study was made possible by grants from the National Geographic Society and the Geological Society of America. Their support is gratefully acknowledged. The cooperation and assistance of James Gualtieri (U. S. Geological Survey) played a significant role in execution of the field work. Capable field assistants included Alan Williams (1972), Thomas Hefner (1973), Chris Erikson, and Shawn Erikson. David Hoover assisted during the analytical stage of the study, and Pauline Masters prepared Fortran translations of PL-1 computer programs.

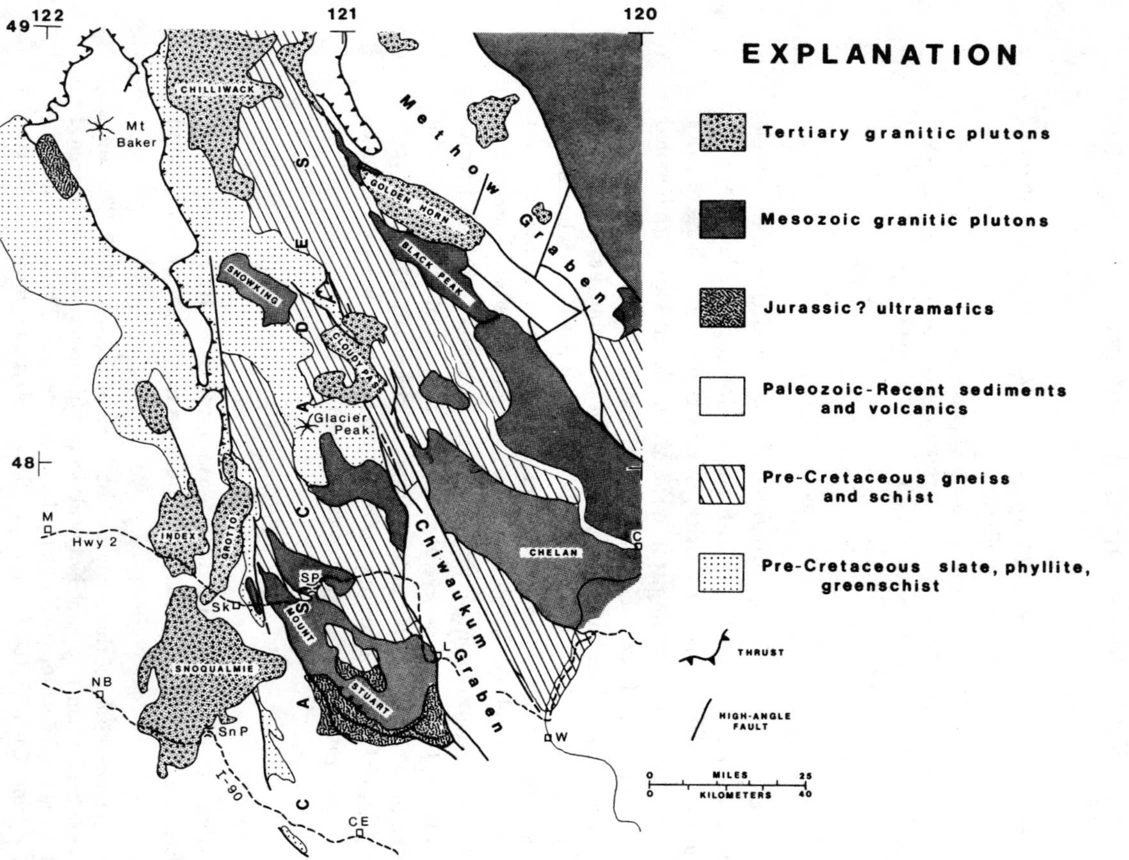

FIG. 1. Generalized tectonic map of the northern Cascade Range, Washington, and vicinity. C = Chelan; C E = Cle Elum; L = Leavenworth; M = Monroe; N B = North Bend; Sk = Skykomish; Sn P = Snoqualmie Pass; S P = Stevens Pass. (After Hunting et al., 1961.)

(fig. 1). The excellent exposures and rugged relief of most of this area facilitate detailed studies of the structural and petrological character of these plutonic rocks.

The Mount Stuart batholith and its outlying stocks are exposed over more than 500 square kilometers in the central Cascade Mountains (fig. 1). They have invaded the Chiwaukum Schist, a major pre-Cretaceous unit of the North Cascades, and a Jurassic mafic-ultramafic complex. All these plutonic rocks are cut by several generations of mafic Tertiary dikes. The batholith and its host rocks comprise the Mount Stuart horst, a northwesterly trending early Tertiary structure (fig. 1). This horst is bounded on the west by the Deception-Straight Creek fault and on the east by the Leavenworth fault and the Chiwaukum Graben. The southern margin of the horst is defined by arcuate zones of shearing within the serpentinized mafic-ultramafic complex.

Methods of Study

Nearly four complete field seasons were spent in the Mount Stuart area, 1970-1973. Major element analyses were performed on 93 rocks from the batholith using atomic absorption techniques and analytical standards from Mount Stuart rocks and the U. S. Geological Survey. More than 400 thin sections were studied in detail. Additional chemical data incorporated in this study were gathered by Pongsapich (1974), particularly his microprobe analyses of Mount Stuart minerals, and by Smith (1904).

General Characteristics of the Mount Stuart Batholith

K/A dating of coexisting biotite-hornblende pairs in rocks of the batholith has established a Late Cretaceous age of crystallization (88±3 million years) (Engels and Crowder, 1971). Fission track ages of apatite and other minerals from the Mount Stuart rocks range from 27 to 94 million years (Engels and Crowder, 1971; Erikson and Williams, 1976).

Evidence for igneous origin and multiple emplacement relies upon the following criteria: 1, Systematic cross-cutting relationships; 2, the chemical and mineralogical homogeneity of intrusive phases comprising the batholith; 3, flow-foliation paralleling the contacts of separate intrusives; and 4, rock composition, mineralogy, and texture. Intrusive phases range in size from small plugs and dikes to plutons, which comprise large portions of the batholith (fig. 2). Related stocks have been recognized outside the batholith by previous workers. Cognate mafic inclusions, transformed by varying degrees of recrystallization, appear in all but the most leucocratic intrusives.

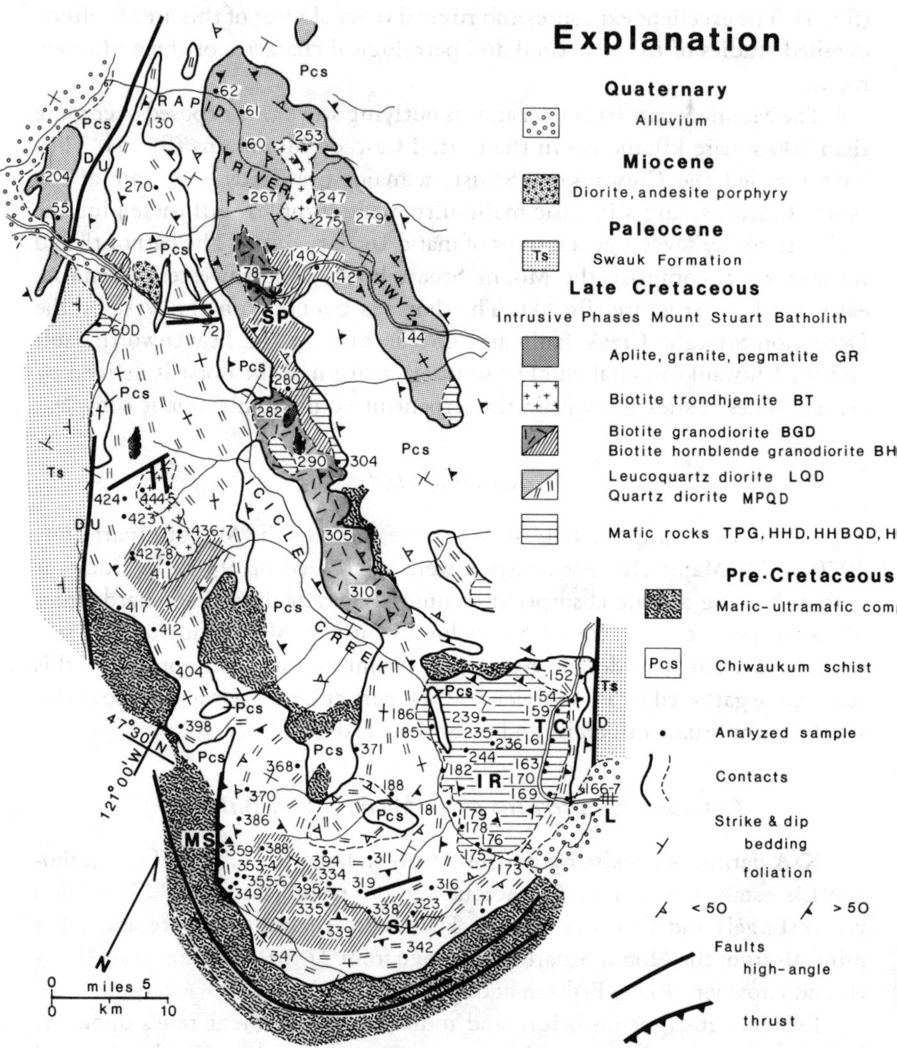

FIG. 2. The Mount Stuart batholith. IR = Icicle Ridge; L = Leavenworth; MS = Mount Stuart; SL = Snow Lakes; SP = Stevens Pass; TC = Tumwater Canyon.

Most Mount Stuart rocks are foliated (fig. 2). Foliation is largely the result of flow alignment of early-formed hornblende and plagioclase, rarely biotite. Protoclasis is locally developed adjacent to pluton margins. The over-all structural fabric of individual plutons is identical to that of a gneiss dome.

Emplacement

Emplacement of the batholith as a whole was strongly controlled by the structures of the enclosing Chiwaukum Schist. This is suggested by the elongation of the batholith parallel to foliation and compositional layering within the schist. Emplacement began as mafic magmas invaded host rocks in the Icicle Ridge area (fig. 2). The upward movement of successively younger magmas, generated by fractionation at depth, stopped and dismembered older plutons. They rose as sill-like intrusives and semicrystalline diapirs, progressively wedging apart the Chiwaukum Schist along its northwesterly trending structural grain. The motions of these magmas are defined by flow-foliation patterns within them. Smaller, more granitic stocks, generated by higher-level fractionation, rose forcefully within their host plutons. Their hosts were, in some cases, incompletely crystalline as indicated by the stretching of cognate inclusions. Based upon minerals formed in the wall rocks during intrusion, magma temperatures exceeded 725°C. at pressures less than 4 kilobars.

Intrusive Series of the Mount Stuart Batholith

The intrusive series of the batholith ranges from two-pyroxene gabbro (norite) systematically through mineralogic varieties of early gabbro, diorite, abundant quartz diorite, and granodiorite to lesser trondhjemite and minor amounts of granite (fig. 3). Accumulate rocks include pyroxenite and hornblendite, some containing olivine. The youngest phases include small amounts of aplite and granite pegmatite. Hornblende- and plagioclase-enriched rocks occur at several stages in the intrusive suite and are spatially associated with their parent rocks. Mafic minerals and plagioclase exhibit systematic changes in their composition and sequence of crystallization throughout the rock series.

Petrochemical Relationships

Chemical variations of the Mount Stuart intrusive series (fig. 4) correspond to trends typical of calc-alkaline magma suites with two prominent exceptions. The soda/potash ratio maintains relatively high levels throughout the series in comparison with other magma suites. This corresponds to their higher ratio of sodic plagioclase to potash feldspar and is related to initial low levels of potash present in the parent magma. The sum of the alkali oxides is similar to other batholithic suites.

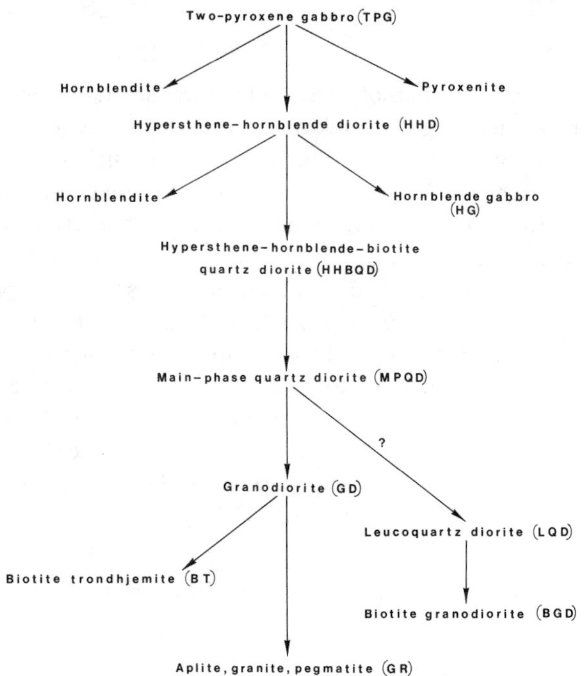

FIG. 3. The intrusive series and liquid line of descent of the Mount Stuart batholith.

The second unusual characteristic is the high magnesium level of the mafic and intermediate rocks of the Mount Stuart series. These rocks are strikingly more magnesian than are corresponding rocks of other intrusive and volcanic suites.

Evolution of the Mount Stuart Magma Suite

All mineralogical and petrological features of the Mount Stuart intrusive suite are consistent with the hypothesis that it has evolved from a single batch of magnesian high-alumina basalt by successive fractional crystallization of ascending residual magma. The main arguments for this model include the following: 1, Systematic changes in the composition of minerals and their host rocks throughout the intrusive series; 2, intrusive phases become increasingly more granitic with decreasing age; and 3, computer simulations of this fractionation process provide quantitative proof that the subtraction of early-formed minerals from their magmas are capable of producing the Mount Stuart rock association.

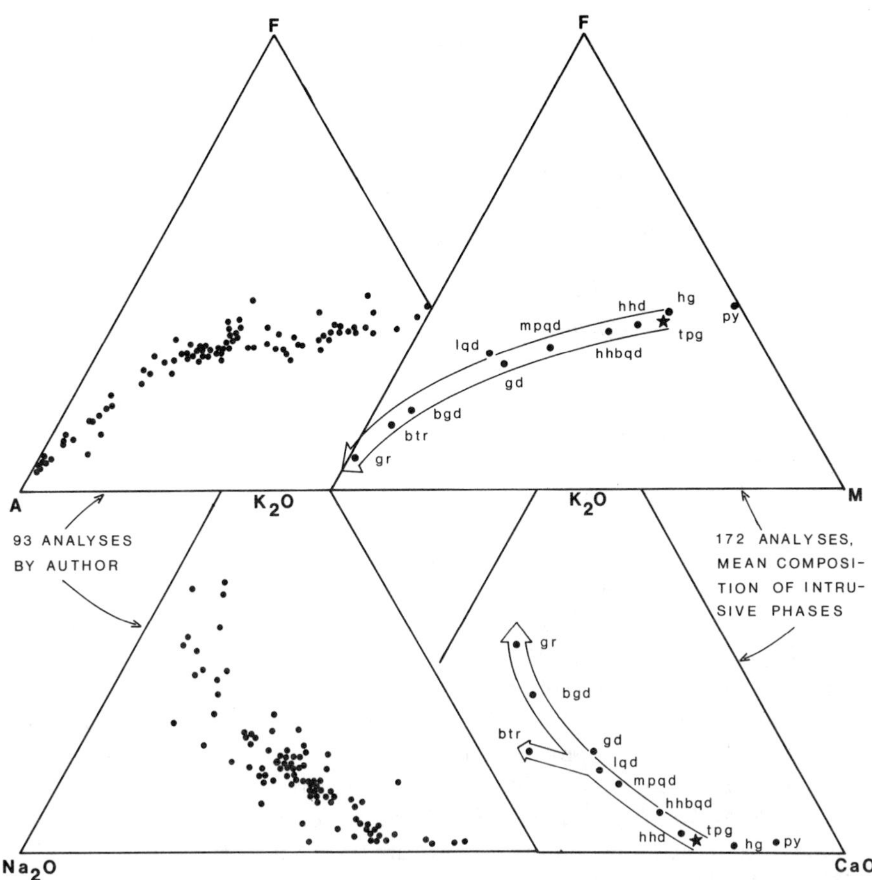

FIG. 4. Triangular plots of chemical trends from rocks of the Mount Stuart batholith. A = total alkalies, F = iron as Fe_2O_3, M = MgO. For analyses of rocks by author (on left), see Erikson 1977. Mean compositions of intrusive phases (on right) are labeled after figure 3 and incorporate data of Smith (1904) and Pongsapich (1974).

Parental Magma. The oldest rock identified in the batholith is believed to represent the parental magma for this suite. Two-pyroxene gabbro (TPG), which occurs as inclusions in gabbro and diorite, has a fine-grained subporphyritic texture characteristic of chilled magma. Mafic minerals and plagioclase of succeedingly younger intrusives define compositional trends away from the TPG minerals. Younger hornblendes and pyroxenes exhibit decreasing MgO/MgO+FeO and plagioclase exhibits decreasing CaO/CaO+Na_2O. Furthermore, subtraction of olivine, hypersthene, augite, and sodic labradorite (identified as early-formed minerals) from TPG can produce the successively younger rocks found in the batholith.

TPG corresponds to the composition of a magnesian high-alumina basalt. High-alumina basalts are recognized as one variety of primary basaltic magma. Their widespread distribution and associated rocks have been documented in the circum-Pacific region, particularly in Japan, and in the High Cascades of Washington and Oregon. The Mount Stuart intrusive suite, although more magnesian, parallels the fractionation trends observed from high-alumina basalt associations of those regions.

Emplacement-fractionation Model. The evolutionary model envisioned here is one of initial emplacement of a single batch of high-alumina basalt at depths of 8 to 10 kilometers followed by inward crystallization and fractionation producing pyroxenite (now present as inclusions) and liquids resembling the younger hypersthene-hornblende diorite (fig. 3). Early separation of olivine (Fo 90-77), hypersthene (En 77), augite (Di 76), plagioclase (An 65-50), and ilmenite-magnetite produced a residual magma of diorite composition. The diorite magma moved upward, invading the crystalline walls of the parental magma chamber and producing the observed field relations at higher structural levels. Eruption of parental and younger magmas was presumably simultaneous with their emplacement. In this manner, successive differentiation, followed by the rise of progressively more granitic magmas, would account for the intrusive sequence and the rock associations observed in the batholith. However, to produce the abundance of quartz diorite observed in the batholith, more mafic rocks would have to be present at depth.

Computer Modeling. The proposed fractionation process was evaluated by means of a linear-programming least-squared computer program designed by Wright and Doherty (1970).

The results of these calculations indicate that it is possible to derive the entire Mount Stuart suite from the initial basaltic parental magma by subtraction of early formed minerals *actually* appearing in these rocks. Considering the mass-balances of basalt fractionation, reasonable amounts of residual granite liquid are produced, 2-3 percent of the original TPG parent. Granitic rocks comprise about this amount of the exposed batholith. However, this model required that large amounts of mafic rocks (which are crystals subtracted from the parent magma) must lie hidden at depth. By contrast, an andesitic parent magma is not ruled out by these calculations, and this composition of parent would require lesser amounts of hidden cumulate rocks at depth. However, it would not account for intrusive relations among mafic members of the batholith.

Conclusions

Computer modeling of the proposed fractionation process and all the available petrologic and field relations indicate that the Mount Stuart intrusive suite can be derived from a high-alumina basalt—the oldest rock in the batholith. The consanguinity of the intrusive suite is indisputable. The model presented here is *not* intended to suggest that *all* composite batholiths are derived from basaltic magma.

REFERENCES

ENGELS, J. C., and CROWDER, D. F.

1971. Late Cretaceous fission-track and potassium-argon ages of Mount Stuart granodiorite and Beckler Peak stock, North Cascades, Washington. U. S. Geol. Surv. Prof. Pap. 75OD, pp. D39-D43.

ERIKSON. ERIK H.

1973. Degranitization of the Late Cretaceous Mount Stuart batholith, central Cascades, Washington. Geol. Soc. Amer. Programs of Meetings, vol. 5, no. 1, p. 939 (abstract).

1976a. Computer modeling of magma fractionation: The Mount Stuart batholith. Program, Northwest Science Meetings, Eastern Washington College, Cheney, 1976, p. 52 (abstract).

1976b. Petrology and structure of the Mount Stuart batholith, Cascade Mountains, Washington. Geol. Soc. Amer. Programs of Meetings, vol. 8, no. 3, p. 372 (abstract).

1977. Petrology and petrogenesis of the Mount Stuart batholith: Plutonic equivalent of the high-alumina basalt association? Contr. Min. Petrol., vol. 60, pp. 183-207.

ERIKSON, ERIK H., and WILLIAMS, A. E.

1976. Implications of apatite fission track ages in the Mount Stuart batholith, Cascade Mountains, Washington. Geol. Soc. Amer. Programs of Meetings, vol. 8, no. 3, p. 372 (abstract).

HUNTTING, M. T.; BENNETT, W. G.; LIVINGSTON, V. E., JR.; and MOEN, W. S.

1961. Geological map of Washington. Washington State Division of Mines and Geology, Olympia, Washington.

PONGSAPICH, WASANT

1974. Geology of the eastern part of the Mt. Stuart batholith, central Cascades, Washington; 170 pp. Unpublished Ph.D. dissertation, University of Washington.

SMITH, GEORGE OTIS

1904. Description of the Mount Stuart Quadrangle. U. S. Geol. Surv. Atlas, Mount Stuart folio (no. 106), 10 pp.

WRIGHT, THOMAS L., and DOHERTY, P. C.

1970. A linear-programming and least squares computer method for solving petrologic mixing problems. Geol. Soc. Amer. Bull., vol. 81, pp. 1995-2007.

Yeats, R. S.; Erikson, E. H.; Frost, B. R.; Hammond, P. E.; and Miller, R. B.

1977. Structure, stratigraphy, plutonism, and volcanism of the central Cascades, Washington. *In* "Geological Excursions in the Pacific Northwest," E. H. Brown and R. C. Ellis, eds., Geol. Soc., Amer. Ann. Meetings, Western Washington Univ., Bellingham, Wash.

Erik H. Erikson, Jr.

The "Acropolis" of Aphrodisias in Caria: Investigations and Excavations of the Theater and the Prehistoric Mounds, 1971-1977

Principal Investigator: Kenan T. Erim, New York University, New York City.

Grant Nos. 926, 1037, 1038, 1139, 1285, 1353, 1435, 1493, 1571, 1646, 1712. In support of exploration and excavation of the Greek and Roman archeological site at Aphrodisias, Turkey.

Between 1971 and 1976, the theater of Aphrodisias and its approaches witnessed intensive as well as extensive activities.[1] By 1974, most of the theater structure *per se* was brought to light (fig. 1). The remaining portion of the south *cavea* was gradually cleared and several of the damaged tiers of seats were restored. The excavation of the stage building was continued and revealed that the southern half of the *skene* paralleled the previously uncovered northern half. Two medium-sized rooms were located beyond the central tunnel dividing the stage building, one communicating with it, the other opening onto

[1] For previous reports on the Acropolis excavations see *National Geographic Society Research Reports, 1966 Projects* (1973), pp. 89-112, and *1968 Projects* (1976), pp. 79-112. Other preliminary reports: *Türk Ark Derg,* 20-1 (1973), pp. 63-87; 21-1 (1974), pp. 37-57; 22-2 (1975), pp. 73-92; and 23-1 (1976), pp. 25-50. Also in "Archaeology in Asia Minor," *AJA,* 76 (1972), pp. 172 and 184-185; 77 (1973), pp. 174 and 188-189; 78 (1974), pp. 126-127; 79 (1975), pp. 219-220; 80 (1976), pp. 277-278; 81 (1977), pp. 296 and 305-306; 82 (1978) pp. 119-120 and 324-325. *Anatolian Studies* 22 (1972), pp. 35-40; 23 (1973), pp. 119-124; 24 (1974), pp. 20-23; 25 (1975), pp. 17-21; and 26 (1976), pp. 24-30. See also my "Aphrodisias" article in the *Princeton Encyclopedia of Classical Sites,* pp. 68-70; my "Afrodisiade," in Enciclopedia dell'Arte Antica Classica e Orientale, Supplemento, 1970, pp. 9-17; and my "Il Teatro di Afrodisia" in D. De Bernardi Ferrero, *I Teatri Classici in Asia Minore,* vol. 4, pp. 162-166; and *Tenth International Congress of Classical Archaeology,* vol. 2, pp. 1065-1084. The recently discovered portraits have been published in J. Inan and E. Alföldi-Rosenbaum, *Römische und Frühbyzantinische Porträtplastik aus der Türkei,* Mainz am Rhein, 1979. See also my contribution to A. Alfoldi, *Aion in Merida und Aphrodisias* (in press).

The campaigns of 1971 through 1977 received occasional support also from the Andrew W. Mellon Foundation, the Robert Owen Lehman Foundation, the Irvine Foundation, the Charles E. Merrill Trust, the Anne S. Richardson Fund, and the National Endowment for the Humanities.

the stage corridor. A third, adjacent smaller chamber lay at the southern end. Next to the door of this room a cubicle similar to the north "chapel," with Byzantine fresco fragments on its walls, was discovered.[2] As did the parallel northern rooms, these also bore informal inscriptions on their lintels or jambs recording the gear kept there by various performers.

Most of the half columns of the *proskenion* screening these chambers were found *in situ* or collapsed in the debris of the upper story. They were subsequently reerected (see fig. 1). The inscribed architrave blocks were all accounted for and advertised that the *logeion* and *proskenion* with all their decorations were dedicated to Aphrodite and to the Demos by G. Ioulios Zoilos, ten times consecutively *stephanephoros.* Zoilos was described here as a "freedman of the son of the divine Julius Caesar." Consequently, the construction of this portion of the theater must be dated in the thirties B.C. Such evidence is naturally most significant not only for the chronology of the theater but also for the dating of the decorative elements of the *proskenion.* Indeed, a great number of these were found either trapped in the backstage corridor or fallen on the *pulpitum.* The most exciting of them proved to be a handsome Nike statue carrying a trophy (fig. 2) and several intricate *akroteria* (fig. 3, left). In addition, an abundance of other sculpture was extracted from the southern stage area. Among them, the body and inscribed base of the large Demos (fig. 2, right) found in 1970,[3] a full portrait statue of a notable Aphrodisian of the 4th century, and an almost intact relief bust of the Aphrodite of Aphrodisias (fig. 3, right) must be mentioned. Several heads and fragments of statuary discovered in earlier seasons, particularly the two pugilists, were also recorded.[4]

The Byzantine history of the theater continued to be supplied with interesting data. The hollow area of the orchestra, following the collapse of the stage building probably caused by an earthquake, was at first used as a dumping ground. Subsequently, a number of makeshift houses were built over the *cavea,* often with seat fragments used in their foundations. This small quarter must have especially developed when the whole Acropolis was transformed into a fortress from the 11th century onward after Seljuk and Turcoman raids required the establishment of a safer inhabitable citadel. Evidence pertaining to the earlier Byzantine use of the theater itself, on the other hand, was uncovered on the stage and the central *cavea.* In addition to the creation of "chapels"

---

[2] *National Geographic Society Research Reports, 1968 Projects* (1976), pp. 90-91, figs. 8, 9.

[3] *National Geographic Society Research Reports, 1968 Projects* (1976), pp. 92-93, fig. 11.

[4] *National Geographic Society Research Reports, 1968 Projects* (1976), p. 99, fig. 16.

FIG. 1. Aphrodisias, theater. Bottom: Stage and *proskenion* looking south.

FIG. 2. Aphrodisias, 1971-72, theater. Late Hellenistic statue of Nike carrying trophy from the *scaenae frons* decoration. Right: Demos statue from stage decoration.

at each end of the stage corridor, the intercoluminations of the *proskenion* were blocked with masonry and their side facing the audience was covered with frescoes. Only the lower parts of these paintings remain in a number of cases and show the legs of several indeterminate figures. Numerous graffiti mentioning the Greens and the Blues were deciphered on seats and in at least one of the backstage chambers.

The layout of the area east of the theater, i.e., behind and beyond the stage building, was gradually brought to light in excavations from 1973 on. A solid wall, erected out of architectural and occasional sculpture and epigraphical fragments, blocked the complete length of the stage building and

FIG. 3. Aprhodisias, 1971-72, theater. Late Hellenistic *akroterion* from stage decoration. Right: Relief bust of Aphrodite of Aphrodisias.

formed part of the eastern flank of the Byzantine Acropolis fortress. In its northward extension, it jutted out at a right angle, then continued for a few meters but resumed a westward direction after another right angle, thus creating a sort of "bastion" (fig. 4). A series of steps was discovered between the bastion and the large, early buttressed wall that supported the north *analemma* area.[5] A well-preserved rectangular room was contained within the bastion. It communicated by means of a vaulted passageway with the late Roman vaulted hall built over the north *parodos* and facing the "archive wall" of the stage building.[6] The function of this room remains unclear. It may have been used once as a guards' room. Several coins and terra-cotta lamps of the 6th century found at its floor level would indicate that it was in full use at that date. How-

[5] It is likely that these steps are to be connected with one of the *vomitoria*.

[6] *National Geographic Society Research Reports, 1968 Projects* (1976), p. 84. The "archive wall" Imperial letters will soon be published in a volume, *Aphrodisias and Rome,* by Joyce Reynolds et al.

FIG. 4. Aphrodisias, theater. Bastion of Byzantine stage-blocking wall.

ever, it certainly antedated the transformation of the Acropolis into a Byzantine fortress and the construction of the bastion, within which it was intentionally included. The room featured an arcuate niche and air vents or windows as well as a shelf built out of masonry and fitted with two marble mortars. It was once vaulted. Construction of the bastion considerably damaged its eastern end and upper walls.

Like its stage-blocking extension, the bastion itself also included reused architectural fragments. The most striking of these were nine frieze blocks reset in an orderly yet not original sequence in an upper course of the east wall. The frieze was of a type much favored in Aphrodisias, namely, heads of masks

FIG. 5. Aphrodisias, "piazza," or *tetrastoon,* behind stage building of theater, with central fountain arrangement to left and theater baths in background (bottom; see also fig. 9).

joined by elaborate swinging garlands. These blocks probably came from a building closely connected with the theater. A candidate might be one of the porticoes of the "piazza" extending to the east.

Indeed, immediately beyond the stage building, a large paved open and approximately square area was gradually revealed by excavations between 1972 and 1976.[7] It was at first labeled a "piazza" and thought to have been created here in the latter part of the 4th century. Recent epigraphic evidence, however, suggested the name *tetrastoon* for it.[8] A stylobate ran on all four sides of this *tetrastoon* (fig. 5) forming porticoed areas and supporting high column bases, except on the east side. Several of these bases and their columns as well as Corinthian capitals were found felled, but *in situ.* A great many, however, appeared to have been incorporated in the construction of the Byzantine stage-blocking wall.[9] The eastern side of the *tetrastoon,* on the other hand, featured columns resting on low bases. Several of these were discovered in place. The stylobate also proved to be interrupted here at about the middle of the portico for a width of about 5 meters. A sondage dug eastward revealed large, well-cut slabs. The size and nature of these stones suggested a street leading toward the east.[10]

At the approximate center of the *tetrastoon* a circular platform was uncovered. It consisted of a 1.50-meter-wide edge and had a total diameter of 6 meters. A separate element in the center featured an upright terra-cotta pipe fragment, perhaps part of a fountainlike arrangement.[11] A round altar was also found imbedded in the northeastern section of the "piazza." Its body was

---

[7] The pavement was often in good condition and consisted of slabs of blue-gray marble. Many featured letters or mason's marks cut on their faces.

[8] The dismantling of part of the northern section of the stage-blocking wall in 1976 and 1977 produced a large number of architectural, sculptural, and epigraphical fragments. Among the latter, one must mention several pieces pertaining to the Imperial letters of the "archive wall" as well as a round base belonging to a statue of the emperior Julian later replaced by one of Theodosius and put up by a governor named Antonius Tatianus. The inscription adds that Tatianus built "all the work of the *tetrastoon* from the foundations up." There can be little doubt that this base once stood near the stage building and that the *tetrastoon* can only be the 4-porticoed "piazza."

[9] Their disparate style and lack of uniformity suggest that these had also been pilfered from an earlier structure and reused here.

[10] Another less elaborate passage or alley was discovered off the south portico running southward and separating the basilica hall of the theater baths from a series of rooms of as yet indeterminate character.

[11] It is probable that this was not the original function of the platform. Its blocks betray clear indications of reuse. A circular altar, a statue, or a monument may have originally stood here.

FIG. 6. Aphrodisias, 1972, *tetrastoon,* northwest portico. Full portrait statue of Flavius Palmatus.

decorated with relief figures or motifs, now almost completely erased. Its top surface was cut with lines and featured barely legible words, suggesting reuse as a sundial or similar instrument.

Two statue bases were discovered in front of the west portico near the northwestern corner of the *tetrastoon.* One, columnar-shaped and broken, referred to an individual whose name is lost, much praised for having driven civil strife from the city. The second base once supported a portrait statue of Flavius Palmatus, a "vicar of Asia," which was found fallen in front of its base. Palmatus was shown in full toga with broad *contabulatio,* holding the *mappa* in his right hand and a scepter in his left (fig. 6). The style of this remarkable statue suggests a date in the late 5th century. To the south of Palmatus, another well-carved body of a young boy also in full toga but earlier in date (probably 1st century) was discovered. Its head was inserted separately. An excellent portrait found nearby probably belonged to it. The head shows a melancholy young man with delicate features wearing an elaborate diadem consisting of separately inserted stones. He was a prince of the Constantinian house, perhaps Constantine II. It also appears likely that the original portrait was cleverly reworked in the 4th century to represent the Constantinian prince (fig. 7). Another head similarly and more obviously reworked was also recovered within the northwest portico.

On the opposite southwestern corner of the *tetrastoon* an oblong room was built within the portico against the stage-blocking wall. Many sculpture fragments and early Byzantine lamps were found here. The most unusual item was a large *krater,* still unfinished, carved out of local gray-blue marble and later fitted into a drainage system of terra-cotta pipes. Other fragments included a female head, possibly a posthumous, idealized portrait of Agrippina Major, mother of Caligula, and a statuette of Tyche. Immediately to the south of this chamber, a podiumlike stepped construction was uncovered, also nestled against the stage-blocking fortification wall. This arrangement consisted of nine well-fitted steps joined at a right angle by eight steps perpendicular to the stage wall. The precise function of this podium is unclear, but it is evident that a number of its steps were pilfered from the *vomitoria* of the theater. A hoard of 100 coins, all copper *dodecanummia* of the mint of Alexandria ranging in date from Justinian I (527-565) to Maurice Tiberius (582-602) and perhaps Phocas (602-610), was discovered in front of the eastern steps of the podium. It must represent the contents of a purse, namely, the value in copper of a simple fraction of the gold *solidus.*

An inscribed statue base extracted from the Byzantine stage-blocking wall near the podium honored a certain Dulcitius, perhaps Aelius Claudius Dulcitius, a proconsul of Asia in 361-363, and indicated that it had been "set

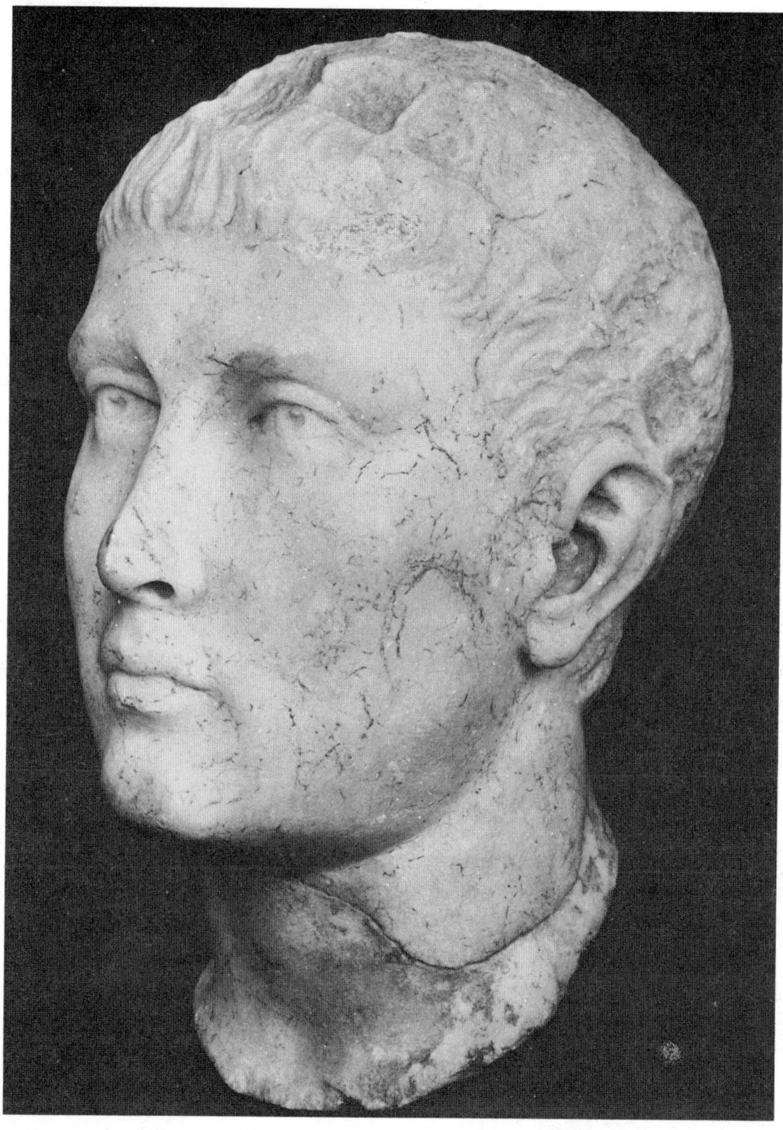

FIG. 7. Aphrodisias, 1972, *tetrastoon,* northwest portico. Head of Constantinian prince.

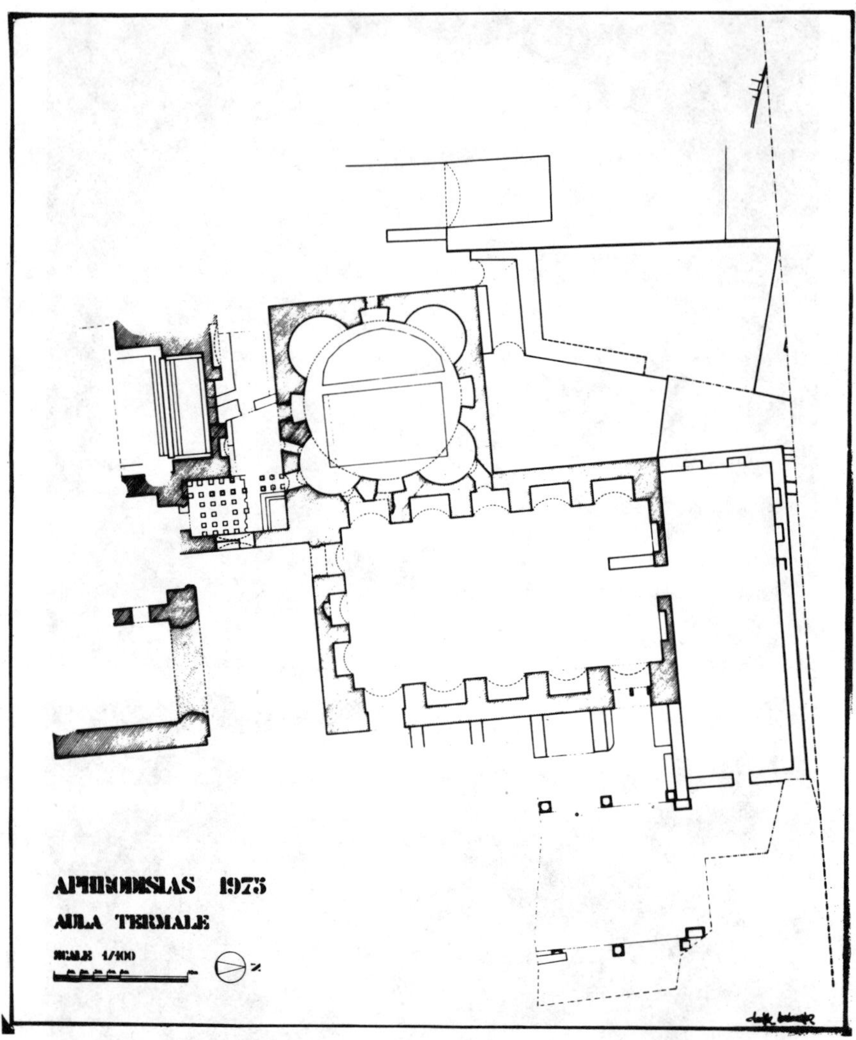

FIG. 8. Aphrodisias, 1975, plan of theater baths, or *aula termale-nymphaeum* complex. (See also fig. 5, bottom.)

up in front of the baths." A candidate for such a thermal establishment was partly excavated in a complex of ruins extending to the south of the theater and the southwestern slope of the Acropolis (fig. 8). Labeled initially "*aula termale* and *nymphaeum* complex," after individual units, it came to be referred to as the theater baths (fig. 5, bottom). Because of numerous water pipes inserted into its masonry, a large hall immediately south of the *tetrastoon* was tenta-

FIG. 9. Aphrodisias, 1976, theater baths, including *nymphaeum* and basilica hall units (see also fig. 5).

tively identified as a *nymphaeum* or fountain-house. It was sporadically excavated between 1973 and 1975. It featured walls preserved to a height of over 10 meters and cut by a series of arcuate recesses or niches. Its west wall was cut by five such niches, which were paralleled across on the east wall. However, in lieu of closed recesses to the north and south, doors opened there toward the east. Several trenches dug beyond these doors in 1975 and 1976 brought to light a great part of a lavishly decorated hall in basilica plan (figs. 9, 10). Oriented north-south, this hall featured a nave separated from its aisles by Corinthian columns of local blue-gray marble on high bases. In the east and west aisles, short curtain walls formed small rooms or cubicles.[12] The

[12] The pavement of the basilica was extremely well preserved and consisted of closely fitted large marble slabs.

FIG. 10. Aphrodisias, 1976, theater baths. Basilica hall, looking northeast.

most attractive element of the hall proved to be its northern end. Two rectangular pillars of blue-gray marble aligned with the aisle columns were nestled against two impressive pilasters framing the nave there. Both of these pilasters were intricately carved in the "peopled scrolls" style so much popularized by Aphrodisian sculptors (fig. 11). Lions, stags, and Erotes leaped, hunted, and frolicked among elaborate intertwining swirls of acanthus on the interior as well as the south sides of the pilasters.[13] There were also found a number of

[13] The dismantlement of the upper portions of these pilasters was initiated in the Byzantine period. Some of these blocks were dragged away and were discovered in 1973 before the bastion of the stage-blocking wall. Cf. supra.

fragments decorated with equally elaborate scrolls of acanthus leaves and flowers on one face. One of these even showed the upper face of a Medusa head. The imperceptibly curved shape of these blocks suggested that they formed part of an archway joining the two "peopled scrolls" pilasters, the Medusa head being its keystone.

The precise function of such an arcuate doorway remains uncertain. It framed a chamber or *oecus,* which was adjacent to the south portico of the *tetrastoon,* and presented a well-preserved pavement of black and white marble slabs.

An additional antechamber or hallway of size was added to the northwestern corner of the theater baths in late Roman or early Byzantine times, between the basilica and the theater (fig. 11, left). It communicated with both the so-called *nymphaeum* hall and the *oecus* of the basilica unit and included a series of shallow niches or recesses in its west and north walls. Attractive *opus sectile* floors decorated its floor, while traces of colored frescoes were apparent on the lower courses of some of its walls.

The most spectacular part of the theater-baths complex, however, proved to be the so-called *aula termale.*[14] This circular structure (fig. 12) located to the west of the *nymphaeum* was joined to it by means of two small vaulted corridors. Its state of preservation was remarkable, its walls standing erect to a height of over 10 meters. Its roof surely was once domed, and it featured four arcuate, apsidal niches opposite one another at the cardinal points. Two of these niches had smaller, equally vaulted subsidiary doors: the southeastern one had three, one communicating with the *nymphaeum* hall, the other two leading to a *calidarium* arrangement partly excavated to the south. The northeastern niche was also broken by a vaulted tunnel leading to the *nymphaeum.* Four smaller arcuate but almost rectangular recesses came to light between the higher apsidal ones.[15]

The internal layout of the *aula termale* consisted of two contiguous pools separated by a low wall. The pool to the west was shallow and half polygonal in shape (fig. 12, right), while the adjoining one to the east was rectangular, larger, and occupied more than half of the interior of the hall. It also included a system of upright terra-cotta pipes and tiles at its eastern end. Part of the pool arrangement may be due to modifications of the baths in early Byzantine times. The four large apsidal niches were also used as shallow basins or receptacles at a later period.

[14] The fill that was excavated out of the hall was well over 12 meters. Most of the marble revetments and sculpture had unfortunately been stripped or removed. Only a torso of a Nike was found in the northeastern apsidal niche.

[15] At a later date two doors were roughly pierced through the west and south smaller niches.

FIG. 11. Aphrodisias, 1976, theater baths. Antechamber adjacent to basilica hall, looking east, and (right) "Peopled scroll," east pilaster of basilica hall.

FIG. 12. Aphrodisias, 1976, theater baths. *Aula termale* unit, showing (right) interior arrangement with pools.

Trenches opened to the south of the *aula termale* beyond the vaulted passageways of the large southeastern niche, and the smaller southern one led to the discovery of a hypocaust forming part of a vaulted *calidarium,* as already noted. This area appeared to have undergone many transformations at a later date. A large amount of early Byzantine small oil or perfume flasks was extracted between the columns of the hypocaust. A section of a stepped pool with some of its marble revetments still in place but also betraying signs of repairs was excavated to the south. It was connected with the *calidarium* by means of a water channel.

Finally, investigations in the north theater area uncovered the early buttressed fortification wall over which the village mosque of Geyre had once stood.[16] The relationship of this wall with the north *analemma* is not clear. Its original construction date, however, is most likely late Hellenistic, i.e., contemporary with and even anterior to the building of the theater. On close inspection, its five strong buttresses betray an uneven surface and clear indications of subsequent reworking, which must be connected with the transformation of the Acropolis into a stronghold in the 11th or 12th century.

Objectives for continued investigations of prehistoric Aphrodisias were satisfactorily completed in 1971 and 1972. Subsequently, actual excavations were interrupted and activities focused on study of the abundant archeological material recovered and concomitant laboratory work and research.[17] Trenches numbered 8 and 9 were staked out and dug farther up the west slope of the Acropolis mound. Their aim was to seek and consolidate evidence for the Late Bronze and Iron Age habitation sequences of the site. Efforts were often impeded by the angle of the slope and the complex late intrusions of the Byzantine and Turkish periods. Each of these late habitation phases had indeed created its own terracing and freely reused earlier building material. Numerous walls, fireplaces, packed earth, or plaster floors marked these levels. No evidence for any substantial Roman building or occupation was uncovered in this area. In the eastern end of Trench 8, mud-brick walls on stone foundations were uncovered with relevant material of the 2d millennium B.C. The pottery revealed gold or silver wash as well as red-brown to blackish painted linear designs. Small finds associated with these levels included spindle whorls, pierced ceramic disks, and crescents, as well as stone implements.

---

[16] A great part of the mosque had collapsed by 1974. A number of primitive "frescoes" painted on its walls were, however, recorded and salvaged by the expedition.

[17] For previous articles on prehistoric Aphrodisias, see B. Kadish, *AJA,* 73, 1 (1969), pp. 49-65; *AJA,* 75, 2 (1971), pp. 121-140; and R. T. Marchese, *AJA,* 80, 4 (1976), pp. 393-413.

Investigations in 1972 further supplied additional evidence for the chronological sequence of these levels. In Trench 8, part of a structure featuring a central hearth was excavated and dated to the Late Bronze Age. In Trench 9, on the other hand, an interesting complex came to light in the eastern sector. Sherds gathered here showed traces of fire and betrayed exposure to extreme heat. This may suggest some kind of intensive "industrial" activity. A hearth area and two refuse pits with ashes and charcoal were also located. The stratigraphy here revealed a continuous series of burnt layers and implied constant use of fire. A date between the Late Bronze and Early Iron Age (i.e., 1200-1000 B.C.) must be tentatively envisaged for this area.

Beginning in 1975, study leading to a computer analysis of the vast quantities of prehistoric pottery fragments accumulated from both the Acropolis and Pekmez mounds investigations between 1968 and 1972 was initiated by Martha S. Joukowsky and Anna S. Benjamin.[18] Attention was focused first on the evidence collected from the five Late Bronze to Iron Age strata of Acropolis trenches. Over 7,500 sherds were classified and a type series of 300 factors, including forms, ware-fabric, and decoration was added to a type series initially established. A systematic analysis of the Chalcolithic and Early Bronze Age material unearthed between 1967 and 1970 in *Pekmez,* the second prehistoric mound of Aphrodisias, was completed by 1977. The computer study was extended to the ceramic finds of these early levels of the mound. Documentation of small finds such as idols, pyramidal spindle whorls, ceramic disks, whetstones, and hammer and burnishing stones was finished. A comparative analysis of the Chalcolithic pottery from other southwestern Anatolian sites was launched and revealed that the prehistory of Aphrodisias developed earlier than hitherto presumed, probably from the end of the 6th millennium B.C. It appeared also that the traditionally accepted views of one-settlement Chalcolithic sites did not hold true for Aphrodisias, the early levels of which betrayed overlapping cultural traits as well as continuous evolutionary development. Contacts with Hacilar and Late Chalcolithic Beycesultan were reflected in the Pekmez ceramics, which also provided a link thus far not documented for these two important prehistoric Anatolian sites. The character of the excavated portion of the Pekmez mound indicated that the settlement remained essentially unchanged during its evolution. Although pottery

[18] An article, "Computer Use in Pottery Studies at Aphrodisias," describes the application of the computer to our ceramic finds (see M. S. Joukowsky, *Journal of Field Archaeology,* 5, 4 [1978], pp. 431-442).

statistics revealed the impact of new fashions, the greater percentage of the material demonstrated that its manufacturers remained attached to a variety of ware-fabrics as well as traditional ceramic forms.[19]

KENAN T. ERIM

[19] A detailed study, analysis, and evaluation of the early levels at Aphrodisias is being completed and prepared for publication by M. S. Joukowsky.

Occultation of Beta Scorpii and Companion by Jupiter, May 13, 1971

Principal Investigator: David S. Evans, University of Texas, Austin, Texas.

Grant No. 922: To observe the occultation of Beta Scorpii and companion by Jupiter on May 13, 1971.

The moon and planets move against the background of the stars and, from time to time, pass in front of a star, a phenomenon known as an occultation. A common occurrence in the case of the moon, occultations of naked-eye stars by Jupiter are very much rarer and occur only about once in 30 years. Jupiter occulted the bright star Sigma Arietis on November 20, 1952, the very much brighter star Beta Scorpii in 1971, and will occult no more bright stars during the rest of the 20th century.

William Baum and Arthur Code observed the disappearance of the star in 1952 and produced the theory of the phenomenon used by all subsequent observers of occultations by the major planets. When a star is occulted by the moon it disappears because a solid body obstructs its light. The dimming of light by Jupiter occurs not through obstruction of the starlight by the planetary disk seen in the telescope but by dispersion or defocusing of light in transparent layers at somewhat higher levels in the Jovian atmosphere. The atmospheric density and hence also the refractive index (capacity of a substance for bending light rays) decrease with height in the atmosphere. When a ray of starlight passes through the upper layers of the atmosphere of Jupiter it traverses tens of thousands of kilometers of the atmospheric gases and is bent so as partially to follow the curvature of the atmospheric layers. The dispersion or defocusing occurs because this bending at any one point varies with height in the atmosphere. The computation of the total effect predicts that when Jupiter nears a star the light of the latter will decrease with time following a curve that first takes a rapid turn down and after a steady rapid reduction will decrease to zero at a slow and decreasing rate, giving the light curve a long tail. However, if in the atmosphere of Jupiter there are layers of constant refractive index (constant temperature or "isothermal" layers) the atmosphere will momentarily stop dispersing the light, and, since the absorption in the gases is small, the star will suddenly for an instant flash almost to full brilliance. Baum and Code did not observe this phenomenon, possibly because at that time the technical means for observing very rapid fluctuations of brightness in astronomical objects were not as highly developed as they now are. Flashes were, however, observed at the occultation (an even more rare event) of a rather faint star by Neptune on April 7, 1968.

Advance prediction of these events is essential since they are observable only from limited regions on the surface of the earth; they last only a matter of minutes and demand the facilities of an established observatory for their observation. Gordon E. Taylor, a staff member at the Nautical Almanac Office at the Royal Greenwich Observatory at Herstmonceux in England, has for 20 years been predicting these events.

The prediction that the bright naked-eye star Beta Scorpii would be occulted by Jupiter on May 13, 1971, caused a flurry of activity in astronomical circles. The event, predictable to better than a minute of time, took place with Jupiter almost in opposition (at its nearest approach to the earth). The star had been well studied by many astrometric and other observers. Its outstanding feature is its visual duplicity. The star system, as it should more correctly be called, consists of a bright blue star of visual magnitude 2.63 and spectral type B 0.5 V, meaning that it has a surface temperature near 25,000°C. and a spectrum containing only a few absorption lines, with hydrogen prominent. The bright star has a companion of magnitude 4.92 with a slightly lower temperature distant from it 13.6 arc seconds, an angle equal to about one-third of the angular diameter of Jupiter. There would thus be four occultation events, namely, the disappearance and reappearance of Beta Sco A, both not far from Jupiter's south pole, and the disappearance and reappearance of the fainter companion, called Beta Sco C, both of which would occur a little south of Jupiter's equator. In all cases the star concerned was brighter than that occulted in 1952. The companion is called Beta Sco C because Beta Sco A is believed to have yet another companion star, Beta Sco B, so close to A that it cannot now be separated in a telescope, and rather faint, though the latter is a debated point. To complicate matters still further, Beta Sco A is itself an extremely close pair never visually separable, and in the course of this work we obtained evidence that Beta Sco C may actually also be a close pair. So in fact there may be five component stars in this system, but because of the closeness of some of the separations and the faintness of some of the components it could be treated as if it consisted of only two bright stars, Beta Sco A and Beta Sco C. If this assumption turns out not to be justified, some modification of the results of the 1971 observations may be necessary, though not, it is thought, of a fundamental kind. It may be possible to settle the matter after 1976 when the first of a series of occultations of this system by the moon will occur. When multiple stars are occulted by the moon they are obliterated in turn and it is possible to determine the number and relative luminosities of the components.

The Jupiter occultation of 1971 was to be observable from a considerable area of the earth's surface, but the best position, namely, the one where it would occur directly overhead, was in the middle of the Indian Ocean, almost directly south of India and in the latitude of northern Australia, that is, not far from the antipodes of Austin, Texas, hundreds of miles from any land, and thousands of miles from any established observatory.

The Department of Astronomy at the University of Texas at Austin and the McDonald Observatory have specialized experience in high-speed photometric measurements as well as strength in planetary astronomy, one faculty member, Dr. William B. Hubbard, being expert in problems of the structure of Jupiter.

Occultation observations were expected to determine a value for the mean molecular weight of the gases in the upper atmosphere of Jupiter. This would be inferred from a quantity known as the atmospheric scale height, which in turn would be deduced from the rate at which the standard form of light curve deduced from the Baum and Code theory would be described. Scale height means the height in kilometers through which an ascent reduces a quantity, such as atmospheric pressure, through a standard ratio, usually taken to be the mathematical constant $e = 2.718$. In the lower part of the earth's atmosphere the scale height is about 8 kilometers, but it depends on the mean molecular weight of the atmosphere, the temperature, and the intensity of the gravitational attraction. In the case of Jupiter the scale height deduced from the Baum and Code observation was about 8 kilometers. Apart from some uncertainty in temperature this indicated a high value (3.3) of the molecular weight, and hence that the Jupiter atmosphere, presumably largely hydrogen, contained a higher proportion of helium than is found in the sun. Since helium is thought to be formed only in nuclear transmutations occurring in the interior of stars, this raised possibilities concerning the constitution of Jupiter not borne out by other theoretical and observational lines of argument. The precise value of the scale height of the Jupiter atmosphere is also important in computing the drag experienced by a space craft passing close to the surface of the planet. The scientific objective of the observations was the determination of the scale height of the Jupiter atmosphere and the inference of the mean molecular weight and hence helium content of its atmosphere.

To carry out these observations successfully with only the six months' notice at which the prediction was published involved hectic activity and a series of risky gambles. The team assembled consisted of Dr. Hubbard, who supplied the theoretical guidance and the theoretical analyses; Dr. R. Edward

Nather, the chief inspirer of the high-speed photometry program at Texas; Dr. Robert G. Tull, an outstanding instrumental designer; Dr. Brian Warner, a well-known observer; and two graduate students, Donald C. Wells (now Dr. Wells at Kitt Peak) and Wayne van Citters. The two last named were both experts in programming and operation of minicomputers. The team was completed with reserve observer Dr. Paul Vanden Bout, now well known for his researches in millimeter wave astronomy, and the writer who had some experience in high-speed photometry of occultations by the moon and wide international contacts.

It was decided to mount three separate expeditions and to obtain facilities at three observatories as near to the coasts of the Indian Ocean as possible. This was done and use of the facilities guaranteed before there was even a dollar in the treasury. Secondly, we had to design and commission suitable equipment under the same conditions. The team worked together with remarkable smoothness, and very little time was spent in group discussions since everyone knew what he had to do. By courtesy of the respective observatory directors, facilities were granted at the Government Observatory of Western Australia at Bickley, near Perth, the observing team being Robert G. Tull and Donald C. Wells; at the Uttar Pradesh Observatory at Naini Tal, India, in the foothills of the Himalayas, where the team consisted of Dr. Brian Warner and Dr. R. Edward Nather; and of the Republic Observatory, Johannesburg, South Africa, to which went David S. Evans and Wayne van Citters.

Several other institutions were also seeking facilities at the limited number of observatories available. A team from Smithsonian-Cornell went to Bloemfontein, South Africa, and a French team to Pretoria, South Africa. Observations were made also by resident astronomers in southern India, Indonesia, and Cape Town, South Africa. Before the instruments were even half designed, the Texas group had to make plausible guesses at dimensions, weights, and values and to talk to airlines and customs both in the United States and overseas. Funds were raised with the necessary swiftness not only from the National Geographic Society but also from the Research Corporation, a private donor, the University of Texas, and the National Science Foundation. In those less inflationary days the total cost of the expeditions (excluding salaries for personnel) was about $23,000, including special instrument construction and transport, living expenses, and most of the publication costs, so that the National Geographic Grant covered over 40 percent of the cost.

While one member was wrestling with logistics, much aided by scientific attachés in Washington and airline executives, others were solving the technical problems. The prime difficulty in observing the dimming of a star as it passes behind Jupiter is the intense light of Jupiter itself. If one observed the total visual light of both stars and the whole of Jupiter, the loss on disappearance or reappearance of one of the stars would have been only a few percent of the total illumination, and thus itself not determinable with that proportionate accuracy which the problem demanded. A standard maneuver in this situation is to restrict the range of wavelengths in which the observation is made. To a rough approximation the spectrum of Jupiter is that of the sun, since its light is solar light only slightly modified. The solar spectrum contains a pair of extremely strong lines due to ionized calcium in the violet part of the spectrum, and these lines are not present in the spectra of the B stars of Beta Scorpii. By the use of interference filters in this range the light of Jupiter could be greatly dimmed leaving the star light unreduced. Secondly, a small diaphragm could be introduced that would restrict the area of sky observed around each star as it disappeared or reappeared. This would involve resetting the telescope slightly at each of the four events so as to center it precisely on the star being observed. However, when this was done each diaphragm would, at the critical moment, contain not only the star image but also part of the edge of Jupiter, and if the guiding wobbled a little, as it inevitably would, both because observers are fallible and because of the instability of the earth's atmosphere, a little more or a little less of the limb would be recorded and the record would jump up and down, not in response to the dimming of the star but because there was more or less of Jupiter in the field. The photometers were therefore designed to scan the field by incorporating a rocking plate. In the course of 1 second they would measure the brightness of a series of sky patches starting on the disc of Jupiter, crossing the star and on to the sky giving 20 points on a bell-shaped curve the outer ends of which represented the level of light from the Jupiter disc and scattered light, while the increases above this level would represent the contribution from the star image. This image would be spread out, as star images always are, to a slight extent, both by the effects of the earth's atmosphere and by the inevitable spreading effects that all telescopes produce. In this way the light due to the star alone could be separated from the background light. Since the scan would be completed in 1 second or less, and since the dimming and brightening phenomena were each expected to last at least 30 seconds, later analysis of all the many scans could produce a light curve for each event. From careful calculation of the circumstances for each station, and from details of the telescopes to be used, the three photometers could be tailored to give the same image scale. Each was provided with preset stops for axial rotation to get the scans in the right direction perpendicular to the edge of Jupiter. All the observer would have to do would be to rotate his photometer to the appropriate stop, center the Jupiter disc on the guiding target, and let the equipment reel off the brightness measures.

The data acquired at such high speeds were to be recorded by means of minicomputers (Data General Novas), of which three were available. However, memory capacity was limited, and some way had to be found to dump and record the data for each event before the next one came along, by a method that would ensure that no garbling had taken place. Paper tape generated by teletype machines would have been cumbersome to transport and too slow in action. The time between the two closest events (Nos. 3 and 4 at Naini Tal) was only 17 minutes. The solution devised by the programmers was to display the actual figures representing a section of the memory on a cathode ray screen and to photograph these with a polaroid camera. In this way it proved possible to dump the entire memory contents twice over at each observing station between each pair of events.

The teams left Austin on May 2, 1971, each with two cases containing the computer, photometer, cathode-ray display, scanning photometer, and auxiliary apparatus, all matched to the conditions and electric supply at the observatory of destination. The only thing to be purchased on the spot in each case was a 12-volt car battery. The journeys were relatively uneventful except for an engine failure on one plane and a customs officer who impounded all the equipment of one team. In due course everybody arrived on site. The prudent programmers had provided a spare memory board with the control program in place, a wise precaution, since at two observatories temporary electric incompatibility caused the original version of the program to be completely wiped out. Fortunately the spare version could be copied into the original memory board.

The weather behaved as well as may be expected on most expeditions, that is to say, untypically, though the average success rate hit the 50-percent level we had counted on beforehand. In Australia, where it was expected to be cloudy, the weather was fine until a matter of hours before the events. In India, the monsoon arrived two weeks early, and the observations were impeded, though the last two yielded good results. In Johannesburg, in the middle of the official dry season, it rained, hailed, and thundered persistently but cleared in time to give good observations of all four events. Visual observation was distinctly dramatic, since, particularly for Beta Scorpii A, the phenomenon of flashing showed up in striking fashion. Instead of occupying only some 30 seconds to 1 minute as had been expected each event ran on for literally minutes, straining the memory capacity of the computer to its limits and making data dump in the time available a "near run thing."

The data were returned to Austin and analyzed by Hubbard. All the scale heights came out much higher than the Baum and Code value, with an indication of variation with position around the Jupiter limb (i.e., latitude on Jupiter), a not unexpected result when it is considered that Jupiter is in very rapid rotation and in consequence has a markedly oval outline. Near the equator the scale height was 31 kilometers, while in the latitude where the brighter star was occulted it was 24 kilometers, both tending to support the view that the abundance of helium in the Jupiter atmosphere has the normal solar value. It was noticed that the flashes on the various traces were correlated, indicating that the isothermal layers that produced them must be rather extensive and possibly rather permanent features of the Jupiter atmosphere. When the operation was proposed it was thought that the atmospheric temperature of Jupiter was well known and its molecular weight uncertain. With this revelation of a complicated variation of atmospheric temperature it was possible also to turn the problem around and plot variations of temperature with height. The results seemed to show that the atmosphere was hotter nearer the equator and that at the very top there was a warmer exosphere where the hydrogen-rich atmosphere was escaping into space.

All the observations were keyed into the Universal Time System through the local time services in the three countries. In addition, it was possible to use some timings made elsewhere, including those made under positively heroic conditions at the South Pole by two American scientists. The diameter of the earth is less than 10 percent of that of Jupiter, so that although the occultation of a particular star will take place at a different point on the edge of Jupiter for observers in different places the maximum possible displacement cannot exceed 10 percent of the Jupiter diameter. Multiple observations of two of the component stars gave four sections of the Jupiter edge where a series of points could be plotted corresponding to observations from various stations. From these an extremely accurate profile of Jupiter could be drawn giving a shape for the planet's oblateness sensibly less than had previously been deduced and reconciled with theories of the interior of the planet.

An unexpected bonus to this rich harvest of results was the fact, predicted by Gordon Taylor, that from some region of the earth an occultation of Beta Scorpii C by one of Jupiter' satellites, Io, was possible. Since Io is only 3,660 kilometers in diameter, occultations by such a body are of almost inconceivable rarity, and one would have to be in precisely the correct position on the surface of the earth (the total latitude range is about equal to the satellite's diameter) to observe it. A reliable prediction was difficult since a small uncertainty in the position of the star generates a big uncertainty in the position of the best observing station. For a while cables flew around the world, and the

Texas Johannesburg team was alerted to observe the phenomenon. They did in fact observe but saw no occultation, since by that time a revised version had fingered the Virgin Islands as the favored spot. Even with three photometric teams in the field, Texas's astronomy director Harlan J. Smith was able to raise a fourth, consisting of a Swiss visitor, Paul Bartholdi, and student Frazer Owen, and to find a telescope at the College of the Virgin Islands. With jury-rigged equipment this team successfully observed the occultation, demonstrating that Beta Scorpii C is probably a double star (it disappeared and reappeared in two steps), and these observations, combined with some others made in the Caribbean region, enabled Hubbard and T. C. van Flandern from the U. S. Nautical Almanac Office to derive the diameter of Io with an uncertainty of only about 3 kilometers (making this easily the best measured satellite in the solar system after the moon) and to infer that it had no sensible atmosphere. However, below the limits of density set by these observations later observers have found traces of sodium vapor surrounding Io. Any information concerning Io is extremely welcome since, in some way not properly understood, it exercises a controlling influence on the emission of radio waves from Jupiter itself.

REFERENCES

EVANS, DAVID S.; ELLIOTT, JAMES LUDLOW; and PETERSON, DEANE M.
1978. Occultation astrometry of the Beta Scorpii system. Astron. Journ. vol. 83, no. 4 (April), pp. 438-441.

EVANS, DAVID S., and HUBBARD, WILLIAM B.
1971. Jupiter and Beta Scorpii. Sky and Telescope, vol. 42, no. 6, pp. 337-341, illus.

HUBBARD, WILLIAM B., et al.
1972. The occultation of Beta Scorpii and Io:
I. Jupiter: By W.B. Hubbard, R. E. Nather, David S. Evans, R. G. Tull, D. C. Wells, G. W. van Citters, B. Warner, and P. Vanden Bout. Astron. Journ., vol. 77, pp. 41-59.
II. Io: By Paul Bartholdi and Frazer Owen. Ibid., pp. 60-65.
III. Astronometry: By W. Hubbard and T. C. Van Flandern. Ibid., pp. 65-74.

DAVID S. EVANS

Petrology of Andean Metamorphic Rocks from Colombia and Ecuador

Principal Investigator: Tomas Feininger, Université Laval, Québec, Province de Québec, Canada.[1]

Grant No. 969: For study of the petrology of Andean metamorphic rocks from Colombia and Ecuador.

Under National Geographic Society grant 969 I was able in 1971 to make extensive field studies of metamorphic rocks in Ecuador. The first year's work took place in the Eastern Cordillera of the Ecuadorian Andes, whereas the second year's work was in the coastal metamorphic belt in El Oro Province, adjacent to the Peruvian border. Subsequently, two additional years of fieldwork at the latter location were financed by an agency of the Ecuadorian Government, and the expenses of publication of the final report with a colored geologic map are being borne by my host institution, the Escuela Politécnica Nacional, Quito. Results of my work in El Oro Province will appear as a "Special Paper" of the Geological Society of America. None of the work here described would have been possible without the generosity of the Society which made available the initial grant.

Background and Results of Fieldwork

Regionally metamorphosed rocks crop out in Ecuador in the Eastern Cordillera of the Andes, and in the coastal Andean foothills of El Oro Province adjacent to the Peruvian border (see map, fig. 1). The rocks of the Eastern Cordillera appear spatially to be a physical continuation of the metamorphic rocks of the Central Andean Cordillera of Colombia to the north.

Prior to my work under the Society's grant, I had had five years' experience of geologic mapping in the Colombian Central Cordillera with the U. S. Geological Survey (Feininger, 1975). The metamorphic rocks of that Cordillera are characterized by a broad range of grades, all under a low-pressure facies series. Shortly before my return to the United States I had the opportunity to make a single traverse across the Eastern Cordillera of Ecuador at Baños. I found the rocks to belong to a single metamorphic grade, probably within a

[1] Formerly, Departamento de Geología, Escuela Politécnica Nacional, Quito, Ecuador.

medium-pressure facies series. Thus my initial impression, later substantiated by laboratory work undertaken by myself on samples at the Smithsonian Institution, was that the rocks were unrelated to those in Colombia. The "physical continuity" of the metamorphic belt was only apparent.

The first problem involved the continuity of the metamorphic belt of the Colombian Central Cordillera and the Eastern Cordillera of the Ecuadorian Andes. By earlier field and laboratory work I had established that fundamental differences exist between the metamorphic rocks of the Central Cordillera of the Colombian Andes, and those of the Eastern Cordillera of the Ecuadorian Andes. These differences are summarized in the following tabulation:

	Colombia	*Ecuador*
Grade	Low greenschist to medium amphibolite	Medium greenschist
Facies series	Low pressure	Medium pressure (?) Diagnostic minerals not found.
Rock types	Pelites, marbles, mafic rocks	Pelites
Garnet in pelites	Scarce: spessartine-rich	Common: almandine-grossularite
Biotite in pelites	Widespread	Scarce
Plagioclase	Oligoclase or more calcic	Albite
Age	Paleozoic	Cretaceous(?)

During 1971 I was able to make four new traverses across the Eastern Cordillera rocks and to repeat the Baños traverse. My findings were as follows:

1. The Eastern Cordillera rocks belong to a medium-pressure facies series. Kyanite, a diagnostic mineral, occurs in abundance locally east of Cuyuja on the Papallacta-Baeza traverse.

2. Rocks on the Oyacachi and Sarahurcu traverses are like those at Baños.

3. Rocks on the northmost traverse, just south of the Colombian border, are mostly igneous and metaigneous, with only minor schists. Strikes of foliation of these rocks depart markedly from the regional north-south Andean trend and range from N 30° E to N 60° E. This structural change suggests a

FIG. 1. Map of western Ecuador, showing areas of regionally metamorphosed rocks (stippled areas). Taken from the Geologic Map of Ecuador (Quito, Ministerio de Comercio e Industrias, 1969). Note: the Government of Ecuador does not recognize all of the international borders here shown.

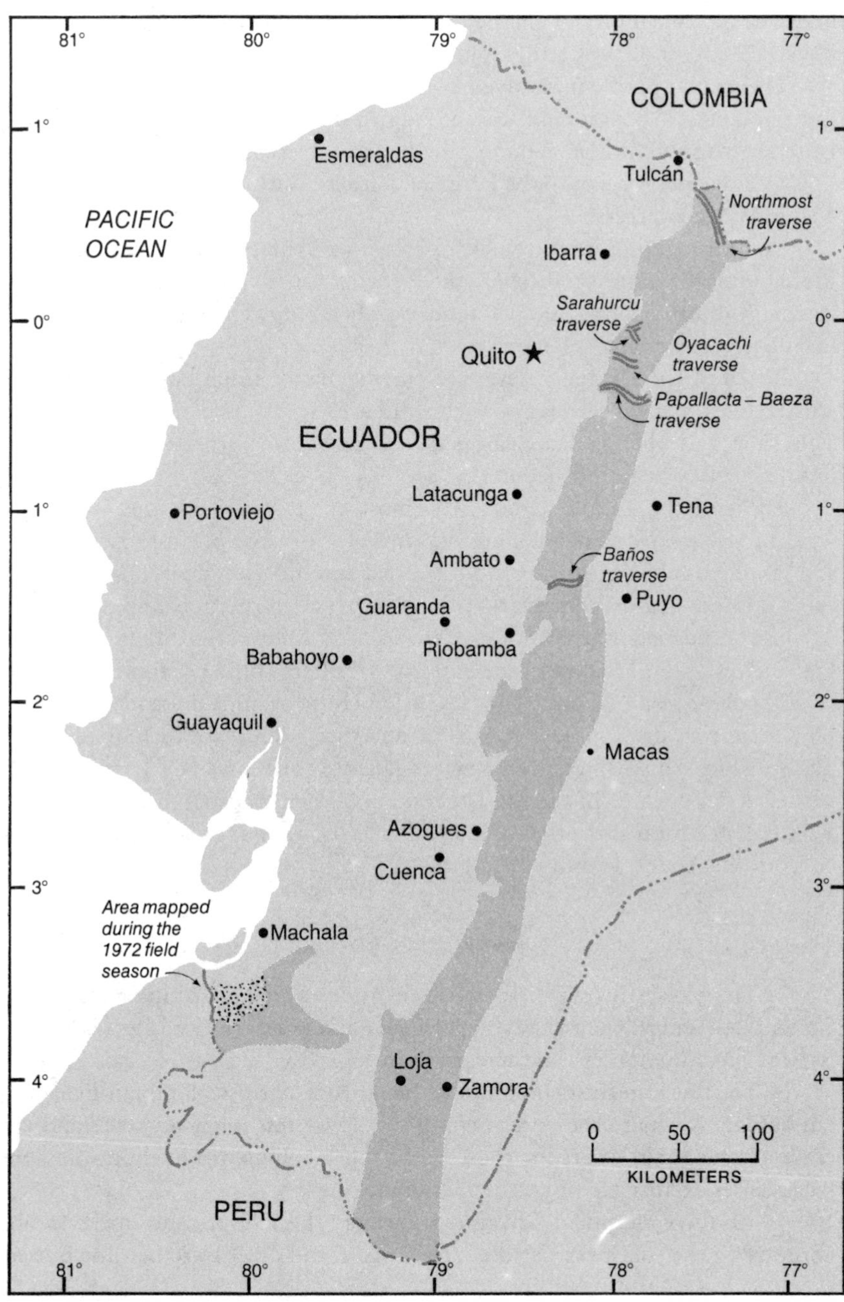
81°
80°
79°
78°
77°
1°
0°
1°
2°
3°
4°
COLOMBIA
Esmeraldas
Tulcán
Northmost traverse
PACIFIC OCEAN
Ibarra
Sarahurcu traverse
Oyacachi traverse
Quito
Papallacta – Baeza traverse
ECUADOR
Latacunga
Tena
Portoviejo
Ambato
Baños traverse
Puyo
Guaranda
Riobamba
Babahoyo
Guayaquil
Macas
Azogues
Cuenca
Area mapped during the 1972 field season
Machala
Loja
Zamora
0 50 100
KILOMETERS
PERU

break in the continuity of the belt at the latitude of the Colombian border, physical support of the petrographic evidence.

The second problem involved the nature of the metamorphic rocks in El Oro Province. I spent a field season (August 17 to October 14, 1972) doing geologic mapping in the metamorphic rocks of the coastal Andean foothills of El Oro Province adjacent to the Peruvian border. With two students I mapped 432 square kilometers.

Excluding minor igneous rocks, I recognized three major groups of rocks. From oldest to youngest, these are the Precambrian (?) Piedras Group, the Paleozoic Tahuín Group, and a Cretaceous harzburgite body and associated high-pressure metamorphic rocks.

Rocks of the Piedras Group are chiefly mafic: amphibolite and greenschist. They may be correlative with similar rocks exposed around Medellín, Colombia, but I had had no prior personal experience with them and they are unknown elsewhere in Ecuador.

Rocks of the Tahuín Group, the most extensive of the area, are overwhelmingly pelitic. They belong dominantly to a low-pressure facies series and range from low greenschist to the top of amphibolite grade. Their chemical and mineralogical compositions, and style of deformation are very similar to those of the metamorphic rocks of the Central Andean Cordillera of Colombia, and quite unlike those of the Eastern Cordillera of the Ecuadorian Andes.

The large body (about 25 square kilometers) of high-pressure metamorphic rocks contained in the harzburgite body are unique and include eclogite, glaucophane schist, hornblende-garnet-kyanite rock, and pelitic schist with garnet, kyanite, and chloritoid. The finding of these unusual rocks is especially interesting for it is the first occurrence of eclogite and isofacial rocks reported from the Andes (Feininger, in press).

Summary of Findings

1. The physically continuous belt of Andean metamporphic rocks of the Colombian Central Cordillera and the Ecuadorian Eastern Cordillera is actually two belts quite unlike one another petrologically.

2. The break in the belt occurs at the latitude of the Colombian-Ecuadorian border. Rocks to the north belong to a low-pressure facies series and include a broad range of grades; those to the south belong to a medium-pressure facies series exclusively of greenschist grade.

3. At the Colombian-Ecuadorian border, the low-pressure rocks swing abruptly to the southwest (strikes are N 30° E to N 60° E) to become buried

beneath young, chiefly volcanic deposits of the Central Andean Valley of northern Ecuador.

4. The low-pressure rocks reappear in El Oro Province in the coastal Andean foothills adjacent to the Peruvian border. Here I have mapped these rocks as the Tahuín Group. They rest on chiefly mafic Precambrian(?) rocks of the Piedras Group.

5. High-pressure metamorphic rocks contained in a harzburgite body in El Oro Province represent the first occurrence of eclogite and isofacial rocks reported from the Andes.

REFERENCE

FEININGER, TOMAS

1975. Geologic map of eastern Antioquia Department, Colombia. U. S. Geol. Survey Miscell. Invest. Series Map I-860 (two sheets, 1:100,000).

1980. Eclogite and related high-pressure regional metamorphic rocks from the Andes of Ecuador. Journ. Petrology, vol. 21, no. 1, pp. 107-140.

TOMAS FEININGER

Laysan Albatross: Mortality, Survival, Breeding, and Changes in Breeding Populations

Principal Investigator: Harvey I. Fisher, Department of Zoology, Southern Illinois University, Carbondale, Illinois.

Grant No. 1028: For a study of Laysan albatross on Midway Island.

Field research was conducted on Midway Atoll from November 15, 1972, to January 1973 by the following persons whose travel was supported by the National Geographic Society: Dr. Earl Meseth of Elmhurst College, Illinois; and Mr. Donald Sparling, Miss Margaret Van Ryzin, and the principal investigator, all of Southern Illinois University, Carbondale. Through the cooperation and financial support of the Explorers Club of New York, these students also participated: Mr. George Jobanek of Oregon, Mr. Mitchell Stokes of Vermont, and Mr. Peter H. S. Wood of New York.

Summary of Results

More than 15,000 previously banded Laysan albatrosses *(Diomedea immutabilis)* were recaptured. The long-time records on these birds enabled the completion of studies of breeding dynamics, mortality, survival and longevity, and changes in breeding populations, which have culminated in the papers cited in the references.

CHANGES IN BREEDING POPULATIONS

My studies in earlier years had revealed low breeding populations in 1960, 1964, and 1968. The sparse literature pertaining to the 1956 population on Midway also indicated a probable low in that year. This information suggested that the colony as a whole might have a four-year cycle in breeding. The 1972 season was thus critical, for, in line with the above concept, breeding numbers were expected to be low. This decline did not occur, however, and from figure 1 it is evident that breeding populations have more than doubled in 12 years. The failure of many experienced breeders to attempt breeding is thought to be the major reason for significant drops in the number of those breeding in certain seasons (Fisher, 1976, p. 133).

AGE AT FIRST BREEDING

Van Ryzin and Fisher (1976) analyzed records of 847 albatrosses of known age and sex, and breeding for the first time, recaptured during this expedition. Males tended to initiate breeding a year sooner than females, mean ages being 8.4 and 8.9 years, respectively. Unknown seasonal factors seemingly influenced the age at which many birds began reproduction. In one season when great numbers of experienced breeders failed to breed, first-time breeders were significantly younger.

AGE COMPOSITION OF THE BREEDING COLONY

A stabilized breeding colony of these albatrosses may consist of 15 percent young breeders of no great reproductive significance, since most fail to raise chicks; 54 percent prime, reproductive birds 10 to 19 years old, the main strength of the colony; and 31 percent albatrosses 20 or more years old (Fisher, 1976).

There was a mean 14 percent annual recruitment of first-time breeders, and all came from the Midway colonies.

FREQUENCY OF BREEDING

Although these albatrosses were capable of breeding each year, after the second season of their reproductive life, the mean observed frequency was 0.82 to 0.86 percent of the seasons by pairs with long-term pair bonds. This frequency is remarkable when it is known that attempts to breed are influenced by availability of food, the monogamous nature of the pair bond and the time required to form it, and the success in reproduction (Fisher, 1976, p. 141).

Reproduction was attempted in only 60 percent of the first 5 years of the pair bond, and more than half of these young pairs did not try to breed in the season after the first attempt.

MORTALITY

It has been found in a 13-year study of more than 27,000 banded albatrosses (Fisher, 1975c) that mortality at different stages of the life cycle is 3 to 5 percent as eggs (6,543 nests); 3 to 17 percent as chicks in the nest; approximately 13 percent among fledglings departing from the colony (4,492 birds); a mean of 6.8 percent in each of the first 4 years and of 1.8 percent in each of the next 4 years (sample of 7,000); 3.7 to 4.0 percent per year among young birds in their first 9 breeding seasons; and 5.3 to 6.3 percent among 3,305 breeders of all ages.

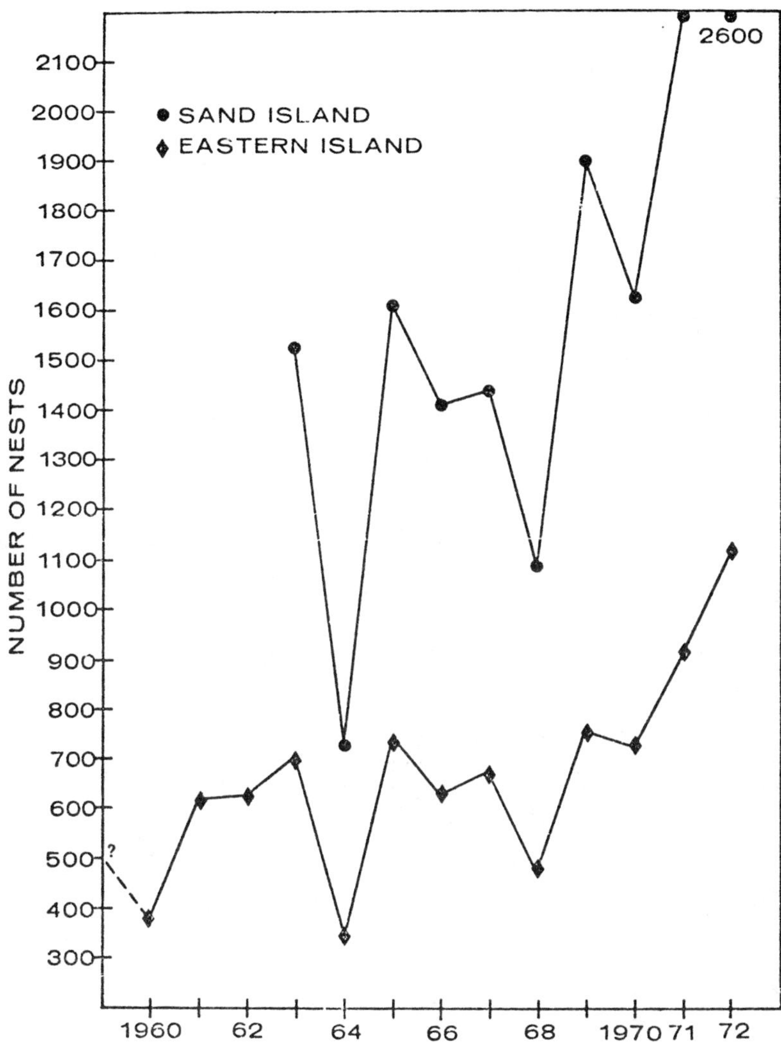

FIG. 1. Number of Laysan albatrosses breeding in study plots on the islands of Midway Atoll, North Pacific Ocean.

Birds which initiated reproduction at earlier than usual ages did not exhibit increased mortality rates (Fisher, 1975b).

There was no consistent sexual variation in mortality.

SURVIVAL AND LONGEVITY

Approximately 40 percent of the breeding albatrosses lived a minimum of 12 years, 30 percent to 14 years, 25 percent to 16 years, 20 percent to 18 years, and 13 percent to 20 years (Fisher, 1975c, p. 279).

In my study of longevity (1975a) I was able to extend the information on survival beyond the age of 20 years, based upon the recapture of more than 200 birds banded prior to July 1944. Unfortunately, the banding laboratory of the U. S. Fish and Wildlife Service has never reported to me on more than 100 badly worn bands, and my views on minimum survival beyond 20 years are based upon 135 recaptures. Perhaps more than 9 percent live to 30 years, 7 percent to 38 years, and 3 percent to 40 or more years.

Laysan albatrosses may have a breeding life expectancy of some 16 to 18 years.

REFERENCES

FISHER, HARVEY I.

1975a. Longevity of the Laysan albatross, *Diomedea immutabilis.* Bird-Banding, vol. 46, no. 1, pp. 1-6

1975b. The relationship between deferred breeding and mortality in the Laysan albatross. Auk, vol. 52, no. 3, pp. 433-441.

1975c. Mortality and survival in the Laysan albatross, *Diomedea immutabilis.* Pacific Sci., vol. 29, no. 3, pp. 279-300.

1976. Some dynamics of a breeding colony of Laysan albatrosses. Wilson Bull, vol. 88, no. 1, pp. 121-142.

VAN RYZIN, MARGARET T., and FISHER, HARVEY I.

1976. The age of Laysan albatrosses, *Diomedea immutabilis,* at first breeding. Condor, vol. 78, no. 1, pp. 1-9.

HARVEY I. FISHER

Excavations at Rattlers Bight—A Late Maritime Archaic Settlement and Cemetery in Hamilton Inlet, Labrador

Principal Investigator: William W. Fitzhugh, National Museum of Natural History, Smithsonian Institution, Washington, D. C.

Grant Nos. 947, 1045, 1101. For a study of environmental archeology and cultural systems in Hamilton Inlet, Labrador.

In the early 1900's Warren K. Moorehead made some startling archeological discoveries in Maine. Excavating in farmers' potato fields and trash pits he found evidence of prehistoric graveyards containing powdered red ocher and tool types unknown in the common coastal shell mound sites which were thought to be ancestral to the historic Indians. The cemeteries seemed to be older. Pottery was not present and skeletons and bone tools were not preserved. Also distinctive was the presence of tools of beautiful translucent chert resembling frosted glass, the origin of which remained unknown until archeological surveys revealed quantities of this material in Labrador (Strong, 1930; Bird, 1945).

The identity of the "Red Paint" or Moorehead culture and its relationships to the north remained obscure for many years. Recent field work—much of it sponsored by the National Geographic Society—has greatly advanced knowledge of this early period of prehistory. Sites have been excavated in Maine, New Brunswick, Newfoundland, and Labrador. An important cemetery at Port au Choix in northern Newfoundland, replete with skeletons and bone preservation, provided a means for redefinition of Moorehead culture as part of a larger Maritime Archaic tradition (Tuck, 1971), aspects of which extend from southern Maine to northern Labrador during the Late Archaic, ca. 4000-3500 B.P. These excavations revealed a seasonally maritime-oriented society with specialized technology and complex ritual and burial forms which contrasts strongly with the adaptation known for historic Northeastern Indians.

Within this larger pattern, archeological work in central Labrador conducted by me in a series of Smithsonian-National Geographic expeditions between 1971 and 1974 has served to place the northernmost Maritime Archaic cultures in perspective and adds considerably to our understanding of the unique adaptation of these early sea hunters and fishermen of the Northeast.

Intensive research has been conducted at the site of Rattlers Bight (fig. 1) at the northern entrance of Groswater Bay east of Hamilton Inlet, central Labrador coast (see References). The site was discovered in 1969 with the assistance of fishermen's children intent on pointing out a number of "pirates' " graves to our survey party. While the graves were those of early settler children only a hundred years old, they were dug into an old beach terrace containing the remains of a large 4,000-year-old living and ceremonial site. Between 1969 and 1974 excavations were conducted here and at other Rattlers Bight period sites in the vicinity. In addition, other sites have been found that extend the Maritime Archaic development for another 3,000 years. These excavations are reported elsewhere in preliminary fashion (see References), with more detailed analysis currently in process.

Rattlers Bight is located on the outer coast of central Labrador in what is today a transition zone between the boreal forest/parkland and arctic tundra. The site is presently in tundra vegetation with small isolated patches of stunted spruce, birch, and willow. Forest grows in the more protected bays several miles to the west. Food resources are predominantly maritime—seals, fish, sea birds, and whales are common. Bear, caribou, and woodland species are less available but can be found in the forest to the west.

Research at Rattlers Bight has included reconstruction of the local environment through the study of fossil pollen, flora, and dietary remains. Pollen analysis (Jordan, 1975) suggests that the area was deglaciated about 9,000 years ago, after which tundra conditions prevailed until the arrival of the spruce forest about 5000 B.P. Slight cooling may have occurred after 4000 B.P. with subsequent minor oscillations until the present. Plant macrofossils in peat deposits indicate former expansion of trees in present-day tundra areas, and forest fires resulted in thick charcoal layers dating to 3000 B.P. in peats at the Hound Pond 4 site. Large amounts of culturally derived charcoal and wide mats of paper-birch bark in the Rattlers Bight burials also suggest that firewood (predominantly identified as spruce) was locally abundant, while access to large birch trees—themselves not present in Groswater Bay—must have been by trade from farther south or from western Hamilton Inlet. There the effects of warm hypsithermal climates would have been more pronounced than on the coast where the Labrador Current produced localized cooling and depressed conditions for vegetation growth. Large paper birch do not grow in Groswater Bay today. Thus, while pollen and other data do not indicate warmer or more forested conditions at the coast during the Rattlers Bight occupation, they do suggest a stronger thermal and vegetation gradient existed from the coast to the interior.

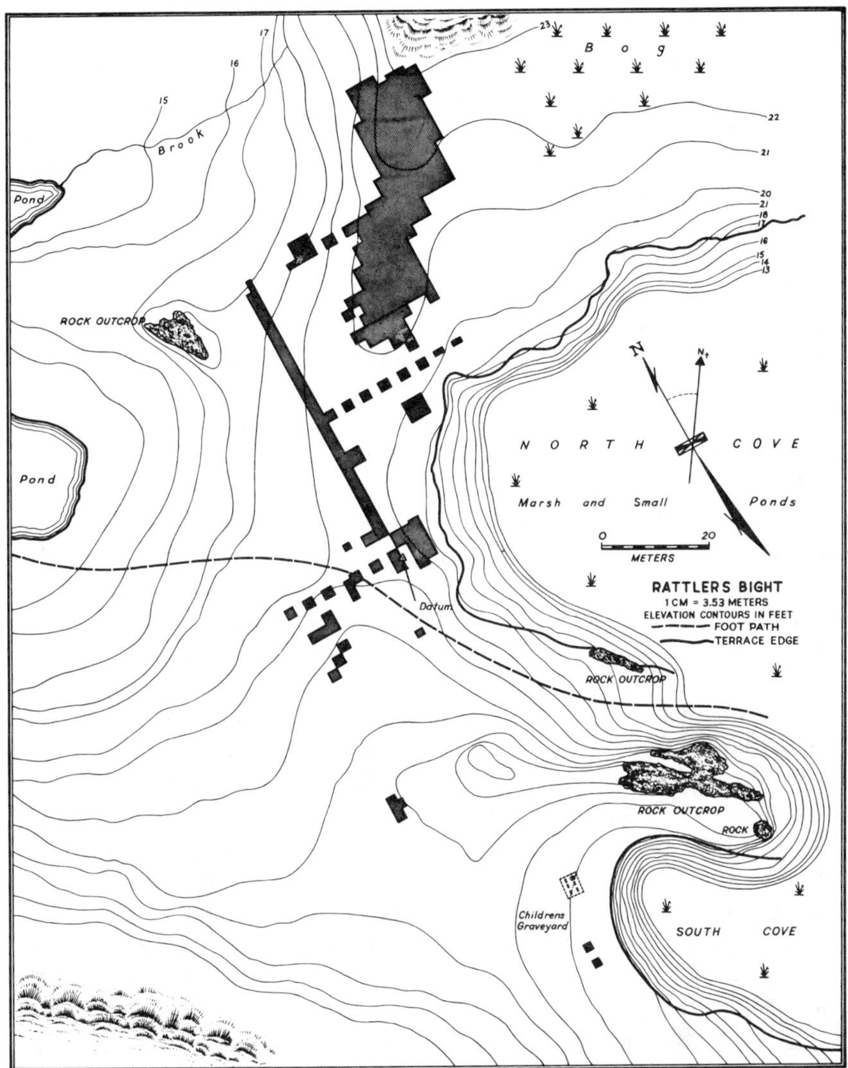

FIG. 1. Map of Rattlers Bight showing living area excavations at top, test trenches, and cemetery area to right of datum mark.

The similarity to present climatic and vegetation conditions seems to apply also to the former availability of land and sea animals. Food remains from the site include several seal species, walrus, and various sea birds and ducks together with lesser quantities of land game: caribou, black bear, fox, hare, otter, beaver, and muskrat. Fish must have been present but are not preserved. Over all, the economy was based on marine species and, of these, all except walrus are present in the area today. The presence of seasonally available species indicates site occupation in spring and fall, and probably during summer as well. No winter sites are known from the coast. It is presumed they exist in the interior and that caribou hunting was the economic mainstay at this time of year.

This settlement pattern is different from that used by ethnographic Indians and Eskimos on the Labrador and Quebec coasts. Montagnais-Naskapi Indians rarely came to the outer coast in summer, preferring to fish and hunt at river mouths and at the heads of the bays and protected inner passages; during winter, caribou hunting occurred from interior sites. The Labrador Eskimo pattern included winter settlement on the islands and inner bays and summer hunting in the outer islands, as has been suggested for the Rattlers Bight period. Hence, the proposed late Maritime Archaic settlement pattern combines elements of both Labrador Eskimo and Montagnais-Naskapi seasonal rounds but is not accurately paralleled by either ethnographic group.

The geographic setting of the site is also important in interpreting its living and ceremonial functions. The site now stands 7 meters above sea level, but during occupation the beach had only recently emerged from the sea as a terraced sand bar between two islands. The bar created two narrow coves, one of which would always be calm and suitable for boat landing. As the easternmost harbor in Groswater Bay, Rattlers Bight was strategically located in terms of coastal movement and must have figured prominently in the trade route along which various materials, especially Ramah chert, would have moved. Undoubtedly Rattlers Bight either controlled a stage of this trade or participated actively in the excursions to obtain it from northern Labrador. Other exotic materials found in the site, such as copper, slate, mica slabs, and soapstone, indicate that movements of scarce resources, for technological, social, and religious functions, may have played an important part in the life of Rattlers Bight people.

Excavations at the site proceeded in three stages. Initially, trenching and test pitting were done to identify different function areas and spatial patterning in the whole locale. This was followed by extensive areal stripping where heaviest artifact and feature concentration occurred. A third stage involved excavation of a portion of the cemetery. As a result, an integrated view of the settlement has begun to emerge. The heaviest domestic occupation was at the northern end of the site and consisted of hearth pits, rock features, lithic manufacturing areas, and middens (fig. 2). Artifacts and faunal remains, usually associated with slab-lined hearth pits, were abundant. No clear pattern of in-

FIG. 2. North area excavation at close of 1971 field season.

terrelationship between these features emerged, nor could the outlines of dwellings or other enclosures be identified. It seems possible that dwellings were located elsewhere; if they existed on the site they must have been of a light skin construction without stone foundations. An unusual feature of the site was a trench 10-20 centimeters deep, which ran for 30 meters down the center of the site parallel to the shore. This trench contained charcoal, mica fragments, tools, and faunal remains. This feature may be a smudge pit used for drying or smoking fish hung on racks above the fire.

Other areas of the site served different domestic and technological functions. Large slab grindstones surrounded with slate flakes, ocher and stains of ocher, and powdered slate mark stations where adzes, axes, and gouges were manufactured. Heavy deposits of Ramah chert flakes show where chipped stone tools were sharpened, and the distribution of fitting fragments from individual tools demonstrates the behavioral aspects of technology and provides synchronic relationships between different functional areas in the site. Areas where broken adz fragments occur suggest heavy woodworking or large sea-mammal butchering. Ocher grinding areas have also been identified. Taken

FIG. 3. "Lotus" burial (Feature E) rockpile before dismantling. Sterile surrounding deposits have been removed exposing the feature intact. A dog burial was found in the petal-like leaves of slab rock which lie on top of two separate burial pits at the base of the rocks.

together, these data suggest varied activities of a group returning periodically to a site where they spent the ice-free months in subsistence hunting and fishing, maintaining their technology, traveling and trading for raw materials, making contacts with visitors, exchanging tools, raw materials, and spouses, and burying their dead.

Discovery of the cemetery was made in 1974 when a rock cluster, previously thought to be a geological feature, proved to mark the center of a burial ground at the the southern end of the site. Nine burial features (see figs. 3, 4) were excavated, each consisting of a small oval pit about 1.5 meters below

FIG. 4. Cemetery excavations, 1974. Stephen Loring records dimensions of rock slabs covering Feature D.

the surface. Some of the burials were marked by surface boulders while others were not. Skeletal remains were recovered from only one burial, but it seems likely that the pattern for this feature—that of a single flexed or bundled interment—pertained to the others as well. All features contained large birch bark mats and quantities of red ocher, but beyond this feature individuality was expressed in diverse deposits of chipped and ground stone tools, mica slabs, plummets, copper, and raw material blanks—each grave being quite distinct in the types and abundance of materials found. This individuality has been noted at other Maritime Archaic cemeteries, especially at Port au Choix.

Analysis of these burials and comparison with the breakage patterns and tool types from the adjacent living site are beginning to show a number of interesting patterns. Most important is the obvious contemporaneity between the two areas; we can confidently state that they are part of a single cultural system, although not of one year's occupation. The contrast between the poverty of both chipped and ground stone remains in the living site and the large size and lavish expenditure of energy on tools found in the burial deposits highlight concepts of individual versus communal wealth and redistribution of goods. The disposal of exotic raw materials and large exquisitely made tools appears to be an important element in supporting the exchange systems and movement of materials and ideas that characterizes Late Maritime Archaic cultures in general. It is an extension of this system that results in the Labrador raw material and finished tools that have been found in sites as far south as Maine.

The excavation of Rattlers Bight therefore affords a rather unusual view of a flourishing Late Maritime Archaic society whose adaptation to the rich Labrador marine resources permitted participation in a widespread and unique cultural pattern stretching from the Arctic fringe to the temperate forest coasts of southern New England. The location of other similar but earlier cultures in Labrador shows that this pattern was not introduced from Late Archaic cultures of the south; its roots extend several thousand years earlier, ultimately perhaps to late Paleo-Indian hunters of the now submerged continental shelf.

The importance of the Rattlers Bight site lies in the large collection of tools, technological and functional information, faunal materials, and the geographic and environmental setting into which this cultural data can be placed. The large size of the site and presence of both domestic and mortuary activities make it a northern keystone in interpreting an early, new type of culture pattern in the prehistory of northeastern North America.

REFERENCES

BIRD, JUNIUS

1945. Archaeology of the Hopedale area, Labrador. Anthrop. Papers Amer. Mus. Nat. Hist., vol. 39, no. 2, pp. 117-186.

FITZHUGH, WILLIAM

1972a. Environmental archeology and cultural systems in Hamilton Inlet, Labrador. Smithsonian Contr. Anthrop., no. 16, 245 pp., illus.

1972b. Preliminary report of the Hamilton Inlet archeological project, 1972. Can. Archaeol. Assoc. Bull. no. 4, pp. 89-98.

1973. Smithsonian archeological investigation on the Labrador coast, 1973: A preliminary report. Can. Archaeol. Assoc. Bull. no. 5, pp. 77-90.

1974a. Smithsonian field work on the central Labrador coast: 1974. Can. Archaeol. Assoc. Bull. no. 6, pp. 209-217.

1974b. Hound Pond 4: A Charles Complex site in northern Groswater Bay, Labrador. Man in the Northeast, vol. 7, pp. 87-103.

1974c. Ground slates in the Scandinavian Stone Age with reference to circumpolar maritime adaptations. Proc. Prehist. Soc., vol. 40, pp. 45-58.

1975a. A comparative approach to northern maritime adaptations. Pp. 339-386 *in* "Prehistoric Maritime Adaptations of the Circumpolar Zone," William Fitzhugh, ed., 405 pp.

1975b. A Maritime Archaic sequence from Hamilton Inlet, Labrador. Arctic Anthrop., vol. 12, no. 2, pp. 117-138.

JORDAN, RICHARD

1975. Pollen diagrams from Hamilton Inlet, central Labrador, and their environmental implications for the northern Maritime Archaic. Arctic Anthrop., vol. 12, no. 2, pp. 92-116.

STRONG, WILLIAM D.

1930. A stone culture from Labrador and its relation to the Eskimo-like cultures of the Northeast. Amer. Anthrop., vol. 32, pp. 126-144.

TUCK, JAMES A.

1971. An Archaic cemetery at Port au Choix, Newfoundland. Amer. Antiq., vol. 36, no. 3, pp. 343-345.

1976. Ancient people of Port au Choix. Papers Inst. Social and Econ. Res., Mem. Univ. Newfoundland, no. 17, 261 pp.

WILLIAM W. FITZHUGH

Biology of Snail-killing Flies of the Pacific Northwest (Diptera: Sciomyzidae)

Principal Investigator: Benjamin A. Foote, Kent State University, Kent, Ohio.

Grant No. 918: For a study of snail-killing flies (Sciomyzidae) of the Pacific Northwest.

During the summer of 1971 an investigation into the larval feeding habits and life histories of the snail-killing flies (Sciomyzidae) of the Pacific Northwest was undertaken by the principal investigator and two graduate students, Robert Mangan and Thomas Sluss. Approximately one month of effort was expended in southern and central Alaska, and two months of collecting and rearing work were devoted to northwestern Montana.

The only previous taxonomic work that deals comprehensively with the snail-killing flies of Alaska is that of Steyskal (1954), which records 30 species of 9 genera of Sciomyzidae from the state. The only early paper that contains biological observations on the Alaskan species is that of Berg (1953).

Methods employed during the research effort included sweeping suitable habitats with insect nets, establishing adults of desired species in rearing chambers, and making observations on a variety of life-history parameters. Information was obtained on adult longevity, courtship behavior, premating and preoviposition periods, and fecundity; on larval feeding habits and duration of the three larval instars; and on pupation sites and duration of the pupal period. Observations were made also on the habitat and seasonal distributions of each species.

Adults were killed in cyanide, placed on insect pins, and labeled as to locality and date of collection. Larvae and puparia were killed in hot water and subsequently preserved in 70 percent ethanol. Collections of immature stages were assigned rearing numbers and labeled as to locality and date of the rearing effort. Voucher specimens were deposited in the biology collections at Kent State University. Eventually all preserved material will be transferred to the National Museum of Natural History at Washington, D. C.

Results

Partly as a result of the month-long collecting effort during the summer of 1971, an additional 23 species of Sciomyzidae have been recorded for Alaska. Steyskal (1954) listed 30 species for the state; so the total Alaskan sciomyzid fauna now consists of 53 species. Four new species, all in the genus *Pherbellia,* will be described by specialists at the National Museum. *Pherbellia,* with 20 species, is the largest genus of Alaskan Sciomyzidae. *Tetanocera* contains 16 species, but the remaining 8 genera each contain only 1 to 4 species. Seven species, mostly in the genus *Pherbellia,* are apparently restricted to Alaska; 11 species are known only from northwestern North America; 7 are transcontinental across Canada and the northern United States; an additional 23 species are similarly transcontinental but extend also southward in the western mountains; and 5 species have very wide distributions in the Nearctic Region. Twenty of the 53 Alaskan species, or 37.7 percent, are holarctic in distribution, as they have been recorded also from the Palearctic Region. In contrast, only approximately 13 percent of all the North American species of Sciomyzidae occur also in the Palearctic Region. A further indication of the strong affinity of the Alaskan sciomyzid fauna with that of the Old World is the fact that 9 of the 10 genera are also recorded from Palearctic localities.

The well-watered southern coastal areas of Alaska were particularly productive of sciomyzid species, although the huge inland area of the state centered on Fairbanks was also quite rich. Very few species have been obtained from the North Slope bordering the Arctic Ocean or from the adjacent Brooks Mountain Range. Wetlands containing extensive stands of grasses, sedges, and horsetails were the most productive habitats. In contrast, muskeg environments, perhaps because of their acid waters and consequently depauperate snail faunas, provided very few species. Moist, forested areas, particularly those consisting of a mix of deciduous and coniferous tree species, contained a small but well-defined sciomyzid fauna composed of species having larvae that prey on slugs and terrestrial snails.

Biological information was obtained for 31 of the 37 species that were collected in Alaska during the summer of 1971. Eleven species were found to have larvae that feed on nonoperculate aquatic snails, 17 species attack shoreline-inhabiting snails, 2 species are associated with terrestrial snails occurring in woodlands, 1 species preys on slugs, and another species has larvae that attack only fingernail clams belonging to the family Sphaeriidae. Rearings of 4 previously unstudied species were obtained. Larvae of *Tetanocera bergi* Steyskal and *T. stricklandi* Steyskal were predators of aquatic snails, those of *Renocera brevis* (Cresson) attacked fingernail clams, and larvae of *Pherbellia prefixa* Steyskal were found to be associated with stranded operculate snails belonging to the aquatic gastropod genus *Valvata.* Some evidence was obtained that larvae of *Tetanocera brevihirta* Steyskal, another previously unreared species, feed on marsh-inhabiting snails belonging to the genus *Oxyloma.* In summary, life-history information is now available for 41 of the 53 species of Sciomyzidae currently reported from Alaska. Observations on the larval feeding habits of certain of the Alaskan species are available in Foote (1971, 1973) and Foote and Knutson (in preparation).

Extensive collecting in northwestern Montana during the tenure of the grant resulted in the discovery of 6 species previously unknown for the area. Habitat data were obtained for 25 species, and new life-history observations were acquired for 16 species. Larvae of the Montanan species were discovered to feed on aquatic, shoreline, and terrestrial snails; snail eggs; slugs; and fingernail clams.

Particularly interesting was the discovery in Montana of *Sciomyza varia* (Coquillett), a species previously thought to be restricted to eastern North America. As in the Eastern States, adults of *S. varia* collected in Montana deposited eggs on shells of living but stranded *Lymnaea* snails. The larvae were parasitoids in that they were highly host specific, killed only one snail during their larval life, and fed singly within the host snail.

A more complete rearing of *Pherbellia prefixa,* a species also studied in Alaska, was obtained from adults collected in drying sedge marshes near Swan Lake, Montana. Eggs were deposited on litter and low herbaceous vegetation occurring in the vicinity of stranded individuals of *Valvata sincera* Say, an operculate aquatic snail, which served as the larval host.

This rearing is significant in that very few species of Sciomyzidae are known to utilize operculate snails.

A new, undescribed species of *Pherbellia* was reared from puparia found in the woodland-inhabiting snail *Discus cronkhitei* (Newcomb). A complete life cycle was obtained, and the immature stages are being described.

REFERENCES

Berg, Clifford O.

1953. Sciomyzid larvae (Diptera) that feed on snails. Parasitology, vol. 39, pp. 630-636.

Foote, Benjamin A.

1971. Biology of *Hedria mixta* (Diptera: Sciomyzidae). Ann. Ent. Soc. Amer., vol. 64, pp. 931-941.

1973. Biology of *Pherbellia prefixa* (Diptera: Sciomyzidae), a parasitoid-predator of *Valvata sincera* (Gastropoda: Valvatidae). Proc. Ent. Soc. Washington, vol. 75, pp. 141-149.

Foote, Benjamin A., and Knutson, Lloyd V.

_____. Sciomyzidae of Alaska. (Diptera). (In preparation.)

Steyskal, George C.

1954. Sciomyzidae of Alaska (Diptera). Proc. Ent. Soc. Washington, vol. 56, pp. 54-71.

Benjamin A. Foote

Mountain Gorilla Research, 1971-1972

Principal Investigator: Dian Fossey, Ruhengeri, Rwanda.

Grant Nos. 952, 1049, 1138. In aid of long-term field observations of behavioral patterns of the mountain gorilla *(Gorilla gorilla beringei)* in central Africa.

Research on the mountain gorilla was begun in January 1967 in the Kabara area adjacent to Mount Mikeno within the Parc des Virungas of Zaire (formerly known as the Parc Albert of the Congo) where three groups totaling 50 animals were observed for 267 hours. In July 1967 that part of the study was terminated due to political upheavals. The second part, still in progress, was begun in September 1967 on Mount Visoke (fig. 1), approximately 5 miles from the original study site, within the Parc des Volcans of Rwanda.

The gorilla research was initiated by the late Dr. L.S.B. Leakey, whose enthusiasm for procuring knowledge of the great apes was also responsible for launching Jane Goodall into her totally successful, long-term chimpanzee project and, as well, Biruté Galdikas-Brindamour into an equally enlightening study of the orangutan. The Wilkie Brothers Foundation supported the first year of the gorilla research. Since then the project has been generously sponsored by the National Geographic Society with some specific projects aided by the Leakey Foundation. I remain deeply indebted to all who have made this research possible; in particular to the National Geographic Society for its continued support, enthusiasm, and interest in the results.

The Albert National Park, Africa's oldest national park, was established in 1925 by the Belgian Government. At that time it encompassed only the three western inactive volcanoes of the Virunga chain, Mikeno, Visoke, and Karisimbi. In 1929 the remaining five mountains of the chain were incorporated into the park system—the three eastern mountains, Muhavura, M'Gahinga, and Sabinio plus the two active volcanoes Niragongo and Nyamlagira. Mountain gorillas are confined to the six inactive volcanoes and their adjacent saddle areas.

Discussion of the work accomplished during 1971 and 1972 is concerned with both the results of the gorilla census counts made on five of the previously mentioned mountains and with the research output of the central camp.

The main study area is located at the base of the southern slopes of Mount Visoke (see fig. 1) at an altitude of 10,000 feet and at approximately long. 30°

FIG. 1. Aerial view of Mount Visoke (3,711 meters) and its adjacent saddle area, within the Parc des Volcans of Rwanda to the east of the crater and within the Parc des Virungas of Zaire to the west of the crater. North is at the top of the photograph. For identification of vegetation and location of camp, see figure 2.

E. and lat. 1° S. The camp lies within a montane rain forest and is situated against the steep mountain slopes of Visoke at 12,172 feet (3,711 meters). The 25 square kilometers of working area covered from the central camp include both the mountainous terrain as well as an extensive saddle area lying to the south, southeast, and west toward Mount Karisimbi and Mount Mikeno. The four main study groups of gorillas within this area were contacted at between 8,500 and 13,000 feet, both within the Parc des Volcans of Rwanda and the Parc des Virungas of Zaire, the border of the latter being slightly more than a kilometer from the central camp.

Within the working area are six main vegetation zones (see fig. 2): 1, Saddle (figs. 1, 3): A gentle, rolling terrain interrupted occasionally by small hills or ridges and heavily treed with numerous *Hagenia* and *Hypericum* trees. Food is abundant and of high quality within the saddle zone. 2, Nettle: A flat terrain lying betwen the western slopes of Mount Visoke and the saddle area. Trees are scarce and many other herbs have been choked out by the density of

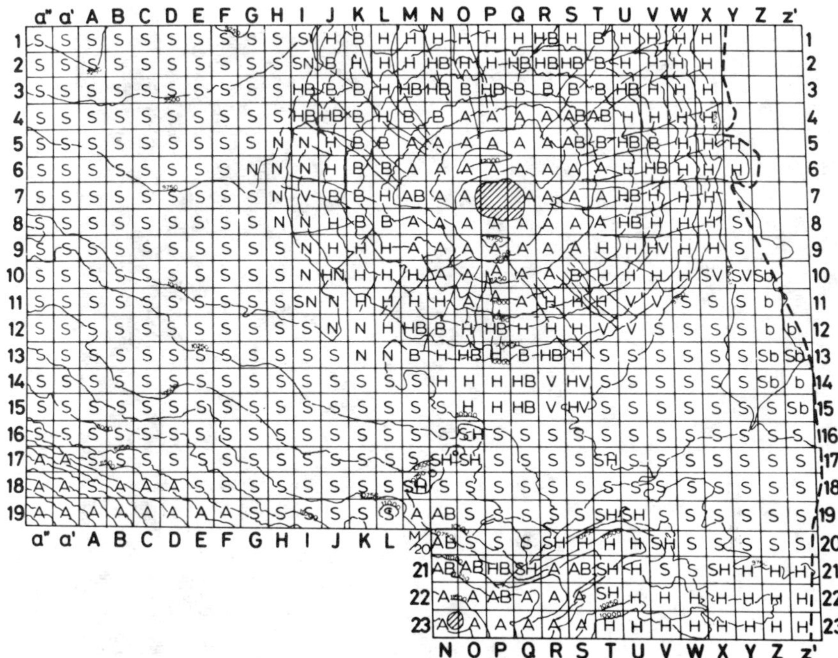

FIG. 2. Distribution of vegetation zones in the study area (north is at top of vertical lines). Each grid square is 0.25 kilometer on a side (area 0.625 square kilometer). Initial indicates dominant vegetation and/or location of the square: (A) Alpine, (B) brush ridge, (b) bamboo, (H) herbaceous, (N) nettle, (S) saddle, (V) Vernonia. Camp is located at the top right of square 0-14. And the crater of Mount Visoke is the diagonally ruled area centered on P-7. North is at the top.

the nettle growth. 3, Brush ridge (fig. 3): This area forms the edges of deep ravines and is widespread on the mountain slopes. Ridges support a vegetation containing shrubs and trees not as commonly found in other parts of the gorillas' habitat, and offering little of the herbaceous ground foliage that forms the majority of the gorillas' diet. 4, *Vernonia:* Areas on and adjacent to the slopes of Mount Visoke containing small clusters of *Vernonia* trees are treated as a separate zone because such trees form an important food source for the gorillas. In fact their consistent use of the trees has substantially reduced the zone since the study began in 1967, especially where group ranges overlap. 5, Herbaceous slopes (fig. 3): These areas consist of fairly low, thick herbs such as celery, thistle, and rumex, and are found commonly on the mountain as well as in the saddle. The gorillas spend more time regularly in the herba-

FIG. 3. Southern facing slopes of Mount Visoke, illustrating brush ridge zones and herbaceous slopes (untreed areas); saddle area in the foreground.

FIG. 4. Sub-alpine and alpine zone on the southern facing slopes of Mount Visoke at approximately 3,300 meters illustrating the scarcity of vegetation at this altitude. The saddle terrain is shown some 300 meters below.

ceous zone than in any other, and the core areas of all four main study groups are centered on and around herbaceous slopes. 6, Sub-Alpine and Alpine (fig. 4): This zone begins at approximately 3,300 meters on the slopes of Mount Visoke and offers little food vegetation for gorillas. What foods are there are not common in other zones but do not appear to offer sufficient incentive for regular or prolonged usage of the area by the gorillas.

Home Ranges Within Study Area

The home ranges of the groups have not remained constant throughout the study period, but there have been only minor changes in the core areas, the areas of heaviest regular use. To measure group movements and range area, a contoured 1:50,000 map (1965, Sheet 3, Provisional Trace of the Belgian Centre National de Volcanologique) was enlarged to approximately 1:17,000, and gridded (see fig. 2) with squares of side 0.25 kilometer (0.625 square kilometer). The observed positions and/or trails of the groups were then assigned grid reference numbers. When a group was recorded only within the square in which it was contacted, it is possible that the range size was underestimated; however, the probabilities of underestimation have been shown to be reduced over a prolonged period of time (7 years). Another disadvantage of the grid method that contributes to underestimation of range size is that it does not correspond to the ground area, because of the irregularity of the terrain. Schaller (pers. comm.) tried to correct for the unevenness of terrain by simply adding 10 percent of a known range area to the total sum of miles and arrived at an estimation of 10 to 15 square miles for the home ranges of the Kabara groups.

Table 1 shows the yearly and total range sizes, 1971 and 1972, of the four main study groups. As could be expected, the group most consistently followed (4) had a larger portion of its range represented than the other groups. With all groups, however, it may be seen that there was considerable variation in the percentage of the same grid squares used exclusively or shared with other groups between the two years. This was considered to have been primarily a direct result of the number of interactions between groups; secondly, a result of a gradual incorporation of "new" terrain into the range areas. Most groups expanded their ranges, chiefly into the saddle because of the marked decrease of human encroachers in that area. Availability of food resources was not felt to have been a major factor influencing range usage.

Table 2 shows the number and kind of interactions observed throughout 1971 and 1972 and the total number and type of grid square in which they occurred. All auditory interactions (those in which the proximity of one group

TABLE 1. Comparison of Changes in Range Size 1971-1972.

Group	*Contacts*		*Total range area*		*Area of exclusive use*			*Area shared with other groups*			*Tot. range var. betw. 1971 & 1972*	
	No.	*Pct.*	*Grid sqs.*	*km²*	*Grid sqs.*	*km²*	*Pct. of range*	*Grp.*	*Grid sqs.*	*Pct. of range*	*Grid sqs.*	*Pct.*
A - 1971 (4 main study groups)												
4	162	71	62	3.88	44	2.75	71	5	6	10		
								8	11	18		
								9	1	1		
5	34	15	25	1.56	19	1.19	76	4	6	24		
8	29	13	20	1.25	8	.50	40	4	11	55		
								9	1	5		
9	4	2	4	.25	2	.13	50	4	1	25		
								8	1	25		
B - 1972 (3 main study groups)												
4	202	64	66	4.13	46	2.88	70	5	8	12		
								8	12	18		
5	88	28	45	2.81	37	2.31	82	4	8	18		
8	27	8	15	.94	3	.19	20	4	12	80		
C - 1971-1972 Combined (4 main study groups)												
4	364		85	5.31	23	1.44	27	5	3	3	55	65
								8	5	6		
5	122		56	3.50	10	.62	18	4	3	5	43	77
8	56		32	2.00	0	-	-	4	5	16	27	84
9[a]	4		4	.25	-	-	-	-	-	-	-	-

[a]No 1972 contacts.

TABLE 2. Interactions (Auditory, Visual, Physical) and Their Locations, 1971-1972.

	Interactions		*No. Grid squares involved*		*Interaction type*						*Grid squares*			
					1971			*1972*			*Shared*		*Exclusive*	
Gr. no.	*1971*	*1972*	*1971*	*1972*	*Aud.*	*Vis.*	*Phys.*	*Aud.*	*Vis.*	*Phys.*	*1971*	*1972*	*1971*	*1972*
4	34	32	23	22	22	9	3	28	0	4	8	9	15	13
5	7	9	6	5	4	0	3	5	0	4	2	0	4	5
8	9	13	10	8	5	2	2	9	0	4	3	6	7	2
9	1	-	1	-	1	-	-	-	-	-	-	-	1	-
Tot.	51	54	40	35	32	11	8	42	0	12	13	15	27	20

to another could be clearly determined by vocalizations and/or chestbeats exchanged between two groups or one group and another individual) occurred in grid squares of exclusive use. Visual interactions were those that occurred when the observer was in contact with one group and could see another group or individual from his contact spot with the group under observation. Such interactions were usually always auditory at some stage and could become physical (intermingling of members of two different groups) dependent upon the groups involved and the "purpose" of the interaction. The same held true for solely auditory interactions. Because of the above two reasons, very few general conclusions should be drawn about group interactions; impressions gained from field observations were, however, that physical interactions, which almost always resulted in aggressive behavior due to attempted "kidnappings" of young females, appeared to have been avoided whenever possible by the group with females to lose. Consequently, physical interminglings amounted to only 19 percent of all interactions, while auditory and visual interactions made up the remainder. Of the 20 known physical interactions that occurred during 1971 and 1972 between the 4 main study groups, 14 (70 percent) involved exchanges of 6 young females either between the groups or between a group and a lone silverback. Of these, 3 (15 percent) were considered to have been mild interactions and appeared, to the observer, to have been almost accidental, or at least not intentional. The remaining 3 (15 percent) appeared to serve as preliminaries toward the exchange of females. Since all physical interactions occurred in grid squares of shared usage, it was to the advantage of the group with females to lose or "drop" that part of their range when another group was in proximity; an impression that has been reinforced throughout the long-term study.

Probably both intergroup interactions and the decrease in encroachers within the saddle areas were the two factors most responsible for the decrease in range overlap between groups. As is evident in table 1, less than half of each year's group range was used in the same manner during both years. All core areas were contained within the sections of repeated use and on the herbaceous slopes of Mount Visoke. As previously mentioned, the majority of expansion occurred into the saddle area. The most dramatic example of this was seen in the case of Group 5 whose exploratory sallies into "new" saddle terrain eventually resulted in 19 new grid squares (34 percent of their total range) accumulated by the end of 1972. The usual method of expansion resulted in somewhat amoebalike protrusions into a new area (followed by quick retreats back to the mountain slopes) and gradually extensions made on both sides of the initial investigatory route. It appeared that limitations affecting random expansion were due to meetings with "fringe" groups, or individuals, who frequented the "new" area; to encounters with poachers; to an apparently strong inclination toward investigating all parts of the new terrain covered; or to the food resources being either unavailable or temporarily depleted by other species such as elephant and buffalo.

Comparisons with the Lowland Gorilla

Another interesting speculation concerning the increased usage of the saddle area was brought up by Dr. Jorge Sabater Pi who spent 19 working days at camp in August 1972 under the sponsorship of the National Geographic Society. In a 10-page report Dr. Sabater Pi described the macrobiotopic distribution on the slopes of Mount Visoke as contributive toward the gorillas' vegetation requirements. However, because of the increasing erosion of the mountain slopes, there has been a subsequent growth of microbiotopic vegetation which contributes little toward gorillas' food needs. Other specific observations made by him that included comparisons between the feeding habits and ecological influences of the mountain (eastern) and lowland (western) gorillas of the Río Muni and the Cameroons were (Jones and Sabater Pi, 1971): 1, The western gorillas, unlike the mountain gorillas, are a "guest of man" and need reforested areas or heliophilia zones to supply their food needs; 2, fruit is far more important in the diet of the western gorilla, especially during the cold dry season from November to February, whereas with the mountain gorillas no similar comparison can be made, since the two main species of fruit occupy only 1 percent of their total diet; 3, lowland gorillas almost always utilize food vegetation for the construction of their night nests, whereas this has rarely been observed among mountain gorillas, the most obvious reason for this difference being that the main food plants of the mountain gorillas (nettles, thistles, celery, *Galium*) are not conducive to nest construction while the more common herbaceous plants (*Senecio, Hypericum* branches, *Lobelia*) are not only more accessible but also lend themselves to a firmer and more "comfortable" night nest (see Fossey and Harcourt, 1977).

Feeding

Sabater Pi listed 79 different kinds of plants, including some domestic, eaten by the western gorillas. Among the mountain gorillas, 44 different kinds were observed being consumed, but no authenticated reports of consumption of cultivated plants have been received, though two groups occasionally entered cultivated areas. Of the feeding time, 60 percent was spent on

FIG. 5. Uncle Bert, dominant silverback of group 4. Photo by Bob Campbell © National Geographic Society.

the 3 most commonly eaten species and 20 percent on the next 6 most common. Idiosyncratic vegetation ingestion, primarily seen in younger animals and accounting for an additional 18 plant species, were not listed because they amounted to less than one percent of all records. Gorillas apparently do not have the requisite gut structure (thus microflora) to synthesize vitamin B12 from plant material. It seems quite likely that they obtained this vitamin from the numerous grubs they obtained from decayed wood, stalks, and leaf surfaces.

Observations

General and specific observations based on study of the four main groups during 1971-1972 are here summarized. Gorillas normally rose between 06:00 and 06:45 and night-nested between 18:00 and 18:45 hours. Only in exceptional circumstances did gorillas move during the night, and such movement was always connected with interactions with another group or individual. The two main study groups (4 and 5) had similar activity patterns and spent about 25 percent of the day feeding. Climate definitely affected activity patterns of all groups. In the rain, animals sat and huddled almost motionless, and on sunny days adults tended to rest longer during the midday period to bask in the sun. It seemed likely that they compensated for this inactivity by increased locomotion and feeding during the remainder of the day.

Behavioral observations became increasingly more profitable with Groups 4 and 5 as their acceptance of observers increased dramatically, especially during 1972. The compositional changes and transitions that occurred in the 4 main groups during the 2-year period study are noted in the following paragraphs.

Group 4. There were 13 members in Group 4 at the beginning of 1971 and 10 by the end of 1972, under the inexperienced but diligent protection of Uncle Bert (fig. 5). Only 1 of the losses was due to death; 3 were females who were taken into other groups; only 1 newly born was known to have been alive at the end of the period concerned. The transfer of the females Maisie and Macho into Group 8 and Bravado into Group 5 appeared to have involved aggressive behavior, as injuries were noted on the adult males of all groups following the interaction. The elderly female Mrs. X returned to Group 4 after a 2-month consortship with the lone silverback Amok (formerly of Group 4). All group members, in particular Mrs. X's 37-month-old infant, Simba II, showed a considerable amount of interest in and attention to her almost right up until the time of her death. Of the 4 births by Group 4 females, 2 occurred while the females were traveling with their transfer groups, and the infants were undoubtedly sired by the silverbacks of these groups. Of the 2 births by older females within the group itself, one (Flossie's) appeared normal in every respect. The second (Old Goat's) was possibly a nonviable birth and was unlike any previously seen. Old Goat, accompanied by her 41-month-old son Tiger, traveled at distances of up to half a mile from the group, and it was the group that followed her. After several days of such behavior she deposited copious amounts of blood into her day and night nests, and on the connecting trails. On the third day her infant's body was only briefly sighted as she dragged it off by one arm following a day resting period. Shortly after this observation an extremely violent outbreak of prolonged screams was heard coming from the group, in the direction in which she had disappeared. Despite intensive search along all the trail routes taken by the group for several more days, the body of the infant was never found.

Group 5. There were 15 members in Group 5 at the beginning of 1971 and the same number at the end of 1972; however, quite a number of compositional changes were made during the 2-year period. No losses were attributed to death; 1 loss occurred when the least dominant silverback, Bartok, left the group after 6 known months of traveling peripherally to them; a second loss involved the transfer of a young female, Baffle, to a lone silverback, Nunkie, who frequented part of Group 5's newly acquired range territory in the saddle. During the 2-year period, 2 births occurred, 1 from a female transfer from Group 4. This female, Bravado, might well have been responsible for maintaining 3 days of auditory, visual, and physical interaction between Groups 4 and 5. Over half of this time 3 younger members of Group 5 and Bravado, who was probably in estrous at the time, intermingled freely with Group 4 members in play behavior. Bravado, a mature female at the time, behaved more in the manner of a juvenile as she "renewed" her acquaintanceship with members of her home group she had not seen for 10 months. After 2 days of physical interactions, Bravado was literally herded away from her home group by Beethoven, the silverback of Group 5. There was no indication of her having been unwilling to return with him. The impression was received that Uncle Bert was trying to hold her in his group by his constant "vigilance" over her and the numerous, exaggerated "bluff" displays he directed toward Beethoven. However, Uncle Bert was not as experienced a leader as Beethoven and offered no more than token objection when Bravado was herded away.

Group 8. There were 4 members in Group 8 at the beginning of 1971 and also 4 at the end of 1972; however, as in Group 5, many compositional changes occurred during that time. No losses were attributed to deaths but two of the group's adult males, Samson and Geezer, left and the subsequent fate of Geezer is not known. Rafiki was then able successfully to entice 3 females into his group (2 adults from Group 4 and 1 very young female from Group 9) but lost one of these to Samson. Based upon trail evidence alone, this female was thought to have given birth between June and August of 1972 but was not seen with an infant in 1973 when still traveling with Samson. Rafiki became noticeably more protective in his role as a leader once the very young female (Tynker) from Group 9 had been added and she, in turn, formed a close attachment toward him which resulted in her sharing his proximity more than did the two older females. By the end of 1972 Peanuts was the only other remaining "original" member of Group 8; however, owing to his increasing maturity, he was observed much less frequently near Rafiki and the transfer females. It is believed that it was Rafiki who was responsible for the maintenance of distance.

Group 9. The lack of data on Group 9, especially during 1972, does not allow any concise statements concerning changes in their group composition. From a fairly well-habituated, robust group of 14 members in 1970 their number was reduced to 7 in May 1971 and to 5 by November 1971. Also, at this later date the silverback Geronimo appeared to be in ill health and was exceedingly nervous. The reason for reduced contacts with Group 9 was due to their dramatic range shift from the western facing slopes of Mount Visoke over to the northwestern slopes and the northern saddle toward Mikeno. As this region was known to have been regularly used by poachers, it was felt that the decline in group membership might have been due to a fatal encounter with a poacher group. In March 1973 both visual and tracking evidence suggested that the maturing young silverback of the group, Gabriel, possibly took some of the group members away from the older and perhaps ailing Geronimo (this was also the time when Tynker transferred back from Group 8). Additional evidence, based upon noseprint sketches and photographs, would be needed to determine the extent of the changes that took place between 1971 and 1973, but all available evidence seems to support the fact that Geronimo had died, or at least was no longer with the group.

"Fringe" Groups. In addition to the 4 main study groups there were also 2 "fringe" groups on Mount Visoke (composition of the 6 groups, totaling 71 animals, is shown in table 3). "Fringe" groups are those that infrequently visit the study area and interact with the well-known groups, though no transfers of members were known to occur between the two study groups, at least within this study period. Of the 2 most commonly encountered "fringe" groups, Group 6 almost always appeared from a lower-altitude terrain on the eastern slopes of Visoke; Group 7 nearly always came from the uppermost summits and from a northerly direction. Only 9 contacts were made with both of these groups throughout 1971 and 1972 but the trend was one of increased usage of

TABLE 3. Composition of Groups on Mount Visoke, 1971-1972
(Transferred animals counted with their home groups.)

	Main				*Lone*	*Fringe*		*Total*
	4	*5*	*8*	*9*	*1*	6	7	
Silverback (SB)	2	3	1	1	1	1	2	11
Blackback (BB)	0	0	3	1	-	1	1	6
Adult, sex unknown (A)	0	0	0	0	-	0	0	0
Female without dependent young (F)	7[a]	4	0	4	-	2	2	19
Juvenile (J)	3	2	0	4	-	2	2	13
Infant[b] (J)	3	3	0	2	-	2	2	12
Young Adult (YA)	1	4	0	2	-	2	1	10
Totals	16	16	4	14	1	10	10	71

[a]One adult death during period.

[b]During period, 8 births occurred; 2 infants died shortly after birth.

the study area. Other "fringe" groups, from Mikeno and Karisimbi, were also encountered less frequently. Obviously there is a high degree of observer error in attempting to account for the frequency with which such groups entered the study area (25 square kilometers) as they were not usually encountered unless interacting with one of the main groups. There were also lone silverbacks (1 to 3) who interacted with the study groups and who were known to take females away.

In Summary. The 6 groups combined showed a ratio of adult to immature animals of 1:1 and of known adult males to females of 1:1.2; the mean and median group size was 12; and there were 2.8 known gorillas per square kilometer within the study area and on and around Mount Visoke. "Fringe" groups, in addition to totally unknown groups were also encountered by census workers who surveyed the northern and eastern slopes of Mount Visoke during 1971 and 1972; but since these latter groups were not known to interact with the main study groups and did not usually frequent the 25 square kilometers of the study area, they were not included in these calculations.

Census

During 1971 a census was conducted on the Visoke slopes outside the working area, on a southern ridge section on Karisimbi, and on one of the three eastern volcanoes, Mount Sabinio, and its adjacent saddle and bamboo hill area. In 1972 the census was concentrated on the 3 eastern volcanoes,

Sabinio, M'Gahinga, and Muhavura, and a small amount of time was spent in repeating the census on Karisimbi. The sites of the 6 separately established census camps are shown in my 1969 report (fig. 2); at different times there was a repetition of sites because of their physical advantages and also for comparison of results between years.

The major aim of the census was to establish a precise count of the Virunga gorilla population and, whenever possible, to verify the range estimation and determine the degree of overlap of each of the groups encountered. At the same time information was collected on the illegal use of the Park by encroachers and on the effects of elephant, buffalo, and encroachers upon the gorilla. An evaluation was also made of the quality of the habitat and its long-term potentialities for supporting gorillas.

The methods involved systematic searching of areas surrounding each census camp. Both old and new gorilla sign (feeding remnants, dung deposits, nests, and trails) were recorded on the 1:17,000 contoured maps; this gave some idea of gorillas' usage of an area in time. Whenever a fresh trail was encountered it was followed. Once a group was contacted, individuals of the group were identified whenever possible by means of a "nose-print" (a simple line drawing of the nostril shape and wrinkle pattern along the bridge of the nose). This type of record served to identify individuals of one group from those of another. These records were supplemented by written descriptions of physical and behavioral variations between individuals of different groups. The composition of any group was confirmed by no less than 5 separate night-nest counts. All group counts or individual identifications were considered suspect until visual observations plus consistency of nest counts certified both identification as well as the number of animals within each group.

The census workers found that gorillas in the eastern sections of the Virungas showed far more fear (manifested by silent, rapid retreats or bluff charges) than did those in the western mountains, Karisimbi and Visoke. Tracking time also varied consistently between the two areas; following daily routes of western groups could take an average of 4 hours from one afternoon's contact point to that of the next morning, whereas on Karisimbi only an average of an hour a day was spent in following a group. Differences in population density, structure, and behavior appeared to have been caused in part by variations in the abundance and quality of food (lusher in the western area) and, in the eastern section, by a much higher proportion of competition with elephant and buffalo and by constant interactions with human encroachers. These latter included poachers, cattle grazers, wood cutters, honey gatherers, and large parties of smugglers. The above factors undoubtedly affected the equanimity of the eastern gorillas.

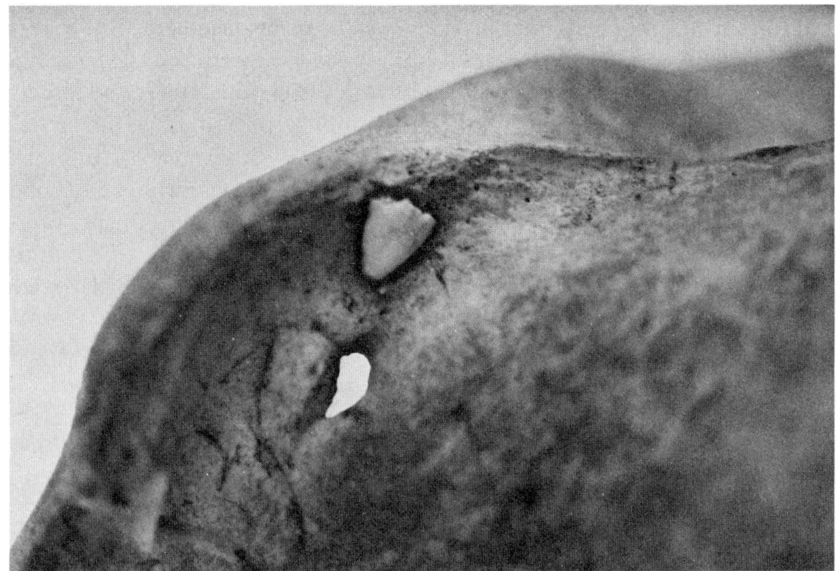

FIG. 6. Gorilla canine cusp embedded in left supraorbital torus of older silverback.

In summary, the census results show a ratio of adults to immature animals of 1.9:1; of adult males to females, 17:9 (this figure lacks accuracy, as 19 percent (n = 21) of all adults could not be sexed); a median group size of 5 and a mean group size of 6 (both exclude lone silverbacks); and 1.5 gorillas per square kilometer within the 70-square-kilometer area covered by the workers in 1971 and 1972. When the census count is merged with that of the main study camp, including "fringe" groups, there is a ratio of adults to immature animals of 11:7.3; of adult males to females, 2:1.4 (this figure lacks accuracy as 11 percent (n = 21) of all adults could not be sexed); a median group size of 6 and a mean group size of 8 (both exclude lone silverbacks); and 1.9 gorillas per square kilometer within the 95 square kilometers in the main study area plus that covered by the census workers in 1971 and 1972.

Skeletal Material

A record was kept of the sites of recovery of either bodies or gorilla skeletal remains found up to the end of 1972. Of the 31 known deceased, at least 12 were known to have been killed by poachers and only 2 were known to have died of natural causes. Quite a number of interesting observations have been made on the 31 specimens but only a few will be mentioned here. One silverback skeleton was found in a deep crater pit together with the skeleton of a young leopard (the cat, despite its youth was, as of June 1972, the largest leopard specimen in the Smithsonian Institution's collection). Arthritis was found in a number of adult specimens, though it is possibly nonexistent in the lowland gorilla; healed wounds, most likely resulting from bites, were found in the skulls of all age and sex classes; in each of 2 silverback specimens, a single canine cusp tip was found embedded in the upper skull (fig. 6); all individuals with either broken canines or incisors, at least 6 animals, were silverback males.

In 1971 Nick Humphreys and Colin Groves from Cambridge University visited camp for the primary purpose of examining a portion of the skeletal collection there at the time. They arrived at some tentative conclusions based upon 11 adult and immature skulls. They found a marked asymmetry, the left side being longer than the right, a condition more apparent in males than females. In only one case was injury suspected as the cause. Both considered it possible that the asymmetry was a secondary consequence of masticatory apparatus, or a tendency to chew more on the left than on the right. They noted that similar asymmetry was absent in the lowland gorilla. They queried as to whether asymmetry in the skull could be related to anatomical asymmetry of the cerebral hemispheres or merely a consequence of asymmetrical behavior. Among mammals, lateralization of brain function has thus far been demonstrated only in man and is assumed to be associated with language capacity (Groves and Humphrey, 1973).

Motion Pictures

For nearly 11 months during parts of 1971 and 1972, approximately 46,500 feet of 16-millimeter film were taken by Bob Campbell of many previously undocumented aspects of gorilla behavior. A total of 67,000 feet had been shot by May 1972, when this portion of the research study was completed. Editing of the film was then begun for presentation at a National Geographic Society lecture in Constitution Hall the following year. This film was one of the more outstanding achievements of the project.

Conclusions

In the October 1971 issue of *National Geographic* a second article was published concerning new developments and findings among the gorillas, whose numbers we now know are far more reduced than previously thought. Since that time, research has continued to reveal more and more insights into the life of the mountain gorilla, due to the prime advantage of having been able to continue this work as a long-term study project.

REFERENCES

FOSSEY, DIAN
1970. Making friends with mountain gorillas. Nat. Geogr. Mag., vol. 137, no. 1, pp. 48-67.
1971. More years with mountain gorillas. Nat. Geogr. Mag., vol. 140, pp. 574-585.
1972. Living with mountain gorillas. Pp. 208-229 *in* "The Marvels of Animal Behavior." National Geographic Magazine, Washington.
1974. Observations on the home range of one group of mountain gorillas *(Gorilla gorilla beringei).* Anim. Behav., vol. 22, pp. 568-581.
1976a. Development of the mountain gorilla *(Gorilla gorilla beringei)* through the first thirty-six months. *In* "Perspectives on Human Evolution (Great Apes)," vol. 5, D. Hamburg and J. Goodall, eds. Staples, W. A. Benjamin, Inc., Menlo Park, California.
1976b. The behaviour of the mountain gorilla. A dissertation submitted to the University of Cambridge for the degree of Doctor of Philosophy. 365 pp., illus. Cambridge University Library Microfilming Service.
1976c. Mountain-gorilla research, 1967-1968. Nat. Geogr. Soc. Res. Rpts., 1968 Projects, pp. 131-140, illus.
1978. Mountain gorilla research, 1969-1970. Nat. Geogr. Soc. Res. Rpts., 1969 Projects, pp. 173-186, illus.

FOSSEY, D., and HARCOURT, A. H.
1977. Feeding ecology of free-ranging mountain gorilla *(Gorilla gorilla beringei).* Pp. 415-447 *in* "Primate Ecology: Studies of Feeding and Ranging Behaviour in Lemurs, Monkeys and Apes," T. H. Clutton-Brock, ed. London, Academic Press.

GROVES, COLIN P., and HUMPHREY, NICHOLAS
1973. Asymmetry in gorilla skulls: Evidence of lateralized brain function? Nature, vol. 244, no. 5410 (July 6), pp. 53-54.

JONES, C., and SABATER PI, JORGE
1971. Comparative ecology of *Gorilla gorilla* (Savage and Wyman) and *Pan troglodytes* (Blumenbach) in Rio Muni, West Africa. Bibl. Primat., vol. 13, p. 1096.

KABAGABO, PH.
1975. Rapport de mission à la 14e session de l'assemblée générale de l'O.I.A.C. Bull. Agr. Rwanda, April, vol. 2, pp. 110-115.

LEAKEY, LOUIS S.B.
1969. Animals of East Africa, 199 pp., illus. National Geographic Society, Washington, D. C.

SCHALLER, GEORGE B.
1963. The mountain gorilla: Ecology and behavior, x + 260 pp., illus. University of Chicago Press, Chicago and London.

DIAN FOSSEY

The Bakhtiyārī Tribe: Its Organization and Role in Iran

Principal Investigator: G. R. Garthwaite, Associate Professor, Dartmouth College, Hanover, New Hampshire.

Grant No. 966: For study of the Bakhtiyārī Tribe and its role in the history of Iran.

In 1971, thanks to the support of the National Geographic Society, I spent five weeks in London microfilming and studying the papers of Sir Henry Layard and 19th-century Persian manuscripts at the British Museum, diplomatic correspondence and reports at the Public Record Office and India Office Library, and, briefly, Sir Arnold Wilson's diaries at the London Library. I had earlier gathered Persian and Bakhtiyārī sources in Iran and was especially searching for materials dealing with the nature of the office of īlkhānī, paramount tribal chief, with inheritance in the Bakhtiyārī among the khāns and its relation to the transfer of wealth, power, and land, and with the concepts of power and authority within the Bakhtiyārī and as it relates to the central government. Manuscripts are in preparation. In addition I was looking for corroborative evidence and information to support the diary of Hosain Qoli Khān Īlkhānī (d. 1882). A Persian text, with translation, annotation, and analysis of this diary, is in preparation.

Iranian and Western images of the Bakhtiyārī, no matter how distorted, have historical roots and involve two major interrelated characteristics of the Bakhtiyārī—pastoralism and tribalism, the former involving their economy and the latter dealing with political loyalty and identification, which suggest certain changes that have recently occurred in the relationship between the Bakhtiyārī and the central government. Most significantly, the latter has replaced Bakhtiyārī political leadership at the highest level within the tribal confederation. This together with integration into the national economy, improved communication, and a host of government activity at the local level is initiating the gradual transfer of loyalty and identification from the tribe to the nation-state.

Accurate Bakhtiyārī census figures are not to be found, but Rawlinson's estimate in 1836 of 28,000 families and one from 1963 for 80,000 families (or about 500,000 individuals) appear to be reasonable. The term Bakhtiyārī actually refers not only to the people but also to the territory they occupy, an area of approximately 20,000 square miles, some 60 percent of which encompasses the rugged central Zagros Mountains. Low hills along the narrow fringe of the northeast Khuzistān plain provide the tribes with their winter (garmsīr or qishlāq) encampment and also fields and pastures for sedentary agriculturalists; the intermontane valleys of the Zagros furnish the summer (sardsīr or yailāq) pastures for the Bakhtiyārī; and the broad valleys of the central plateau, which is broken by lower mountain ranges, form not only the summer pastures for part of the tribes but also the permanent habitat of a sedentary village population. Bakhtiyārī reside year round in agricultural settlements throughout the territory except at the highest elevations.

The winter rains in the winter encampment, about 12-14 inches annually, are usually sufficient for pastures and cereal agriculture, and with irrigation rice, cotton, melons, and cucumbers may also be raised. In early spring some of the flocks are taken to still lower elevations. Higher temperatures and increasing desiccation in late March and early April spur most of the nomads to begin their slow, usually 6-week, move toward higher and better pastures in the yailāq. A portion of the nomads remain in the garmsīr until the wheat is harvested. In the summer pastures the higher precipitation, up to 40 inches annually in the form of snow, and the cooler summer temperatures create conditions for relatively lush vegetation. In the autumn, before returning to the garmsīr, some of the tribesmen plant winter wheat which they will harvest on their return.

This migratory quest for pastures underlies the central economic role of sheep and goats, the largest and most important group of animals owned by the tribesmen. These animals provide the Bakhtiyārī not only with food and wool for their own subsistence but also with products for economic exchange with sedentary society.

The Bakhtiyārī segmentary structure begins with the family (khānivādah or vārgah, lit. tent)—classification and terminology follows Digard (1979). The nuclear family, which owns the flocks and works together in the agricultural cycle, constitutes the key economic unit. The yield of the flocks and of the land is largely utilized for family consumption; similarly, marketing is a family concern. Extended, or related, families come together as oulad, or tash, approximating a descent group, which functions as a camp (māl) of from 3 to 12 tents and shares common herding, migrating, and defense interests. At this level of segmentation decisions are reached by heads of family. The tīrah (roughly subtribe) forms the next level and constitutes the maximum group of related camps and functions primarily during the migration. Tīrahs are represented by kadkhudās. Tīrahs come together to form ṭāyafah, some of which number 25,000 and are headed by kalāntars appointed from the group by the khāns. Pasture rights derive from membership in the ṭāyafah, which exists as a named group with its own identity and, probably, as an endogamous unit. Even though it may not have always acted as an entity, the ṭāyafah, indeed even the Bakhtiyārī confederation, provides a conceptual framework for organizing people politically and attaching them to leaders.

Continuing with the segmentary pyramid, all ṭāyafah are a component of one of eight bāb; each bāb has a dominant lineage from which khāns are chosen. The bāb are grouped in one of the two moieties (bakhsh or bulūk) of the Haft Lang or Chahār Lang, and finally the confederation (īl) of the Bakhtiyārī.

The confederation, Īl-i Bakhtiyārī is the inclusive unit and encompasses those who live, or lived, in the territory, speak the Bakhtiyārī dialect of Persian, and acknowledge the leadership of the khāns and īlkhānī. The existence of the khāns, and the īlkhānī, differentiate the Bakhtiyārī from other major segmentary systems.

Both the factors of the migration and the necessity for exchange with sedentary society may sharpen the potential for internal conflict. This, added to the pressures generated by external conflict with other tribes and the defense of territory, and the demands of the larger community, especially the central government, seem to necessitate the existence of khāns or like leaders as mediators and intermediaries. These leaders usually have "common" ancestors with their people. Or lacking that, they possess the characteristics of wisdom, courage, and generosity necessary for their chiefly function, which includes coordination of the migration, assignment of pastures, appointment of kalāntars, mediation of intertribal disputes, leadership for raids, defense and battle, and awarding of levies, taxes, and fines.

The khāns are usually selected from those born into the chiefly families of the bāb. Khāns have the greatest economic resources and widest ties both within the tribe and confederation and outside the tribe with sedentary society and other pastoral nomads. They are the executives and retain the greatest coercive power within the tribe. Their seemingly absolute power is in turn limited by the power of the various segments of the tribes to withhold their support or to throw this support to a rival within the chiefly family or to another khān or even to one outside the tribe.

The tribal confederation is a further elaboration of the tribe's political structure, and like the bāb khān, the īlkhānī can seldom count on the support of all the constituent tribes and subtribes. The khāns and their tribesmen frequently have different interests and may actually seek to weaken the power and ability of the īlkhānī to intervene, and, especially, to collect taxes.

The power of the khāns and īlkhānī is both personal and vested in their chiefly office: it is based on the benefits that they are able to dispense, the respect they may command through their birth, their coercive capabilities within the tribe as a result of loyal armed retainers, and the support given them by the central government or outside sources of power, such as the British. This latter association was beneficial only to a few, other than the most important khāns and their supporters.

The Iranian government's demands were comparatively simple—recognition and submission characterized by payment of taxes, conscription of recruits, and observance of royal suzerainty. The Qājār government in the 19th century maintained its position not so much by its military superiority, for the army, what there was of it, was often poorly trained and equipped, but because of its greater prestige and authority, access to Great Power support, and ability to reward and divide by utilizing inter- and intratribal rivalries.

Both historians and anthropologists have made the erroneous assumption that the late 19th-century organization of the Bakhtiyārī into a confederation, albeit a loose one, under an īlkhānī appointed by the Shāh, had long been the characteristic political organization of this tribe. Available documentation suggests that the office of īlkhānī of the Bakhtiyārī did not appear until Nāṣir al-Dīn Shāh (r. 1848-1896) in 1867 conferred the title and its prerequisites on Ḥusain Qulī Khān with a farmān, or imperial decree. The earliest historical reference to a group with the name Bakhtiyārī dates from the 13th century, although the confederation would not appear to be a major force in Iranian history until the 18th century.

Ḥusain Qulī Khān had the requisite lineage, tribal support, the cooperation and collaboration of his sons, brothers, and nephews—at least until just before his assassination in 1882. Governmental support in Tehran and Isfahān, the income from landed properties in Chahār Maḥāll, the agricultural region on the eastern edge of the Bakhtiyārī, and Khūzistān, and revenue collecting rights conferred with his appointment as īlkhānī, gave him both the legitimacy and the income to maintain his preeminent position. In 1864 Ḥusain Qulī Khān was first designated "Nāẓim" of the Bakhtiyārī and then in 1867 "Īlkhānī."

Īlkhānī, as Ḥusain Qulī Khān is always known after 1867, greatly increased his singular wealth and power with the awards of new incomes and additional lands, many of them tax exempt. He regarded the Bakhtiyārī as autonomous but recognized the Shāh as sovereign, generally obeyed his orders, and accepted his awards of land and incomes. Nāṣir al-Dīn Shāh on his part never sent a military force to challenge Īlkhānī's autonomy nor was military action taken in Īlkhānī's sphere of influence, the territories immediately adjacent to the Bakhtiyārī, without his assistance.

Rivalry within the Bakhtiyārī had never been a visible problem for Īlkhānī until about 1878-1880 when his half-brother, Riẓā Qulī Khān, later

Īlbigī, and his nephew, Muḥammad Ḥusain Khān, son of his full-brother Imām Qulī Khān, later Ḥājjī Īlkhānī, secretly began to undercut Īlkhānī's position with the Shāh and the royal governors.

Within the Bakhtiyārī itself, the tribesmen were expected to obey the Īlkhānī, and during Īlkhānī's lifetime the only recourse for those in opposition to him was flight. Following his death and the formation of the three factions, the "Īlkhānī," the "Ḥājjī Īlkhānī," and "Īlbigī"—the sons of Īlkhānī and his two brothers—it became possible for tribesmen to express disagreement by giving their support to a rival. Under the bastigān system this becomes a major factor in Bakhtiyārī instability. It grew out of attempts to emulate Īlkhānī's ability to maintain his power by maintaining private retinues of armed relatives, supporters, and servants (bastah, pl. bastigān). Each khān sought both political alliances and economic resources—among the sedentary peoples as well as with the tribes—to increase their power. They particularly sought governorships outside the Bakhtiyārī during and after the Persian Revolution of 1906-1911 because similar opportunities within the Bakhtiyārī were restricted to senior khāns.

From 1882-1894 the position of īlkhānī moved from one faction to the other as each jockeyed for imperial support. In 1894 the Īlkhānī and Ḥājjī Īlkhānī, with the support of Nāṣir al-Dīn Shāh, drew up an agreement excluding the Īlbigī faction and choosing the īlkhānī and īlbigī (the assistant īlkhānī) on the basis of primacy of age from these two families. This dual division was then officially recognized both by the Shāh's government and by the British.

Three additional factors exacerbating the rivalry within the Bakhtiyārī and linking the khāns' rivalry to their national ambitions appear at about this time. The first was the removal of the senior khāns either to Tehran or to one of the provincial capitals. Second, responsibility for governing the Bakhtiyārī was left in the hands of the junior khāns, two of whom were designated acting īlkhānī and īlbigī. The pool of junior khāns from which these acting officials could be chosen had grown considerably, placing a strain on economic resources and intensifying local level rivalry. Finally, there was the opposition of the other tribes—especially the Qashqā'ī, and Shaikh Khaz'al, the paramount Arab chief in Khūzistān—and of the urban populations in Iran to the increasing role of the Bakhtiyārī khāns on a national level.

The more the Bakhtiyārī khāns participated in national politics the closer they were to greater personal rewards. Conversely, they were also subject to the greater danger of the loss of their power base and tribal support, diminishing their ability to compel obedience, as they moved away from problems of immediate tribal interest.

In summary, the Bakhtiyārī political system differs from the segmentary lineage systems by having a hierarchy of khāns. But the Bakhtiyārī do share the division into segmented levels, with certain relationships, activities, and responsibilities associated with each segment, instability and change in these relationships, and diffusion of military power. This instability in relations and diffusion of military power is not only characteristic of the Bakhtiyārī but the Iranian political system as a whole. The Bakhtiyārī use military force directly against one of the other tribes or settled areas despite the basic notion that they are all subjects of the Shāh, and during the Persian Revolution the Bakhtiyārī used force against the Shāh himself. Within the Bakhtiyārī the various tribes and subtribes use force against each other, against their khāns, and against their īlkhānī. Significantly, the highest authority at even the lowest level can, in effect, negotiate treaties, form alliances, and conclude peace independently of higher levels of authority. Thus, like a segmentary lineage system intergroup, and even intragroup, relations are based on a balance of power at each level—ṭāyafah, īl (confederacy), or even national. Groups that oppose each other on one occasion may unite on another in opposition to some third group.

The balance of power in a segmentary system is between territorial groups, all of whose members are politically equal and act on the basis of internal consensus. In the Bakhtiyārī system, the balance of power is between the various members of the chiefly hierarchy who compete for the support of both their superiors and their subordinates, and at the same time conclude alliances with members of other tribes to strengthen their position. Thus, the īlkhānī of the Bakhtiyārī competes with rival claimants to his position by seeking the support of ṭāyafah khāns, by concluding agreements with a Qashqā'ī khān or Arab shaikh, and by gaining support of a superior authority, the central government, or the British. The ṭāyafah khāns maintain themselves in the same manner. Like model segmentary systems, moreover, Bakhtiyārī alliances are not based primarily on a theory of common descent, unless it suits the immediate purpose, but are extensively modified by contractual alliances based on negotiation and mutual agreement. Since these alliances derive from considerations of expediency rather than categorical loyalties, they tend to be brief in duration. Exchange of daughters and sealed Korans at the conclusion of these alliances, however, helps to strengthen them.

The failure of the Bakhtiyārī khāns to solve their internal division was aggravated by external problems and resulted in their failure to achieve greater power down through World War I, despite possible British support.

After World War I the khāns were unable to resolve their differences and Riẓā Shāh removed the threat posed by the Bakhtiyārī to his sovereignty and to Iran emerging as a nation-state through a series of military, economic, and administrative maneuvers.

In summary, the position of īlkhānī disappeared and the family from which he was chosen ceased to be a tribal power. An element of the Īlkhānī-Ḥājjī Īlkhānī families, however, with the restoration of some estates and incomes during and following World War II, has continued to play an important role in Iran not unlike that of great nontribal families.

The demise of the institution of the īlkhānī and its power resulted from the withdrawal of imperial support and the appointment of civil administrators who assumed some of the roles of the khāns, the confiscation of economic resources, and the physical transfer of the Īlkhānī-Ḥājjī Īlkhānī khāns from the tribal territory; and this demise was hastened by the next generation of khāns, who were educated outside the Bakhtiyārī itself.

Having effectively destroyed the political power of the ruling khāns, Riẓā Shāh was less successful in forcibly settling the Bakhtiyārī.

Following the accession of Muḥammad Riẓā Shāh, 1941, and especially after 1962 with the promulgation of land and other reforms and the greatly increased incomes from oil, the central government has achieved a monopoly of force and has consolidated its own power. This it has accomplished not only with its well-equipped military and security forces but also with the gradual integration of Bakhtiyārī into the national economy, promoting an "Iranian" identity through education and new national symbols.

REFERENCES

'ABD AL-GHAFĀR NAJM AL-MULK
1341/1963. Safarnāmah-yi Khūzistān, ed. by Muhammad Dabīrsīyaqī. Tehran.

ALĪ QULĪ KHĀN SARDĀR ĀS'AD
1333/1914-1915. Tārīkh-i Bakhtiyārī. Lith. Tehran (?).

BELL, COLONEL MARK S.
1885. Military report on southwestern Persia including the provinces of Khuzistan, Luristan, and parts of Fars. Simla.

BISHOP, ISABELLA LUCY
1891. Journeys in Persia and Kurdistan. London.

CURZON, GEORGE N.
1892. Persia and the Persian question. London.

D'ALLEMAGNE, H. R.
1909. Du Khorassan au pays des Bakhtiaris. Paris.

DE BODE, BARON C. A.
1843. Extracts from a journal kept while travelling in January 1842 through the country of the Mamaseni and Kughilu. Journal of the Royal Geographical Society, vol. 13, pp. 75-107.

DIGARD, JEAN-PIERRE

1973. Techniques et cultures des nomades Baxtyari. Thesis, Université René Descarte, Paris.

1975. Campements Baxtyari. Studia Iranica, vol. 4, no. 1, pp. 117-129.

1979. De la nécessité et des inconvénients, pour un Baxtyari. . . . *In* "Pastoral Production and Society," Cambridge (in press).

GARTHWAITE, G. R.

1969. Pastoral nomadism and tribal power. Paper delivered at Conference on the Structure of Power in Islamic Iran, University of California, June 26-28, 1969. (Forthcoming *in* "State and Society in Islamic Iran," Amin Banani, ed.; Society of Iranian Studies, in press.)

1972a. The Bakhtiyārī khāns, the government of Iran, and the British, 1846-1915. International Journal of Middle East Studies, vol. 3, no. 1 (January), pp. 24-44.

1972b. The Bakhtiyārī Īlkhānī: An historical view. American Anthropological Association, New York.

1972c. The Bakhtiyārī in the twentieth century. Paper delivered at Middle East Studies Association, November 1972 meeting, Binghamton, N.Y.

1974. The Bakhtiyārī khāns as landlords and governors. Paper delivered at Middle East Studies Association, November 1974 meeting, Boston, Mass.

1975a. Two Persian wills of Ḥājj 'Alī Qulī Khān Sardār As'ad. Journal of the American Oriental Society, vol. 95, no. 4 (October-December), pp. 645-650.

1975b. Rivalry and alliances: Bakhtiyārī kinship. Paper delivered at Middle East Studies Association, November 1975 meeting, Louisville, Ky.

1977. The Bakhtiyārī Īlkhānī: An illusion of unity. Intern. Journ. of Middle East Studies, vol. 8, no. 2, pp. 145-160.

——. Shāhs and khāns: A documentary analysis of the Bakhtiyārī in Iran. (In press.)

LAYARD, SIR HENRY

1887. Adventures in Persia, Susiana, and Babylonia. New York.

LORIMER, D. L. R.

1954. The popular verse of the Bakhtiārī of southwestern Persia I. Bulletin of the School of Oriental and African Studies, vol. 16, no. 3, pp. 542-555.

1955. The popular verse of the Bakhtiārī of southwestern Persia II. Bulletin of the School of Oriental and African Studies, vol. 17, no. 1, pp. 92-110.

1963. The popular verse of the Bakhtiārī of southwestern Persia III: Further specimens. Bulletin of the School of Oriental and African Studies, vol. 26, pt. 1, pp. 55-68.

MINORSKY, VLADIMIR

1936. Lūr-Lūristān. Vol. 3, pp. 41-53, *in* "Encyclopaedia of Islam." London.

RAWLINSON, MAJOR H.

1839. Notes on a march from Zohab through the Province of Luristan and Kirmanshah in the year 1836. Journal of the Royal Geographical Society, vol. 9, pp. 26-116.

UZHĀN, SARHANG ABU AL-FATH
1345/1967. Tārīkh-i Bakhtiyārī. Tehran.
WILSON, SIR ARNOLD TALBOT
1909. Military report on S. W. Persia, vols. 1-3, 5. Simla.
1926. The Bakhtiaris. Journal of the Royal Central Asian Society, vol. 13, pp. 205-225.

G. R. GARTHWAITE

Papyrus and the Ecology of Lake Naivasha

Principal Investigator: John J. Gaudet, University of Nairobi, Nairobi, Kenya.

Grant Nos. 1003, 1244, 1546, 1759. For a study of aquatic weeds such as papyrus, and the effects of papyrus swamps on the ecology of Lake Naivasha.

Lake Naivasha is located in the center of the eastern Rift Valley in Kenya (see figs. 1, 2). Most of the water input comes from the Aberdare Mountains in the north via the Malewa River. This lake is the only large freshwater lake in the Rift Valley in Kenya. The other important Kenyan lakes, such as Rudolf, Nakuru, and Elmenteita (shown in fig. 2), as well as Lakes Magadi and Baringo, are all saline to some degree. Lake Naivasha has remained fresh for some time, and the interesting question is how this has happened, since it is located in a closed basin with no outflow and in an area of high evaporation. It has been proposed by Richardson and Richardson (1972) that deflation of salts, burial of alkaline sediments, and underground seepage are responsible for maintaining the freshness of the lake. They also suggested the removal of nutrients by aquatic plants as a possibility. Gaudet and Melack (1979) consider in detail the whole subject of the chemical limnology of this lake, including the removal of salts. This study shows that salt removal by seepage, water use, and sedimentation in the lake are all significant factors in maintaining the freshness of this lake. Also, the incoming water in the Malewa River is very dilute, so that the salt input is low to begin with. This salt balance may be shifted, however, especially if the nutrient load of the incoming water is increased. This could occur in the future if sewage effluent is not rigorously treated before being discharged into the Malewa River. Sewage effluent reaching the river at present is minimal, but plans are being put forward to install a modern sewage treatment facility in Naivasha Town. In order to monitor changes in the nutrient load, several studies have been done of the present river (Gaudet and Melack, 1979; Gaudet, in press; and Njue, 1976). This work is valuable in that it provides the first basic study of this type on a Kenyan river and will also serve as a baseline for any future analysis of the water quality in this river.

Why is it important for this lake to remain fresh? This question can best be answered by looking at Lake Naivasha as a natural resource. The lake supports a wide variety of animal and plant life and is routinely included on bird watchers' itineraries. Because the tourist industry is the most important foreign exchange earner in Kenya today, the value of this lake cannot be

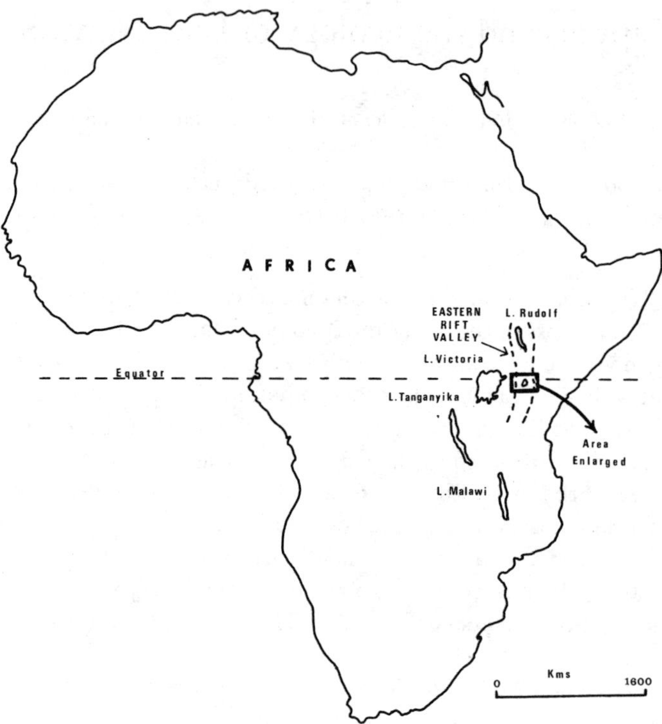

FIG. 1. Africa, showing Rift Valley area, near Lake Victoria.

overstated. For the tourist the lake offers bird watching at its best, sports fishing for black bass (originally introduced by Theodore Roosevelt), camping, and game viewing (a large island on the lake is a wild animal sanctuary). A small commercial fishery and lakeside agriculture also depend on the fresh water of the lake. If the lake were to become saline, most aquatic animal species would disappear, followed by aquatic plants, such as papyrus, which cannot tolerate saline water, and the remaining lake-edge vegetation. The result would be a lake similar to Oloidien Lake which lies only 0.5-1.0 kilometer to the south of Lake Naivasha. Oloidien is much more saline with an electrical conductivity of 1000 micromhos per centimeter, compared to 330 in Lake Naivasha, and presents quite a dismal picture, with only a few species of very small fish, several species of salt-tolerant aquatic plants, and a dense growth of blue-green algae. In general very few species are supported by such a simple system, compared to the species supported by the system complex of Lake Naivasha.

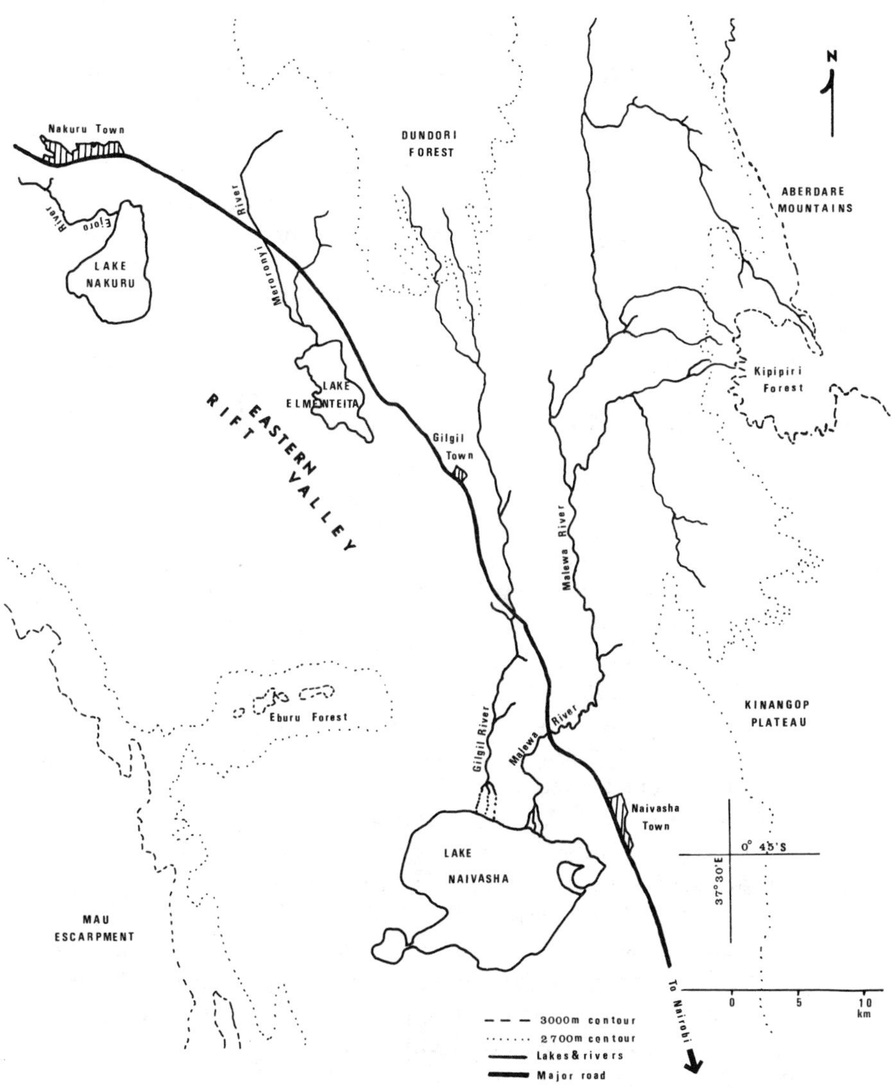

FIG. 2. Lake Naivasha area, in eastern Rift Valley.

Much of my recent research has been done on the relationship of the vegetation along the edge of the lake to the production of nutrients close to shore. This in turn is related to the annual flooding and subsequent retreat of water from the lake edge. Each year a lush lake-edge vegetation is seen to spring up on the exposed soil during the dry season, only to die and rot when flooding takes place during the rainy season. This phenomenon, general in many lakes, but especially pronounced in the tropics, is referred to as the annual "drawdown," a term originally used to describe the annual drop in water level in manmade lakes due to water use. During drawdown the wet mud around the lake edge is exposed, offering a temporary habitat for wet-mud weeds. Wild and domestic animals graze on this flora, and subsequently the area is reflooded as the rain and river-discharge cause a rise in lake level and inundate the lake edge (Gaudet, 1977a). This inundation of lake-edge plants and dung brings about an increase in dissolved substances in the water, a phenomenon first noted in African lakes by McLachlan (1970), who detected a rise in conductivity, alkalinity, and potassium. Recently one of my students (Njuguna, 1976) found a rise in nitrogen and phosphorus in the inshore waters of Lake Naivasha. This corresponds to the decrease noted by Gaudet (1977a) in soil nitrogen, phosphorus, and carbon when swamp soil close to shore is exposed and allowed to dry out before reflooding. We have found that this loss of soil nutrients can be ascribed to uptake by the wet-mud weeds, which accumulate in appreciable quantities during the dry season. These in turn lose the same nutrients back to the water after they decompose. Another student (F. Muthuri) is now monitoring the flux of total nitrogen, phosphorous, and sulphur at the lake edge. He is trying to determine the exact magnitude of the changes, and to see if they are statistically correlated with lake level change.

This annual cycle of wetting and drying at the lake edge has considerable effect on inshore nutrient cycling and must be included as one of the important components in any future model of this lake.

In 1957 Dr. J. Talling of the Freshwater Biological Association (U.K.) published a paper that showed for the first time that papyrus swamps affected the water of the White Nile as it flowed through the Sudan on its way to Egypt. This early paper was the basis for a second project, undertaken by me in 1971, to look further into the role of papyrus swamps in Africa. The project began on Lake Victoria in papyrus swamps in Uganda, but has now shifted to the papyrus swamps on Lake Naivasha in Kenya.

Much ground has been covered since 1971 including: a complete chemical analysis of papyrus plants from 10 different localities throughout Africa (Gaudet, 1975b), an assessment of the uptake and loss of chemical nutrients by papyrus (Gaudet, 1977b), and a study of nutrient composition and release by the organic matter (detritus) in papyrus swamps (1976). A complete review of the literature on the ecology of papyrus has also been compiled (Thompson and Gaudet, 1979).

All of this is fundamental and was needed before the final work on water in the swamps could be monitored. This final phase was begun in 1975 when nine collecting stations were established along the Malewa River passing under a papyrus swamp into Lake Naivasha. Monthly samples were collected which included water from rivers, swamp, swamp edge, and lake. Chemical analyses were carried out to determine conductivity, pH, potassium, sodium, calcium, magnesium, bicarbonate, carbonate, chloride, fluoride, sulphate, iron, and manganese. These analyses spanned one year and included the wet and dry seasons of 1975-76. Toward the end of this study monthly samples were then collected for analysis of ammonia, nitrate, organic nitrogen, orthophosphate, total phosphorus, oxygen, total organic matter, silicate, silt, chlorophyll, and phytoplankton.

This last study was completed in 1977, and it is hoped that all the information collected can then be used to assemble a model of a functional papyrus swamp. Recently this work was brought up in a discussion with Dr. Talling, over 20 years after his historic paper on this subject, and he pointed out that this study will open up many new avenues of research in these swamps.

Among the important findings so far are the following:

1. Small organic particles (detritus) from the swamps are the single most important aspect of nutrient relations between these swamps and other aquatic ecosystems.
2. Papyrus swamps supply large amounts of fixed nitrogen to tropical lakes and rivers every year thus allowing an increase in animal and plant production at the swamp edge.
3. The swamps act as sediment traps.
4. The swamps also trap a large portion of inorganic sulphate from river water and convert this to organic sulphur which is more slowly released, once outside the swamp. The effect on water quality is large in respect to the organic nutrients, but the effect of the swamp on salinity depends on the rate of flow of the river passing under the swamp (Gaudet, 1979a, 1979b).

How then do papyrus swamps affect the major rivers in Africa such as the Zaire (Congo) and White Nile? The whole picture is now emerging in which this unique type of swamp acts as an ecological "buffer zone," by which I mean it acts to moderate changes along a river system by regulating nutrient flow and recycling. For the most part this is accomplished by production of an organic nutrient output at the expense of an inorganic nutrient input. The organic nutrients serve as an energy source to a very diverse tropical fauna and flora, which in turn supports a profitable shallow water fish industry in many parts of Africa.

REFERENCES

GAUDET, JOHN J.

1975a. Papyrus valued from ancient times. Africana, vol. 5, no. 9 (April), pp. iii-iv.

1975b. Mineral concentrations in papyrus in various African swamps. Journ. Ecol., vol. 63, no. 2, pp. 483-491.

1976. Nutrient relationships in the detritus of a tropical swamp. Arch. für Hydrobiol., vol. 78, no. 2, pp. 213-239.

1977a. Natural drawdown on Lake Naivasha, Kenya, and the formation of papyrus swamps. Aquatic Botany, vol. 3, pp. 1-49.

1977b. Uptake and loss of mineral nutrients by papyrus. Ecology, vol. 58, pp. 415-422.

——. Effect of a tropical swamp on water quality. Verh. Int. Ver. Limnol., vol. 20. (In press.)

1979a. Seasonal changes in nutrients in tropical swamp water. Journ. Ecology, vol. 67, no. 3. (In press.)

1979b. Nutrient dynamics of papyrus swamps. Paper presented at the Second International Congress of Ecology, Jerusalem. (In press.)

GAUDET, J. and MELACK, J.

1979. The chemical limnology of the Naivasha Basin, Kenya (in preparation).

MACLACHLAN, S. M.

1970. The influence of lake level fluctuation and the thermocline on water chemistry in two gradually shelving areas in Lake Kariba, Central Africa. Arch. für Hydrobiol., vol. 66, no. 3, pp. 499-510.

NJUE, A.

1976. Chemical analysis of the Malewa River. Unpublished report on a project for final year students in Botany. Department of Botany, University of Nairobi, Kenya.

NJUGUNA, S. G.

1976. Analysis of N, P and K in the plants, mud and water at the lake edge on Lake Naivasha. Unpublished report on a project for final year students in Botany. Department of Botany, Universtiy of Nairobi, Kenya.

RICHARDSON, J., and RICHARDSON, A.

1972. History of an African Rift lake and its climatic implications. Ecological Monographs, vol. 42, no. 4, pp. 499-534.

TALLING, J. F.

1957. The longitudinal succession of the water characteristics in the White Nile. Hydrobiologia, vol. 11, pp. 73-89.

THOMPSON, K., and GAUDET, JOHN J.

1979. The role of papyrus in tropical swamp ecology. Ergebnisse der Limnologie (in preparation).

JOHN J. GAUDET

Thermal Ecology of the American Alligator (*Alligator mississippiensis*)

Principal Investigator: Frederick R. Gehlbach,[1] Baylor University, Waco, Texas.

Grant No. 1007: For study of the thermoregulation and ecology of the American alligator.

The American alligator is the largest ecothermic vertebrate of the United States, ranging through the Southeast along the Atlantic and Gulf Coastal Plains. Despite its status as an endangered species, its economic value (leather), role in swampland and marsh ecology, and use as an indicator of subtropical paleoclimates (Hibbard, 1960), the species' physiological ecology is poorly known. The investigators used a multichannel, temperature and heart rate radio-transmitter (Smith, 1974) to investigate alligator thermal and cardiac ecology in Texas (Smith et al., 1974; Smith, 1975).

Deep body (core), ventral and dorsal surface temperatures, and heart rate were monitored, while behavior was observed with binoculars and a starlight spotting scope (night). Captive animals were studied in Waco, and free-living individuals with and without radio-transmitters, at the Welder Wildlife Refuge, Sinton, Texas. Ancillary observations were made elsewhere and include a determination of the species' southern border of natural range in Texas. In historic time alligators south of the Rio Nueces drainage were introduced. The Rio Grande population is entirely unnatural.

Adult alligators (longer than 2 meters) maintain core temperatures of about 30-34°C throughout the diel period in the summer, although they are active all year and often at lower body temperatures. For example, a 1.5-meter individual with a core temperature of 17°C was observed as it fed upon an American coot *(Fulica americana)* in 17-18°C water when the air temperature was 12°C (22:30 hrs., March 30, Welder Refuge).

Terrestrial basking is critical thermoregulatory behavior, during which the dorsum may heat at 0.09°C/min. Terrestrial basking is always preceded by prebasking behavior in shallow water parallel to the shoreline with the dorsum exposed to the air in "high float" position. Core temperature increases markedly only upon reentry into the water. Alligators may maintain their

[1] Coinvestigators in this project were E. Norbert Smith, W. Eugene Crowder, and Robert D. Allison, of Baylor University.

core temperatures in the 30-34°C preferred range during periods of negative heat loading by endogenous heat production and cardiovascular change.

Heating rate exceeds cooling rate under controlled conditions, and heart rate during heating is double that during cooling at a core temperature of 20°C. On a summer day, alligators normally remain below the water surface, rising only to breathe, and submergence is not accompanied by bradycardia. If approached by man, however, submergence and bradycardia coincide and may permit the alligator to escape predation by prolonging its dive.

Ability to remain active at relatively low ambient temperatures, even at less than preferred body temperatures, suggests that the present range of the alligator is not restricted by short periods of cold weather. Three or more successive winter days of below freezing temperatures are unusual but not unknown within the natural range. Historically, the alligator is strictly a temperate zone creature. Perhaps a reinterpretation of its paleoclimatic significance is in order.

REFERENCES

HIBBARD, C. W.

1960. An interpretation of Pliocene and Pleistocene climates in North America. President's address, pp. 5-30 *in* "Michigan Academy of Sciences, Arts, & Letters, Report, 1959-60."

SMITH, E. N.

1974. Multichannel temperature and heart rate radio-telemetry transmitter. Journ. Appl. Physiol., vol. 36, pp. 252-255.

1975. Thermoregulation of the American alligator, *Alligator mississippiensis.* Physiol. Zool., vol. 48, pp. 177-194.

SMITH, E. N.; ALLISON, R. D.; and CROWDER, W. E.

1974. Bradycardia in a free ranging American alligator. Copeia, 1974, pp. 770-772.

FREDERICK R. GEHLBACH

Collections, Observations, and Illustrations of the Flora of Tierra del Fuego, 1971-1973

Principal Investigator: Rae Natalie Prosser Goodall, Estancia Harberton, Tierra del Fuego, Argentina.[1]

Grant Nos. 1013, 1164: For continuing support of plant exploration to provide collections, observations, and illustrations of the flora of Tierra del Fuego.

Support by the National Geographic Society in 1971 and 1973 enabled me to continue research on the vascular plants of Tierra del Fuego begun under the Society's initial grant made in 1970 (Goodall, 1978). As under the earlier grant, the main emphasis was on collecting plants in as many and as varied localities and habitats as possible and especially trying to reach formerly unexplored areas.

The plants collected were pressed and up to eight sets of duplicates were made to send off to universities on four continents. The first set of all collections was held in my herbarium, formerly located at Estancia Harberton on the Beagle Channel but later moved to my new laboratory in Ushuaia, where it is more accessible to visiting scientists. Duplicates were sent to Leicester University, England; the U. S. National Arboretum in Washington, D. C.; the Missouri Botanical Garden; the Instituto Nacional de Tecnología Agropecuaria in Buenos Aires; Christ Church, New Zealand; and others. Also, most of the rarer flowers were preserved in FAA solution.

Detailed botanical drawings were made, especially of the rarer plants. Partial and complete studies have been made on nearly 200 species. Some of these will be published in Dr. T. R. Dudley's work on the flora of Staten Island, Tierra del Fuego (in press), and others in the *Flora of Tierra del Fuego* (Moore and Goodall, in preparation).

Along with collecting and drawing the plants, bud collections for chromosome counts were taken when possible, and notes were made on flowering times, habitats, and variation.

Through these grants I was able to obtain a Ford pick-up truck, which enabled me to become independent and cover much more ground than formerly,

[1] Dr. David M. Moore, Botany Department, University of Reading, England, acted as an associate investigator and adviser; he was the main recipient of the collections and provided most of the plant determinations.

and a new microscope, which made better drawings possible. The grants also helped me to obtain several part-time assistants, who greatly eased the load of pressing, processing, and labeling the plants and provided companions on expeditions. In Tierra del Fuego it is often difficult to go collecting alone.

Special Expeditions

Within Tierra del Fuego work was concentrated on interior and mountainous regions that have been seldom collected (see fig. 1). In all, I collected about 1,400 specimens (with their appropriate duplicates), as well as 401 numbers collected jointly with Dr. David M. Moore and 120 jointly with Emily Lutkin, who assisted me during parts of 1974 and 1975. Toward the end of this period, emphasis was changed from collecting *everything* at each locality to collecting only the rarer and more unusual species, while noting the others on special species charts prepared by Dr. Moore. We are now very familiar with the common plants, circumventing the necessity of collecting herbarium specimens of them.

From October 11 to November 14, 1971, I was able to participate in a botanical expedition to Staten Island, off the east coast of Tierra del Fuego, aboard the R. V. *Hero.* I had been there before, by plane, but this 5-week trip afforded me a magnificent chance to observe and collect on this rarely visited island. Dr. T. R. Dudley, Garrett Crow, and I jointly collected over 1,600 specimens, each with numerous duplicates, of plants of the eastern tip of Tierra del Fuego and Staten Island. I am greatly indebted to Dr. Henry Imshaw, Dr. Dudley, the National Science Foundation, and the crew of the *Hero* for this experience.

In addition to the expeditions within Tierra del Fuego, I had the opportunity to collect plants in several other areas in Argentina and Chile, which greatly broadened my knowledge of the vegetation of southern South America and increased my herbarium with representative plants from sites farther north.

In January 1973 I attended a conference in Comodoro Rivadavia, Chubut Province, Argentina. There I was able to make collections of the plants of northern Santa Cruz, around the Comodoro Rivadavia area, and the Valdez Peninsula. I had never been in central Patagonia before and found its semidesert and beach habitats very interesting.

In November 1973, while attending a botanical conference in the Province of Corrientes, I made a joint collection with French botanist Cristiane Tirel of 400 specimens of the plants of Corrientes and Entre Ríos provinces.

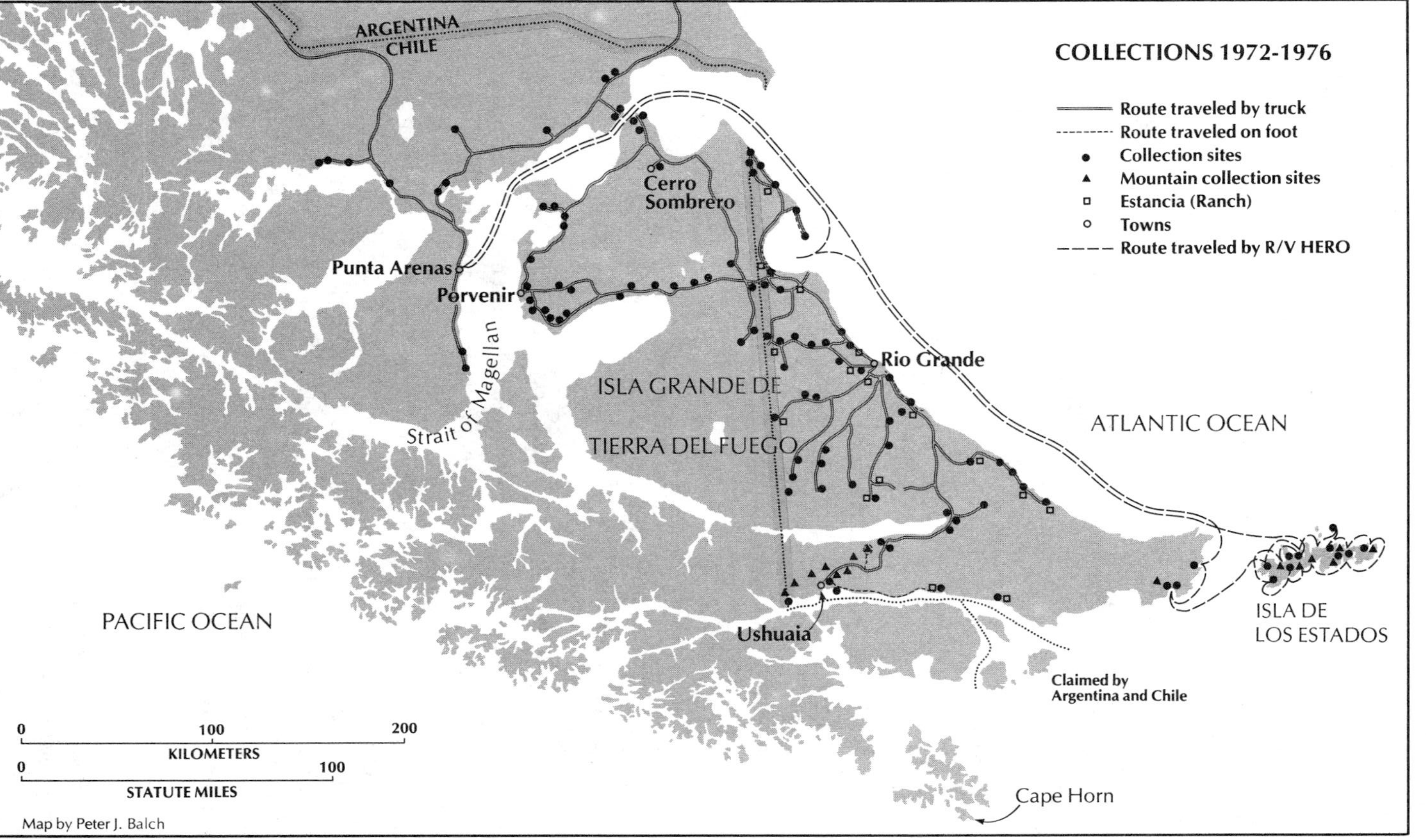

FIG. 1. Area in which collections were made 1972-1976.

During December 1975 I joined an Argentine botanical expedition in the area north of Río Gallegos, Province of Santa Cruz, and in December 1971 and March 1976 I collected in the Paine Mountain area north of Punta Arenas and along the Strait of Magellan, Chile. These expeditions enabled me to see northern extensions of our Fuegian plants, as well as the new plants that appear as one moves north.

My husband, Thomas D. Goodall, while serving as radio operator aboard the R. V. *Hero,* collected 96 specimens of flowering plants in the Chilean Patagonian channels. Many of these I had never seen before. He brought back several live plants that I was able to plant and use for preparation of botanical drawings.

Special Visitors

A great many scientists, teachers, and others have visited us and consulted my herbarium. Among the foremost of these were Argentine botanists Ing. Agron. Osvaldo Boelcke and Dra. M. N. Correa, who collected with us in November 1971 and determined my specimens of their specialties, orchids and Cruciferae.

Dr. David M. Moore stayed with us for 2½ months in 1971, during which we collected many plants, made preparations for publications, and completely checked and identified the whole collection. While he was here, we served as consultants to a British Broadcasting Corporation team making a movie of the wildlife of Tierra del Fuego.

Early in 1974, Dr. Ralph Slayter of the Australian National University and Juliana Mulroy of Duke University stayed with me. We identified plants in several mountainous zones in conjunction with their study of the alpine habitats of the Americas.

Near the end of 1975 Dr. David Ashton, also from Australia, and I visited several places in the mountains and along the Beagle Channel.

During this time my husband and I worked closely with the R. V. *Hero,* which had made its home port in Ushuaia. We met and advised most of the visiting scientists, and many of them were able to use their short time here to best advantage through the use of the pick-up and the camping and cooking gear made available through the National Geographic Society grants.

Botanical Results

Four new native species were found for Tierra del Fuego. They were *Androsace pusilla, Lathyrus nervosus, Rumex longifolius,* and *Benthamiella patagonica*

(Moore and Goodall, 1974). The *Rumex,* based on four of my collections, was also new for Argentina (Perez-Moreau and Crespo, 1972).

New collections were made of many plants that were very rare in Tierra del Fuego or had been collected only once before. Among these were *Oreopolus glacialis, Valeriana sedifolia, Tapeinia obscura, Philesia magellanica, Samolus spathulatus,* and *Phaiophleps lynkholmii. Frankenia chubutensis* was found both north and south of the Strait of Magellan; it had not been found in Tierra del Fuego since 1898.

A very large number of new introduced plants were found for Tierra del Fuego. Many of these are still being determined and a publication is in preparation.

Many more specimens were found of the hybrid *Caltha* (Moore and Goodall, 1973), including another strange *Caltha,* which may be a hybrid.

After more work in the mountain area, several of the plants thought to be the rarest were found to be very common on some mountains.

About 180 seed collections were made and sent to England for growing experiments.

Progress continued on the flower drawings, with the addition of missing items, such as fruit, seeds, etc., to former drawings and the preparation of new ones.

During several winters a long series of experiments on the dye properties of the local plants on native hand-spun wool were conducted. This study, representing about 200 species, was presented at the convention of the Sociedad Argentina de Botánica in November 1973 and is being prepared for publication.

I prepared flower-illustrated maps to be used as end sheets for two volumes of the *Flora Patagonica* (Correa, 1971, and in press). Many of my botanical collections are reported as well in this publication. Large murals on the local flora and fauna were prepared for the government of Tierra del Fuego for use in an exhibition in Buenos Aires.

I have gathered together maps of many of the farms and estancias of Tierra del Fuego with the view of preparing detailed vegetation maps.

The herbarium collection has been well organized, housed in metal cabinets, processed, labeled, and poisoned. It is available to any scientist visiting Ushuaia; some plants have been sent on loan to other institutions.

Related Activities

During this period I completely revised and enlarged the flora and fauna sections of my guide book to Tierra del Fuego (Goodall, 1975).

While walking the beaches, I took notes on the extent of damage from the *Metula* oil spill (1974), and the numbers of dead birds (mostly penguins and cormorants) were noted. As late as 1977 layers of oil-covered rocks could still be seen on the beaches.

Also, while checking the beaches for plants, I began to pick up a few dolphin bones as a curiosity. After a visit from whale experts Dr. Robert L. Brownell, Jr., Dr. Edward Mitchell, and Dr. James Mead, who were astounded at the number of rare species I had, I began to collect them more seriously. At one site on San Sebastian Bay, we found 88 specimens of dolphin and whale bones in one day! By July 1976 I had over 300 specimens of 14 species, more than doubling the world's records for some of them (Goodall, 1977). And nearly all these collections were just incidental while I was looking for plants! The whale collection is numbered RNP to differentiate them from the plants, which are labeled RNPG.

Apart from the whales and dolphins, four skulls of crabeater seals and one of a leopard seal were found. These represent first records for Tierra del Fuego.

A filing system has been set up for each species of plant, mammal, and bird, in order to collect data for a future *Field Guide to Tierra del Fuego.*

Numerous slide lectures on the local flora and fauna were given to groups of tourists and on tourist ships and annual classes in flora and fauna were taught to the tourist guides in Ushuaia. My flora and fauna maps have introduced many people to the wildlife of Tierra del Fuego.

REFERENCES

Correa, Maevia N., ed.

1969, 1971. Flora Patagonica. Colección Científica de INTA, vol. 8, pt. 2, 219 pp.; pt. 3 (in press); pt. 7, 451 pp. Instituto Nacional de Tecnología Agropecuaria, Buenos Aires.

Dudley, Theodore R.

——. A contribution to the flora and vegetation of Isla de los Estados (Staten Island), Tierra del Fuego, Argentina. American Geophysical Union Antarctic Research Series: Terrestrial Biology, vol. 30, illus. (In press.)

Goodall, Rae Natalie P.

1975. Tierra del Fuego, ed. 2, 253 pp., illus. Ediciones Shanamaiiam, Buenos Aires.

1976. Preliminary report on the small cetaceans stranded on the coasts of Tierra del Fuego. Paper presented at meeting of Subcommittee on Small Cetaceans, Scientific Committee, International Whaling Commission, London, June 7-9, 1976. (Abstract published in IWC 27th Ann. Rpt., p. 505, 1977.)

1978. Collections, observations, and illustrations of the flora of Tierra del Fuego. Nat. Geogr. Res. Rpts., 1970 Projects, pp. 217-222, illus.

GOODALL, RAE NATALIE P.—continued
_____. Dyes obtained from native plants of Tierra del Fuego. Paper submitted to Jornadas Argentinas de Botánica, Paso de los Libres, Corrientes.
MOORE, DAVID M., and GOODALL, RAE NATALIE P.
1973. Interspecific hybridization in Fuegian *Caltha* L. Bol. Soc. Argentina Bot., vol. 15, pp. 72-76, illus.
1974. Further additions to the native vascular flora of Tierra del Fuego. Bot. Notiser, vol. 127, pp. 38-43, illus.
_____. The flora of Tierra del Fuego. (In preparation.)
PÉREZ MOREAU, R L., and CRESPO, S.
1972. Notas sobre el génro *Rumex* (Polygonaceae). Bol. Soc. Argentina Bot., vol. 14, no. 4, pp. 325-329, illus.

RAE NATALIE PROSSER GOODALL

Reproductive Cycles and Biogeographic Relationships of Tropical *Anolis* Lizards

Principal Investigator: George C. Gorman, University of California at Los Angeles, Los Angeles, California.

Grant No. 964: For study of *Anolis* lizards in the West Indies.

From September 1971 through December 1972 I was based in the Caribbean region, where I was engaged in a series of studies relating to the biogeography, ecology, and evolution of *Anolis* lizards. I was a research associate of Harvard University's Museum of Comparative Zoology and was supported primarily by a National Science Foundation grant to Dr. E. E. Williams. The funds received from the National Geographic Society immensely aided my travel and field support while in this region. My research projects there fell into a series of independent, but interrelated disciplines.

Reproductive Cycles of Tropical Anolis *Lizards*

Most people who dwell in the temperate zone tend to think of tropical climates as being uniform throughout the year. Although it is true that day length and temperature fluctuate much less radically than in temperate latitudes, it is becoming increasingly evident that there is strong seasonality in the tropics. Most conspicuous, perhaps, are the regular patterns of rainfall—the partitioning of the year into wet and dry seasons. More subtle, but still measurable, are changes in temperature or photoperiod.

In conjunction with Dr. Paul Licht, of the University of California at Berkeley, I studied the annual reproductive cycles of six species of *Anolis* lizards from Puerto Rico and the Virgin Islands (Gorman and Licht, 1974; Licht and Gorman, 1975). We were able to demonstrate strong seasonality in a seemingly stable climate. Virtually all species cycled, i.e., had peak and minimum reproductive periods. All species were in phase with one another. That is, they were not breeding at different times of the year in similar localities. By careful analysis we were able to show that reproductive cycling is under environmental control and that temperature, not rainfall, seems to be the key factor. For example, reproductive decline *within* a species (several populations studied) occurs earlier and more severely in montane rain forest (where it is cooler but wetter) than in the lowlands.

Experimental transplantation of highland lizards to the lowlands, and the reverse, indicated that the differences observed in cycling were strictly under environmental and not genetic control. That is, lowland lizards transported to outdoor cages in the mountains responded exactly the same as free-living montane individuals, and not as their former neighbors of the lowlands. The reciprocal transplantations yielded similar results.

Biogeographic Relationships of Remote Populations

In previous studies, I had examined the chromosomes of all *Anolis* populations of the Caribbean east of Hispaniola, with three exceptions. Chromosome studies have proven to provide very valuable information for defining species groups and interpreting biogeographic history. I had also studied the display behavior of all the island forms of a southern Lesser Antillean species group. Again, stereotyped behavior patterns provided valuable insight into patterns of relationships (Gorman, 1968; Gorman and Atkins, 1969).

My only missing bits of information were from Mona Island, which lies between Hispaniola and Puerto Rico; Redonda, which is a tiny emergent volcano between Nevis and Montserrat; and La Blanquilla, a tiny island that belongs to Venezuela and lies between Grenada of the Lesser Antilles and Bonaire, far to the west. Each of these islands has an endemic species of *Anolis,* i.e., a species restricted just to that tiny island. Each of these islands is relatively remote, essentially uninhabited, hence difficult to reach. NGS funds were used for boat hire (Redonda and Blanquilla) and charter flight (Mona). The chromosomes of the three forms have now been studied (Gorman and Stamm, 1975). The Redonda and La Blanquilla species provided no surprises. The chromosome complement was identical to that of their presumed closest relatives in their respective species groups. The Mona species *(Anolis monensis)* had been presumed to be most closely related to, in fact, perhaps the same species as, *Anolis cristatellus,* a very widespread form on Puerto Rico. We were able to demonstrate that in chromosomes it differs significantly from *A. christatellus.* In fact, it is indistinguishable from another Puerto Rican species, *A. cooki,* that is restricted in distribution to the most arid, southwestern section of Puerto Rico.

The behavioral study of *Anolis blanquillanus* indicated that it was apparently intermediate between a St. Lucia species and a Bonaire species. Thus the apparent colonization route was from St. Lucia to Bonaire, with La Blanquilla serving as a stepping stone.

A major focus of my research deals with a biochemical analysis of protein differences between populations. This gives a measure called "genetic distance"which in turn provides a way of examining relationships between populations and their divergence times in a quantitative manner. The methodology and interpretation need not be spelled out here. Interested readers are referred to Selander et al., 1971 and Nei, 1972. My laboratory has incorporated the genetic data of these three species into analyses of the genetic evolution of their respective species groups. *Anolis monensis* is biochemically most similar to *A. cooki* and not to *A. cristatellus*. This confirms the chromosome observation. *Anolis blanquillanus* is genetically most similar to *A. bonairensis* (it was originally described as a subspecies of *bonairensis*), and both *blanquillanus* and *bonairensis* are most closely related to the St. Lucia species *A. luciae* (Yang et al., 1974). Thus the genetic data support the behavioral data.

The Lizards of Malpelo Island

Isla Malpelo is a barren rock about one mile long and 1,300 feet high that emerges from the Pacific about 250 miles west of Colombia at a latitude of about 3° N. The island is very peculiar because it has virtually no primary productivity (green plants), but was known to have abundant populations of an endemic anole *(A. agassizi)* and a large lizard related to the alligator lizards of North America, known to the scientific world as *Diploglossus millepunctatus*. Sea birds breed on the island, and the insects that they attract are apparently sufficient to form the base of a food chain that can support the lizards. I was keenly interested in studying this remote *Anolis* population. In 1972, the Smithsonian Tropical Research Institute, in conjunction with the United States Navy, arranged for a field trip to Malpelo. I used funds from my National Geographic grant to fly to Panama to join the expedition.

A study of the chromosomes of the Malpelo lizards indicated that they belonged to primitive groups in their respective genera. The *Anolis* was similar to several South American and southern Lesser Antillean forms (Stamm and Gorman, 1975). Biochemical studies confirmed a general relationship between the Malpelo anole and the Lesser Antillean forms.

In conjunction with A. S. Rand and William Rand (Rand et al., 1975) I studied the social behavior and ecology of *Anolis agassizi*. Unlike most anoles, which are highly arboreal (perch on trees) and highly territorial (i.e., defend sites from intruders of the same species), this species dwells on the rocks (it has little choice!), and swarms all over the place. Territorial interactions were few and far between. Many unusual items, ranging from jellied candy to packages of film, attract great swarms of anoles. We were able to show that they were particularly attracted to orange and yellow colors, and we speculated that they might feed on broken eggs from the nesting sea birds. There is no other yellow or orange on the entire gray-drab island. There was little doubt that these anoles exhibit social facilitation. When one individual sees something of interest and moves toward it, others are likely to follow.

REFERENCES

GORMAN, G. C.

1968. The relationships of *Anolis* of the *roquet* species group (Sauria: Iguanidae). III. Comparative study of display behavior. Breviora, no. 284, pp. 1-31.

GORMAN, G. C., and ATKINS, L.

1969. The zoogeography of Lesser Antillean *Anolis* lizards. An analysis based upon chromosomes and lactic dehydrogenases. Bull. Mus. Comp. Zool., vol. 138, pp. 53-80.

GORMAN, G. C., and LICHT, P.

1974. Seasonality in ovarian cycles among tropical *Anolis* lizards. Ecology, vol. 55, pp. 360-369.

GORMAN, G. C., and STAMM, B.

1975. The *Anolis* lizards of Mona, Redonda and La Blanquilla; chromosome 5, relationships and natural history notes. Journ. Herpetol, vol. 9, pp. 197-205.

LICHT, P., and GORMAN, G. C.

1975. Altitudinal effects on the seasonal reproductive cycles of male *Anolis* lizards from Puerto Rico and the Virgin Islands. Copeia, 1975, pp. 496-504.

NEI, M.

1972. Genetic distance between populations. Amer. Nat., vol. 106, pp. 283-292.

RAND, A. S.; GORMAN, G. C.; and RAND, W. M.

1975. Natural history, behavior, and ecology of *Anolis agassizi* Stejneger. Pp. 27-38 *in* "The Biological Investigation of Malpelo Island, Colombia," Jeffrey B. Graham, ed., Smiths. Contr. Zool., no. 176.

SELANDER, R. K.; SMITH, M. H.; YANG, S. Y.; JOHNSON, W. E.; and GENTRY, J. B.

1971. Biochemical polymorphism and systematics in the genus *Peromyscus*. I. Variation in the Old-field mouse *(Peromyscus polionotus)*. Pp. 49-90 *in* "Studies in Genetics VI," Univ. Texas Publ. 7103.

STAMM, B.; and GORMAN, G. C.

1975. Notes on the chromosomes of *Anolis agassizi* (Sauria, Iguanidae) and *Diploglossus millepunctatus* (Sauria, Anguidae). Pp. 52-54 *in* "The Biological Investigation of Malpelo Island, Colombia," Jeffrey B. Graham, ed., Smiths. Contr. Zool., no. 176.

YANG, S. Y.; SOULÉ, M.; and GORMAN, G. C.

1974. *Anolis* lizards of the eastern Caribbean: A case study in evolution. I. Genetic relationships, phylogeny, and colonization sequence of the *roquet* group. Syst. Zool., vol. 23, no. 4, pp. 387-399.

GEORGE C. GORMAN

Archeological Investigations at Chalcatzingo, 1972, 1973

Principal Investigator: David C. Grove, University of Illinois, Urbana, Illinois

Grant Nos. 997, 1136: For study of the archeology of Chalcatzingo, Morelos, Mexico.

Mesoamerica's first truly complex culture, the Olmec, has its apparent heartland in Mexico's tropical Gulf Coast region. However, artifacts and art identified by scholars as Olmec occur in widespread and diverse regions throughout central and southern Mexico and at least as far south as Costa Rica. The nature and significance of this diffused Olmec manifestation, while speculated upon for many years, are just now being subjected to archeological testing. The site of Chalcatzingo, in the central Mexican State of Morelos, about 85 miles southeast of Mexico City, is a site with such a manifestation. It is the only archeological site north of the Gulf Coast with a quantity of monumental bas-relief carvings executed in the Olmec art style. The first of these carvings were reported by Guzman nearly 40 years ago (1934) and subsequently discovered bas-reliefs have been reported and discussed by a number of scholars (Cook de Leonard, 1967; Gay, 1966, 1972; Grove, 1968). The site has long been recognized as of great importance but only small scale excavations had been undertaken at Chalcatzingo prior to the excavations discussed in the following pages. These prior excavations were carried out by Mexican archeologist Roman Piña Chan in 1952 and consisted primarily of a series of stratigraphic test pits (Piña Chan, 1955) which located no Formative period architectural features. During those investigations a small Classic period mound was excavated and partially reconstructed. The excavations by Roman Piña Chan were not of sufficient magnitude to provide data on settlement patterning, life ways, or the nature of Olmec influences at the site. Even if these data had been recovered, little comparative data on Olmec culture were available in 1952, even from Gulf Coast sites.

The Chalcatzingo Archeological Project, initiated in 1972, was created to investigate the nature of the archeological manifestation at Chalcatzingo. The 1972 field season was in a sense a "pilot project" to provide background data for more extensive excavations planned for 1973 and 1974. The over-all project did not restrict itself solely to Chalcatzingo, for no archeological site ever existed in a cultural vacuum. Thus to understand Chalcatzingo it was necessary also to understand something of simultaneous cultural developments throughout a far wider region. The investigations, both on and off the site, involved such aspects as excavations, ecological analyses, palynology, settlement pattern analyses, studies of agricultural land use, and irrigation patterns.

Both Mexican and U. S. investigators participated in the project. The over-all project was directed by Dr. David C. Grove of the Department of Anthropology, University of Illinois. Project codirector in 1972 was Professor Jorge Angulo of Mexico's Instituto Nacional de Antropología e Historia (I.N.A.H.), who is also in charge of the Instituto's regional center for the states of Morelos and Guerrero, located in Cuernavaca, Morelos. In 1973 a second codirector joined the project, Professor Raul Arana, also affiliated with the Instituto Nacional. Numerous Mexican and U. S. graduate and undergraduate students participated in the investigations and while it is impossible to mention each individually, there was not one of them who did not make a significant contribution to the over-all goals of this research.

The labor force for the excavations came from the present-day village of Chalcatzingo. A weekly rotational system was established in the village to allow all adult males the opportunity to work. A similar system was arranged for village women who assisted in washing the artifacts and in cataloging all artifacts in the field.

Both the 1972 and 1973 field seasons were supported by research grants from the National Geographic Society (nos. 997 in 1971 and 1136 in 1972) and from the National Science Foundation (GS 31017). The 1974 field season, not discussed in this report, was funded by the same NSF grant.

From the two field seasons, 36 radiocarbon dates were processed. These dates are included, where relevant, in the following discussion.

Investigations in 1972

The 1972 field season, which ran from late January until early June, began with an intensive surface survey of the entire site area to determine its nature and extent. This was carried out in conjunction with extensive clearing and burning of the heavy overgrowth of tall, thick weeds covering Chalcatzingo's terraced hillside. A preliminary master map, drawn from an aerial photograph, enabled us to give each terrace and agricultural field an identification number (see fig. 1). It was decided that each of these units (fields or terraces) should be considered as individual sub-sites which would receive their own excavation datum and grid system. This proved to be a practical method of

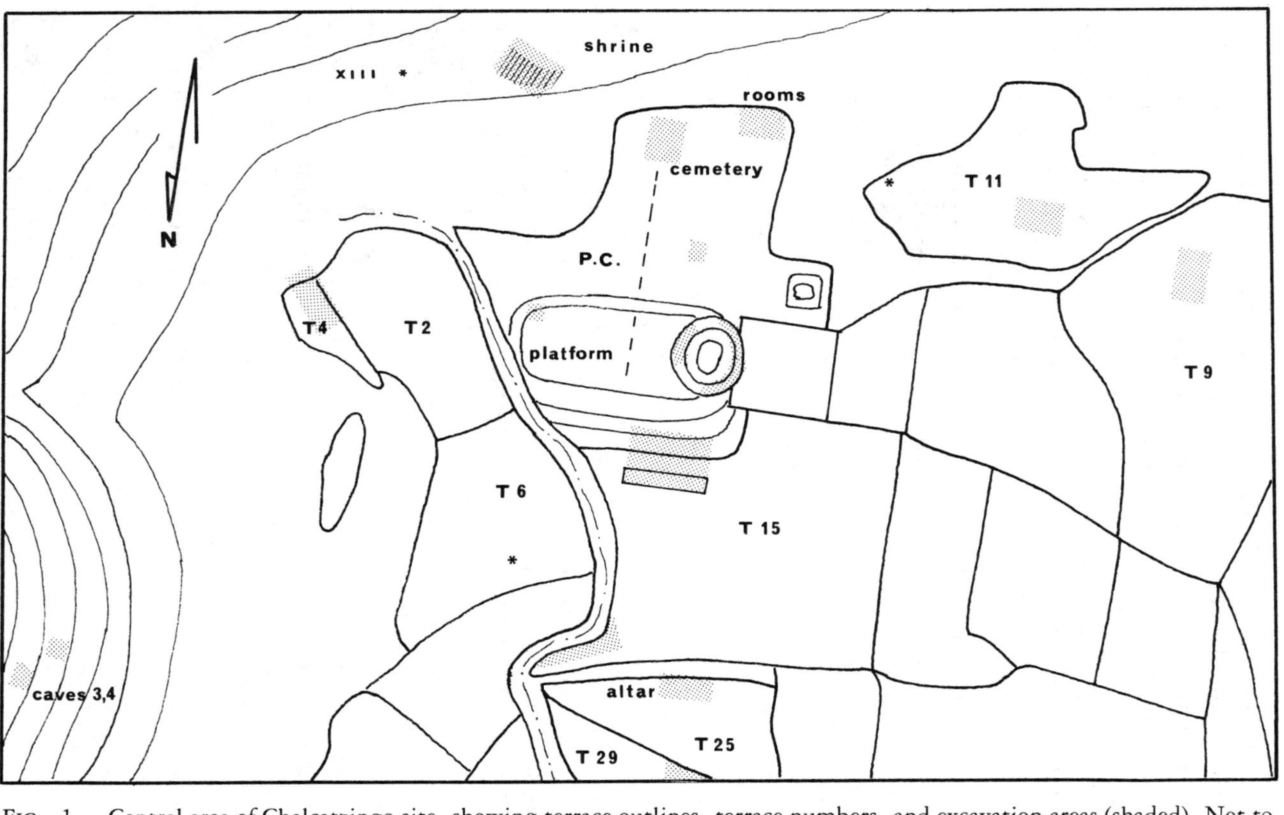

FIG. 1. Central area of Chalcatzingo site, showing terrace outlines, terrace numbers, and excavation areas (shaded). Not to scale.

dealing with a large archeological site with dispersed occupation and ceremonial zones. All sub-site units were then tied into the site's master datum.

The first excavations were conducted on the uppermost large terrace of the site, a terrace we termed the "Plaza Central." This terrace was chosen because it lies directly below the reliefs on the mountainside and because its downhill (northern) edge is delimited by a low, 70-meter-long platform mound. On the western end of the platform mound is a pyramid mound, about 8 meters in height. A 100-meter-long trench line was laid out running north-south across this terrace from the center of the platform mound southward to the talus slopes of the mountainside. Stratigraphic pits 1 by 3 meters were excavated at 10-meter intervals along this trench line, and a number of these were enlarged so that eventually we had a nearly complete 50-meter-long stratigraphic section bisecting the terrace (fig. 2). This long trench, which was excavated to bedrock, uncovered several buried architectural features including one structure running parallel to the south side of the long platform mound. In profile, these two structures, taken together, resemble a ballcourt. Radiocarbon dates from the stratigraphic trench (N-1407-N-1410), taken mostly from lower strata, range from about 1090 to 740 B.C. (all dates given are approximate and do not include one-sigma variations, etc.).

A 2- by 2-meter test pit excavated 120 meters south of the platform mound (location of our datum) on the north-south trench line, uncovered stone alignments, fragmentary human skeletal remains, and broken ceramic vessels, at a depth of only 30 centimeters below the surface, well within the lower edge of the plow zone. Several other test pits were excavated in adjacent grid squares and as each new square was opened to about 30 centimeters depth similar remains were discovered. It was readily apparent that we had located a Middle Formative cemetery area which due to erosion existed today at a very shallow depth. We were well aware that cemetery areas, while yielding data regarding the "way of death" (rather than the culture's way of life), can be of value in determining such things as patterns of rank or stratification. Comparative skeletal morphology could also be used to determine whether two different morphological populations inhabited Chalcatzingo (hypothetically a local population and perhaps a small population from the Gulf Coast Olmec heartland, these latter perhaps associated with different burial furniture). Our methodology was to open the area square by square to only 30 centimeters depth in order to first ascertain the dimensions of the cemetery zone. The total area opened in 1972 was approximately 160 square meters. The southern and eastern boundaries of the cemetery were clearly delimited by the remains of a well-constructed stone wall, almost 50 centimeters in width. Incomplete wall lines occur to the west and north but were so destroyed by plowing, etc., that

FIG. 2. 1972 Plaza Central excavations, looking north. Classic period pyramid mound is to the left, on the west end of the platform mound running across the center of the picture.

these boundary limits were determined by the presence and absence of burials. Within the cemetery limits over 30 identifiable human skeletons were uncovered, both at the 30-centimeter level and, as excavations began, level by level downward. A number of very fragmentary remains had been found at the 30-centimeter level but at times identification as "human" was made on the basis of the presence of one or two human teeth. Four burial types, probably related to rank or status, can be defined: flexed burials (relatively rare), extended burials, extended burials within crypts constructed of stone slabs, and stone crypt burials associated with jade artifacts (nearly all burials were associated with ceramic vessels). Associated with one crypt burial was a carved stone head with Olmec-like features, which apparently had been knocked off of a statue (it does not fit the headless Chalcatzingo statue in the Museo Nacional de Antropología). Ceramic vessels associated with the burials are generally similar to Zacatenco phase ceramics in the Valley of Mexico (Tolstoy and Paradis, 1970).

The walls delimiting the Plaza Central cemetery area suggest that the burials are in actuality subfloor burials within a major houselike ceremonial structure. The floor and upper levels of this structure have long since been destroyed by erosion and plowing. Five radiocarbon dates (N-1402 through N-1406) from the cemetery indicate that the uppermost burials date to around 600 B.C., while burials at deeper levels may date to as early as 800 B.C.

Excavations following a prehistoric manmade water channel crossing the mountainside's talus slopes discovered wall lines on the southwest edge of the Plaza Central, about 40 meters west of the cemetery area. Excavations have shown these walls to be part of a series of rooms, part of at least two houselike structures. Within these structures we were able to determine two floor levels. Other floors may have been destroyed by erosion or plowing. In one room area, 9 ceramic vessels were aligned along the uppermost floor. The lower floor in the same structure was heavily burnt in one section. This fired section was sampled by Dr. Dan Wolfman, who in 1972 was associated with a University of Oklahoma research project on archeomagnetism. Dr. Wolfman has since communicated the laboratory results obtained from those samples, an ancient magnetic declination of 5.6°E. ± 4.8°. Present-day declination is 7.5°E. The wall alignment of this structure is 2°E. This latter is pointed out because some scholars are investigating the possibility that Gulf Coast Olmec sites were aligned by means of a compass needle. A wall alignment of 2°E. is about halfway between the archeomagnetic declination and true north, neither confirming or denying either as a basis of alignment.

These room structures were in all probability not domestic habitation structures, as no domestic artifacts such as grinding stones were associated with the rooms. On the other hand, various "ritual" artifacts including a carved stone "padlock" (Spanish: *candado*) were found, suggesting a ritual-ceremonial function for these structures. We were also able to ascertain the major building materials used in the construction of these structures. In the excavation levels associated with the burned floor we also found quantities of burned mud plaster adjacent to the stone wall lines. Impressions in this plaster indicate that the walls were constructed of *chamiza* (Compositae), the thick stems of a relative of the sunflower which grows in profusion today at the site. These *chamiza* walls were coated with a smoothed mud plaster. No postmolds were found in any structures excavated in 1972 but the data suggest that the supporting wall posts were set within the stones of the wall base.

Excavations on Terrace 4 uncovered a 4- by 6-meter rectangular stone-faced platform, constructed with at least two superpositions. Middle Formative vessels occurred on the floor of one of the superimposed structures. Excavations north of the platform uncovered an extensive series of walls, apparently part of several destroyed structures. Excavations on Terrace 9 disclosed the first of a number of habitation structures excavated during the project. Although the structure's floor levels are within the plow zone and thus destroyed, the structure's outline is present in the substructural walls. Eight subfloor burials were excavated. In addition to the human burials, a dog burial was also uncovered below the house floor, and a peccary burial was found in excavations to the south of the house structure. Radiocarbon dates for the T-9 excavations include two (N-1414 and N-1415) from Classic period intrusions and two (N-1416 and N-1417) on the house and subhouse levels; these range from 850 to 1170 B.C.

At the beginning of the project, the clearing and burning of the heavy vegetation cover exposed stairlike stone alignments on the mountainside talus slopes south of the Plaza Central terrace. These alignments were cleared and found to be the remnants of an extensive, wide stairway and platform complex which ran uphill to the base of a group of boulders which include bas-relief carvings (Relief II; see any of the previously cited works on Chalcatzingo for the location of this). We have labeled this complex the *"adoratorio"* (shrine). This construction is apparently Postclassic in age, as it is coated with lime plaster and numerous Postclassic sherds and fragmentary vessels were discovered during its excavation. The fact that this complex continues up the hill to the base of the Relief II boulder group suggests to me that this "shrine" was dedicated to Relief II, meaning that Relief II (an Olmec-style relief) was known and venerated by Postclassic inhabitants of the Chalcatzingo region. The Spanish chronicler Duran writes of a famous Postclassic shrine, *Teocuicani,* which existed in this region (Duran, 1971: 257-258; Grove, 1972), although the possibility that Duran is speaking of Postclassic Chalcatzingo remains to be demonstrated. At the end of the 1972 field season the *adoratorio* complex was reconstructed (fig. 3).

Four previously unknown bas-relief carvings were uncovered during the 1972 field season. Relief XII was reported to us by several of our workers who had known of its discovery by looters about 5 years previously. The looters, unable to remove it because of its size, had reburied it, and fortunately our workers were able to rediscover it. Of all of the Chalcatzingo bas-reliefs known to date, Relief XII is perhaps the most Olmec stylistically. The relief depicts a human figure flying through the air holding a torch in his right hand (fig. 4). A parrot is depicted flying below the person while above him fly two quetzal birds. The depiction of a flying personage carrying a torch is also known from Gulf Coast Olmec jades (Cervantes 1969, figs. 7, 9, 10, 11). The clothing and over-all execution of the personage on Relief XII is nearly identical to the "flying" human figures represented on La Venta Stela 3 (Drucker, Heizer, and

FIG. 3. Reconstructed Postclassic stairways and platforms on the mountainside below the boulder group containing Relief II.

Squier 1959, fig. 68). The headdress worn by the personage is apparently canine, but quite similar in style to the serpent headdress worn by the seated figure in La Venta Monument 19 (1959, fig. 55). It is hard for me to conceive of this relief having been carved by someone who was not intimately familiar with La Venta carved art.

Relief XIII, "The Governor" (fig. 5), a fragmentary relief discovered during brush clearing operations on the hillside near Relief II, depicts a cleft-headed baby-faced figure seated within the mouth of an earth monster (which iconographically represents a cave). The earth monster mouth is nearly identical to those depicted in Chalcatzingo Reliefs I and IX (Grove 1968, figs. 1, 7).

Reliefs XIV and XV are located high on the mountainside in the area of Reliefs I, VI, VII, VIII, and XI (Gay 1972, fig. 9a; Grove 1968, figs. 1, 2) and were uncovered by clearing operations in that area. Both reliefs represent small iguana-like animals crouched upon scroll motifs. Below the scrolls are squash plants while a stylized rain cloud with falling raindrops hangs over

FIG. 4. Relief XII, "The Flying Olmec." Size about 1.4 by 1.4 meters.

each animal (Relief XV is highly weathered and difficult to discern). The animal/rain-cloud/squash plant scene depicted in these reliefs is basically identical to those of Reliefs VI, VII (this, previously unidentified, was seen in 1972 to be the animal crouched upon a scroll), VIII, and XI, although these latter two lack squash plants. (See fig. 6.)

In addition to excavations, ecological investigations were an important part of our 1972 research and remained important in the subsequent research conducted in 1973 and 1974. Ecological zones both on the site and throughout the surrounding region were studied and sampled. All excavation units, including room floors and strata profiles, were sampled for fossil pollen. Modern pollen samples from all major ecological zones in central and eastern Morelos were collected to provide comparative data. Studies of current agricultural practices, irrigation systems, land use, crop yields, etc., were conducted over the three years of field work. Extensive soil tests were also carried out on the site zone.

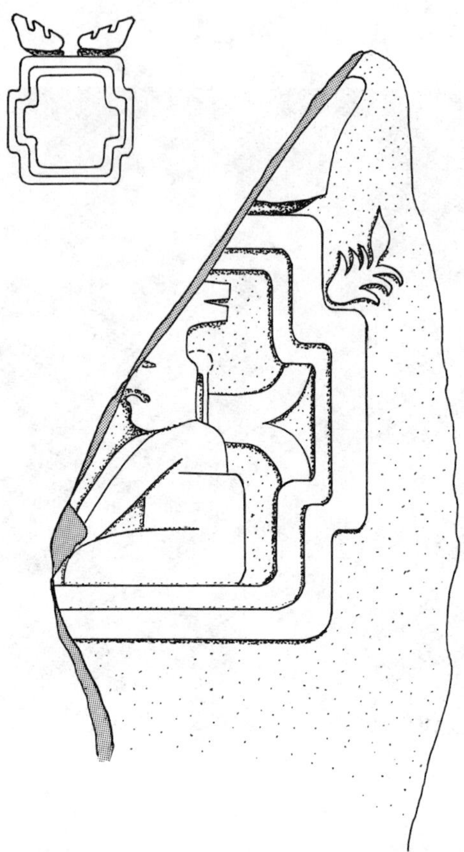

FIG. 5. Relief XIII, "The Governor." Total height approximately 2.5 meters. The inset at upper left is a suggested reconstruction of the relief's earth-monster face.

All artifacts were washed and cataloged on the site before moving them to laboratory facilities in Cuernavaca provided by I.N.A.H. Ceramic analyses began during the 1972 field season and continued to the beginning of the 1973 excavations.

Investigations in 1973

Our 1973 field research began in January and continued until July. From the initial conception of the project it was our belief that in order to understand properly the cultural situation at Chalcatzingo we must also understand the nature of the Formative culture in the region surrounding Chalcatzingo. Chalcatzingo is situated in the center of the Amatzinac-Tenango River valley,

FIG. 6. Relief XIV. The total height of the carved area is about 1.3 meters.

a valley which because of surrounding ecological patterns we believed could be considered, for purposes of our research, an isolated geographic unit. A major phase of our 1973 research involved an intensive surface reconnaissance of this approximately 600-square-kilometer region, in order to locate all archeological sites within the area, to map and surface-collect each site, and to study each site in terms of such criteria as location, proximity to natural resources, ecology, and land-use patterns. Air photographs of the reconnaissance area with a scale of 1:5000 were obtained from an agency of the Mexican government. These photos were covered with an acetate overlay and in the fieldwork all sites located were plotted directly onto the acetate. Over 330 archeological sites from Early Formative through Late Postclassic were located in the five months of reconnaissance.

Four Early Formative sites were located by the reconnaissance crew. This is in sharp contrast to the heavy Early Formative occupation of the Río Cuautla Valley 15 miles west of Chalcatzingo or the Izucar de Matamoros area 35 miles to the east. The valley's ecology and lack of good surface water sources is probably the main reason for a low population during the Early Formative. Chalcatzingo is one of the four Early Formative sites, and one of the few locations with accessible surface water in the valley. A marked population increase is seen during the Middle Formative with 57 archeological sites, of which Chalcatzingo is the largest. Data indicate a nucleation of settlements clustering around Chalcatzingo, a phenomenon not apparent in nearby areas such as the Valley of Mexico. In fact our survey located nearly as many Middle Formative sites in our survey area as previous surveys have recorded for the entire Valley of Mexico region (60). This suggests the obvious importance of Chalcatzingo during the Middle Formative.

In all, 60 Late Formative sites, 67 Early Classic sites, and 52 sites corresponding to Teotihuacan III and IV were recorded. During this latter period the largest settlement is in the area of the southern valley, an area we believe to have been important in cotton production. Intensive irrigation is implied by the Classic settlement patterning; 64 Early Postclassic and 201 Late Postclassic sites were located, these appearing primarily in the northern valley, often associated with colonial period irrigation systems. This indicates that the colonial systems are in many cases simply re-used prehispanic systems. The site of Tetla, the Postclassic zone at Chalcatzingo on the east side of the mountain, was apparently the major site for the valley during the Early Postclassic. Tetla, I believe, is the actual Postclassic Chalcatzingo, a site tributary to Chalco in the Valley of Mexico.

Because of the complex nature of the terrain and the time needed for other phases of our investigations, topographic mapping of Chalcatzingo (including the Tetla zone) by transit and stadia became impractical. Funds were provided by the National Geographic Society which allowed a photogrammetric map to be made by Compañía Mexicana Aerofoto from aerial photographs specially flown for this purpose. The map produced by this method covers over 2 square kilometers at a scale of 1:1000, with contour levels of 1 meter.

The 1973 excavations continued work on the Plaza Central cemetery area and 15 additional burials were excavated, including 5 crypt burials. Associated with the skeleton inside one crypt was a serpentine "were-jaguar" figurine. Cemetery burials occurred to a depth of only about 2 meters, below which we came upon portions of a packed clay house floor with some fragmentary sections of the mud-plaster wall base still in situ.

Excavations of the Plaza Central ceremonial rooms were reopened and it was decided to cut through preserved floor areas in several of the rooms to determine if these were underlain by any earlier features. Ten subfloor burials were discovered. Ceramic vessels associated with these burials are identical to those associated with cemetery area burials. Three carbon-14 dates (N-1706-N-1708) range from 940 B.C. for prestructure deposits to 620 B.C. for floor levels of the structure.

The north-south trench cut across the Plaza Central in 1972 did not continue onto the platform mound on the north end of the terrace. In 1973, 3 stratigraphic trenches were excavated on the mound itself. Two of these excavation units eventually reached bedrock at 5 meters in depth. The stratigraphic profiles indicate that the mound was constructed in the Middle Formative, and as such represents the largest architectural structure reported in central Mexico in this time period. The third excavation unit, on the edge of the platform mound, uncovered a Middle Formative burial, the richest discovered in 1973. In addition to the associated ceramic vessels, the burial had green jade earspools and jade beads at the throat and pelvis (1974 excavations uncovered further "status" burials along the platform edge).

The western end of the Plaza Central platform mound is marked by a large pyramid mound. Our 1973 excavations cleared portions of this structure and exposed a faced stone exterior which originally had been coated with lime plaster. The pyramid's stairway faces a small plaza area on the west (this plaza was noted and excavated by Piña Chan in 1952). The pyramid is Classic in age and, surprisingly, is round, a form not uncommon in the Postclassic but exceedingly rare in central Mexico during the Classic. The walls and staircase area exposed by our excavations were reinforced and reconstructed.

Excavations were continued on Terrace 4, and further walls were followed in an effort to delimit room areas, etc. Excavations also uncovered an intrusive circular feature, slightly larger than 2 meters in diameter, which proved to be a stone-faced cylinder with a depth of almost 2 meters. The stone facing is to the interior and the stones were set in a mud mortar which later was fired to a high temperature. Classic period sherds occurred in the interior fill of this feature and in the lowest 50 centimeters of the interior we uncovered a layer of 1500 limestone rocks and below that, charcoal. There seems little doubt that this was a Classic period lime kiln (others were found in 1974). Radiocarbon date N-1694, of A.D. 690, confirms this.

In order to uncover further Middle Formative house structures, excavations were carried out on terraces 11, 24, and 29. In addition to uncovering a series of stone sub-structural walls, the T-11 excavations located 14 pit features. In most cases these pits seem to postdate the walls. The first use of these pits seems to have been for food preparation, probably through the use of fire-heated stones. Faunal material recovered includes dog and deer bone. Later the pits appear to have been utilized for refuse. Radiocarbon dates N-1696 and N-1709, of 810 and 630 B.C., relate to the wall features, while date N-1697, of 580 B.C., is from the interior of a pit feature.

The house structures uncovered on terraces 24 and 29 were both heavily destroyed by erosion (it was not until 1974 that a house area undisturbed by erosion was located). Both excavations yielded small fragments of jade ear-spools, etc., in addition to grinding stones and quantities of ceramics.

A Classic period ballcourt structure on Terrace 15 was partially excavated and reconstructed. This ballcourt utilized a portion of the northern side of the Middle Formative Plaza Central platform mound to form the south side of the playing area. A cache of Classic figurines was located in the center of the ballcourt's playing alley.

Early in the project our investigations of possible water control systems disclosed a large "dam" or "dike" projecting like a thumb from the northeast corner of Terrace 15. This "dike" served as a major water control feature on the drainage system that delimits the east side of the Plaza Central and T-15 terraces. This structure is nearly 35 meters long and 7 meters high. Our excavations show that it was built at the time of the terracing (early Middle Formative), and was constructed across the original watercourse of the drainage system. During the rainy season when rain water runoff from the mountains turns this normally dry stream into a rushing torrent, this diversion "dike" serves to slow the currents by diverting them through two nearly 90° bends. This served to protect the lower terraces and the rich valley bottom lands from destruction. This structure is one of two such constructions at Chalcatzingo, and these represent the earliest known water-control features in the Morelos-Valley of Mexico region.

Two areas of caves occur at the site, both on the Cerro Delgado, the smaller of the two mountains bordering the site. Four caves were tested or

FIG. 7. Gulf Coast style altar discovered in 1973. Length of the altar is approximately 4 meters.

excavated, two on the mountain's east side and two on the west side. On the east side of the mountain, 18 1- by 1-meter squares were excavated in Cave 1. A Postclassic occupation with some traces of plaster floors comprised the upper levels, while a Middle Formative occupation, including two burials, was distinguished in the lower levels. Cave 2, a dry cave just below Cave 1, although heavily destroyed by looting, yielded a quantity of prehispanic vegetal material including cotton, cotton bolls, cotton thread, maguey fiber cordage, charred sticks, leaves, nuts, corn cobs, gourd fragments, and maguey quids. Worked wooden implements, apparently tools used in spinning and weaving cotton, as well as some woven cloth fragments were found. This material appears to be Postclassic.

Cave 3, on the western face of Cerro Delgado has several crude red paintings on the cave walls. While Formative and Classic sherds were found by our test excavations, the cultural deposit was shallow and primarily Postclassic. On the other hand, Cave 4, slightly higher on the mountainside, contained a series of rooms with stone wall foundations. Painted Postclassic plaster floors and a small plaster shrine were uncovered. Classic and Formative levels were also excavated. Continued excavations in Cave 4 in 1974 disclosed a Middle Formative mud brick floor above bedrock.

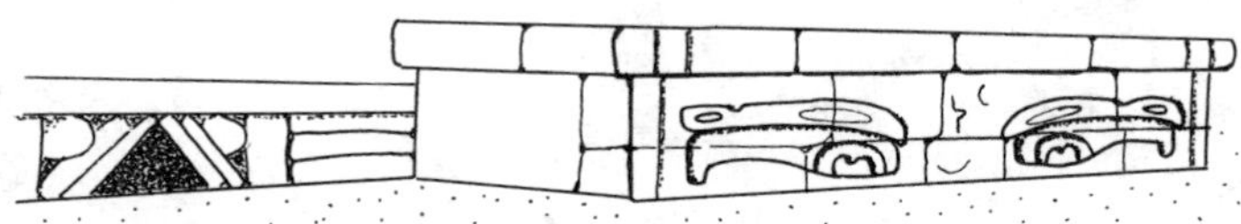

FIG. 8. Drawing of the overhang and the carved bas-relief earth-monster face on the front of the Chalcatzingo altar that is shown on page 301.

Perhaps the most exciting discovery of 1973 began as three flat stones exposed in a plow furrow on Terrace 25 were found to be faced and carved. When fully excavated these stones were found to comprise the upper edge of a large rectangular stone altar, essentially identical in form and execution to the monolithic stone altars found at Gulf Coast Olmec sites. The Chalcatzingo altar even has the overhanging upper "lip" and a carved bas-relief earth-monster face on its front side (figs. 7, 8). Unlike Gulf Coast altars it does not have a front niche area and is not monolithic. This latter point seems important in ascertaining the degree of social power any "Olmec elite" at Chalcatzingo had upon the local population, for suitable boulders lie only 100 meters from the

T-25 altar, yet it was constructed of smaller rectangular blocks. The altar is part of a low walled enclosure and within this area 18 human burials were uncovered, including child burials at each corner of the altar itself. Six radiocarbon dates (N-1700-N-1703, N-1710, N-1711) appear to date the altar and burials at about 700-600 B.C., although we are aware that the situation is somewhat more complex and at least 3 building and rebuilding phases occurred.

Other stone carvings located during the 1973 field season include a small round stone "altar," with a carved bas-relief scroll motif, found on Terrace 6, and a carved *maqueta* (site model) of the site on T-11. Carved on this latter are the two mountains, drainages on the mountainside, and carved stairways. Although no carved stairways were known from the actual mountainside at the time of the discovery of the *maqueta,* two sets of carved steps were found above T-11 soon thereafter.

In 1973 laboratory facilities were rented in Cuautla, and since that date all analyses have been conducted there on a year-round basis. These include ceramics, lithics, and a computerized analysis of over 3000 figurine fragments.

The data from the two years of fieldwork indicate Chalcatzingo was probably the first formal ceremonial center in the Morelos-Valley of Mexico region, and we believe that it was a center established by the Gulf Coast Olmec for the purpose of controlling the exploitation of highland raw materials (including obsidian, jade, iron ore, and probably cotton) and channeling these materials to Gulf Coast centers. These hypotheses and others received further investigation in fieldwork conducted at Chalcatzingo in 1974.

REFERENCES

CERVANTES, MA. ANTONIETA

1969. Dos elementos de uso ritual en el arte Olmeca. Anales, Mexico, 1967-1968, Ser .7, vol. 1, pp. 37-51.

COOK DE LEONARD, CARMEN

1967. Sculptures and rock carvings at Chalcatzingo. *In* "Studies in Olmec archaeology," pp. 57-84. Contr. Univ. California Arch. Res. Facility, no. 3.

DRUCKER, PHILIP; HEIZER, ROBERT F.; and SQUIER, ROBERT J.

1959. Excavations at La Venta, Tabasco, 1955. Bur. Amer. Ethnol., Bull. 170.

DURAN, FRAY DIEGO

1971. Book of the gods and rites and the ancient calendar. Transl. and ed. by Horcasitas and Heyden. University of Oklahoma Press.

GAY, CARLO T. E.
1966. Rock carvings at Chalcatzingo. Natural History, vol. 76, pp. 28-35.
1972. Chalcacingo. International Scholarly Book Services, Portland (also Graz, Austria, 1971).

GROVE, DAVID C.
1968. Chalcatzingo, Morelos, Mexico: a reappraisal of the Olmec rock carvings. Amer. Antiq. vol. 33, pp. 486-491.
1972. El Teocuicani "cantor divino" en Jantetelco. Bol. Inst. Nac. Antr. Hist., Mexico, ser. 2, vol. 3, pp. 35-36.

GUZMAN, EULALIA
1934. Los relieves de las rocas del Cerro de la Cantera, Jonacatepec, Morelos. Anal. Mus. Nac. Arqueol. Hist. Etnol., ser. 5, vol. 1, no. 2.

PIÑA CHAN, ROMAN
1955. Chalcatzingo, Morelos. Informes, Inst. Nac. Antr. e Hist., no. 4, Mexico.

TOLSTOY, PAUL, and PARADIS, LOUISE I.
1970. Early and Middle Preclassic culture in the Basin of Mexico. Science, vol. 167, pp. 344-351. Washington, D. C.

DAVID C. GROVE

Systematics and Evolution of the Family Thelotremataceae (Lichens) in the Lesser Antilles

Principal Investigator: Mason E. Hale, Jr., National Museum of Natural History, Smithsonian Institution, Washington, D. C.

Grant No. 934: For study of systematics and evolution of the Thelotremataceae in the Lesser Antilles.

The lichen family Thelotremataceae is a large group of crustose lichens characterized by craterlike fruiting bodies. They occur almost exclusively in the tropics and appear to be particularly developed in the West Indies and in Southeast Asia. My preliminary results from Dominica indicated a very rich flora, and I decided to expand the study to all of the Lesser Antilles. This latter work has been supported by a research grant from the National Geographic Society.

The main goals were to ascertain the size of the thelotreme flora, the probable pathways of evolution and migration which have contributed to the present rich flora, and the relationship to the thelotreme floras of neighboring regions.

Summary of the Flora

The following islands were visited: Guadeloupe, Dominica, Saint Lucia, Grenada, Saint Vincent, and Trinidad. The only major island not visited in the itinerary was Martinique. The approximately 800 collections included 68 species as follows:

Ocellularia: alborosella, antillensis, berkeleyana, cavata, comparabilis, concolor, *conglomerata, dilatata, *dominicana, efformata, exanthismocarpa, fecunda, glaziovis, *maculata, mordenii, *nigropuncta, olivacea, orthomastia, papillata, perforata, plurifaria, pyrenuloides, rhodostroma, *rimosa, *sorediata, subcavata, subemersa, sublilacina, terebrata, terebratula, and *thryptica.

Phaeotrema: *aggregatum, disciforme, leiostomum, leprieurii, and *obscurum.

*Indicates new species.

Thelotrema: carassense, citrinodiscum, clandestinum, conforme, *confusum, depressum, *dominicanum, glaucopallens, *guadeloupense, interpositum, leucinum, leucomelaenum, *norsticticum, *papillosum, praestans, stylothecium, *subsimile, *tenue, and tuberculiferum.

Leptotrema: bahianum, *bisporum, *deceptum, fissum, laeviusculum, lepadodes, *microglaenoides, occultum, phaeosporum, spondaicum, subcompunctum, trypaneoides, and wightii.

Dominica has the largest number of species, 47 (Hale, 1974). The poorest island was Grenada where a hurricane in the 1950's had destroyed much of the forest vegetation. I collected only 4 species there. I estimate that Dominica, the most intensively collected island, eventually will be found to have 55 species. The other large islands, especially Guadeloupe, may approach this number, but they have much less undisturbed forest area than has Dominica.

Of the total 68 species, 19 were described as new (see the listings above). Of these, 15 are endemic to the Lesser Antilles according to our present knowledge. This represents 22 percent of the flora. By comparison, Panama, another region where I have collected intensively, has 86 species of which 27 percent are endemics. Cuba, the only other well collected island in the West Indies, has about 53 species and only 6 percent of these are endemic.

Having established that the Lesser Antilles do indeed have an unusually large thelotreme flora, we can now examine several factors that may have contributed to it.

Habitat Requirements

On all islands in the Lesser Antilles the thelotremes are almost totally confined to undisturbed virgin rain forest or relatively intact mixed primary-secondary forest. Only three species readily invade secondary forests or planted citrus groves: *Leptotrema compunctum* (including *occultum*), *L. spondaicum,* and *Ocellularia exanthismocarpa.* In long-established secondary forests, such as that covering the slopes of Souffrière on Saint Vincent following destruction by an eruption about 60 years ago, *O. subcavata* invades on canopy branches.

The area where species are most numerous is a zone of lush rain forest between 300 and 800 meters elevation. Here one finds a characteristic thelotreme flora on tree bases and buttresses: *O. concolor, O. papillata, O. perforata,* and *Thelotrema glaucopallens.* In the canopy, however, *O. olivacea, O. subcavata, O. terebratula,* and *Thelotrema praestans* dominate.

Above 800 meters the rain forest becomes stunted and intergrades with a wind-swept elfin forest of *Clusia* where few thelotremes are found. Some species, however, are confined to this zone: *Thelotreme tuberculiferum* (first described from Guadeloupe in 1914 and rediscovered on Dominica), *T. guadeloupense,* and *T. leucomelaenum* (a widespread tropical montane species).

The thelotreme flora is also very depauperate in the dry thorn forests on the leeward coasts of all the islands. The characteristic species are *Leptotrema bahianum, L. occultum, L. wightii,* and *Phaeotrema disciforme.*

Origin of the Flora

The Lesser Antilles are volcanic in origin and, geologically speaking, Recent. Most plant groups and foliose lichens are much more poorly represented here than on the large West Indian islands (especially Hispaniola and Jamaica). The thelotremes are exceptional in that they are much more abundant in the Lesser Antilles than in the western Caribbean. Our problem is to explain how this situation came about by analyzing how many species can be accounted for by migration from adjacent or more distant regions and how many actually evolved in the Lesser Antilles. Two factors make discussions of this nature tentative if not foolhardy. For one we know nothing of the means of reproduction in the thelotremes. It is assumed that spore dispersal, the only obvious means in evidence, is the chief process. Secondly, the level of collecting is notoriously poor in the thelotremes since the specimens are so inconspicuous and the characteristic fruiting bodies can only be detected with a hand lens.

The high level of endemism in the Lesser Antilles seems to indicate that species have indeed evolved there and have not simply migrated there. The midelevation rain forest has provided the ideal site for speciation. A similarly high level of speciation has been found in the Panamanian rain forests.

Continued collecting efforts in the Caribbean region will undoubtedly show that some "endemics" are more widespread than anticipated. *Thelotrema papillosum,* for example, was described from Dominica, but has recently been collected in the mountains near Caracas, Venezuela. *Thelotrema norsticticum* was known only from Trinidad until I collected it again in Panama. A very striking case is *T. subsimile,* which I described from Trinidad but which has also been found in the Philippines.

We cannot rule out the Lesser Antilles as the point of origin for these species, however, since the prevailing easterly trade winds could easily carry spores westward to the western Caribbean, northern South America, and Panama. This could include at least some of the 24 species, almost half of the thelotreme flora of the Lesser Antilles, which are more or less common in the Caribbean basin. Certainly some evolved in the Lesser Antilles and migrated westward.

The pan-tropical element comprises those species that occur around the world. There are 14 species in this category, most also occurring in the Philippine–Malaysian region.

A continental element which would be characteristic of the South American landmass is, perhaps, expectedly, not well developed in the Lesser Antilles. For example, Trinidad, which is virtually a part of South America, has five conspicuous species that do not occur northward in the Lesser Antilles: *Ocellularia glaziovii, O. sublilacina, Phaeotrema leprieurii, Thelotrema citrinodiscum,* and *T. norsticticum.* In these cases the potential invaders may have been cut off by the trade winds.

Perhaps as significant in interpreting the thelotreme flora is an analysis of species which do not occur in the Lesser Antilles but which are known from Cuba or other larger islands and neighboring landmasses. This group comprises 31 species, for example, known from Cuba and Jamaica, about half the flora of the western Caribbean. Some of these may have evolved in the Lesser Antilles, migrated out, and then become extinct in the Antilles. Most probably evolved in the western Caribbean, and in fact many of them seem to be common in relatively low secondary or drier forest.

The more geographically remote Panamanian thelotreme flora has 42 species in common with the Lesser Antilles and, perhaps significantly, this is about half the total flora of 86 species, the same proportion as the western Caribbean. Many of the species which do not also occur in the Lesser Antilles are found at higher elevations in Panama.

The evidence for chemical evolution is still under investigation (see Hale, 1974). Generally speaking, no new substances seem to have evolved in the Lesser Antilles. The commonest acids are psoromic acid and protocetraric acid. The "cinchonarum" unknown, so common in the thelotreme flora of South America, is very rare.

Further speculation on the origin of the thelotremes in the Lesser Antilles will have to await field studies in Cuba, Jamaica, Central America, and northern South America.

REFERENCES

HALE, M. E.

1973a. Studies on the lichen family Thelotremataceae. 1. Phytologia, vol. 26, pp. 413-420.

1973b. Studies on the lichen family Thelotremataceae. 2. Phytologia, vol. 26, pp. 490-501.

1974. Morden–Smithsonian Expedition to Dominica: The lichens (Thelotremataceae). Smithsonian Contr. Bot., no. 16, 45 pages.

MASON E. HALE, JR.

Chromosomes, Speciation, and Evolution of Mexican Iguanid Lizards

Principal Investigator: William P. Hall III, Museum of Comparative Zoology, Harvard University, Cambridge, Massachusetts.[1]

Grant Nos. 864 and 957. For study of the biogeography of karyotype variation in the iguanid lizard (1970) and comparative population cytogenetics and evolutionary roles of vertebrate genetic systems (1971).

Background

Many evolutionary biologists have believed for a long time, almost as a dogma, that essentially all animal speciation is initiated by the separation of ancestral species into geographically isolated subdivisions, and that only if these subdivisions are isolated long enough to evolve incipient reproductive isolating mechanisms will they remain evolutionarily independent species if they come into secondary contact (Mayr, 1942, 1963, 1970). Bush (1975) and White (1968, 1978) among others, however, have asserted and have fairly convincingly shown in their recent major works that there are probably a variety of qualitatively different modes of speciation, at least for animals with relatively limited dispersal abilities. Less convincingly, they claim that geographic isolation may be involved as an initiating factor in only a small fraction of all speciation events. My research on Mexican iguanid lizards represents an attempt to reconstruct in detail speciation patterns for this one group of vertebrates; such a study should provide some solid statistical evidence relative to this controversy.

The revolutionary difference in the views of the two groups of biologists cited above probably results from the different scientific paradigms (Kuhn, 1970) followed by each, and this difference needs to be understood before the approach followed by my research can be assessed. One paradigm (oversimplified), begins with a hypothetical model of species formation which is then tested by finding cases that fit it and by demonstrating that the model rarely can be disproved as a plausible explanation for any case. Since the formation of

[1] Present affiliation Department of Genetics, University of Melbourne, Parkville, Victoria 3052, Australia.

most species can be plausibly accounted for by models involving geographic isolation and since it is very difficult to prove that an alternative explanation must apply to any given case, it has been accepted by workers following this paradigm that most speciation is geographic. The other paradigm is based on the still poorly understood and nowhere explicitly formulated paradigm of comparative biology (Ghiselin, 1969, 1977; Hull, 1973, 1974; Platnick and Gaffney, 1978; see also Salmon, 1967; Skyrms, 1975). Briefly (and also oversimplified) this paradigm begins with the assumptions that each process resulting in speciation is a unique and unrepeatable sequence of events, but that there are probably only a relatively few (but possibly more than one) underlying stochastic mechanisms, or "natural laws," involved. The methodology followed is then: (1) to survey nature to see if distinctive modes of correlated phenomena can be found among the totality of those potentially related to speciation; (2) to develop as many different hypotheses as seem reasonable to explain each of the modes of correlation; and (3) to develop a better understanding of the actual reality of speciation processes by attempting to falsify, at least in a statistical sense, assumptions, logic, and/or predictions of one or more of the hypotheses offered to explain given modes. When the comparative paradigm is used for studying evolutionarily closely related organisms, it gains utility and power from the fact that many extraneous variables can be controlled or kept constant because the species are genetically similar, and much of their biology and history is shared. Properly selected "natural experiments" should vary primarily in the phenomena of interest.

The lizard family Iguanidae has been stable in its definition and content of genera at least since the time of Cope (1900), and there is no reason to believe that it is anything but a monophyletic grouping of species (Paull et al., 1976). With about 50 genera and probably more than 600 species, the family offers a rich resource for comparative biology. The North American segment of the family offers about 14 well-known genera (depending on the taxonomist), which include 130 named species. All but 22 of these belong to a natural group of 9 closely related genera that form the sceloporine division of the family (Etheridge, 1964; Presch, 1969; Hall, 1973; Paull et al., 1976). In the sceloporine radiation *Sceloporus* is probably the most recently derived, yet it includes 64 named species with an actual count that I believe to be at least 75. No other iguanid genus endemic to North America includes more than 14 species by anyone's taxonomy (Paull et al., 1976).

My undergraduate advisor, Don Hunsaker II, pointed out this situation to me and suggested that it would be a good research problem to try to explain why the phylogenetically recent *Sceloporus* have proliferated a vast array of species over a phylogenetically short time when compared with the other 8 related, and probably older, sceloporine genera, all of which have few species. From results obtained in an undergraduate cytogenetics course project, I found that *Sceloporus* appeared to be chromosomally more variable than other iguanid genera (Painter, 1921; Matthey, 1931; Cavazos, 1951; Schroeder, 1962; Zeff, 1962). It occurred to me that the phenomena of possibly unusual chromosomal variability and anomalously prolific speciation in *Sceloporus* might be causally related, and that the excess number of species might have resulted from the fact that the genetic system of *Sceloporus* allowed alternative modes of speciation not possible for the related genera (Hall, 1963). My initial explorations in the southwestern United States and adjacent Mexico to test the correlation convinced me that the concentration of chromosomal variation in *Sceloporus* was probably real (Hall, 1965). For my Master's degree work under Ralph W. Axtell, I explored the sceloporine radiation for recent cases of anomalously rapid speciation and/or chromosomal differentiation not associated with speciation, and for appropriate controls for any such cases. Partially supported by Society Sigma Xi funds in 1966 and the National Science Foundation (grant to the Evolutionary Biology Committee at Harvard) and Sigma Xi in 1968, I further confirmed the concentration of chromosomal diversity in *Sceloporus* and its absence in the other sceloporines. As a Ph.D. student at Harvard University under Ernest E. Williams, in the 1968 field season I finally located a case of chromosomal variation of the kind normally fixed between species in what was believed to be a single species, *Sceloporus grammicus*. I then requested support from the National Geographic Society for detailed studies of the chromosomal variability and other aspects of the biology of *Sceloporus grammicus* and for comparative studies of other sceloporine species.

The most important goals of the expeditions supported by the Society were: (1) to document the nature of the chromosomal variability both within and between populations in the *grammicus* complex, (2) to do control studies on presumably chromosomally invariant relatives, and (3) to determine the genetic interactions of chromosomally different populations meeting in geographic contacts. Subsidiary, but essential, goals were to learn as much as possible about the cytogenetics and other aspects of the biologies of the other sceloporines so the various factors involved in the origin of the other species could also be reconstructed.

Methodology and Material Examined

After colchicine pretreatment of the whole animal, karyotypes were determined by direct cell suspension methods similar to those of Evans et al. (1964) and Patton (1967). Testis, bone marrow, spleen, and the mucosal epithelium of intestine were all used as sources of dividing cells. To have rapid feedback for directing collection efforts, most chromosome preparations were made and initially scored in Mexico, working with portable laboratory facilities set up either in motels close to collecting areas or in available laboratory space. Lic. Ticul Alvarez S. of the Escuela Nacional de Ciencias Biologicas of the Instituto Politecnico Nacional in Mexico City and Dr. Rene Millon of the Teotihuacán Mapping Project in San Juan Teotihuacán, both kindly provided laboratory space in close proximity to the most important study areas. Most karyotyped specimens were preserved and are entered in the herpetological collection of the Museum of Comparative Zoology, along with several hundred additional specimens collected but not karyotyped, thereby adding significantly to the reference collections for Mexican herpetology. Methods of tissue preparation—starch-gel electrophoresis, and protein staining used in allozyme analyses (Hall and Selander, 1973)—were similar to those of Selander et al. (1971), as modified for lizards by Webster et al. (1972) and McKinney et al. (1972).

During the 2 years of National Geographic Society support, collections were made in all states of Mexico north of the Isthmus of Tehuantepec, except Aguascalientes. In 1970 I was in the field from June 19 through October 16, assisted through mid-September by Scott M. Moody, who then returned to classes. He was replaced by Timothy Dickinson, a part-time curatorial assistant from the Museum of Comparative Zoology herpetology department. Moody, a Harvard undergraduate, developed his Honors Thesis (Moody, 1971) from materials and observations he collected during the expedition. Most work in 1970 focused on northern and western parts of the Mexican Plateau and on the contacts between the P1 and F6 populations of *Sceloporus grammicus* along the eastern divide of the Valley of Mexico. Moody and I roughly determined the nature and geography of the P1 × F6 contact by spot sampling. Then, with the aid of Ticul Alvarez and some of his students, we surveyed a 600-meter-long transect across the hybrid zone and collected a large series of individuals whose collection localities were recorded accurately to the nearest 2 meters. These were karyotyped in Mexico and immediately frozen on dry ice for transport to Robert Selander's laboratory at the University of Texas where they were electrophoresed. Chromosomal and electrophoretic markers were then used to reconstruct the dynamics of the hybridization known to occur in the contact zone. In 1971 I made one solo trip, from March 21 through May 10, to northern Baja California to collect chromosomally primitive sceloporines, down along the west coast of Mexico via Guadalajara to collect a primitive relative of the *grammicus* complex, and then to the Valley of Mexico to make behavioral observations on *grammicus* populations in the area of the previous year's transects. During the summer I was in the field from June 24 through October 5, assisted by Harvard undergraduates R. B. Stamm and Seth Reichlin. Most work during this period focused on the eastern and southern parts of the Mexican Plateau and on the contact between the S and FM2 populations in the Teotihuacán Archeological Zone. In the Teotihuacán study we were very greatly assisted by the availability of the 1:6000 base map of the Archeological Zone prepared by the Teotihuacán Mapping Project, kindly provided by Dr. Rene Millon (see Millon, 1970).

During the 2 years of the project, over 900 individuals of the *Sceloporus grammicus* complex and about 500 of other species were karyotyped. These, along with specimens from earlier collections, bring the karyotypic data for analysis to about 1,250 individual *grammicus* and over 1,000 individuals of all other species combined. The papers by Cole (1970; 1971a,b; 1972) and his colleagues (Cole and Lowe, 1968; Cole et al., 1967), and by Pennock et al. (1969), and Gorman (1973) among others, add data on perhaps another 300-400 individual sceloporines. Altogether, 57 of the 75 *Sceloporus* species I currently recognize have been karyotyped, and all but 3 of these are represented in my own karyology collection. Also, 30 of the other 44 sceloporine species have been karyotyped.

These data, combined with other biological observations, distributional data, and information from the massive literature on the biology and systematics of sceloporines allow the phylogenetic history of most of the genera to be reconstructed well enough to enable mechanisms to be ascribed to a large proportion of at least the last rounds of speciation events. Unfortunately though, due to a 4-year delay caused by the conflicting demands of my employment, only a few papers have yet been published on this synthesis (Hall and Selander, 1973; Smith and Hall, 1974; Dassmann and Smith, 1974; Paull et al., 1976; Hall and Smith, 1978), and some aspects of the data reduction are still incomplete. However, several papers that will present the major findings of the research are currently in active preparation, and the results of these are summarized here in preliminary form.

Results

1. With over 50 percent of the species in each of the 9 sceloporine genera karyotyped, no genus other than *Sceloporus* shows interspecific differences in karyotypes—all species are characterized by closely similar 2n = 34, xy♂ patterns. Most speciation outside of *Sceloporus* itself can plausibly be associated with evident Pliocene and Pleistocene ecological or geographic barriers (e.g., Norris, 1958; Morafka, 1977). No sceloporine genus other than *Sceloporus* includes more than 14 species.

2. All sceloporines except the primitive *Petrosaurus* (Etheridge, 1964; Presch, 1969) derive from a common ancestral species which had evolved a suite of skeletal, nasal, and behavioral features which enabled individuals to submerge themselves in loose sand for sleeping and escape cover—a suite of characters which would probably be selectively favored only in sandy desert conditions. This implies that differentiation of the various sceloporine genera from a *Petrosaurus*-like ancestor probably did not occur until the xeric adapted Madro Tertiary Geoflora became established in the Miocene (Axelrod, 1950).

3. As suggested by Smith (1939) *Sceloporus* divides into 2 major lineages, a small-sized, small-scaled branch and a large-sized, large-scaled branch. The small-scaled species are morphologically and (usually) chromosomally more conservative than the large-scaled species (Hall, in preparation). Of 16 small-scaled species, 11 are known or suspected on the basis of their relationships, to retain the primitive 2n = 34xy♂ karyotype. This radiation centers on the Chihuahuan desert; and, like the other sceloporine genera, most speciation in it is ascribable to evident ecological and geologic barriers.

4. The small-scaled species include at least 2 independent sequences of chromosomal derivation. One leads by a sequence of 6 centric fissions to the 2n = 46xy♂ *S. merriami*. It may involve only this species, although there is unconfirmed evidence that at least one population of *S. maculosus* may be karyotypically intermediate in the evolution of the *merriami* karyotype (Carol Axtell, unpublished). The other leads, by a sequence of centric fusions, to the 2n = 24xy♂ species *S. aeneus* and *S. scalaris*. The possibly recently extinct *S. goldmani* has not been karyotyped, but based on morphological relationships it could conceivably be karyotypically intermediate in the *scalaris* lineage. Both *merriami* and *scalaris* stocks are highly specialized. *S. merriami* live on vertical cliff faces and *scalaris, aeneus,* and *goldmani* are close or obligate commensals of bunch grass.

5. The large-scaled branch of *Sceloporus* includes only 4 species which retain the primitive 2n = 34xy♂ karyotype: *orcutti, hunsakeri, licki,* and *nelsoni* (Hall and Smith, 1978). These species are either restricted to Baja California or the Mexican mainland opposite the southern end of the Peninsula. These 4 large-scaled species are morphologically more closely related to the small-scaled species than are any of the other large-scaled species, and clearly represent direct survivors of the ancestral large-scaled stock. The stock appears to derive from portions of the small-scaled radiation still centered in the Chihuahuan desert. The separation of these 4 conservative species is most plausibly associated with the formation of the Gulf of California and the separation of the Cape Region of the Peninsula from the Mexican mainland some 5 million years ago by plate tectonic processes (Atwater, 1970; Anderson, 1971). All

the remaining 53 or more large-scaled species are chromosomally derived with regard to the ancestral karyotype. Two major sublineages trace from a common ancestor with a derived 2n = 32 xy♂ karyotype and include 52 of the 53 chromosomally derived large-scaled species.

6. One of these 2 branches evolved still lower chromosome numbers. Surviving species with intermediate karotypes retain 2n's of: 30 (*S. graciosus* and *S.* [*magister*] *zosteromus*), 29x_1x_2y♂ (*S.* [*magister*] *rufidorsum*), and 26 + pericentric inversion of chromosome pair 1 (the mainland *S. magister*). Twenty-three species are known or suspected by their close relationships to have 2n = 22 or even more derived karyotypes. I regard it highly significant: (a) that the entire sequence of chromosomal derivation seems to have been confined to a possibly short period of the Pliocene and to the area around the upper end of the Gulf of California, where there is no evidence for major geographic barriers; (b) that the chromosomally most derived forms have expanded geographically to cover the entire North American continent except Baja California and adjacent deserts still occupied by chromosomally more primitive relatives; and (c) that chromosomally different lineages are frequently sympatric while there is little sympatry among chromosomally similar stocks.

7. The 23 2n = 22 species form 2 distinctive species groups: the northern egg-layers (egg-laying is a primitive trait) with 10 species, and the southern live-bearers (a derived trait), with about 13 species. Speciation in the egg-players is easily ascribable to isolation in refugia during Pleistocene glacial periods. Too little is known about the southern live-bearers to even allow an accurate determination of the number of species the group includes. It is interesting, however, that the live-bearers include at least 2 pairs of syntopic siblings (*S. formosus* and *cryptus*, and *formosus* and *adleri*) which show no obvious chromosomal differences.

8. The second major branch of lineages deriving from the 2n = 32xy♂ stock includes many species which still retain a 2n = 32 in females but have evolved a 2n = 31x_1x_2y♂. Evidently the common ancestor of this branch of lineages was also polymorphic for a great enlargement of chromosome pair 9 (the Em 9 mutation). This mutation appears to have been established as a polymorphism in the Pliocene. Two lineages trace back to the 2n = 32xy♂ polymorphic Em 9 stock, and both retain the Em 9 mutation, either still present as a polymorphism (!), or fixed in some species and lost in others.

9. The first lineage involves a sequence of 4 centric fissions leading to the 2n = 40xy♂ *S. clarki* and the 2n = 39x_1x_2y♂ *S. melanorhinus*. Both species are polymorphic for the Em 9 mutation. No intermediates in the fission sequence appear to survive. *Clarki* occupies the western drainage of the Sierra Madre Occidental, immediately adjacent to the Sonoran Desert at the head of

the Gulf of California, where it is believed that the ancestral 2n = 32 stock once lived, and ranges south to the Río Grande de Santiago. No geographic barriers are evident in its derivation. Although *clarki* and *melanorhinus* differ in their sex chromosomes, they are also presently separated geographically by the Río Grande de Santiago, which also separates several other pairs of closely related species. *S. melanorhinus* ranges south from this river to Guatemala.

10. The second lineage deriving from the 2n = xy♂ polymorphic Em 9 stock includes only live-bearing species which have evolved a unique 2n = 31 male with an x_1x_2y sex chromosome system different from that of *S. melanorhinus*. Females retain the 2n = 32 karyotype. *S. asper*, the morphologically least specialized species in the radiation, is a tree lizard found at intermediate elevations in the western Sierra Volcánica Transversal. It is fixed for the Em 9 mutation. All the remaining species in the live-bearing lineage are specialized behaviorally and morphologically for using one or another form of crevice for cover: rocks, wood, or between the dried leaves of *Agave*.

11. The rock-crevice users include about 11 species (8 karyotyped) which occupy all rocky areas on the Mexican Plateau south to the Isthmus of Tehuantepec. One species *(S. serrifer)*, secondarily a tree-crevice user, is found on the eastern coastal plain and extends as far as the Yucatán Peninsula. There is no evidence for chromosomal variation within any of the 8 rock-crevice users karyotyped; all are fixed for the ancestral condition of pair 9 and all have the 2n = $31x_1x_2y$♂ karyotype. All speciation can easily be accounted for by isolation of populations on "insular" outcroppings of rock in a "sea" of alluvium. Frequently 2 species are sympatric but they usually differ enough in size so that they probably exploit different sized crevices. Often the outcrops are small enough so that founder effects could potentially play important roles in speciation.

12. There is only 1 species of *Agave* crevice user, *S. megalepidurus*, as shown by finding clear intergrades in my 1971 collections (Dassmann and Smith, 1974). Its morphological distinctiveness suggests that it was an early derivative of the crevice-using radiation, but details of its origin are obscured by the apparently more recent radiation of the wood-crevice users of the *S. grammicus* species group. *S. megalepidurus* is fixed for the Em 9 mutation and has the 2n = $31x_1x_2y$♂ karyotype.

13. The wood-crevice users include at least 4 morphospecies: *S. shannonorum*, *S. heterolepis*, and 2 presently included in *S. grammicus grammicus* (the nomenclature is ambiguous because both morphospecies are included among the syntypes of *grammicus* Wiegmann 1828). Three of the morphospecies are restricted to intermediate elevations along the western and southern sides of the Mexican Plateau: *shannonorum*—limited to areas north of the Río Grande de

Santiago; *heterolepis*—limited to areas between the Río Grande de Santiago and the Río Balsas; and *S. grammicus grammicus* sensu Smith (1939) and Smith and Laufe (1945)—found south of the Balsas. The fourth morphospecies (Smith's *S. g. microlepidotus* and *S. g. disparilis* subspecies) occupies the remainder of the Plateau and parts of the Gulf of Mexico coastal plain. Speciation of the 3 western forms is clearly associated with the major ecological barriers formed by the valleys of the Río Grande de Santiago and the Río Balsas, which completely separate the present populations. If the fourth species is derived from a *shannonorum*-like ancestor, as I believe likely, although the species are now almost certainly in contact, it probably became separated during a Pleistocene glacial epoch by climatic barriers along the crest of the Sierra Madre Occidental. Except for the chromosomally derived populations of the *grammicus* complex, all species have $2n = 31x_1x_2y♂$ karyotypes. The Em 9 mutation may be established in *S. grammicus grammicus* sensu Smith, and it is clearly absent in all of the remaining crevice users.

14. The morphospecies formed by *S. grammicus microlepidotus* and *S. g. disparilis* is a complex of 7 geographically parapatric cytotypes, whose distributions bear little relationship to the formally named subspecies:

S (standard—retains the $2n = 31x_1x_2y♂$) must have originally ranged over the area of the Mexican Plateau not held by the other 3 wood-crevice-using species, before it was then geographically displaced from parts of this range by the chromosomally derived stocks.

F6 ($2n = 33x_1x_2y♂$, fixed for a fission of pair 6) ranges from the Nevado de Colima in Jalisco to central portions of the Sierra Volcánica Transversal. In the area of the Valley of Mexico, F6 is found above 2,400 meters on the south and west, and between 2,400 and 3,200 meters on the east. Presently disjunct populations of F6 are also found in relict mesic areas of the Sierra Madre Occidental in San Luis Potosí, Tamaulipas, and Nuevo León.

P1 ($2n = 31\text{-}33x_1x_2y♂$, polymorphic for a fission of pair 1) is found on the eastern divide of the Valley of Mexico from 3,200 meters elevation to the treeline at about 4,000 meters, for a total range of about 700 square kilometers.

F5 ($2n = 33x_1x_2y♂$, fixed for a fission of pair 5) occupies the northernmost portions of the Sierra Madre Occidental in Chihuahua.

F5+6 ($2n = 35x_1x_2y♂$, fixed for fissions of pairs 5 and 6) occupies the southern portions of the Chihuahuan Desert, the low-lying central portions of the Sierra Madre Occidental in the Río de Pánuco drainage, and the Gulf of Mexico coastal slopes and plain northward to the Lower Rio Grande Valley of Texas.

FM1 (2n = 39-43x_1x_2y♂, fixed for fissions of pairs 2,4,5, and 6, polymorphic for fissions of pairs 1 and 3) is found in the northwest corner of Mexico state and central Hidalgo.

The seventh cytotype, *FM2* (2n = 43-45x_1x_2y♂, fixed for fissions of pairs 1,2,4,5,6, and 14, polymorphic for a fission of pair 3) is found in southern Hidalgo and in the northeastern corner of Mexico state.

Given that *S. grammicus* populations appear to be able to use all available wood-crevice cover within their geographic ranges and that such cover is more or less continuously available over the whole of the Mexican Plateau except for extreme areas of the Chihuahuan Desert, there is no evidence that *grammicus* populations were fragmented by the interposition of geographic barriers of the magnitude associated with most other speciation events in the sceloporines.

15. Parapatric contacts probably exist between all *S. grammicus* populations with adjacent ranges, but sampling points outside of the Valley of Mexico are still too widely scattered to have precisely located any of them. Based on more than 73 cytological sampling localities, 5 different kinds of parapatric contacts are likely: S and F6—sample sites about 40 km apart; S and F5+6—sample sites, respectively, 15 and 50 km apart; F6 and F5+6—sample sites about 50 km apart; F5+6 and Fm1—sample sites about 60 km apart; and FM1 and FM2—sample sites about 60 km apart. Based on more than 82 cytological sampling sites in the Valley of Mexico area, 3 different kinds of geographic contacts were precisely located: several contacts between P1 and F6 on the east side of the Valley of Mexico, all within 200 meters elevation of the 3,200-meter contour; contacts between S and FM2 in the Valley of the Río San Juan (mainly in the Teotihuacán Archeological Zone), which appear to follow the contact between igneous hill slopes and alluvial bottomland; and one contact between S and F6 north of Cuernavaca at about 2,400 meters elevation. Chromosomal hybrids were found in all of these situations, but in no case were pure populations on either side of the hybrid zone separated by more than 2 kilometers. The P1 × F6 (1970) and S × FM2 (1971) contacts were studied in detail.

16. Several chromosome sample transects were established across the P1 × F6 contact in the Río Frio area (Hall and Selander, 1973; Hall and others, in preparation). These demonstrated that the chromosomal transition from one pure population to the other was probably no more than about 500 meters wide. Once the approximate distribution and structure of the hybrid zone was established by chromosomal sampling alone, a previously unsampled transect area (west of Cerro Potrero) was selected and accurately surveyed before 153 *S. grammicus* were collected from it for electrophoresis and karyology.

Populations away from the contact were also electrophoresed to give some idea of genic variation within allopatric P1 and F6 populations. The disjunct F6 population on the Nevado de Colima, 500 kilometers to the west, is genetically more similar to F6 populations in the Río Frio area than are P1 populations collected 3 kilometers of dispersal distance to the east of the F6 sample site. Aside from the fixed chromosomal difference between P1 and F6, 3 protein loci, out of the total of 20-21 sampled in the 2 Río Frio-area populations, were fixed for alternative alleles. In the Cerro Potrero transect 2 proteins and the fixed chromosomal difference were used as genetic markers to determine the dynamics of what was happening in the hybrid zone. I conclude from these observations that:

a. Pure parental types meet and hybridize, with very little indication that either cytotype discriminates against mating with the other. F_1 hybrids are found at about the frequency one would expect from random matings of the individuals present in a neighborhood population.

b. The high frequency of individuals with backcross genotypes (heterozygous for 1 or 2 markers but not all 3) shows conclusively that F_1's are at least partially fertile and that first generation backcrosses must also be sufficiently fertile to allow significant introgression beyond the first generation of backcrossing (Hall and others, in preparation—this contradicts one of the conclusions of Hall and Selander, 1973).

c. Very paradoxically, all other evidence indicates that the hybrid zone functions over a very short distance (<3 kilometers) as a complete block to gene flow between the 2 pure populations, despite the evidence for hybrid fertility, successful backcrossing, and "introgression":

(1) P1 and F6 samples 3 kilometers apart, separated only by the continuous population inhabiting the hybrid zone, are genetically more different than 2 F6 populations separated by 500 kilometers and a geographic barrier!

(2) When the genetic structure of the Cerro Potrero transect is analysed microgeographically, 90 percent of the replacement of the genetic markers for one population by the markers for the other population appears to take place over a distance of about 500 meters. This is not an unreasonable dispersal distance for single individuals between the mating of their parents and their own mating. A 100 percent replacement certainly occurs in less than 3 kilometers; and extrapolating from the gene frequency versus distance curve, it appears that the genetic change is probably complete over a distance of about 1,500 meters.

(3) The change in gene frequency versus distance from the center of the hybrid zone appears to be exactly symmetrical on either side.

(4) Despite comments by Hall and Selander (1973) to the contrary,

based on external morphology P1 is probably derived from F6 rather than the chromosomally-more-similar S, and there is no evidence to indicate that P1 and F6 were ever geographically separated, although it is likely that the contact zone changed in altitude along with climatic fluctuations.

17. Similar results on the dynamics of hybridization were obtained from the transect between S and FM2 in the Teotihuacán Archeological Zone, for what is almost a secondary contact situation involving the 2 terminal races in a circle of derivation from the ancestral condition to the most derived. Here 5 fixed macrochromosomal differences serve as markers for the dynamics of hybridization. However, due to the extreme wariness of the *S. grammicus* in this area, and possibly also due to differences in the population structure, we did not obtain a large sample of individuals from the hybrid zone itself. The total sample from the mapped area of the Archeological Zone (Millon, 1970) included 73 pure S, 52 pure FM2, 7 F_1 hybrids (5 were female), 1 backcross to S, and 5 or 6 backcrosses to FM2 (1 could have been an F_2). Additionally, 1 individual was a 3n backcross to FM2, with 1 haploid S genome plus 2 haploid FM2 genomes. Hybrids, backcrosses, and mixed samples from this zone were limited to a belt about 500 meters wide running north-northwest from a line of stone fences crossing the "Street of the Dead" south of the Pyramid of the Sun, where the pure FM2 population was restricted to the wedge-shaped area between this belt and the Street of the Dead. Following Millon (1970) and Mooser (1968), FM2 *grammicus* probably did not enter the Valley of San Juan Teotihuacán until the hill slopes above the ancient city were catastrophically deforested during the period A.D. 200-600. The Street of the Dead, which was cleared of cover suitable for *grammicus* around 1913, appears to serve as a recent, local geographic barrier to impede FM2 west of the street from contacting S individuals on the east side of the street.

18. Aside from the evidence that the S × FM2 hybrid zone involves both hybridization and backcrossing and yet serves as a complete barrier to gene flow, the excessive number of females among the hybrids (although the sample size is too small for the disproportion to be statistically significant) combined with the discovery of a triploid backcross in the hybrid zone (only 3 other triploids, all *S. grammicus,* were discovered among the more than 1,200 *grammicus* and more than 1,500 other iguanids karyotyped), suggest, but do not prove, that some of the F_1 hybrids may have been reproducing parthenogenetically. If so, it may be possible to duplicate the S × FM2 hybridization in the laboratory to observe the origin of parthenogenetically reproducing hybrid clones under controlled conditions.

19. Data on the details of meiosis in the many chromosomally heterozygous individuals collected remains to be extracted from the prepared slides. It

seems probable, however, that meiotic malassortment from fusion or fission trivalents contributes to reduce the reproductive fitness of chromosomally heterozygous individuals relative to homozygotes, as has been demonstrated in mice (Capanna, 1976; Capanna et al., 1976; Cattanach and Moseley, 1973).

Conclusions

Without attempting to detail the logic by which they are inferred from the results, I have reached the following conclusions based primarily on the data collected during the Society-funded expeditions:

1. There clearly are at least two distinct modes of speciation operative in the sceloporine radiation, each with strikingly different evolutionary consequences:

a. By far the most common mode of speciation appears to involve the classical mechanics of geographic separation of large populations for long periods of time by the interposition of geographical, climatic, or ecological barriers (Mayr, 1963). All speciation in 8 of 9 sceloporine genera appears most plausibly to be geographic, and even in the exceptionally speciose *Sceloporus,* about 60 of 75 species show no evidence of chromosomal differences from their nearest relatives. Also, in most species pairs lacking chromosomal differentiation there is positive evidence suggesting that speciation sequences involved geographic isolation. At least for sceloporine lizards, this contradicts the conclusions of White, Bush, and Endler, cited earlier, that the majority of speciation in terrestrial organisms of limited vagility does *not* involve classical geographic isolation. However, although most speciation in the sceloporines has involved geographic isolation, it is also quite clear that such speciation is associated with very slow rates of evolutionary change. Genera showing only evidence for geographic speciation contain comparatively few species and show little ecological diversity.

b. Although only about 15/75 species of *Sceloporus* differ chromosomally from their closest relatives, all but 17 *Sceloporus* have at least 1 event of chromosomal differentiation in their ancestries. Where sequences of chromosomal differentiation leading to these species can plausibly be reconstructed: (1) chromosomal differentiation appears to be directly associated with the establishment of genetic isolation between the chromosomally differentiated populations, (2) there is little or no evidence that this differentiation was associated with the interposition of geographic barriers of the magnitude evident in most speciation events not associated with chromosomal changes, and (3) the observations imply that chromosomally derived populations frequently shift enough ecologically in the process of derivation so that they are quickly (in an evolutionary sense) able to coexist sympatrically with their ancestral stocks. Only in the very recent case of *S. grammicus,* where the chromosomal differentiation has occurred within an already highly specialized stock living in an environment where the surrounding habitat appears to be already saturated with other *Sceloporus* species, has such a shift not occurred. I regard it as highly significant: (1) that although most sceloporine species were evidently formed in geographic isolation, the great proliferations of species in *Sceloporus* all involved a history of chromosomal differentiation, and (2) that the unquestionably most widely distributed, successful, and most ecologically plastic lineage in the whole radiation (i.e., the radiation of $2n = 22$ species) is at the end of a long chain of chromosomal derivation.

From this I conclude that chromosomal speciation may occur without geographic isolation, either in a parapatric relationship as demonstrably seems to be the case in the *S. grammicus* complex, or possibly even in an initially sympatric relationship. Also competitive interactions between the initially small population of the nascent chromosomally differentiated species and its chromosomally conservative ancestral stock will frequently quickly force the derived species to differentiate enough ecologically to use previously underexploited limiting resources. Chromosomal speciation may be completed rapidly, and a linear sequence of such speciation events over short evolutionary times may result in great ecological shifts by comparison to the much more conservative mode of geographic speciation. Each chromosomal speciation event may, therefore, open to the derived lineage a new range of habitats that are sympatric to those used by the ancestral stock. Such forced differentiations will not occur in secondary contact situations between already widely distributed sibling species because competitive exclusion will prevent significant sympatry and because the great genetic inertia of the respective populations away from the areas of contact will slow evolutionary responses to local conditions.

2. The data from *Sceloporus grammicus* suggest a specific model for chromosomal speciation: All the observed chromosomal differences between species in *Sceloporus* have the potential for causing meiotic malassortment in chromosomal heterozygotes (for mechanical reasons), and thereby for reducing the reproductive fitness of chromosomally heterozygous individuals. Such mutations could never become fixed in a large randomly breeding population because selection against the much more frequent heterozygotes would quickly eliminate the initially rare rearrangement from the population. If, however, a species (due to its limited vagility in an environmental mosaic) has a population structure such that it is subdivided into a series of small demes (genetically effective sizes <10 individuals) with comparatively limited gene

flow between them (say <15 percent per generation), then there is a low, but evolutionarily reasonable, probability that such mutations may become fixed by random drift in a deme, despite even fairly strong selection against heterozygotes. If such a rearrangement becomes fixed, and further chance events allow the initially differentiated population to spread over a large enough area so that at least some of its individuals are geographically protected from the risk of hybridization with parental types by an intervening hybrid zone functioning like those demonstrated in the *grammicus* complex, then speciation in a genetic sense is already completed for the central population. For example, probably no P1 population is more than about 5 kilometers distant from the P1 × F6 hybrid zone, which is itself of the order of 500-1,000 meters wide; yet despite the complete absence of reproductive isolation between the 2 species in any classical sense, the P1 population has differentiated genetically to a greater extent than has a geographic isolate 500 kilometers away.

The key to such speciation lies in the dynamics of the genetic events in the zones of parapatric hybridization. If hybrid fitness is reduced for any reason (e.g., chromosomal heterozygosity): (a) A fraction of potentially introgressing genes will be lost in the first generation of hybridization because of more frequent than normal reproductive failures by the less fit hybrid individuals. (b) Also, because of reduced hybrid fitness, fewer individuals will be competing for limited resources in the hybrid zone by comparison to pure populations on either side of it, thus encouraging a net immigration of parental types from the pure populations into the hybrid zone that will result in a net gene flow *toward* the hybrid zone from each pure population. Such a flow will impede the diffusion of genes out of the hybrid zone. (c) Therefore, any genes surviving one passage through less fit hybrid genomes will still tend to be retained in the hybrid zone, where they risk being combined repeatedly in hybrid genotypes until they are inevitably lost. I call this process a hybrid sink, and the *S. grammicus* observations demonstrate conclusively that some such process effectively blocks gene flow through a hybrid zone well before hybrid or backcross fitness is reduced to the point of sterility.

3. The results of the sceloporine study further suggest that positive feedback processes may be involved in chromosomal speciation events to enhance the probability of further chromosomal speciation in chromosomally derived lineages relative to their ancestral stocks. Theoretically, it seems reasonable that the initial probability of chromosomal speciation depends on a variety of parameters of a lineage's genetic system (e.g., mutation rates, meiotic behavior of chromosomal rearrangements in heterozygotes, gametic and zygotic effects of rearrangements in balanced and unbalanced combinations, population structure, mating system, and vagility). Under normal circumstances, even

large changes in many of these parameters would seem to have little or no selective importance for the single individual or its immediate progeny. Therefore, although they may respond to selection over periods of time on the order of thousands or tens of thousands of generations, the frequencies of genes coding such parameters may be expected to show considerable random variability over a species' geographic range. Those demes that have especially favorable combinations of genes are most likely to form the founder populations for chromosomally derived species. Consequently, for thousands of generations, the derived species which evolves from this founder population may be expected to perpetuate an especially favorable combination of speciation parameters relative to the average for the ancestral stock as a whole. The chromosomally derived species will, therefore, be more likely to produce another even more derived species than will be the ancestral species. This second derivative will be still more likely to produce a third derivative than the first will be to produce another second, and so on.

If this positive feedback amplification process is working against selective forces, as no doubt will be the case, subsequent chromosomal speciation will probably occur rapidly—before a derived stock spreads much more geographically—or not at all. One chromosomal speciation event, therefore, may set the stage for an even more rapid progression of nongeographic speciation events in an otherwise conservatively speciating stock. These, for reasons discussed above, may also be associated with radical ecological shifts and the exploitation of new ways of making a living. Such a series of events will most frequently result in phylogenetically relatively long and unbranched chains of species, rather than in highly branched or fan-shaped phylogenies. Also, because they may have little opportunity to spread ecologically, chromosomally intermediate species are less likely to persist for evolutionarily long times than are ancestral and terminal stocks. Furthermore, chromosomal speciation sequences may be expected to involve primarily one kind of chromosomal mutation and to terminate with species that have either "used up" the substrate for that kind of mutation (e.g., sequences of centric fissioning that end in species with completely fissioned karyotypes) or that are polymorphic for the kind of mutations fixed between more primitive species in the chain of derivation. I call this process cascading or chain speciation. All these situations are observed in *Sceloporus* and can be demonstrated as significant modes in a number of insect or other vertebrate radiations (e.g., see White, 1973, 1978).

Finally, it should be noted that all of these models are predictive, at least in a statistical sense, and that they are susceptible to falsification through a variety of approaches involving attempts to refute their various predictions or still weakly substantiated premises. In other words, the National Geographic

Society-financed study has considerably advanced understanding of the species problem, but, as any good research study probably should, it has generated many more fruitful research questions than it has answered.

REFERENCES

ANDERSON, D. L.
1971. The San Andreas Fault. Sci. Amer., vol. 225, no. 5, pp. 52-68.

ATWATER, T.
1970. Implications of plate tectonics for the Cenozoic tectonic evolution of western North America. Bull. Geol. Soc. Amer., vol. 81, pp. 3513-3535.

AXELROD, D. I.
1950. Studies in Late Tertiary paleobotany. Carnegie Inst. Washington, Publ. no. 590, 323 pp., illus.

BUSH, G. L.
1975. Modes of animal speciation. Ann. Rev. Ecol. Syst., vol. 6, pp. 339-364.

CAPANNA, E.
1976. Gametic aneuploidy in mouse hybrids. Pp. 83-89 *in* "Chromosomes Today, vol. 5, Proceedings of the Leiden Chromosome Conference, July 15-17, 1974," 473 pp., P. L. Pearson and K. R. Lewis, eds. J. Wiley and Sons, New York.

CAPANNA, E.; GROPP, A.; WINKING, H.; NOACK, G.; and CIVITELLI, M.-V.
1976. Robertsonian metacentrics in the mouse. Chromosoma, vol. 58, pp. 341-353.

CATTANACH, B. M., and MOSELEY, M.
1973. Nondisjunction and reduced fertility caused by the tobacco mouse metacentric chromosomes. Cytogenet. Cell Genet., vol. 12, pp. 264-287.

CAVAZOS, L. F.
1951. Spermatogenesis of the horned lizard *Phrynosoma cornutum.* Amer. Natur., vol. 85, pp. 373-379.

COLE, C. J.
1970. Karyotypes and evolution of the *spinosus* group of lizards in the genus *Sceloporus.* Amer. Mus. Novitates, no. 2431, 47 pp.
1971a. Karyotypes of the five monotypic species groups of lizards in the genus *Sceloporus.* Amer. Mus. Novitates, no. 2450, 17 pp.
1971b. Karyotypes and relationships of the *pyrocephalus* group of lizards in the genus *Sceloporus.* Herpetologica, vol. 27, pp 1-8.
1972. Chromosome variation in North American fence lizards (genus *Sceloporus; undulatus* species group). Syst. Zool., vol. 21, pp. 357-363.

COLE, C. J., and LOWE, C. H.
1968. The karyotype of a lizard *(Sceloporus virgatus)* and description of a spontaneous chromosomal aberration. J. Arizona Acad. Sci., vol. 5, pp. 128-130.

COLE, C. J.; LOWE, C. H.; and WRIGHT, J. W.
1967. Sex chromosomes in lizards. Science, vol. 155, pp. 1028-1029.

COPE, E. D.

1900. The crocodilians, lizards, and snakes of North America. Ann. Rept. U. S. Nat. Mus., 1898, part 21, pp. 151-1294.

DASSMANN, M. M., and SMITH, H. M.

1974. A new sceloporine lizard from Oaxaca, Mexico. Great Basin Natur., vol. 34, pp. 231-237.

ENDLER, J. A.

1977. Geographic variation, speciation, and clines. Monogr. Pop. Biol., no. 10, 246 pp., illus. Princeton Univ. Press.

ETHERIDGE, R.

1964. The skeletal morphology and systematic relationships of sceloporine lizards. Copeia, vol. 1964, pp. 610-631.

EVANS, E. P.; BRECKON, G.; and FORD, C. E.

1964. An air-drying method for meiotic preparations from mammalian testes. Cytogenetics, vol. 3, pp. 289-294.

GHISELIN, M. T.

1969. The triumph of the Darwinian method, 287 pp. Univ. California Press, Berkeley.

1977. On paradigms and the hypermodern species concept. Syst. Zool., vol. 26, pp. 437-438.

GORMAN, G. C.

1973. The chromosomes of the Reptilia, a cytotaxonomic interpretation. Pp. 349-424 *in* "Cytotaxonomy and Vertebrate Evolution," 783 pp., A. B. Chiarelli and E. Capanna, eds. Academic Press, London.

HALL, W. P.

1963. Cytogenetic studies in the family Iguanidae. (Unpubl. MS, San Diego State University, 1963.)

1965. Preliminary chromosome studies of some Nevada Test Site lizards. Paper read at the 1965 Annual Meeting of the American Society of Ichthyologists and Herpetologists, Lawrence, Kansas. (Unpublished MS.)

1973. Comparative population cytogenetics, speciation, and evolution of the iguanid lizard genus *Sceloporus*. Ph.D. thesis, Harvard University, 250 pp., illus.

——. Cascading chromosomal speciation and the paradoxical role of contact hybridization as a sink for gene flow. (Submitted to Evolutionary Theory. Informally published in 1977 by unauthorized but widespread photocopying from MS.)

——. An evolutionist in an epistemological wonderland. Preface (1979) to cascades and sinks. (Submitted to Evolutionary Theory.)

——. Modes of speciation and evolution in the sceloporine iguanid lizards. I. Solving the problem of iguanid speciation: epistemology and heuristics of the comparative approach. Papéis Avulsos de Zoologia, São Paulo. (In press.)

HALL, W. P., and SELANDER, R. K.

1973. Hybridization of karyotypically differentiated populations in the *Sceloporus grammicus* complex (Iguanidae). Evolution, vol. 27, pp. 226-242.

HALL, W. P., and SMITH, H. M.
1979. Lizards of the *Sceloporus orcutti* complex of the Cape Region of Baja California. Breviora Mus. Comp. Zool., No. 452, 26 pp.

HULL, D. L.
1973. Introduction. Pp. 1-77 *in* "Darwin and His Critics: The Reception of Darwin's Theory of Evolution by the Scientific Community," 473 pp., D. L. Hull, ed. Harvard Univ. Press, Cambridge.
1974. Philosophy of biological science, 148 pp. Prentice-Hall, Inc., Englewood Cliffs.

KUHN, T. S.
1970. The structure of scientific revolutions, ed. 2, 210 pp. Univ. Chicago Press.

MATTHEY, R.
1931. Chromosomes de reptiles. Sauriens, Ophidiens, Cheloniens. L'evolution de formule chromsomiale chez les Sauriens. Rev. Suisse Zool., vol. 38, pp. 117-186.

MAYR, E.
1942. Systematics and the origin of species, 334 pp., illus. Columbia Univ. Press, New York.
1963. Animal species and evolution, 787 pp., illus. Harvard Univ. Press, Cambridge.
1970. Populations, species and evolution, 454 pp., illus. Harvard Univ. Press, Cambridge.

MCKINNEY, C. O.; SELANDER, R. K.; JOHNSON, W. E.; and YANG, S. Y.
1972. Genetic variation in the side-blotched lizard *(Uta stansburiana). In* "Studies in Genetics," vol. 7, Univ. Texas Publ., no. 7213, pp. 307-318.

MILLON, R.
1970. Teotihuacan: Completion of map of giant ancient city in the Valley of Mexico. Science, vol. 70, pp. 1077-1082.

MOODY, S. M.
1971. Aspects of behavior affecting gene exchange between two parapatric sibling species of the *Sceloporus grammicus* complex (Sauria, Iguanidae). B. A. honors thesis, Harvard College, 57 pp., illus.

MOOSER, F.
1968. Geologia, naturaleza y desarrollo del Valle de Teotihuacan. Inst. Nac. Antropol. Hist., ser. Invest., vol. 17, pp. 29-49.

MORAFKA, D. J.
1977. A biogeographical analysis of the Chihuahuan Desert through its herpetolfauna. Biogeographica, vol. 9, 313 pp., illus. Dr. W. Junk B. V., publishers, The Hague.

NORRIS, K. S.
1958. The evolution and systematics of the iguanid genus *Uma* and its relation to the evolution of other North American desert reptiles. Bull. Amer. Mus. Nat. Hist., vol. 144, pp. 247-326.

PAINTER, T. S.
1921. Studies in reptilian spermatogenesis. I. The spermatogenesis of lizards. Journ. Exp. Zool., vol. 34, pp. 281-327.

PATTON, J. L.
1967. Chromosome studies of certain pocket mice, genus *Perognathus* (Rodentia: Heteromyidae). Journ. Mammal., vol. 48, pp. 27-37.

PAULL, D.; WILLIAMS, E. E.; and HALL, W. P.
1976. Lizard karyotypes from the Galapagos Islands: Chromosomes in phylogeny and evolution. Breviora Mus. Comp. Zool. no. 441, 31 pp.

PENNOCK, L. A.; TINKLE, D. W.; and SHAW, M. W.
1969. Minute Y chromosome in the lizard genus *Uta* (family Iguanidae). Cytogenetics, vol. 8, pp. 9-19.

PLATNICK, N. I., and GAFFNEY, E. S.
1978. Evolutionary biology: A Popperian perspective. Syst. Zool., vol. 27, pp. 137-141.

PRESCH, W.
1969. Evolutionary osteology and relationships of the horned lizard genus *Phrynosoma* (family Iguanidae). Copeia, vol. 1969, pp. 250-275.

SALMON, W. C.
1967. The foundations of scientific inference, 157 pp. Univ. Pittsburgh Press.

SCHROEDER, G.
1962. Chromosome studies in the genus *Sceloporus*. (Unpublished MS, San Diego State University).

SELANDER, R. K.; SMITH, M. H.; YANG, S. Y.; JOHNSON, W. E.; and GENTRY, J. B.
1971. Biochemical polymorphism and systematics in the genus *Peromyscus*. I. Variation in the old-field mouse *(Peromyscus polionotus)*. Studies in Genetics, vol. 6, Univ. Texas Publ., no. 7103, pp. 49-90.

SKYRMS, B.
1975. Choice and chance: An introduction to inductive logic, ed. 2, 220 pp. Dickenson Publ. Co., Inc., Encino.

SMITH, H. M.
1939. The Mexican and Central American lizards of the genus *Sceloporus*. Zool. Ser. Field Mus. Nat. Hist., vol. 26, pp. 1-397.

SMITH, H. M., and HALL, W. P.
1974. Contributions to the concepts of reproductive cycles and the systematics of the *scalaris* group of the lizard genus *Sceloporus*. Great Basin Natur., vol. 34, pp. 97-104.

SMITH, H. M., and LAUFE, L. E.
1945. Mexican amphibians and reptiles in the Texas coperative wildlife collections. Trans. Kansas Acad. Sci., vol. 48, pp. 325-354.

WEBSTER, T. P.; SELANDER, R. K.; and YANG, S. Y.
1972. Genetic variability and similarity in the *Anolis* lizards of Bimini. Evolution. vol. 26, pp. 523-535.

WHITE, M. J. D.
1968. Models of speciation. Science, vol. 159, pp. 1065-1070.
1973. Animal cytology and Evolution, ed. 3, 961 pp., illus. Cambridge Univ. Press.
1978. Modes of speciation, 455 pp., illus. W. H. Freeman and Company, San Francisco.

ZEFF, E. W.
1962. A technique for delineation of chromosomal constitution of reptilian leucocytes grown in culture. (Unpublished MS, Univ. California, Los Angeles.)

WILLIAM P. HALL III

The Paleoecology of Dry Cave, New Mexico

Principal Investigator: Arthur H. Harris, Museum of Arid Land Biology, University of Texas at El Paso, Texas.

Grant No. 929: For study of the Pleistocene ecology of Dry Cave, New Mexico.

Dry Cave, at an elevation of 4,200 feet, lies in southeastern New Mexico about halfway between the Guadalupe Mountains to the west and the Pecos River to the east. The area now is semiarid with a vegetation transitional between the Lower Sonoran life zone of the Chihuahuan Desert and the Upper Sonoran life zone. The area is described in some detail by Harris (1970).

The cave consists of mazes on several levels (see fig. 1). These connect vertically by fissure systems, some of which have intersected the ground surface in the past; only one remains unclogged, forming the present entrance to the cave. The entrances, past and present, have served as roosting places for raptorial birds, as pitfalls for unwary large mammals, as dens for smaller mammals and reptiles, and as drainageways for water-carried debris. The resultant deposits have preserved samples of the animal life extant at the times the fissures were open to the surface.

Preliminary investigations of mammals (Harris, 1970), herpetiles (Holman, 1970), and mollusks (Metcalf, 1970), and a subsequent 4-week field expedition had been completed before National Geographic Society aid was requested. The grant allowed a second 4-week expedition, followed by study of the material and data gathered. During the field portion, efforts were directed specifically toward clarifying the age relationships of the various sites as well as increasing samples from various time intervals. Of particular interest was a human vertebra found in 1970 near Pleistocene deposits; unfortunately, some earlier cave explorer obviously had laid the bone where it was found—we hoped to find its source during the 1971 expedition.

Further human remains were uncovered during the 1971 season, but only in post-Pleistocene deposits, despite extensive testing of the Pleistocene levels. The human-bearing strata lie in the present entrance chamber and postdate a C^{14} date of 11,880±250 BP (I-5987) associated with the uppermost Pleistocene fauna at a depth of 3.5 meters; a C^{14} determination of 3135±165 BP (I-6199) from the 80-100 centimeter level both predates and postdates human remains. Thus, although the amount of flowstone on the original vertebra and its position some distance from the nearest post-Pleistocene deposits still strongly suggest a Pleistocene age, the person who moved the bone to the position in which it was found has stymied proof.

The results of dating the various deposits show that there are two major time intervals represented in the cave: from ca. 34,000 to 25,000 BP and from ca. 15,000 BP to the present. The earlier dates are from deposits far back in the cave and, due to almost complete loss of bone collagens, were determined on bone carbonates; their accuracy on a fine scale is questionable, but they show the general order of magnitude.

The earliest date is 33,590±1550 BP (Tx-1773) on a combined sample from Museum of Arid Land Biology (MALB) Locality 26 (Room of the Vanishing Floor) and related Loc. 27 (above Room of the Vanishing Floor). A date of 29,290±1060 BP (Tx-1774) is available from MALB Loc. 1 and 17 (Lost Valley) and a date of 25,160±1730 BP (Tx-1775) from MALB Loc. 5 (Sabertooth Camel Maze). These dates indicate the faunas antedate the last Wisconsin stadial. The faunal evidence shown in table 1 agrees, seemingly representing a time with "temperatures less extreme than those of today and greater effective moisture, at least during the warm season" (Harris, 1978).

TABLE 1. List of Animals Identified From Older Dry Cave Deposits

Sites are: A — Lost Valley (MALB Loc. 1 and 17); B — Sabertooth Camel Maze (MALB Loc. 2 and 5); and C — Room of the Vanishing Floor (MALB Loc. 26 and 27). Identifications should be considered tentative. Extinct taxa are marked by a dagger.

Site A	Site B	Site C	*Taxon*	*Common name*
X	-	-	Osteichthyes	Fish
X	-	X	Amphibia	Amphibians
-	X	X	Chelonia	Tortoises
-	?	X	*Gopherus* sp.	Gopher tortoise
-	-	X	*Crotaphytus collaris*	Collared lizard
X	-	-	*Phrynosoma* sp.	Horned lizard
X	X	-	†*Breagyps clarki*	†Extinct condor
X	X	X	†*Coragyps occidentalis*	†Western vulture
-	-	X	*Falco peregrinus*	Peregrine falcon
-	X	-	†cf. *Parapavo*	†cf. Extinct turkey
-	-	X	†cf. *Strix brea*	†cf. Extinct owl
-	-	X	*Bubo virginianus*	Great horned owl
-	-	X	*Otus* sp.	Screech owl
X	-	?	*Corvus corax*	Common raven
X	X	X	†*Corvus neomexicanus*	†Extinct raven
X	-	-	*Plecotus* sp.	Big-eared bat
X	-	-	*Tadarida brasiliensis*	Brazilian free-tailed bat
cf	X	-	*Tadarida macrotis*	Big free-tailed bat

Site A	B	C	Taxon	Common name
-	-	X	†Edentata	†Sloth
X	X	X	*Sylvilagus* sp.	Cottontail
X	X	X	*Lepus* sp.	Jack rabbit
X	X	-	*Lepus californicus*	Black-tailed jack rabbit
X	-	-	*Spermophilus* sp.	Ground squirrel
X	-	-	*Cynomys* sp.	Prairie dog
X	X	X	Geomyidae	Pocket gophers
-	-	X	*Thomomys* sp.	Thomomys pocket gopher
-	X	-	*Pappogeomys castanops*	Yellow-faced pocket gopher
X	-	-	*Perognathus* sp.	Pocket mouse
X	X	-	*Dipodomys* sp.	Kangaroo rat
X	-	-	*Dipodomys spectabilis*	Banner-tailed kangaroo rat
X	-	X	*Peromyscus* sp.	White-footed mouse
X	-	-	*Onychomys leucogaster*	Northern grasshopper mouse
X	X	X	*Neotoma* sp.	Wood rat
X	-	-	*Sigmodon* sp.	Cotton rat
X	-	-	*Microtus ochrogaster*	Prairie vole
X	-	-	*Canis latrans*	Coyote
-	X	X	*Canis lupus*	Gray wolf
-	X	-	†*Canis dirus*	†Dire wolf
-	?	?	*Vulpes velox*	Swift fox
X	X	?	*Urocyon cinereoargenteus*	Gray fox
-	X	-	*Bassariscus* sp.	Ringtail
X	-	-	*Mustela frenata*	Long-tailed weasel
X	-	-	*Spilogale gracilis*	Western spotted skunk
-	X	X	*Felis* sp.	Cat
-	-	X	*Felis onca*	Jaguar
X	-	-	*Lynx rufus*	Bobcat
X	-	-	†*Tapirus* sp.	†Tapir
X	-	X	†*Equus* sp.	†Horse
X	X	?	†*Camelops* sp.	†Extinct camel
-	-	?	*Odocoileus* sp.	Deer
X	?	X	†*Breameryx* sp.	†Extinct small pronghorn

These older faunas are only now being examined in detail, but Hurley (1972) earlier studied the raptorial birds and Hornedo (1971) included the gray wolf (*Canis lupus*) and jaguar (*Felis onca*) material with her study of the more recent Dry Cave carnivores. A new species of raven currently is being described by Magish and Harris (1976).

The more recent cave deposits are found near the front of the cave, either associated with the present entrance (Entrance Fissure) or nearby Bison Sink. Most of the material reported by Harris (1970), Holman (1970), and Metcalf (1970) was associated with the now closed Bison Sink fissure. Faunal material believed to have originated from that source (MALB Loc. 6) was dated at

14,470±250 BP (Harris, 1970) and probably marks the approximate commencement of sedimentation; material from Loc. 4 is undated, but younger. A date that should be only slightly earlier than the closure date is 10,730±150 BP (I-6200) on bison and horse bone collagen from Loc. 54. Several taxa have been added to those published in 1970, notably the least shrew (*Cryptotis parva*) (Harris, Smartt, and Smartt, 1973). The known fauna is summarized in table 2.

TABLE 2. Taxa Identified From Dry Caves Sites Dating Between ca. 15,000 and ca. 10,700 B.P. (Extinct forms are marked by a dagger.)

Taxon	*Common name*
Osteichthyes	Fish
Ambystoma tigrinum	Tiger salamander
Scaphiopus bombifrons	Central plains spadefoot toad
Scaphiopus hammondi	Hammond's spadefoot toad
Bufo punctatus	Red-spotted toad
Bufo woodhousei	Woodhouse's toad
Pseudacris triseriata	Chorus frog
Rana pipiens	Leopard frog
Phrynosoma douglassi	Short-horned lizard
Phrynosoma cornutum	Texas horned lizard
Crotaphytus collaris	Collared lizard
Sceloporus undulatus	Eastern fence lizard
Elaphe guttata	Corn snake
Salvadora sp.	Patch-nosed snake
Thamnophis proximus	Ribbon snake
Thamnophis sp.	Garter snake
Crotalus atrox	Diamond-backed rattlesnake
Anatidae	Duck
?*Gymnogyps*	?Condor
† *Coragyps occidentalis*	† Western vulture
Cathartes aura (poss. Holocene)	Turkey vulture
Buteo jamaicensis	Red-tailed hawk
Buteo swainsoni	Swainson's hawk
Aquila chrysaetos	Golden eagle
Accipiter cooperi	Cooper's hawk
†?*Buteogallus fragilis*	†?Fragile eagle
Falco sparverius	Sparrow hawk
† *Caracara prelutosa*	† Extinct caracara
Charadriidae	Shorebirds
?*Numenius*	?Curlew
Tyto alba	Barn owl
Asio flammeus	Short-eared owl
Otus sp.	Long-eared owl
Bubo virginianus	Great horned owl
Speotyto cunicularia	Burrowing owl

Taxon	*Common name*
Galliformes	Galliform birds
Piciformes	Woodpeckers
Corvus corax	Common raven
Sorex vagrans	Vagrant shrew
Sorex merriami	Merriam's shrew
Cryptotis parva	Least shrew
Notiosorex crawfordi	Desert shrew
Myotis cf. *velifer*	cf. Cave myotis
† *Myotis* cf. *rectidentis*	† Extinct mouse-eared bat
† *Myotis* cf. *magnamolaris*	† Extinct mouse-eared bat
Eptesicus fuscus	Big brown bat
Lasiurus cf. *cinereus*	cf. Hoary bat
Plecotus cf. *townsendi*	Townsend's big-eared bat
† Edentata	† Sloth
Sylvilagus nuttalli	Nuttall's cottontail
Lepus townsendi	White-tailed jack rabbit
Marmota flaviventris	Yellow-bellied marmot
Spermophilus ? richardsoni	?Richardson's ground squirrel
Spermophilus tridecemlineatus	13-lined ground squirrel
Cynomys (*Leucocrossuromys*) sp.	Prairie dog, white-tailed group
Thomomys bottae	Botta's pocket gopher
Thomomys talpoides	Northern pocket gopher
Pappogeomys castanops	Yellow-faced pocket gopher
Perognathus sp. (small)	Small pocket mouse
Dipodomys spectabilis	Banner-tailed kangaroo rat
Reithrodontomys sp.	Harvest mouse
Peromyscus ? crinitus	?Canyon mouse
Peromyscus cf. *maniculatus*	cf. Deer mouse
Peromyscus leucopus (poss. Holocene)	White-footed mouse
Peromyscus ? boylei	?Brush mouse
Peromyscus cf. *difficilis*	Rock mouse
Onychomys leucogaster	Northern grasshopper mouse
Neotoma cf. *albigula*	cf. White-throated wood rat
Neotoma mexicana or *cinerea*	Mexican or bushy-tailed wood rat
Microtus longicaudus	Long-tailed vole
Microtus mexicanus	Mexican vole
Microtus ochrogaster	Prairie vole
Lagurus curtatus	Sagebrush vole
Ondatra zibethicus	Muskrat
Erethizon dorsatum	Porcupine
Canis latrans	Coyote
Canis lupus	Gray wolf
Vulpes velox	Swift fox
Ursus americanus	Black bear
Bassariscus sp.	Ringtail
Mustela frenata	Long-tailed weasel

Taxon	Common name
Mephitis mephitis	Striped skunk
Spilogale gracilis	Western spotted skunk
Conepatus mesoleucus	Hog-nosed skunk
Taxidea taxus	Badger
Felis sp.	Cat
† *Felis ? atrox*	† Extinct lion
Lynx rufus	Bobcat
† *Equus* cf. *conversidens*	† Extinct horse
† *Camelops ? hesternus*	† Extinct camel
† *Tanupolama* sp.	† Extinct llama
Odocoileus sp.	Deer
Antilocapra americana	Pronghorn
† *Breameryx* sp.	† Extinct small pronghorn
Ovis canadensis	Bighorn sheep
† *Bison* cf. *antiquus*	† Ancient bison

Unlike the deposits of Bison Sink, those of Entrance Fissure form essentially a continuous column some 10 meters deep. Deposits from the lowermost known chamber intersecting the fissure (Charlies Parlor) were C^{14} dated on bone collagen at 15,039±210 BP (I-6201); deposition is believed to have begun only slightly earlier. It is fill of about this age that has spilled from the fissure to form the Animal Fair and Hampton Court deposits (MALB Loc. 22) to the east and west of the fissure respectively; a tunnel driven through the fissure fill verifies the relationship.

A pit from the entrance chamber to Stalag 17 (MALB Loc. 23) allowed continuous sampling from the present into the Pleistocene deposits of the 11,880-year age mentioned earlier. Other tunnels connected this pit with Camel Room (MALB Loc. 25). Still other excavations allowed approximate estimation of the position of a minor passageway intersecting the fissure immediately under Stalag 17 and of the area where the human vertebra was found (Early Man Corridor, MALB Loc. 31). The approximate relationships of the major localities and C^{14} dates are shown in figure 1.

One locality (MALB Loc. 12) lies between the Entrance Fissure and the Bison Sink Fissure and also has received Recent material from the present entrance. Abundant material from trenching awaits study to determine the depositional history of this area.

Several hundred thousand bone elements are available from the cave front deposits, most with some associated chronological data. Study of this material will not be completed for years, but the studies thus far completed already have added immeasurably to our knowledge of the late Wisconsin in the

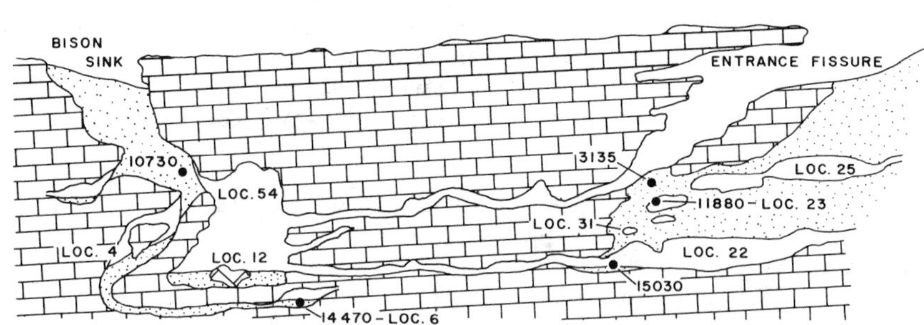

FIG. 1. Vertical relationships of the more recent Dry Cave fossil localities. Horizontal relationships are greatly distorted to bring the localities into a vertical plane. Fill is represented by stipple; C^{14} date localities by dots. Highly diagrammatic and not to accurate scale.

Southwest. These studies include those mentioned earlier (Hornedo, 1971; Hurley, 1972; Harris, 1970 and 1978; Holman, 1970; Metcalf, 1970; and Harris, Smartt, and Smartt, 1973). Additional papers include one clarifying the Pleistocene history of bighorn sheep (*Ovis canadensis*), based in part on a specimen from Charlies Parlor (Loc. 22) (Harris and Mundel, 1974); another involves the Dry Cave mollusks in paleoecological reconstruction (Metcalf, 1978).

Harris (1970) pointed out that Great Basin elements were notable in the Bison Sink material; additional data from the Dry Cave studies have served to emphasize this Great Basin element even more and also to bring out clearly the more complex nature of the Southwestern ecosystems during the late Pleistocene (Harris, 1978). Continued analysis of the material over the next few years should clarify even more the nature and timing of the changes occurring in the Southwest during the last 33,000 years.

REFERENCES

HARRIS, ARTHUR H.

1970. The Dry Cave mammalian fauna and late pluvial conditions in southeastern New Mexico. Texas Journ. Sci., vol. 22, pp. 3-27.

1978. Wisconsin age environments in the northern Chihuahuan Desert: Evidence from the higher vertebrates. Pp. 23-52 *in* "Symp. Biol. Res. Chihuahuan Desert, U. S. and Mexico," R. H. Wauer and D. H. Riskind, eds. Nat. Park Serv., Washington, D. C., 658 pp.

1978a. Paleontology. Pp. 69-77 *in* "The caves of McKittrick Hill, Eddy County, New Mexico," C. E. Kunath, ed. Texas Speleological Surv., Austin, 87 pp.

HARRIS, ARTHUR H., and MUNDEL, P.
1974. Size reduction in bighorn sheep (*Ovis canadensis*) at the close of the Pleistocene. Journ. Mamm., vol. 55, pp. 678-680.
HARRIS, ARTHUR H.; SMARTT, R. A.; and SMARTT, W. R.
1973. *Cryptotis parva* from the Pleistocene of New Mexico. Journ. Mamm., vol. 54, pp. 512-513.
HOLMAN, J. ALAN
1970. A Pleistocene herpetofauna from Eddy County, New Mexico. Texas Journ. Sci., vol. 22, pp. 29-39.
HORNEDO, M.
1971. Pleistocene carnivores of Dry Cave, Eddy County, New Mexico, 57 pp. Unpublished M.S. thesis, University of Texas, El Paso.
HURLEY, P. A.
1972. Late Pleistocene raptors from Dry Cave, Eddy County, New Mexico, 62 pp. Unpublished M.S. thesis, University of Texas, El Paso.
MAGISH, D., and HARRIS, A. H.
1976. Fossil ravens from the Pleistocene of Dry Cave, Eddy County, New Mexico. Condor, vol. 78, pp. 399-404.
METCALF, A. L.
1970. Late Pleistocene (Woodfordian) gastropods from Dry Cave, Eddy County, New Mexico. Texas Journ. Sci., vol. 22, pp. 41-46.
1978. Some Quaternary molluscan faunas from the northern Chihuahuan Desert and their paleoecological implications. Pp. 53-66 *in* "Symp. Biol. Res. Chihuahuan Desert U. S. and Mexico," R. H. Wauer and D. H. Riskind, eds. Nat. Park Serv., Washington, D. C., 658 pp.
VAN DEVENDER, T. R.; MOODIE, K. B.; and HARRIS, A. H.
1976. The desert tortoise (*Gopherus agassizi*) in the Pleistocene of the northern Chihuahuan Desert. Herpetologica, vol. 32, pp. 298-304.

ARTHUR H. HARRIS

Morphological and Ecological Studies of Sponges in Pacific Reef Caves

Principal Investigators: Willard D. Hartman, Yale University, New Haven, Connecticut, and Henry W. Reiswig, McGill University, Montreal, Canada.

Grant No. 995: In support of studies of the morphology and ecology of sponges in Pacific reef caves.

The primary objective of this research was the direct investigation of shallow-water submarine cavern communities in the tropical Pacific, with particular emphasis on extant members of once abundant Paleozoic and Mesozoic sponge groups: the Sclerospongiae, Sphinctozoa, Pharetronida, and Lithistida. These are important elements of an apparently pan-tropical relict fauna that appears to be largely restricted to cryptic submarine habitats within the limits of the euphotic zone. These relict sponges form massive or fused skeletons of calcareous or siliceous material and thus remain potential contributors to modern coral-reef frameworks. This extremely interesting fauna has been the subject of previous investigations in the West Indies (Hartman and Goreau, 1970, 1972) and in the Mediterranean Sea and Indian Ocean (Vacelet 1964, 1967a, 1967b; Vacelet and Vasseur, 1965, 1971). The research reported here represents an extension of earlier preliminary observations by T. F. Goreau and R. H. Randall on the tropical West Pacific representatives of this assemblage.

The activities supported by the present grant included a field trip to the Pacific islands of Guam and Saipan, where direct observation, photography, in situ experimentation, and collection and preservation of the important members of the cryptic sponge fauna were carried out. Preserved specimens were sent to Yale University where they have been and continue to be the objects of more intensive detailed investigations.

Fieldwork

During the fieldwork, carried out between August 2 and September 8, 1971, a total of eight locations were visited, seven on Guam and one on Saipan (see fig. 1). Among the rich and diverse sponge fauna of the submarine cryptic habitats studied, special attention was given to five species of sponges with massive or fused skeletons of calcium carbonate. These are (1) a tabulate sponge, *Acanthochaetetes wellsi* Hartman and Goreau (1975), with a calcitic skeleton made up of contiguous vertical, tabulate tubes into the outer ends of which the living sponge tissue extends; (2) a ceratoporellid sclerosponge, *Stromatospongia micronesica* Hartman and Goreau (1976), closely allied to Caribbean cryptic sponges (Hartman, 1969); (Hartman and Goreau, 1970), with a massive basal skeleton of aragonite in which are entrapped siliceous spicules secreted by the sponge tissue; (3) a sclerosponge, *Astrosclera willeyana* Lister (1900), believed to be a relative of the extinct group Stromatoporoidea (Hartman and Goreau 1970, 1972), with a spherulitic skeleton of aragonite; (4) a living member of the group Sphinctozoa (*Neocoelia crypta* Vacelet, 1977), with an aragonitic skeleton; and (5) a pharetronid, *Murrayona phanolepis* Kirkpatrick (1910), belonging to the class Calcarea and having a skeleton of fused calcitic spicules. The distributions of these species as well as of the lithistid are shown in figure 1.

During the 30 days spent on Guam, a total of 24 SCUBA dives, 5 snorkel dives, and other wading collections were carried out at the seven sites, totaling approximately 42 hours in the water. Transportation, diving equipment, support personnel, laboratory equipment, and facilities were supplied by the Marine Laboratory of the University of Guam at Pago Bay. The major portion of this effort was focused upon caverns at (1) Anae Island, where there is a small cave consisting of three entrances with horizontal tunnel connections extending -4.5 to -11 meters, and at (2) Orote Point, referred to locally as the "Blue Hole" and consisting of a single expansive cavern, opening on the reef platform at -18 meters and extending vertically to a floor at -61 meters. Both sites are inhabited by all five calcareous sponge species.

A major portion of the diving activity in these two caverns included specimen collection, submarine mapping, collection of habitat and distribution data, and underwater photography (black and white as well as color, at extreme close-up and survey distances). The support vessel was utilized as a stable platform upon which the necessarily rapid preservation of freshly collected material was carried out for eventual electron-microscope studies of fine structure. In addition to collections of the important five calcareous sponge species, an extensive survey collection of the entire sponge fauna of these caverns was obtained, totaling perhaps 50 to 100 species. These were preserved on board the support vessel or upon return to the laboratory for subsequent histological examination, identification, and description. The more important nonsponge elements of the communities were also surveyed, representatives identified at the laboratory or preserved for subsequent investigation. Living

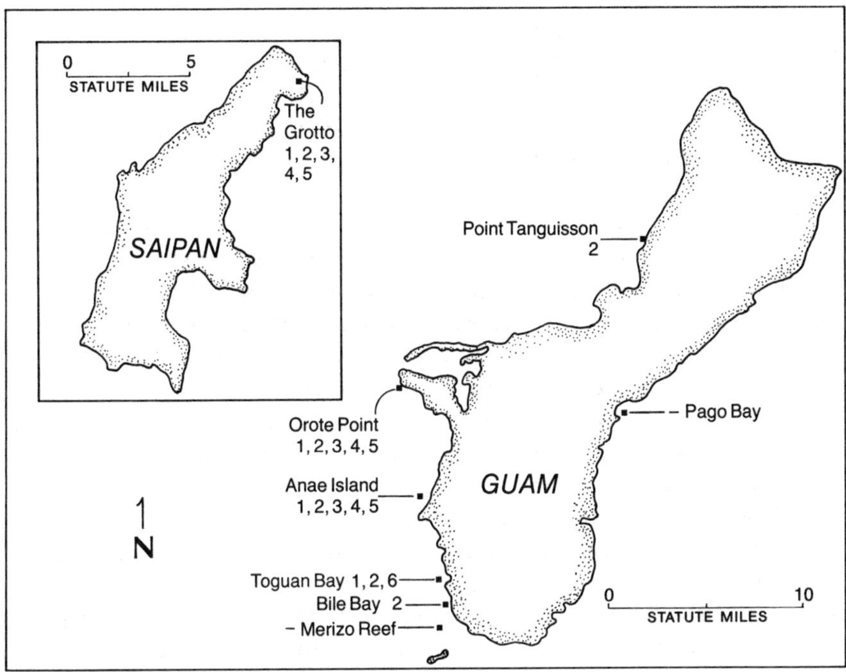

FIG. 1. Occurrence of cave-dwelling sponges on Guam and Saipan, Mariana Islands: 1, Tabulate sponge *(Acanthochaetetes wellsi);* 2, ceratoporellid sclerosponge *(Stromatospongia micronesica);* 3, stromatoporoid sclerosponge *(Astrosclera willeyana);* 4, sphinctozoan sponge *(Neocoelia crypta);* 5, pharetromid *(Murrayona phanolepis);* 6, lithistid sponge.

specimens of the calcareous sponge species were returned to the laboratory, held in running sea-water tanks, and observed for behavioral activity.

More detailed field investigations were carried out in the Anae Island cave. Calcification rates of the target sponge species 1-4 were investigated by vital alizarin-red marking methods (Barnes, 1970). Marking was accomplished by attaching plastic bags to specimens in place on the cavern walls and introducing alizarin solutions into the bags for variable periods of time (2 hours to 2 days) during which time the dye was incorporated into the calcareous skeleton being formed. Subsequent normal growth could then be easily identified distal to the permanent red alizarin band and rates of calcification calculated. Specimens of each species were collected after 2 to 18 days of growth following staining. Stained specimens of each species were also mapped and left in place upon the walls for later collection by University of Guam personnel. These will provide back-up data over a longer growth period in the event that (1) calcification is unresolvable over the short interval of the field trip or (2) calcification rate varies seasonally. One scleractinian coral was marked to provide a check on the activity of the stain solution and the method.

To establish causal factors responsible for restriction of this special fauna to cryptic habitats, water analyses were also carried out at the Anae Island cave. On nine separate visits 6-liter water samples were collected in cleaned polyethylene bags from both inside the cave and on the exposed coral reef less than 20 meters from the entrance. The samples were immediately iced on the support vessel and fractionated upon return to the laboratory. Subsequent analysis of particulate organic carbon and examination of plankton fractions were to be performed upon return to Yale University. Temperature and pH data were also taken on waters inside and outside the Anae Island cave.

Work at the other sites on Guam and in the "Grotto" of Saipan was restricted to collections of specimens, gathering of habitat data, and photography. During the short 2-day trip to the "Grotto" in Saipan, we were able to establish clearly that all five calcareous sponges of the Guam caves were present but in a luxuriance that contrasted dramatically to their conditions in the Guam caverns. The apparent low and decreasing abundance of the Guamanian cryptic sponges could be easily attributed to either of two factors: (1) the effects of the *Acanthaster* decimation of some areas of Guamanian reefs and its inevitable effects upon the spectrum and quality of organic material in the reef waters or (2) the effects of the high human population density on Guam, with its attendant sewage runoff, increased topsoil erosion, and suffocation of filtering faunas in quiet-water habitats (especially caves where sedimentation is enhanced). Inasmuch as the specific caves visited by Goreau in 1968 at Toguan Bay, Guam, had previously supported rich calcareous sponge populations but were now found to be essentially barren, while the immediately local coral fauna escaped the *Acanthaster* predation, the second alternative appears the more likely.

The fieldwork has thus enabled collection of adequate numbers of dried and preserved calcareous cryptic sponges and other elements of the cavern habitats and open reefs of Guam. In all, 28 rolls of 35-millimeter film were taken, most of which document the calcareous sponge fauna of these caverns in their natural underwater situations. Extensive habitat notes and distributional data were obtained for the inhabitants of the sites visited. Further samples included specimens for analysis of calcification rates, material for electron microscope analysis and mineralogical investigation of extant members of these relict sponge groups, and filter-retained material for comparison of cave and exposed reef water quality.

Laboratory Work

Water quality. Analysis of the preserved filters (Reiswig, 1971, 1972) has shown that there is no significant difference between the cave and outer reef waters at Anae Island, Guam, with respect to particulate organic carbon and hence potential food for small particle filter feeders (table 1). All samples investigated are characterized as nutrient-poor waters with microscopic particulate carbon content (large Crustacea and particulate material greater than 0.2 millimeters removed manually) of between 40 and 82 mg C/m^3. An additional 5-10 percent of this value exists as macroscopic material of no potential food value to filtering Porifera.

TABLE 1. Results of Particulate Organic Carbon Analysis (mg C/m^3) on Cave and Outer-reef Waters at Anae Island, August 1971

(Wilcoxan matched pair tests show no significant differences between cave and reef samples. Means differ only by about 0.3 standard deviation or less between habitats.)

Samples	*1*	*2*	*3*	*4*	*5*	*6*	*7*	*8*	*9*	*Mean ± std. error of mean*
CAVE										
micro*	56	81	63	62	43	51	41	56	60	57 ± 4
macro**	2	1	1	1	1	0	1	5	9	3 ± 0.9
total	58	82	64	63	44	51	42	61	69	60 ± 4
REEF 1 EAST										
micro	47	66	50	48	51	61	44	43	69	53 ± 3
macro	2	5	1	12	5	1	1	2	8	4 ± 1.3
total	49	71	51	60	56	62	45	45	76	57 ± 4
REEF 2 WEST										
micro						58	43	48	69	55 ± 6
macro						6	1	1	16	6 ± 3.6
total						64	44	49	85	61 ± 9

* "Micro" designates samples from which macroscopic particulates greater than 0.2 millimeters in largest dimension have been removed by hand.

** "Macro" designates the larger particulate materials removed and analyzed separately.

The lack of difference between cave and adjacent reef waters in temperature and pH supports the hypothesis that water exchange in the Anae Island cave is adequate to prevent water-quality variation between habitats. It thus appears highly unlikely that the restriction of the special cryptic fauna to protected, low-light habitats can be attributed to significant differences in local water masses. Discrete particle-by-particle analyses of the samples have not yet been carried out to determine whether or not qualitative differences exist with respect to the potential food available between habitats.

Electron microscope investigations. The Indo-Pacific sponges that secrete massive or fused calcareous skeletons are each probable representatives of distinct taxonomic units, differing not only widely from one another but also from the major representatives of the three dominant modern classes of the phylum, the Calcarea, Demospongiae, and Hexactinellida. Although small quantities of most of these species had been made available through the brief visits of previous investigators, the materials were insufficient to provide accurate assessment of the relationships between groups. In order to allow inspection of an increased number and range of characters, well-preserved tissue samples of each species were obtained immediately upon collection, providing material for normal histological investigation (paraffin section/light microscopy) and fine structure analysis with the transmission electron microscope.

The fine structure study has been directed to several specific areas: (1) the structure of the choanocyte collar; (2) the interface between living tissues and calcareous skeleton; (3) the organic matrix of the skeleton; (4) the spectrum of symbionts; (5) the fibrous mesogleal (Spongin A) skeleton; (6) other specific cell types. Although this study is only now nearing completion, several preliminary statements can be provided. Briefly, we have found that the anatomy of the choanocyte chamber, the choanocyte, and its collar, does not differ basically from that of other sponge groups (Brien, 1973). The number of villi composing the collar varies from species to species, with reasonably narrow limits within species, but they are not strikingly unlike other Porifera. Likewise, the collagenous fibers of the mesogleal matrix are similar to those of the dominant sponge classes, with structural periodicity varying from species to species. Three of the species, the sphinctozoan, *Astrosclera,* and *?Stromatospongia,* contain a spectrum of mesogleal symbiotic microorganisms that may comprise a living biomass equal to that of the host sponge cells. The symbionts are undoubtedly living and dividing in the sponge mesoglea and in turn are cropped by the host sponge as a food source. These sponge-microbe complexes are thus expected to be uniquely suited to low-nutrient waters, potentially able to utilize dissolved organic matter via the tremendous amounts of water pumped by the sponges, and the microbial cells able to capture dissolved material at high efficiency. The tabulate sponge, *Acanthochaetetes wellsi,* is free of symbiotic microorganisms, as is the pharetronid. The interface between skeleton and tissue as well as the organic matrix of the skeleton differs greatly among these species and will probably form a major character for future assessments of taxonomic relationships. In most cases it is clear that deposition of calcareous material occurs on nonliving membrane surfaces, removed from the sites of living sponge or symbiont cells. In no case are the symbionts implicated as taking part in the process of calcification.

Cell specialization appears to be at a low level in all these calcareous sponge species, although very distinctive cell types do occur in a few species. The anatomical distinction between choanocyte and amoebocyte cell lines is lower than in the Demospongiae proper.

In general, we find surprising conformity at the ultrastructural level between these relict groups and the modern classes of Porifera. These findings reinforce the widely recognized conservatism within this phylum in regard to basic structural components and functional design.

REFERENCES

Barnes, David J.

1970. Coral skeletons: An explanation of their growth and structure. Science, vol. 170, pp. 1305-1308.

Brien, Paul

1973. Les démosponges: Morphologie et reproduction. Pp. 133-461 *in* "Traité de Zoologie," P.-P. Grassé, ed., vol. 3, fasc. 1 (Spongiaires).

Hartman, Willard D.

1969. New genera and species of coralline sponges (Porifera) from Jamaica. Postilla (Peabody Mus. Nat. Hist., Yale Univ.), vol. 137, pp. 1-39.

Hartman, Willard D., and Goreau, T. F.

1970. Jamaican coralline sponges: Their morphology, ecology and fossil relatives. Symp. Zool. Soc. London, vol. 25, pp. 205-243.

1972. *Ceratoporella* (Porifera: Sclerospongiae) and the chaetetid "corals." Trans. Connecticut Acad. Sci., vol. 44, pp. 133-148.

1975. A Pacific tabulate sponge, living representative of a new order of sclerosponges. Postilla (Peabody Mus. Nat. Hist., Yale Univ.), vol. 167, pp. 1-21.

1976. A new ceratoporellid sponge (Porifera: Sclerospongiae) from the Pacific. Pp. 329-347 *in* "Aspects of Sponge Biology," F. W. Harrison and R. R. Cowden, eds. Academic Press, New York.

Kirkpatrick, R.

1910. On a remarkable pharetronid sponge from Christmas Island. Proc. Roy. Soc. London, vol. 83B, pp. 124-133.

LISTER, J. J.
1900. *Astrosclera willeyana,* the type of a new family of sponges. Pp. 459-482 *in* "Zoological Results Based on Material from New Britain, New Guinea, Loyalty Islands . . . during 1895-7," vol. 4, by Arthur Willey.

REISWIG, HENRY M.
1971. Particle feeding in natural populations of three marine demosponges. Biol. Bull., vol. 141, pp. 568-591.
1972. The spectrum of particulate organic matter of shallow-bottom boundary waters of Jamaica. Limnol. Oceanogr., vol. 17, pp. 341-348.

VACELET, JEAN
1964. Étude monographique de l'éponge calcaire pharétronide de Méditerranée, *Petrobiona massiliana* Vacelet et Lévi: Les pharétronides actuelles et fossiles, 125 pp. Thése, Faculté des Sciences de l'Université d'Aix-Marseille.
1967a. Descriptions d'éponges pharétronides actuelles des tunnels obscures sous-récifaux de Tuléar (Madagascar). Rec. Trav. Stat. Mar. Endoume, fasc. hors sér., suppl., vol. 6, pp. 37-62.
1967b. Quelques éponges pharétronides et "silico-calcaires" de grottes sous-marines obscures. Rec. Trav. Stat. Mar. Endoume, Bull. 42, fasc. 58, pp. 121-133.
1977. Une nouvelle relique du Secondaire: un représentant actuel des éponges fossiles Sphinctozoaires. Compt. Rend. Acad. Sci. Paris, vol. 285, ser. D, pp. 509-511.

VACELET, JEAN, and VASSEUR, PIERRE
1965. Spongiaires des grottes et sur-plombs des récifs de Tuléar (Madagascar). Rec. Trav. Stat. Mar. Endoume, fasc. hors sér., suppl., vol. 4, pp. 71-123.
1971. Éponges des récifs coralliens de Tuléar (Madagascar). Tethys, suppl. 1, pp. 51-126.

WILLARD D. HARTMAN
HENRY W. REISWIG

Archeological Investigations at the Murray Springs Clovis Site, Arizona, 1971

Principal Investigator: C. Vance Haynes, Jr., University of Arizona, Tucson, Arizona.

Grant No. 937: For continuation of archeological investigations at the mammoth-kill site near Murray Springs, Arizona.

During June and part of July 1971 excavations at the Murray Springs Clovis site were concentrated in areas 6, 7, and 8 and a small part of area 1 (fig. 1).

Excavations in the Clovis hunting camp in areas 6 and 7 were continued under the supervision of Dr. Larry D. Agenbroad, assistant director of the project, and Gerald Kelso, foreman. In addition to expanding the 1970 excavations in area 7, a system of nonaligned random squares (4 square meters each) was laid out for statistical sampling of the unexcavated portions of the area. The pattern was extended through the previously excavated areas in order to compare the efficiency of the sampling methods. It was found that it would have readily detected the concentration of artifacts uncovered in 1970.

The random sampling was continued into area 6, and a total of 536 square meters of the hunting camp was excavated this season and yielded 478 lithic artifacts, including two Clovis projectile point bases, four flake knives, two blades, and a multiple-use tool resembling one from the type Clovis site found in 1962.

Several flake concentrations were recorded and in conjunction with the microtopography show that there has been a surprising lack of horizontal dispersion of the artifacts in spite of the 11,000 years since their deposition. The abundant insect, rodent, and root holes attest to the high degree to which bioturbation has affected the surface layers consisting of porous white marl, very pale-gray calcareous clay, and loose pale-grayish-brown silt-sand colluvium. Clovis artifacts were found on the contact between the marl and gray clay, within the gray clay, and within the loose colluvium but never entirely within the marl. It is believed, therefore, that the original stratigraphic position was at or in the base of the gray calcareous clay, which may be a pedogenic facies of unit F_1 or F_2 in the kill area.

The assemblage of Clovis artifacts from the hunting camp indicates projectile-point repair and replacement, sharpening and bifacial thinning of some tools, and cutting and scraping activities. The presence of a few fragments of bone and teeth suggests that these activities were related to utilization of the animals killed in areas 1, 3, 4, and 5.

In area 1 (fig. 2) a small portion of unexcavated ground between the F_1 channel and the buried arroyo (unit G_1) was excavated, but only a few bifacial thinning flakes were added to the collection from area 1. However, the F_1 channel was completely excavated and found to be approximately a meter wide and generally less than 20 centimeters deep. It is apparent that gravels along the channel are residual gravels from unit Z.

As in previous years, artifacts of the Cochise Culture were found in the loose silt and on the surface and are readily distinguished from Clovis artifacts by their form, workmanship, and lithology. Two pits filled with loose silt and rubble extend into unit D and may represent attempts by Cochise people to find water. Similar pits discovered in area 5 in 1968 extend from within unit G_2 through F_2 and into unit D and have the appearance of prehistoric wells dug approximately 3,000 years ago, based upon their position within the stratigraphy.

Excavations were resumed in the buried spring conduits of area 8 (fig. 2), and Jeffrey Saunders continued the collection and cataloguing of fossil vertebrate remains, mostly teeth. The most outstanding finds were teeth of a large cat (cf. *Felis atrox*) and a turtle egg that was remarkably well preserved.

This season conduits 1 and 3 were excavated vertically in half-meter sections with the detailed stratigraphy plotted at each section and all important fossil specimens occurring between sections projected to the plane of the previous line. From these plots a chronology within the spring strata can be established. It is apparent from the truncation of the uppermost conduit sands by the contact with the "black mat" (unit F_2) that the springs had become inactive and their deposits partly eroded before deposition of unit F_2. It is not known how much time this hiatus represents, but from stratigraphic evidence the springs were active sometime after the end of unit D deposition, 25,000 years ago, and before deposition of unit F_2, 11,000 years ago.

The relatively unrounded, unpolished aspects of the quartz sands making up most of the spring sediments indicate that the period of spring discharge was brief, but it is not apparent whether this was before deposition of the Coro marl (unit E), during its deposition, or after its erosion and removal from the location of the conduits. If the springs had formed, either by exposure of the aquifer or by rise of the water table, *after* the removal of unit E, one would expect the finer-grained facies of the spring sediments along a spring run down the valley. Instead, the spring sediments are eroded, and such erosion would call for another period of erosion after unit E erosion and before deposition of the "black mat" (unit F_2).

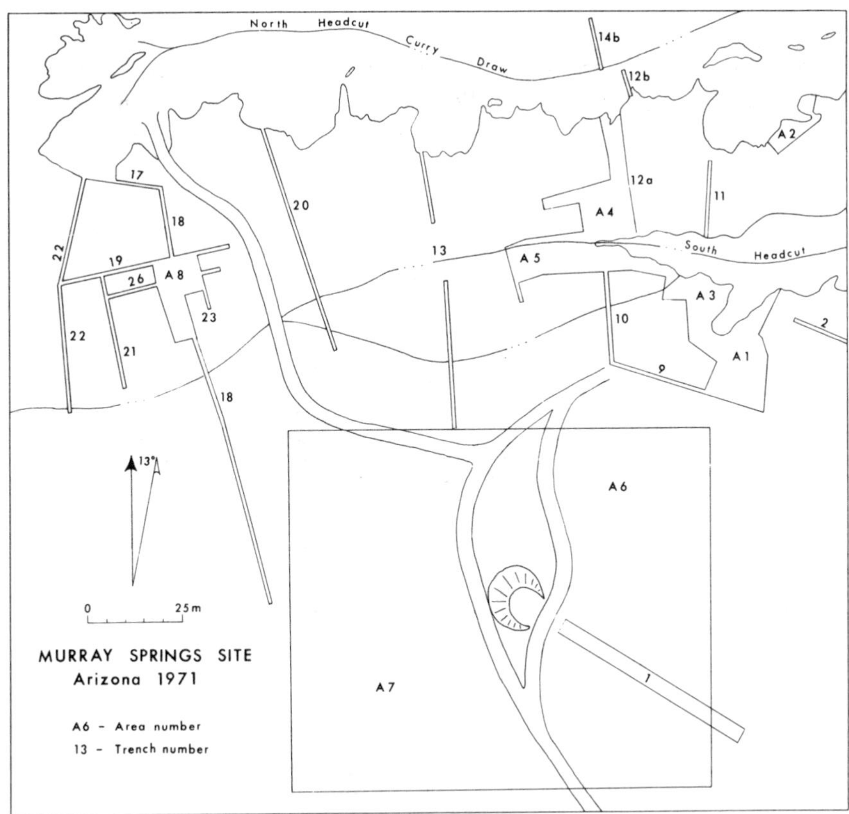

FIG. 1. Map of the Murray Springs site, showing areas of excavations and stratigraphic trenches.

In spite of careful excavations completely around the conduits no outlet or sand layer was found connecting them with the F_1 channel less than 50 yards away as one might expect had the springs been active in F_1 time. This fact plus the absence of Clovis artifacts from the spring sediments and their immediate vicinity also suggest that the springs of area 8 had become inactive and their sediments eroded by the time of F_1 channel filling 11,000–12,000 years ago. The most likely time for erosion of the area 8 spring sediments was during the same episode of erosion that led to the formation of the F_1 channel and the Clovis occupation surface.

From stratigraphic evidence it appears most likely that the period of area 8 spring activity began during unit D deposition and ended sometime during unit E deposition. There is no evidence of either erosion or a hiatus between the green clay (unit D) and the marl (unit E), but occurrences of large-mammal bones in the green clay and in the lower part of the marl indicate a surface stable enough or under shallow enough water to allow the movement

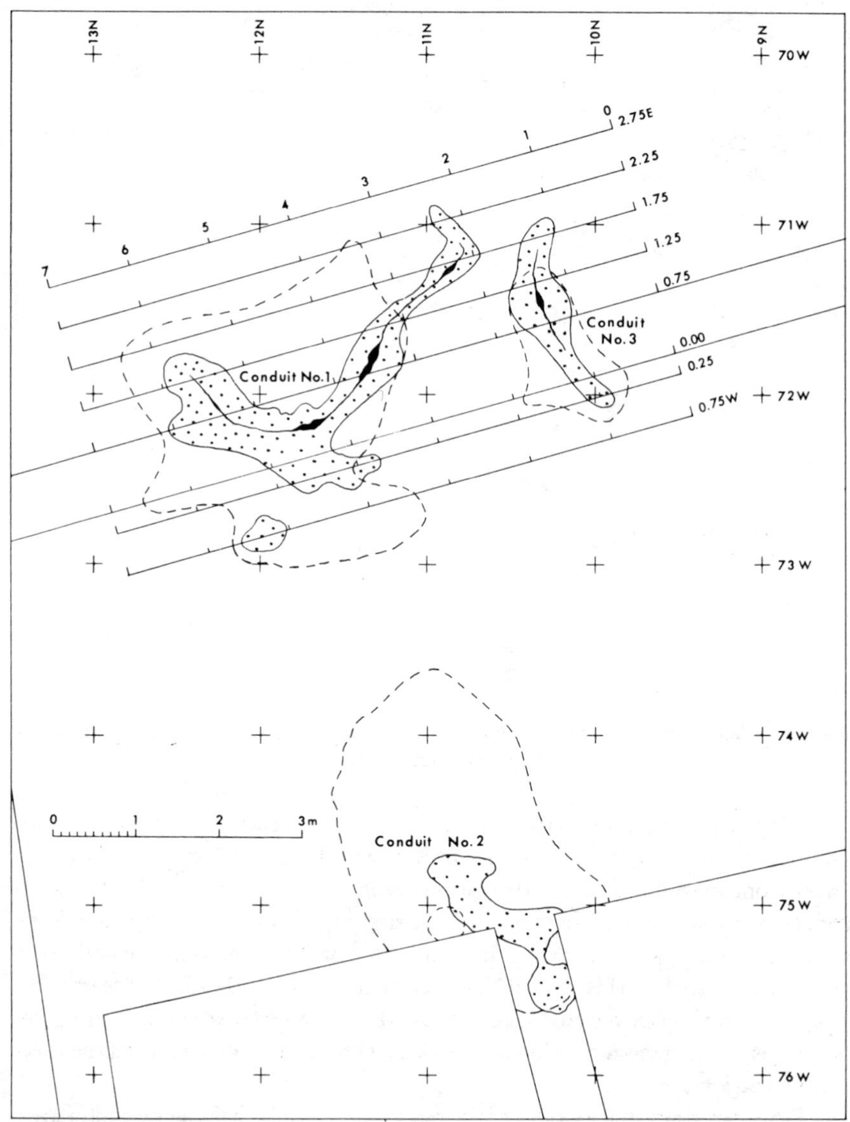

FIG. 2. Map of the Murray Springs site Area 8, showing locations of feeder conduits.

of large animals at least to the point of getting buried in either ooze or quicksand. That either the water depth or depth of calcareous ooze may have increased in the latter part of unit E deposition is indicated by the absence of mammal remains and by the less frequent occurrence of clay partings in the more massive upper half of the marl.

If the springs were active at this time they were probably the source of the carbonate-bearing waters from which the marl precipitated. The absence of calcium-carbonate cement from the spring sands and the dissolution of most of the bones therein might be explained by a high carbonic-acid concentration in the aquifer.

The origin of units D and E appears to be intimately related to the area 8 springs. They provided the source for the water and the calcium carbonate and help explain why no clear-cut channel or deltaic facies have been found. Additional light will be shed upon these problems when the results of current investigations of vertebrate and invertebrate faunas are completed.

Knowledge of the geological stratigraphy (fig. 2) was further improved by the excavation of 1,240 meters of additional backhoe trenches, and charcoal from the F_1 channel was systematically collected at five locations throughout the site area in order to determine the time of F_1 channel activity and its microstratigraphy with as much precision as possible. In addition, aerial photographs from a helicopter were taken on two occasions and allowed our stereo coverage to be brought up to date.

In retrospect it is apparent that during the past 6 years the Murray Springs project has provided an unprecedented amount of data on Clovis activities related to hunting the last of the Pleistocene megafauna in North America (Hemmings, 1970). In addition to projectile points, numerous stone tools were found along with tens of thousands of waste flakes that indicate precisely where various tools were modified, sharpened, or manufactured from materials brought onto the site from as far as 200 miles away. A bone tool of mammoth bone is unique to New World archeology and most closely resembles shaft straighteners from mammoth-hunter camps of eastern Europe and western Russia (Haynes and Hemmings, 1968). An impact fracture flake from the bison-kill area was found to fit a broken projectile point from the hunting camp 80 meters away, and several parts of broken tools were found to fit back together. The tracks of both mammoth and bison were found in the low, muddy kill areas, and the remains of a scavenger wolf were found as well.

By unraveling the geological stratigraphy we have a remarkably complete record of geologic-climatic events over the past 50,000 years as well as excellent records of fossil vertebrates and invertebrates. Unusual organic deposits as well as fossil wood fragments and charcoal have allowed replicate radiocarbon dating of practically all the stratigraphic units within the range of the method, and close interval dating within some units has provided unusually accurate figures on the rates of deposition.

The buried spring conduits and the F_1 channel sands have provided abundant records of late Pleistocene vertebrates, and units E, F_1, F_2, and F_3 have yielded important records of invertebrate fossils. In addition, the buried springs and spring sediments will permit important interpretations of the paleohydrology to be made.

In all aspects the Murray Springs project has been a most rewarding one and when final publications are out will provide some of the most important scientific contributions to Paleo-Indian archeology and paleoecology of modern times. This has all been made possible by the National Geographic Society, which has sponsored the archeology from the beginning; the National Science Foundation, which supported the geochronological studies; the Tenneco West Corporation (formerly Kern County Land Co.), which permitted excavations on its property; Andrea Cracchiolo, who allowed access across his state-lease property and permitted stratigraphic excavations thereon; the Cochise County supervisor, who provided county equipment for the removal of back dirt; the U. S. Army Combat Surveillance School, which made aerial photographs of the area available; the Arizona State Museum and the Department of Geosciences, University of Arizona, which provided equipment and field vehicles and handled administrative matters; the Department of Geological Sciences at Southern Methodist University, which made my time available; Jim Smith, Sierra Vista, Arizona, who performed the expert backhoe excavations; and Louis Escapule and Edward Lehner, who provided important insight and information regarding the occupation of the area by Early Man.

REFERENCES

HAYNES, C. VANCE, JR.

1968. Preliminary report on the late Quaternary geology of the San Pedro Valley, Arizona. Southern Arizona Guidebook III, pp. 79-96. Arizona Geological Society.

1973. Exploration of a mammoth-kill site in Arizona. Nat. Geogr. Soc. Res. Rpts., 1966 Projects, pp. 125-126.

1974. Archeological investigations at the Clovis Site at Murray Springs, Arizona, 1967. Nat. Geogr. Soc. Res. Rpts., 1967 Projects, pp. 145-147.

1976. Archeological investigations at the Murray Springs Site, Arizona, 1968. Nat. Geogr. Soc. Res. Rpts., 1968 Projects, pp. 165-171, illus.

HAYNES, C. VANCE, JR.—continued
1978. Archeological investigations at the Murray Springs Site, Arizona, 1969. Nat. Geogr. Soc. Res. Rpts., 1969 Projects, pp. 239-242, illus.
1979. Archeological investigation at the Murray Springs Clovis Site, Arizona, 1970. Nat. Geogr. Soc. Res. Rpts., 1970 Projects, pp. 261-267, illus.

HAYNES, C. VANCE, JR., and HEMMINGS, E. THOMAS
1968. Mammoth-bone shaft wrench from Murray Springs, Arizona. Science, vol. 159, pp. 186-187, illus.

HEMMINGS, E. THOMAS
1970. Early man in the San Pedro Valley, Arizona, 236 pp. Ph.D. dissertation, University of Arizona, Tucson.

HEMMINGS, E. THOMAS, and HAYNES, C. VANCE, JR.
1969. The Escapule mammoth and associated projectile points, San Pedro Valley, Arizona. Journ. Arizona Acad. Sci., vol. 5, pp. 184-188, illus.

C. VANCE HAYNES, JR.

Source of the Colossi of Memnon on the Theban Plain, Egypt

Principal Investigator: Robert F. Heizer, University of California, Berkeley, California.

Grant Nos. 960, 1010: For an engineering and petrographic study of the colossi of Memnon, Egypt.

For some years at Berkeley we have been interested in developing and applying methods for determining the source of stones used by earlier peoples. Professor Howel Williams and I were able to discover the source of the andesite which the Olmec peoples who built the sites of La Venta, San Lorenzo, and Tres Zapotes sculptured into colossal heads, altars, and stelae (Williams and Heizer, 1965). Further work in Mesoamerica along the same lines was done with obsidian using the analytical methods of x-ray fluorescence.

In 1970 a small research group which had for some time worked together (the present writer, Dr. Fred Stross, and Dr. Thomas R. Hester) discussed the unsolved problem of the quarry source of the stone from which the Egyptian twin colossal statues, one of which was identified in antiquity as that of Memnon, son of Aurora, the goddess of Dawn, and Tithon, the King of Assyria who, in Greek legend, was killed at Troy by Achilles. Numerous opinions had been expressed as to where the stone for these monolithic statues, each weighing 720 metric tons, was secured, but there was no clear proof that any one of the proposed sources was correct. Then, too, the dimensions and weight of the statues as given in the literature were quite varied, and there was no certainty about which was correct. A careful study of the famous statues was clearly desirable, and the National Geographic Society approved our application to carry this out in 1971 and 1972.

The colossi, which stand on the western side of the Nile across the river from Luxor (see map, fig. 1), are in the form of the seated pharaoh, or king, Amenhotep III of the Eighteenth Dynasty, New Kingdom, 14th century B.C. They were placed originally at the eastern end of the processional way leading to the sumptuous mortuary temple which was described at the time of its construction as the most magnificent and costly building ever erected up to that date. Amenhotep III also built, not far to the south, another palace in front of which was dug an artificial lake (called Birket Habu), measuring 2,250 by 927 meters, supplied with water by a canal dug from the Nile, which now

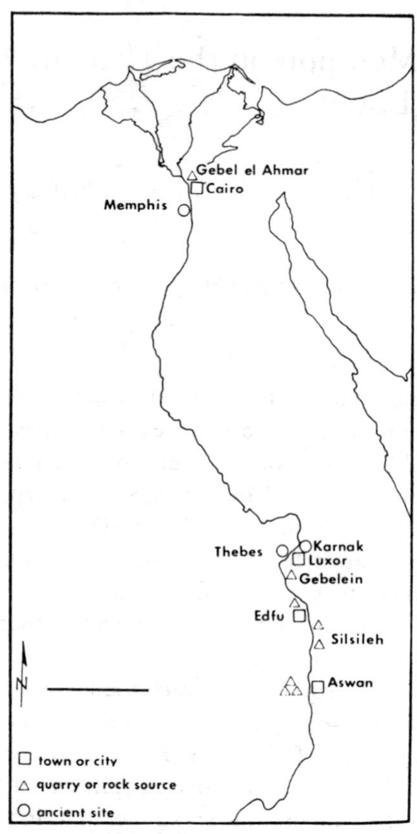

FIG. 1. Location of archeological sites and ancient quartzite deposits related to investigation of the Colossi of Memnon.

runs about a mile to the east. Fragments of sculptures and bits of the mortuary palace have been uncovered through the excavations of W. Petrie and H. Ricke, but of what must have been an incredibly impressive temple and processional way embellished with great sculptures, only the twin colossi and a stela remain today. Precisely how the Greek Memnon became associated with the northern statue of Amenhotep III is not recorded for certain, but this identification seems to have come about as a result of the partial destruction of the northern statue in an earthquake which occurred in 27 B.C. After the toppling of the upper half of the statue it was noted that when the early morning rays of the sun struck the truncated sculpture, sounds variously described as human voices, a harp or lyre when a string has been broken, and clashing cymbals, issued from the stone. The Alexandrian Greeks, always in search of confirmation of the Homeric legend, identified the broken statue as that of Memnon and the sound it issued as his voice greeting his mother, Aurora, as she rose each morning. A kind of cult developed, and visitors came to hear Memnon speak in the first hours of the morning. Many of these, 108 in all, inscribed in Greek or Latin on the legs and lower exposed portions of the northern statue, record their visit (Letronne, 1833; A. and E. Bernand, 1960). The earliest such inscription is that of the Roman emperor, Tiberius (A.D. 20), and the latest is by Septimius Severus in A.D. 196. Here are two of the numerous inscriptions:

> I, Caius Maenius Haniochus, of Corinth, centurion of the Eleventh Claudian Legion, and also the Second Trojan Legion, called Strong, I have heard Memnon, before the end of the first half hour, the 13th of the calends of May under the consulate of Gallicanus and Titianus, and on the same day at the first hour and a half.

> Good luck to Marius Gemellus, the centurion. Thou hast been endowed with speech by thy mother, the rosy-fingered goddess, illustrious Memnon, for me who was desiring to hear thee speak. In the twelfth year of the illustrious Antoninus, when the month of Pachon was thirteen days old, divine being, I heard thy voice twice at the moment when the sun left the magnificent waves of the river. Thou who was once king of the East, the son of Kronos has made thee guardian of stone and has given thee a voice which comes out of the stone. As for me, I, Gemellus, have written these verses here in the presence of my faithful wife, Rufilla, and my children. Good luck to Rufilla, also called Longinia.

In A.D. 197 Septimius Severus ordered the Roman engineers to reconstruct the upper half of the shattered northern statue, a feat which they accomplished by shaping 25 great blocks of quartzite, the largest of which is the head, weighing 58 tons, and setting them in place.

On our research trips in January 1971 and July 1972, we made a great many measurements of both statues, took a large number of samples of the pedestal stones on which the statues rest, sampled the original statues and the reconstruction blocks dating from the second century A.D., photographed the statues from all angles, and put down a number of auger borings around the statues and on the northeastern margin of the Birket Habu Lake. We also secured samples of quartzite from as many quarries as were known in order to compare these source rocks with those of the statues and the pedestal blocks. Since Egypt was still in a state of military readiness, our internal movements were restricted. We did, however, enlist the expert services of an Egyptian geologist, Dr. Ahmed Talaat of the Egyptian Museum of Geology, who secured for us samples of the quartzite from the anciently worked quarries at Gebel el Ahmar, a few kilometers northeast of Cairo, and at Aswan. Dr. Salah Osman of the Egyptian Antiquities Service kindly made collections of quartzite from the deposits near Edfu, about halfway between Luxor and Aswan.

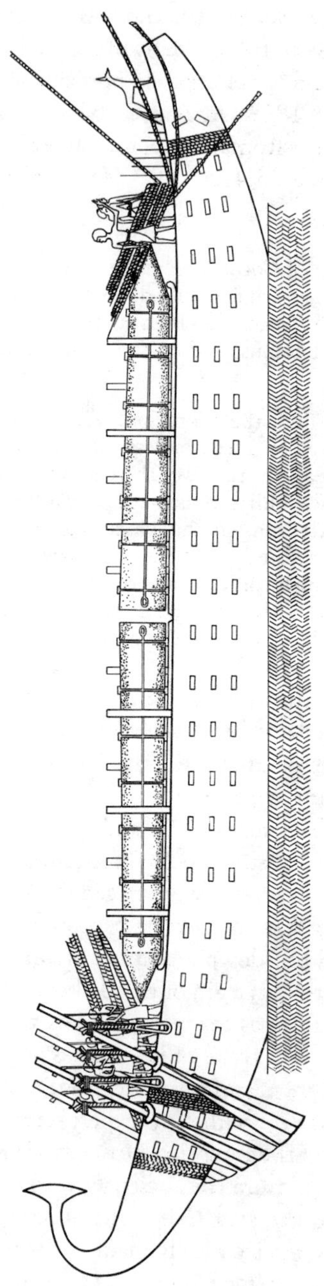

FIG. 2. Queen Hatshepsut's obelisk lighter, Eighteenth Dynasty, as depicted in her mortuary temple at Deir-el-Bahri (based on Naville, plates 153, 154).

After our return to Berkeley, armed with measurement data, statue, pedestal, and quarry samples of quartzite, we determined that the true weight of each of the statues was 720 metric tons, and that they rise to a height of 14.3 meters. The northern statue, although reconstructed, was made to conform exactly to the dimensions of its intact, though somewhat battered, mate that stands to its right on the south.

Drs. I. Perlman, F. Asaro, and H. Bowman of the Lawrence Radiation Laboratory, Berkeley, undertook the comparison of the quarry and statue samples using neutron activation analysis. Based on analysis of 64 samples from 8 quarry sources and 28 samples from the two colossal statues and pedestal blocks, they were able to demonstrate that the statues and their bases came from Gebel el Ahmar, near Cairo, some 676 kilometers north (i.e., downstream) of Luxor. Their results up to late 1973 are contained in Heizer et al. (1973, pp. 1221-1224). Petrographic analysis by Dr. Richard Hay, Department of Geology and Geophysics, Berkeley, confirms these conclusions.

The Lawrence Laboratory analyses are not, as of the date of this report (August 1975) completed. A final report to be published in the Contributions of the Archaeological Research Facility, University of California, Berkeley, is in preparation.

If the statues had proved to come from a geological source near the spot where they were erected, one might readily (and probably correctly) assume that they were dragged from the quarry to the temple by great gangs of men pulling on ropes attached to sledges on which the sculptures rested. But our finding that the source lay over 400 miles away poses a real problem of how these huge weights were transported. We believe, though without any direct proof, that the statues and the great pedestal blocks, each of the latter weighing about 350 metric tons, were carried one at a time on a great lighter, specially built for the purpose and drawn upstream by oared towboats and gangs of draggers walking along one or the other of the banks of the Nile. About a century earlier in the Eighteenth Dynasty, Queen Hatshepsut caused to have engraved on the walls of her temple at Deir-el-Bahri, a few kilometers to the northwest of the colossi, a remarkable relief showing just such a great barge, on whose deck are lashed two granite obelisks, which was towed downstream from Aswan to Luxor (see fig. 2). These two great stone needles weigh, together, 700 tons, so there is no question of the ability of the Egyptians of the time to successfully make and employ such ships—perhaps the largest ships built to that date. Sølver (1940; cf. Ballard, 1920, 1925, 1941, 1947; Anderson 1926, 1941) calculated Hatshepsut's barge to have been 207 feet long, from 69 to 82 feet wide, and to have had a hull weight of about 600 tons. Such a lighter could bear, and indeed did, if we take the carved relief as a literal representation, a cargo weighing at least 700 tons. We believe that it was this means that was used to bring the great statues of Amenhotep III upstream from the Gebel el Ahmar, and that once at Luxor they were brought into the canal leading to the lake of Birket Habu, unloaded, and then dragged to their site a kilometer to the north. The pedestals, of course, would have been brought earlier, and the statues were raised by being drawn up a long inclined earthen ramp to a sufficient height to slide them down to rest upright on their pedestals. There is clear evidence that each of the statues was set in place from the south, so that the northern statue would have been the first to be placed and the southern one last. When the great work was done the inclined ramp would have been removed, and the 3,600 draggers patted on the back, given an extra ration of food, and sent back home.

REFERENCES

ANDERSON, R. C.
1926. Queen Hatshepsut's great lighter. Mariner's Mirror, vol. 12, pp. 447-448.
1941. The towing of the obelisk ship. Mariner's Mirror, vol. 27, p. 82.

BALLARD, G. A.
1920. The transporting of the obelisks at Karnak. Mariner's Mirror, vol. 6, pp. 264-273, 307-314.
1925. Queen Hatshepsut's great lighter. Mariner's Mirror, vol. 12, pp. 221-223.
1941. The great obelisk lighter of 1550 B.C. Mariner's Mirror, vol. 27, pp. 290-306.
1947. The Egyptian obelisk lighter. Mariner's Mirror, vol. 33, p. 158.

BERNAND, A., and BERNAND, E.
1960. Les inscriptions grecques et latines du colosse de Memnon. Institut Français d'Archeologie Orientale, Cairo.

HEIZER, R. D.; STROSS, F.; HESTER T. R.; ALBEE, A.; PERLMAN, I.; ASARO F.; and BOWMAN, H.
1973. The colossi of Memnon revisited. Science, vol. 182, pp. 1219-1225.

LETRONNE, A. J.
1833. Statue vocale de Memnon. Imprimerie Royale, Paris.

NAVILLE, E. H.
1894-1908. The temple of Deir el-Bahari, 7 vols. London, Kegan Paul.

SØLVER, C. V.
1940. The Egyptian obelisk ships. Mariner's Mirror, vol. 26, pp. 237-256.

WILLIAMS, H., and HEIZER, R. F.
1965. Sources of rocks used in Olmec monuments. Contrib. Univ. California Arch. Res. Facility, no. 1, pp. 1-39. Berkeley.

ROBERT F. HEIZER

Studies on the Terrestrial Hermit Crab (*Coenobita clypeatus*)

Principal Investigator: Alex Henderson and Syd Radinovsky, Millersville State College, Millersville, Pennsylvania.

Grant No. 985: In support of ethological studies of the terrestrial (purple-clawed) hermit crab.

Our study of the terrestrial hermit crab was stimulated by our first observation of hundreds of these land-dwelling crustaceans in December 1965 on Big Pine Key in Florida. Representative samples were brought back to the laboratory early in 1966 and a specially designed terrarium was built for them.

Initial perusal of the literature indicated to us that very little had been reported on the life history of this particular species. Subsequent literature search uncovered some additional papers but more or less confirmed our initial observation that little recent work had been reported. Hazlett et al. (1964, 1965, 1966) and Provenzano (1960, 1962) were apparently the most active investigators. Most of the other hermit-crab research available was on the marine crab *Pagurus,* whose behavior, although of interest, we could not assume to be typical of the terrestrial crab *Coenobita.*

Subsequent trips to the Florida keys enabled us to locate additional sources of crabs, particularly on Bahia Honda Key (before construction of the extension to the state park) and on Boot Key just off Marathon. We received reports of other keys supporting populations of varying sizes. At about this time and increasingly thereafter *Coenobita* began appearing in pet shops along the east coast.

Because of the apparent dearth of information in the scientific literature and the absence of anything in the popular literature that might be useful to pet-shop operators and to owners of these "pets" and because of the potential danger of indiscriminate spread of the animals, we decided to pursue our investigation in earnest.

As a result of a personal visit to Dr. Leonard Carmichael, late chairman of the National Geographic Society's Committee for Research and Exploration, and our subsequent submission and the approval of a proposal, we began our study.

Although the two chief investigators collaborated on all aspects of the study, Dr. Radinovsky and his group concentrated primarily on ethology while Dr. Henderson and his students worked on the development and anatomy of the crab and investigated its evolutionary significance. We specifically wanted to investigate feeding habits, reproductive behavior, aggression, shell selection, sexual dichotomy, larval development, learning behavior, influences of environmental conditions including fresh and salt water and tide, external and internal structure, and details on population fluctuation.

Systematic observations were made of the marked crabs in our simulated seashore terrarium, which was arranged with a coral-sand substrate and a low end with slowly circulating sea water, with fresh water available nearby and with a high dry end with rocks and debris simulating the natural habitat of the crabs. A relative humidity gradient of 8 percent was established from "shore" to "high land."

From our personal terrarium observation and subsequent terrarium studies by our graduate students, we were able to conclude that under the laboratory conditions the crabs were most active at night; they tended to aggregate in the high dry zone; drank fresh water; showed water-balancing rhythm; and became very active when rainfall was simulated—climbing on branches above their normal level of activity. It was observed also that in 15 separate simple T-maze choices they made "correct" choices 65 percent of the time. Initial hypotheses on shell selection and aggression were made under these laboratory conditions.

Subsequent to the establishment of the terrarium and coinciding with those observations, field teams were sent to Florida for varying lengths of time and continuing until 1973 to assess what was happening in the natural habitat.

Shell-selection behavior became a prime target of our observations, which soon showed us that shell availability was probably the major limiting factor on terrestrial hermit-crab populations. Provenzano (1960) reached a similar conclusion with respect to the marine hermit crab *Clibanarius*. The shell-encased crab was as impervious to predation as the naked crab was vulnerable. Our study indicated an increasing scarcity of gastropod shells in relation to their increasing size. Since hermit crabs require larger shells as the crabs themselves increase in size, it would seem that availability of larger shell sizes would be important. Hermit crabs apparently obtain shells by chance encounter, by mutual exchange, and by eviction. The latter two methods become more important among the larger forms. On several occasions we observed mass exchanges much like the game of "musical chairs" (Radinovsky and Henderson, 1974). This often left at least one crab with a too-small shell or no

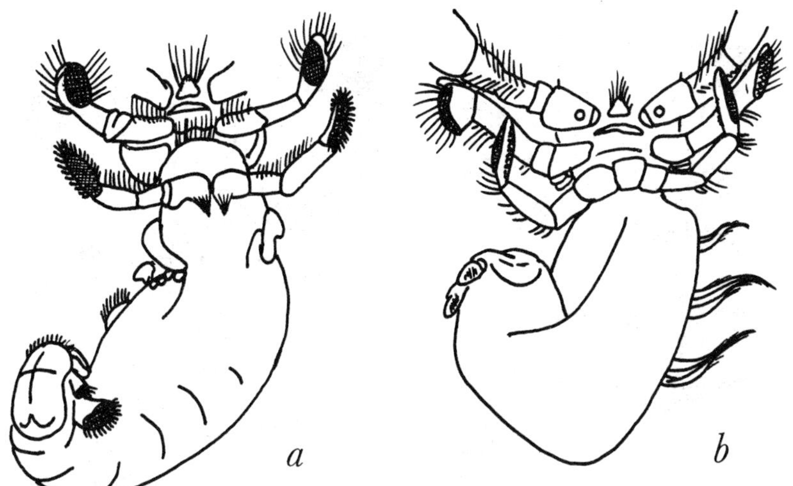

FIG. 1. *a,* Ventral-posterior surface of male *Coenobita. b,* Ventral-posterior aspect of female *Coenobita.*

shell at all. We observed such crabs making use of surrogates like broken light bulbs, shotgun shells, or bottle necks. Borradaile (1903) observed this improvisation using a broken coconut shell in his early observations of *Coenobita* in the Maldive Archipelago. Thompson (1903) noted the glaucothoe of the marine hermit crab *Pagurus* using a broken float bladder of *Fucus.* It seems obvious that opportunism is the result of necessity in these cases. Rocking of the shell and "measuring" of the shell seem to be typical behavior on the part of an aggressor crab hunting for a new home. When mutually beneficial exchange does not occur, active resistance to eviction may develop, but generally blocking of the opening with the large cheliped is an effective deterrent. The overt aggression described by Reese (1962) in the marine hermit crab *Calcinus* is not generally the case in *Coenobita.*

It is virtually impossible to differentiate between the sexes without removing the animal from the shell, unless it is an ovigerous female. The sexual dichotomy becomes obvious upon removing the animal from the shell and examining the thorax and abdomen.

The ventral surface of the fifth pair of pereiopods of the male each has on its proximal segment (coxipodite) a pointed tuft of usually dark setae giving the appearance of a dark papule (fig. 1a). This small protuberance is lacking on the female, but the proximal segment (coxipodite) of the third pair of pereiopods each bears a small but obvious circular opening (fig. 1b).

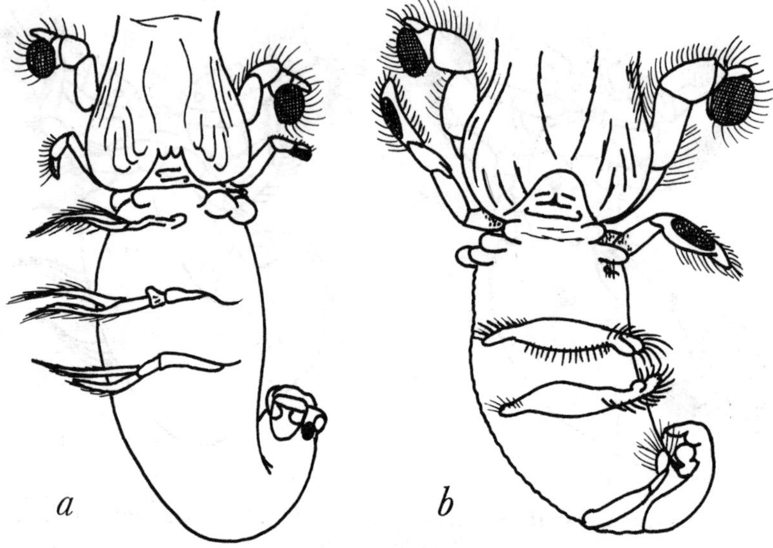

FIG. 2. *a,* Dorsal-posterior aspect of female *Coenobita*. *b,* Dorsal-posterior aspect of male *Coenobita*.

The dorsal surface of the female abdomen bears a biramous appendage on the left side of each of the second, third, and fourth segments. These biramous pleopods are about as long as the abdomen is wide, and each is covered with fine silky setae (fig. 2a). The dorsal abdomen of the male, on the other hand, has no comparable appendages, but there are prominent chitinous ridges across the dorsal surface on the second, third, and fourth abdominal segments. These vestigial structures, located in the region where the tergum would normally be found, have on their right side short rounded protuberances covered with setae, which are rudiments of appendages (fig. 2b).

A sixth pair of abdominal appendages is present in both sexes[1] (figs. 3a and 3b), the one on the left generally being significantly larger than the one on the right. These appendages possess "friction pads," which apparently aid in securing the animal in the shell.

The fourth and fifth pereiopods are also modified with similar "friction pads" whose purpose is apparently to further secure the animal in its borrowed

[1] The female also has a small almost indistinguishable pleopod on the fifth segment. With careful perusal, evidence of this may be seen on the males, particularly the older males.

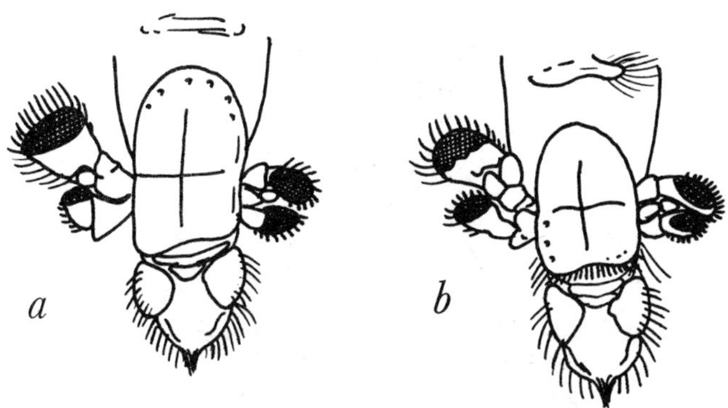

FIG. 3. Last abdominal segments of *Coenobita clypeatus,* illustrating vestigial and sixth pair of abdominal appendages: *a,* male; *b,* female.

shell. The protopodite of the fourth appendage is a dark rounded structure covered with tiny ovoid overlapping scales. The fifth pereiopod contains a similar "friction pad" on its distal surface, except that it is elongated rather than discoidal (figs. 1, 2).

The abdomen of both sexes is asymmetrical, with a dextral half twist. The abdominal appendages, as noted above, are also asymmetrical with those of the female, being better developed on the left while those of the male are less vestigial on the right except for the sixth pair. It is interesting to note that the larval form seems to be symmetrical through the first five stages and develops its dextral half twist only in the sixth stage.

In spite of extensive observations, we were not able to confirm that any of the activities observed were copulation. Neither did Borradaile (1903) nor Provenzano (1962) report these observations.

The eggs are carried attached to the long setae of the well-developed limbs on the left side of the second, third, and fourth abdominal segments of the female.

We collected a number of egg-bearing specimens and placed them in shallow water on the edge of Boot Key. Assiduous and continuous observation enabled us to see the protozoeae being released. This occurred at night after the crabs crawled into shallow water-filled holes in the coral rock. The holes measured 3 to 10 inches in diameter and 1 to 4 inches deep. We collected some alive and carried them to our laboratory for examination. Others we preserved for future use in confirming the data obtained from the live forms. Figures 4a and 4b illustrate the dorsal and lateral aspects of the protozoea we collected.

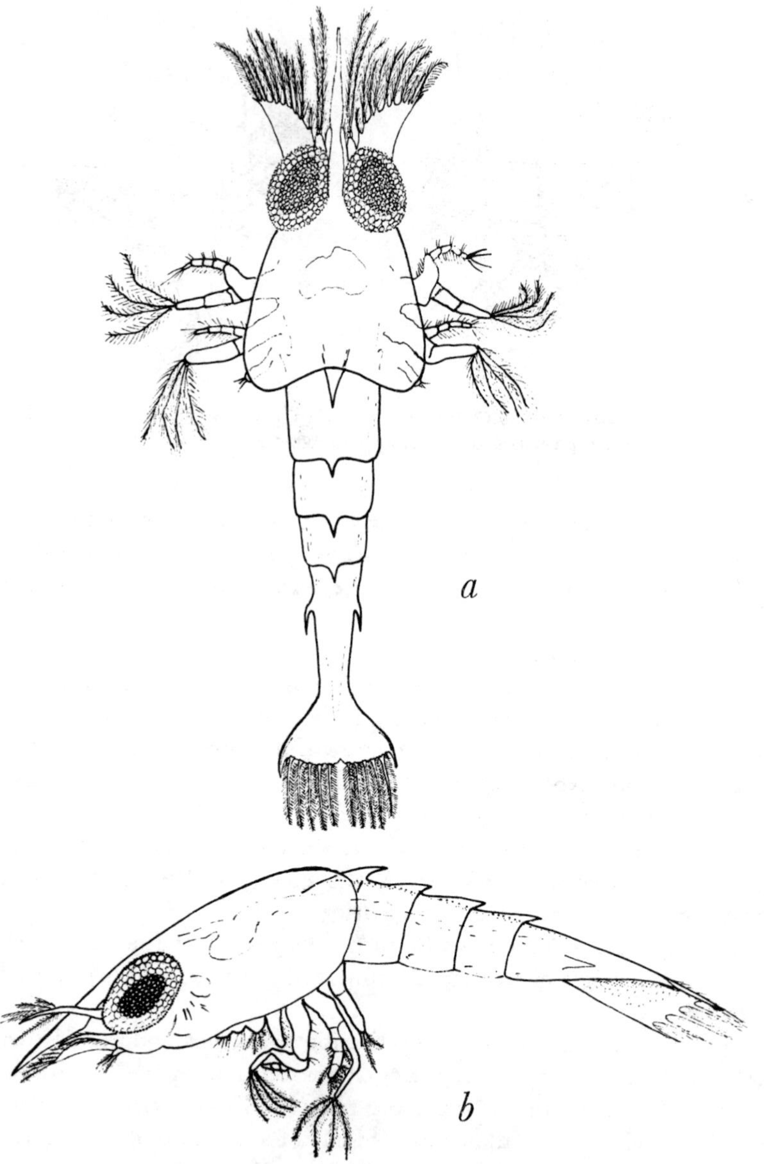

FIG. 4. *a,* Dorsal aspect of *Coenobita clypeatus* protozoea. *b,* Lateral aspect of *Coenobita clypeatus* protozoea.

The evolutionary development of the pagurine[2] crabs is interesting although obscure.

We note that *Coenobita clypeatus* larvae retain the characteristic symmetry and general shape of other decapods. It is not until the sixth stage that the dextral twist necessary for insertion in a molluscan shell obtains. Even if given straight shells or sinistral shells, their abdominal development continues to the right. Thompson (1903) showed that the asymmetrical development is independent of the presence or absence of a shell and is not affected by shell shape.

There are nonpagurine crabs that also have reduced abdominal armor and rudimentary pleopods, but that live in stationary burrows or cracks in bits of wood or rock, e.g., the thalassinids.

Other crabs, particularly the pagurids (Reese, 1962), enter empty gastropod shells in the glaucothoe stage and are able to discriminate among shells of different species, a choice that is independent of previous experience with shells. Provenzano (1960) indicated that *Clibanarius verilli* occupies primarily *Cerithrium* whereas *Pagurus miamensis* lives in *Pyrene* shells.

At the other end of the spectrum are pagurines that seem to be in the process of evolving away from the use of movable homes of empty gastropod shells. *Birgus latro,* the robber crab, when full grown may not carry a shell at all. Its abdomen is more or less symmetrical, and the soft abdominal skin characteristic of pagurines is replaced by a more resistant coat. It, however, lacks abdominal appendages on one side and young individuals may carry shells and may be induced to carry them for several years.

Another interesting variability is the vitality of the various pagurines when confined to either fresh or salt water, as well as the habitat preference. Continuous submersion in water is always fatal to coenobiteds, but there is great variability in this, with submersion in fresh water always being less tolerable. According to Borradaile, *Clypeatus perlatus* showed the greatest vitality in water, followed by *C. rugosus,* with *C. clypeatus* being the most sensitive. In their natural habitats, *C. rugosus* and *C. perlatus* prefer terrestrial areas adjacent to the ocean, whereas *C. clypeatus* may be found at some distance from the sea.

Other than the possible advantage of additional habitats and/or niches there is no satisfactory explanation as to why crabs began inhabiting gastropod shells or why some species moved out onto land—or why some which had adapted very well to terrestrial existence are losing their mobile homes.

---

[2] Borradaile uses the term "pagurine" to refer to the typical hermit crab in the order Pagurinea including families Paguridae and Coenobitidae. He used the term "pagurid" for the Paguridae alone.

Perhaps satisfactory hypotheses may develop as we learn more of the behavior of all genera within the order.

REFERENCES

BORRADAILE, LANCELOT A.

1903. Fauna and geography of the Maldive and Laccadive Archipelagoes, vol. 1, pp. 65-97. Cambridge University Press.

HAZLETT, BRIAN

1964. The social behavior of the Paguridae of Curaçao. Ph.D. thesis, Harvard University.

HAZLETT, BRIAN, and BOSSERT, W. H.

1965. A statistical analysis of the aggressive communication systems of some hermit crabs. Animal Behav., vol. 13, pp. 357-373.

1966. Additional observations on the communication systems of hermit crabs. Animal Behav., vol. 14, pp. 546-549.

HENDERSON, ALEX, and RADINOVSKY, SYD

1978. Some anatomical and ethological adaptations of the purple-clawed hermit crab *Coenobita clypeatus*. P. 50 *in* "Proceedings of the Association of Pennsylvania State College and University Biologists (1969-1977)," vol. 1.

IVERSON, EDWIN S., and SKINNER, RENATE H.

1977. Land hermit crabs as pets. Windward Publishing, Inc., Miami.

PROVENZANO, ANTHONY J., JR.

1960. Notes on Bermuda hermit crabs. Bull. Mar. Sci. Gulf and Caribbean, vol. 10, pp. 117-124.

1962. The larval development of the tropical land hermit crab *Coenobita clypeatus* (Herbst) in the laboratory. Crustaceana, vol. 4, pp. 207-228.

PROVENZANO, ANTHONY J., JR., and DOBKIN, SHELDON

1962. Variation among larvae of decapod Crustacea reared in the laboratory. Amer. Zool., vol. 2, p. 439.

REESE, ERNST S.

1962a. Submissive posture as an adaptation to aggressive behavior in hermit crabs. Zeitschr. für Tierpsych., vol. 19, pp. 645-651.

1962b. Shell selection of hermit crabs. Animal Behav., vol. 10, pp. 347-360.

RADINOVSKY, SYD, and HENDERSON, ALEX

1974. The shell game. Nat. Hist., vol. 83, no. 10, pp. 22-29, illus.

THOMPSON, M. T.

1903. The metamorphosis of the hermit crab. Proc. Boston Soc. Nat. Hist., vol. 31, pp. 147-209.

ALEX HENDERSON

SYD RADINOVSKY

Mass-nesting of Pacific Ridley Turtles on Nancite Beach, Santa Rosa National Park, Costa Rica

Principal Investigators: David A. Hughes and Joseph D. Richard, Rosenstiel School of Marine and Atmospheric Science, University of Miami, Miami, Florida.

Grant Nos. 948, 1009: In support of a field study of ridley turtles nesting in Costa Rica.

During an aerial survey of marine turtle nesting activity along the coasts of Costa Rica in 1970 the authors found two beaches on the Pacific Coast of Guanacaste province (Naranjo and Nancite, see fig. 1) on which Pacific ridley turtles were nesting in large numbers. This find is important, as these two beaches are the only known sites in Central America where this species, *Lepidochelys olivacea,* nests en masse. They bring to a total of only seven the beaches on which mass-nesting has been recorded. The other beaches are all in Mexico where, since the discovery of the first as recently as 1967, the species has been exploited until now only a small proportion of the original population survives.

The endangered status of the species and lack of knowledge concerning most aspects of its biology and behavior inspired the field study reported here.

One of the newly discovered beaches (Nancite) is located within the Santa Rosa National Park. There (see fig. 2), with the considerable help of the Costa Rican National Parks Department, the senior author and his family established camp for 3½ months during the peak nesting season of 1971.

Approximately 2,000 turtles were tagged and a variety of studies were undertaken to determine as much as possible about the mass-nesting phenomenon in the limited time available. In addition, a number of aerial survey flights were conducted along the Guanacaste coastline by the second author (J. D. Richard). Observations were made of the offshore fleets of turtles and their numerical fluctuations were assessed during the nesting season. Some aspects of this study are summarized below.

Mass-nesting ("Arribadas")

During the period of this study an estimated 297,000 turtles nested on the 1,300-meter-long beach and approximately 30 million eggs were laid. Although some turtles nested at other times, the vast majority (about 99

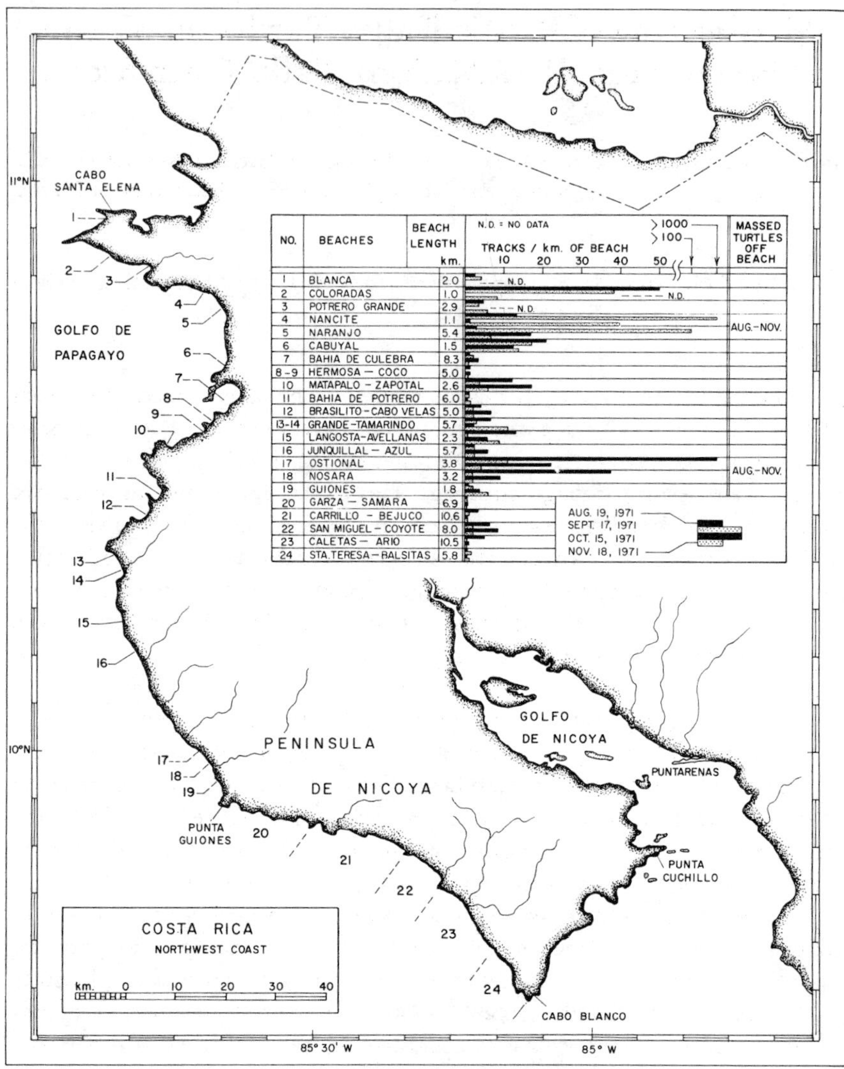

NO.	BEACHES	BEACH LENGTH km.
1	BLANCA	2.0
2	COLORADAS	1.0
3	POTRERO GRANDE	2.9
4	NANCITE	1.1
5	NARANJO	5.4
6	CABUYAL	1.5
7	BAHIA DE CULEBRA	8.3
8-9	HERMOSA — COCO	5.0
10	MATAPALO - ZAPOTAL	2.6
11	BAHIA DE POTRERO	6.0
12	BRASILITO - CABO VELAS	5.0
13-14	GRANDE-TAMARINDO	5.7
15	LANGOSTA-AVELLANAS	2.3
16	JUNQUILLAL — AZUL	5.7
17	OSTIONAL	3.8
18	NOSARA	3.2
19	GUIONES	1.8
20	GARZA — SAMARA	6.9
21	CARRILLO - BEJUCO	10.6
22	SAN MIGUEL - COYOTE	8.0
23	CALETAS — ARIO	10.5
24	STA. TERESA — BALSITAS	5.8

FIG. 1. Observed sea turtle nesting activity along the northwest (Pacific) coast of Costa Rica in 1971 (from Richard and Hughes, 1972).

percent) nested during three "arribadas," as the periods of mass-nesting are called in Mexico. At these times 3,000 to 5,000 turtles were on the beach together (fig. 3) and nesting continued for 3 or 4 days until 100,000 or more turtles had laid their eggs. The crush of animals gives rise to scenes which can

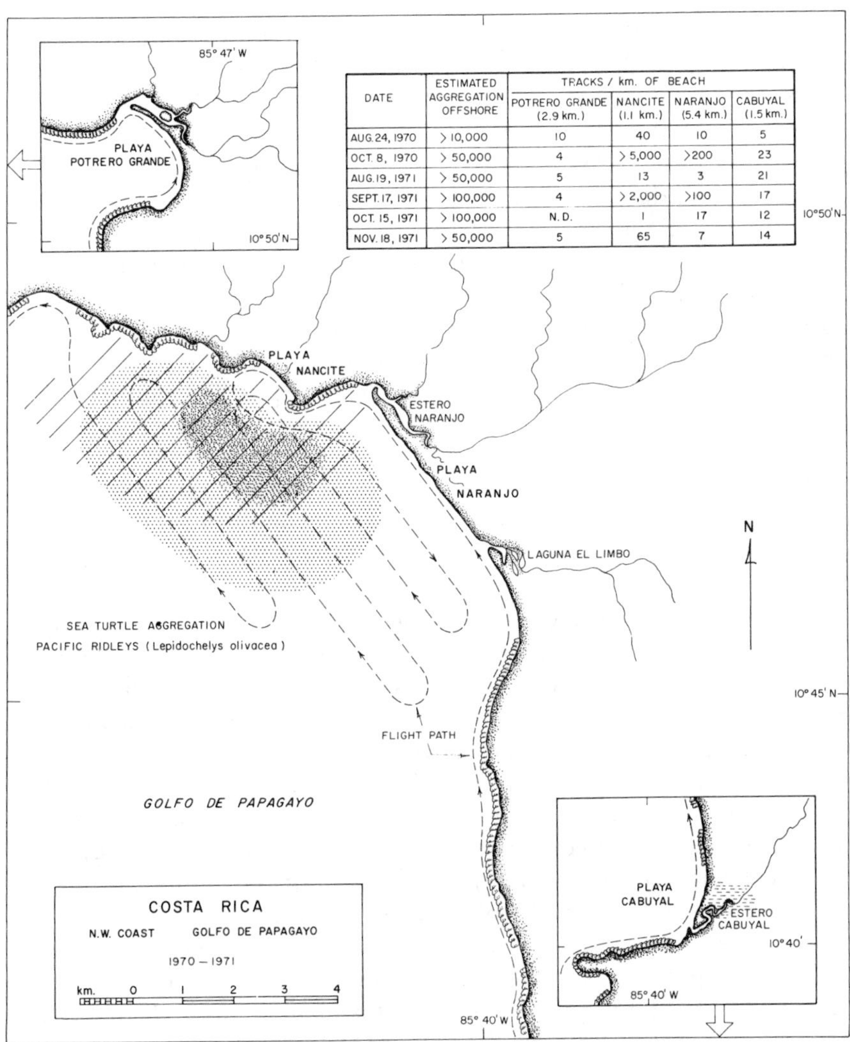

DATE	ESTIMATED AGGREGATION OFFSHORE	TRACKS / km. OF BEACH			
		POTRERO GRANDE (2.9 km.)	NANCITE (1.1 km.)	NARANJO (5.4 km.)	CABUYAL (1.5 km.)
AUG. 24, 1970	> 10,000	10	40	10	5
OCT. 8, 1970	> 50,000	4	> 5,000	>200	23
AUG. 19, 1971	> 50,000	5	13	3	21
SEPT. 17, 1971	> 100,000	4	> 2,000	>100	17
OCT. 15, 1971	> 100,000	N. D.	1	17	12
NOV. 18, 1971	> 50,000	5	65	7	14

FIG. 2. Observed nesting activity of Pacific ridleys *(Lepidochelys olivacea)* at Nancite and nearby beaches (from Richard and Hughes, 1972).

scarcely have their equal anywhere in the animal kingdom. The animals clamber over each other, cover each other with the sand dug from their nests and constantly dig into the nests of others until the beach comes to be littered with eggs, shells, and embryos in various stages of development.

The predictability of arribadas was investigated by assessing the association of nesting with various environmental factors. The data derived from turtles that did not participate in arribadas suggest the optimum conditions for nesting prevail between the times of the last quarter moon and new moon. The factors which may be of importance at this time include the relative lack of illumination, the small tidal amplitude (neap tides), and the occurrence of high tide early in the evening. On the other hand the arribadas remain quite unpredictable and cannot be correlated with any evident environmental factor (fig. 4). It seems probable that synchrony of nesting of all individuals within the population is derived from the action of a pheromone released into the water, but there is as yet no evidence to support this contention.

Furthermore, no evidence was found to support the often quoted notion that arribadas are initiated by, or correlated with, the occurrence of onshore winds.

The evolutionary origin and adaptive significance of mass-nesting require examination, especially in view of our evidence suggesting that hatching success of the eggs laid during an arribada falls far short of expectations. Mass-nesting appears to be less adaptive than would the spreading of nesting effort more evenly along a greater expanse of shoreline, and points are raised here which are fundamental to turtle research concerning the ability of turtles to navigate. The authors take the view, apparently contrary to that of most workers in this field, that turtles do not navigate to and from their nesting beaches but instead are passively displaced by prevailing ocean currents to the vicinity of their "goal" where the latter is "recognized" by readily explicable sensory cues, probably involving the freshwater effluent of rivers, so often associated with mainland nesting beaches. Within the context of this hypothesis, arribadas may be viewed as the mechanism developed by turtles, deposited in often very considerable numbers at particular locations along the coast, to overcome the ravages of predators. By synchronizing the nesting of the entire population of turtles and confining it to only a few days each month, the predator population of the area is minimized and those that remain are effectively overwhelmed during arribadas and at times of hatchling emergence.

In support of our contention that the nest-beach is "recognized" by means of chemical cues we found that direct contact of the turtles with either seepage water on the beach or the water of the estuary behind the beach strongly elicited nest digging even in most unsuitable locations.

FIG. 3. Pacific ridleys *(Lepidochelys olivacea)* nesting on Nancite Beach, Costa Rica in September 1971.

Tagging

Of the nearly 2,000 turtles tagged, 102 were subsequently recovered by us at least once during the period of this study. These returns provided information on several aspects of ridley nesting biology.

It was shown that ridleys generally nest twice in a season, most usually in successive arribadas which, in the case of those witnessed during this study, occurred at intervals of 45 and 22 days. The nesting interval of turtles that did not participate in arribadas appeared to be approximately one month but in the case of individuals that nested solitarily the first time and subsequently joined an arribada was as short as 12 days.

Although many turtles returned to nest a second time on about the same portion of beach on which they were previously tagged, nest-site fixity of a number of individuals was found to be lacking to an apparently unusual degree. Six turtles tagged on Naranjo Beach, immediately to the south of Nancite, were later recovered at arribadas on Nancite Beach. Another, tagged on Naranjo, appeared 13 days later at an arribada on Ostional Beach, approximately 100 kilometers to the south. The same animal subsequently reappeared on Nancite Beach after a further 35 days.

Twenty-nine turtles, tagged in 1971, were found nesting again the following year (Stephen Cornelius, pers. comm.). This figure is large, in view of the limited beach surveillance undertaken in 1972, and it confirms evidence derived by Pritchard (1969) in Surinam to the effect that this species nests annually.

Hatchlings

It was estimated that of the more than 11½ million eggs laid during the arribada witnessed in September 1971 only about 25,000 hatchlings (approximately 0.2 percent) reached the sea. Further observation on Nancite Beach (Stephen Cornelius, pers. comm.) confirms that these incredibly low figures for hatching success appear to be usual. We have speculated (Hughes and Richard, 1974) that the destruction of the many millions of eggs which occurs each season when turtles dig into each others' nests transforms the relatively sterile beach sand into a rich substrate supporting organisms which destroy eggs. In this regard we have calculated that if every available portion of beach were utilized by the turtles there would be room on Nancite for approximately 180,000 nests. Yet the number of nests dug during the period of this study alone exceeded this figure by more than 100,000.

The question of hatching success of the eggs laid during an arribada has far-reaching implications to the development of conservation measures for the

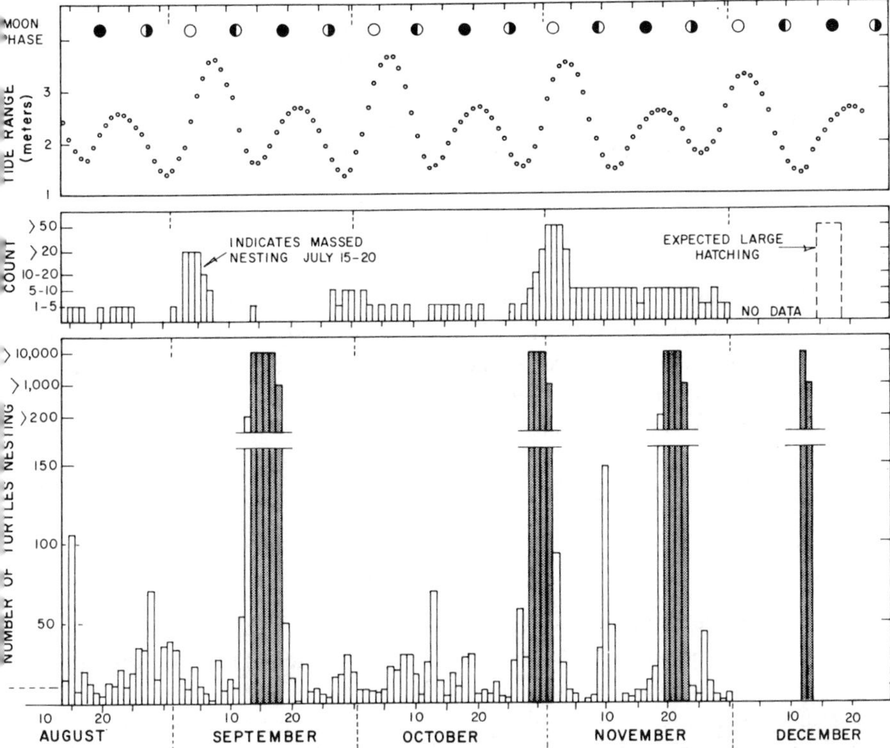

FIG. 4. Daily counts of Pacific ridleys nesting on Nancite Beach in late 1971 (from Hughes and Richard, 1974).

species, particularly as regards the exploitation of eggs on Ostional Beach where the practice has reached alarming proportions. This subject will soon be under investigation on Nancite.

In contrast to the destruction of eggs prior to hatching, the depredations of the many predators on hatchlings appears trivial. And yet it is probable that as many hatchlings as do reach the sea are taken by predators on the beach.

Within the vegetation above the beach, hatchlings are preyed upon by the gecarcinid shore crab *(Gecarcinus quadratus)*, iguanas, snakes, and buzzards. On the beach their chief predator is the black buzzard *(Cathartes burrovianus)*, whose numbers reached over 300 at times. When the emergence of hatchlings was localized on a particular portion of beach, as was often the case, the buzzard population would systematically destroy every hatchling that surfaced.

At least 2,800 ghost crabs *(Ocypode occidentalis)* large enough to capture hatchlings occurred on the beach. These formed a formidable gauntlet which had to be penetrated by the hatchlings to reach the sea.

Frigatebirds *(Fregata magnificans)* in groups of up to 55 patrolled the beach continuously and few hatchlings from a nest discovered by them escaped.

Aerial Survey Flights

The survey flights undertaken in 1971 were confined to the coastline of Guanacaste province and paid particular attention to the populations of ridleys off Ostional and Nancite beaches. They were, in effect, a continuation of the program which, in 1970, first revealed these beaches as major nesting sites of ridley turtles. The flights furnished supportive data on the population size and information on the extent of ridley nesting on beaches in the vicinity of Nancite (Richard and Hughes, 1972).

Conservation Outlook

By extreme good fortune Nancite Beach lies within the boundaries of the Santa Rosa National Park. At the time of proclamation of the park the importance of Nancite Beach was not known. Nevertheless, the National Parks Department is giving considerable attention to providing beach patrols, which will ensure that this population is totally protected during at least one critical phase of its life history.

In view of the drastic exploitation of this species in Mexico, and on the only other beach on which it is known to nest in Costa Rica, it seems probable that, within a short while, Nancite will be the last remaining site in the world where mass-nesting of this endangered species takes place.

REFERENCES

HUGHES, DAVID A., and RICHARD, JOSEPH D.

1974. The nesting of the Pacific ridley turtle *Lepidochelys olivacea* on Playa Nancite, Costa Rica. Mar. Biol., vol. 24, pp. 97-107.

PRITCHARD, P. C. H.

1969. Sea turtles of the Guianas. Bull. Florida State Mus., vol. 13, pp. 85-140.

RICHARD, JOSEPH D., and HUGHES, DAVID A.

1972. Some observations of sea turtle nesting activity in Costa Rica. Mar. Biol., vol. 16, pp. 297-309.

DAVID A. HUGHES
JOSEPH D. RICHARD

Description and Function of *Anolis limifrons* Social Displays

Principal Investigator: Thomas A. Jenssen, Virginia Polytechnic Institute and State University, Blacksburg, Virginia.

Grant No. 1033: To support a descriptive and functional account of the male *Anolis limifrons* repertoire of social signals.

Prior to 1971 most published reports of iguanid-lizard behavior characterized each species' display repertoire as being quite limited, having basically two display types: (1) the courtship display—a series of shallow, rapid head nods with an interspecifically similar pattern—and (2) the assertion-challenge display—a head-nodding pattern that is species-specific. This latter pattern is called the "assertion" display when performed with weak head amplitude and no or few accompanying modifiers (i.e., raised roach, side flattening, gorged throat) during low-intensity social contexts; when this same pattern is performed under intense conflict or motivating situations (i.e, male-male confrontations) it contains exaggerated head movements with many concomitant modifiers and is called the "challenge" display (see reviews by Carpenter, 1967; and Bussjaeger, 1971).

Attempts to ascertain the social functions of lizard displays have been largely by inference from watching enclosed and free-living individuals in uncontrolled situations. Experimental data testing the effects of social displays on conspecifics or systematically recording the elicited displays during controlled social contexts have been minimal and inadequate (Greenberg and Noble, 1944; Hunsaker, 1962; Pyburn, 1955); these results are reviewed elsewhere (Jenssen, 1970). Recently, new approaches to evaluating display social function have been reported (Jenssen, 1970; Stamps and Barlow, 1973). It was Jenssen's (1970) success in applying a film-loop technique to *Anolis nebulosus* displays that prompted the present study. The *A. nebulosus* investigation was of a narrow scope, and Jenssen proposed working with the film-loop technique in a more thorough investigation of display function, using *Anolis limifrons*.

The *Anolis limifrons* study, funded by the National Geographic Society, listed the following objectives:

1. To determine the species' maximum critical flicker-fusion frequency (CFF), a necessity when working with flickering visual stimuli (e.g., cinemagraphic presentations of the film-loop technique).

2. To describe the entire display repertoire of *A. limifrons.*
3. To correlate the use of each display type within the repertoire with specified social contexts.
4. To analyze each display type for range of variability (degree of stereotypy) and kinds of behavioral modifiers.
5. Via manipulated and normal displays portrayed by film loops, to determine those aspects of the various display types that are primarily responsible for message encodement.

Objectives 1-4 were required antecedents to the last objective. The fifth objective employed female response to the film loops as a bioassay to evaluate communicative effectiveness or degree of disruption to the display signal after systematic changes had been made in the film loop portraying a male's display. The experiments were based on the assumption that the female is attracted to a stimulus which simulates her species' recognition signal (the signature display).

Results

CFF Determination. If a light source is flashed on and off in increasingly rapid succession, a frequency will be reached when one no longer perceives the light as a flashing phenomenon but as continuous light. This threshold value is the CFF, which should be determined before presenting motion pictures to animals since the illusion of motion is obtained from the visual system fusing separately flashed pictures into a continuum. The cinema apparatus must produce more Hz than the subjects' maximum CFF. The maximum CFF for *A. limifrons* is about 28 Hz (Jenssen and Swenson, 1974), and the projection equipment used in the film-loop experiments delivered 54 Hz. Jenssen and Swenson (1974) also discovered an ecological correlate to CFF when testing other *Anolis* species. Seven tested congeners had a wide range of maximum CFF values (26-42). The maximum CFF values for the anoles correlated with the general level of insolation in each species' microhabitat, such that the brighter the habitat the higher the CFF.

Repertoire. In contrast to previous studies of iguanid lizards, analysis of 666 filmed male *A. limifrons* displays documented a complex repertoire of five distinct agonistic head-bob patterns (figs. 1 and 2). The A display serves as the species' assertion of signature display (*sensu* Stamps and Barlow, 1973). Characterized by a *one long—three short—one long* bob pattern, the A display is used to signal species identity and to declare territorial occupation. The other four display types (B-E) function in male-male encounters (Hover and

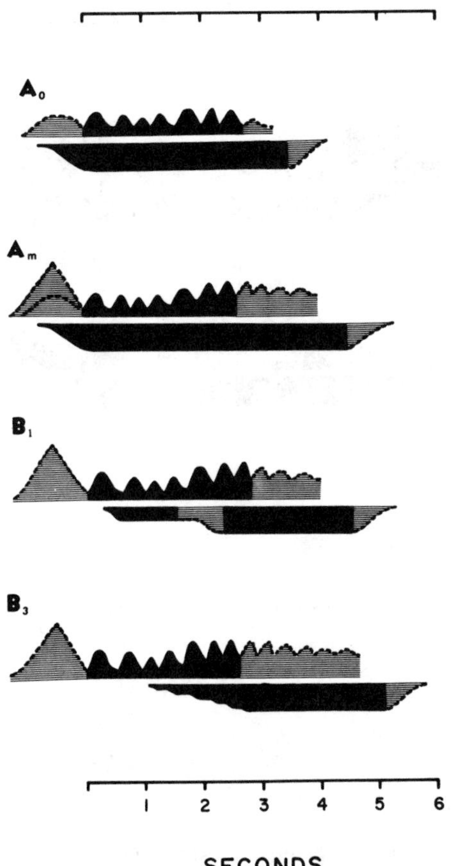

FIG. 1. Generalized head-movement patterns of male *Anolis limifrons* display types A and B. Shaded areas indicate display components not always present. Upper block denotes head amplitude through time and lower block shows dewlap extension through time.

Jenssen, 1976). An unusual aspect to the *A. limifrons* display repertoire was the absence of a pronounced courtship display. After more than 100 hours of observing male-female assemblages, only one display which even remotely resembled courtship bobs was seen.

Social Correlates with Display Type. From experiments and observations under seminatural conditions, the social usage of each display type was examined. Most of these results appear elsewhere (Hover and Jenssen, 1976). However, one set of tests showed that the males performed the C-E displays and

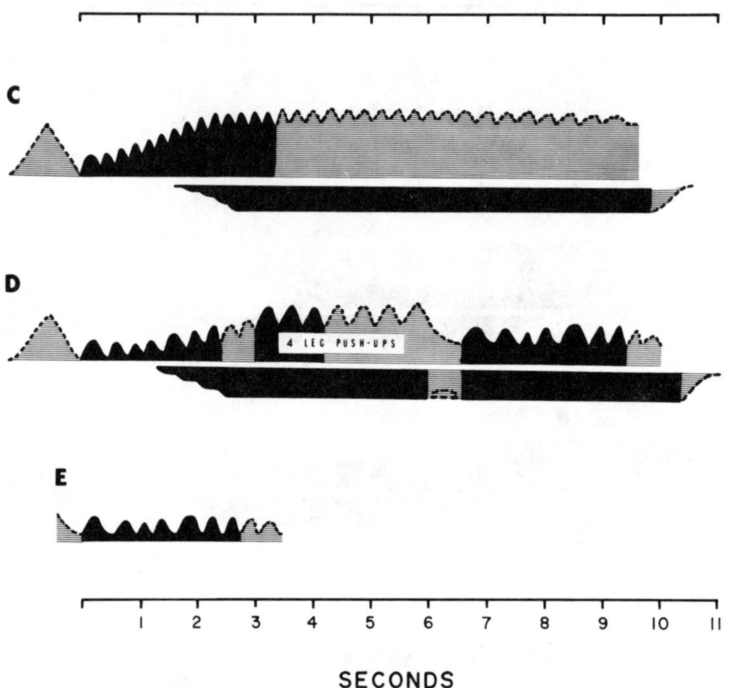

FIG. 2. Generalized head movement patterns of male *Anolis limifrons* display types C, D, and E. See notations of figure 1.

most of the B displays only during male-male encounters. An enclosure measuring (in meters) 2.4 long, 0.6 high, and 0.8 wide was divided into halves by an opaque, removable partition (fig. 3). The glass front was slanted so that the animals inside could not see their own reflections. Simulated forest habitat was duplicated in mirror image at each end of the cage. An adult male and female were placed in each compartment. After at least 24 hours, an hour of observation was conducted with the partition in place, and then continued for an hour after the partition was removed. Besides a twofold increase in number of displays and the appearance of B-E displays, the displays appearing with the partition removed showed a progression from A to E types as distance between antagonists decreased (fig. 4).

Male *A. limifrons* have an expanded aggressive display repertoire of graded behavior patterns. Each of these display types also has variable components (modifiers), which can be added to the basic stereotyped portion of the display to reflect apparent gradation of motivational state (i.e, nuchal crest erected,

FIG. 3. Enclosure used in partition experiments.

side flattening of body, tongue out, exaggerated introductory movements, and increasing number of head bobs). The species has a subtle step-wise progression of behavior indicating relative motivation and social intent.

Display Variability. The dynamics of the A display were analyzed by dividing the display into seven temporal units (fig. 5), and then determining the intraindividual and interindividual variability of each unit. Though the results will appear elsewhere (Jenssen and Hover, 1976), it is important to note that the first seven head bobs of this display were quite stereotyped (fig. 6).

Film-loop Experiments. An enclosure measuring (in meters) 3.3 long, 0.6 high, and 0.6 wide was constructed in a right-angle configuration (fig. 7). In the center chamber was a remote-controlled release box from which a subject (S) started each trial. At each end of the 1.3-meter-long galleries was a rear projection screen and mirror images of simulated forest habitat composed of small tree trunks, vines, and plastic plants. Fluorescent lights were placed over the screen tops of the galleries. A narrow viewing slit for monitoring S behavior was maintained between the top edge of the gallery and the light fixture.

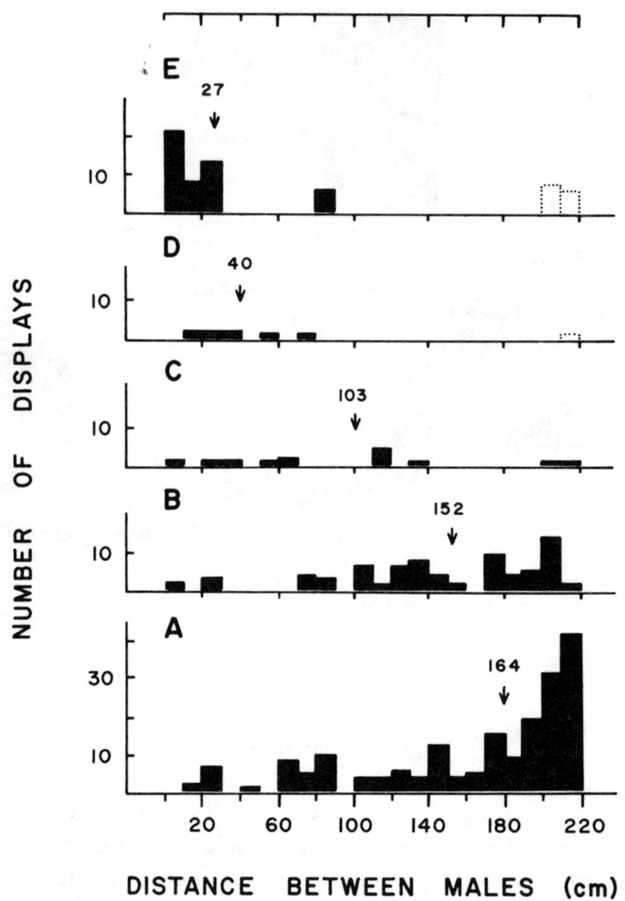

FIG. 4. Number of displays of each type versus distance between male *Anolis limifrons* with partition removed. Arrows indicate mean values, and numbers over arrows show sample size.

All film loops were of a super-8 format portraying a male displaying on a thin perch against a black background. Only those displays during which the male began and finished his display at approximately the same position were selected for making loops. Kodak MFS-8 projectors were used as they could be switched between run and still projection settings from a distance without loss of focus.

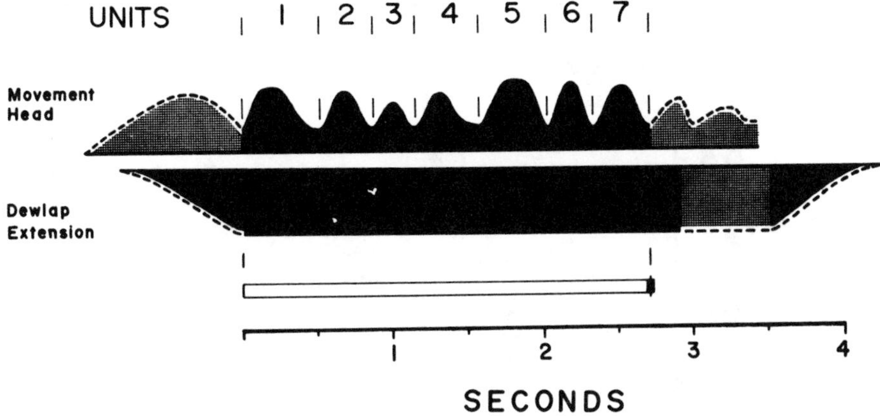

FIG. 5. Generalized type A (signature) display of male *Anolis limifrons*. Stippled areas indicate display components not always present.

The female Ss were all adults (41-49-millimeters snout-vent length) collected from the same general locality (South American side of the Canal Zone, Panama, near Gamboa) and were tested within a week of capture. The females were tested one at a time. The filmed displays to which the Ss responded were of males from the same locality as the Ss. An S was placed into the release box for 10 minutes. The box was then opened. When the S appeared, both projectors were turned on in still mode. The projectors were alternately switched into run mode with two displays being projected during a single run. After 2 minutes the projectors were turned off for 2 minutes. This cycle of 2 minutes on-2 minutes off was repeated three times. The S was allowed a total of 45 minutes to enter one of the galleries or she was scored as "no choice." When half of the Ss of an experiment had been scored, the film loops were switched between galleries.

The effectiveness of the film stimulus was tested by presenting an A display film loop to an adult male. He responded to the stimulus by performing A displays, but his response was not as quick or intense as if a real male had been introduced. As noted above, the male repertoire is complex and use of the various displays appears important in male encounters. Thus, the loop which repeated only one display type was not a totally natural stimulus, but, nevertheless, appeared to be perceived by the male as another male *A. limifrons*.

For the first tests using females, an A display was projected on the screen of only one gallery. During this pilot test it was found that many females did

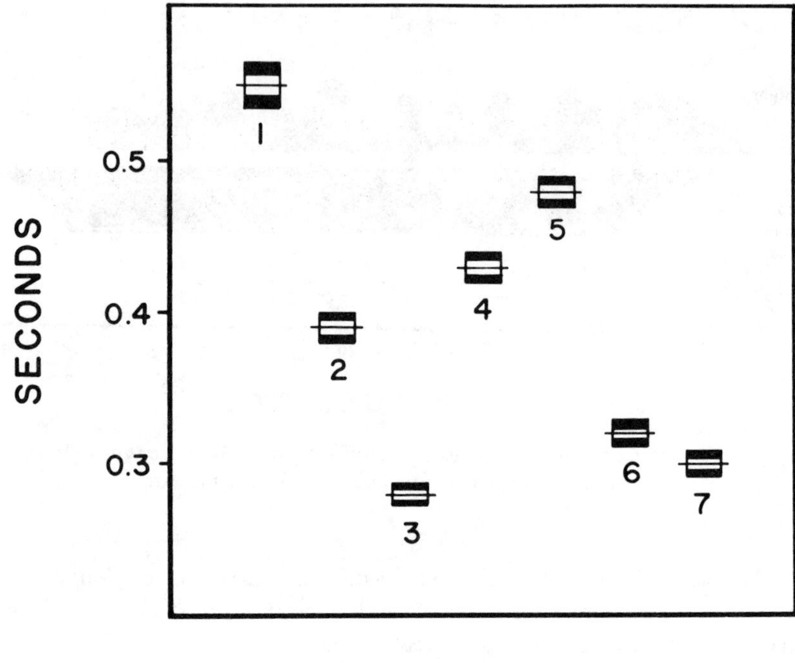

FIG. 6. Mean duration, standard error of the mean, and 95 percent confidence limits of the mean for each of the first seven head bob units in the *Anolis limifrons* type A display. Sample size is 316 displays from 22 males.

not gravitate to the habitat containing the image of the displaying male. This was totally unexpected. It was soon evident that the larger adult females (>45.5mm SVL) entered the habitat without the displaying male, and the smaller adult females mostly chose the habitat with the displaying male. The subsequent experiment demonstrated a statistically significant difference between choice response of large and small Ss (table 1, expt. 1). The same trend held when presenting Ss with a loop portraying a male giving the signature display (A) and the same male displaying in reverse (table 1, expt. 2); the large females did not choose a male giving their species' signal. If the choice was between two similar A displays there was a random response (table 1, expt. 3). When the choice was between a male giving the A display and a male giving the aggressive D display, there was a trend, though not significant, for both size classes of Ss to go to the habitat of the A displaying image (table 1, expt.

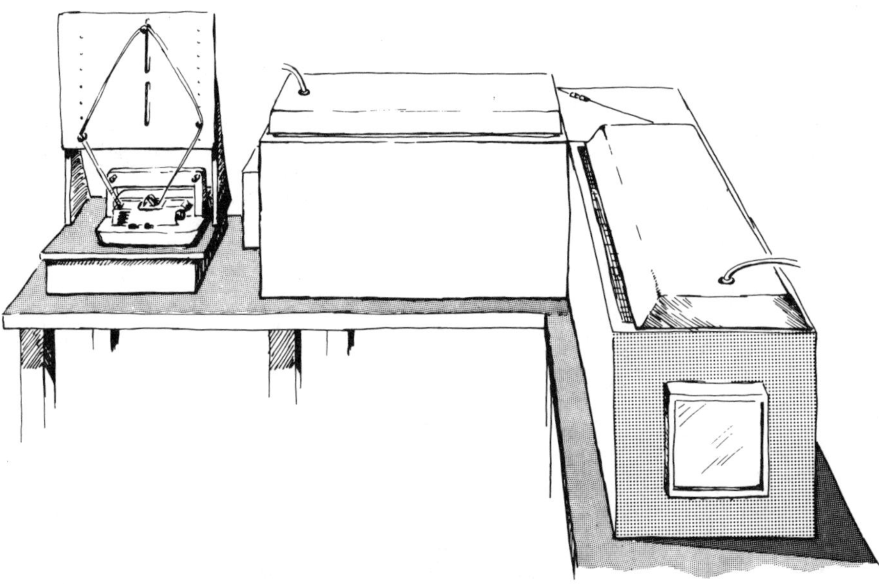

FIG. 7. Choice enclosure composed of central release chamber and two galleries with rear projection screens; one projector fitted with film loop is shown.

4). In the last two experiments, there were 1 and 3 "no choice" females, respectively, possibly indicating some ambivalence. The results from these experiments confirmed that the project's fifth objective could not be met, since the females were not reliable bioassay agents.

The following hypothesis, which, it is hoped, future research will test, is offered to explain the unexpected response of females to the males' displays: To decrease predation pressure, *Anolis limifrons* has integrated the strategy of dispersal into its social organization to the extent that the larger adult sexes are disassociated.

Contrary to most studied anoles, *A. limifrons* adult males and females are of equal size and occupy broadly overlapping structural niches (pers. comm. with A. S. Rand and pers. observ.). Sexual dimorphism related to body size (mouth size) and microhabitat preference are felt to decrease conspecific competition for food resources. *Anolis limifrons* appears to circumvent this competition by adults being spacially separated within the same habitat. While capturing over 70 adult females for the film-loop studies, only on three occasions was an adult male found to be sharing the same habitat cluster with a female. This is in contrast to the usual anoline social organization where the

TABLE 1. Results of Chi-Square Tests (With Yates Correction) Applied to 2 x 2 Contingency Tables of Female Choices to Male Displays

Experiment Number	*Female size (SVL)*	*Stimulus of one gallery*	*Stimulus of other gallery*	*Chi-square value and probability*
1		Habitat with Display *A*	Habitat w/o Display *A*	
	>45.5	0	10	10.21 P<0.01**
	<45.5	8	2	
2		Display *A* 11 head bobs (normal)	Display *A* 11 head bobs (reversed)	
	>45.5	1	10	5.45 0.01<P<0.05*
	<45.5	4	5	
3		Display *A* 7 head bobs	Display *A* 11 head bobs	
	>45.5	6	5	0.18 0.5<P<0.9 N.S.
	<45.5	2	2	
4		Display *A* 11 head bobs	Display *D*	
	>45.5	7	3	0.37 0.5<P<0.9 N.S.
	<45.5	5	2	

** Highly significant.
* Significant.
N.S. Not significant.

adult sexes are paired in coinciding territories. The implication is that adult female *A. limifrons* do not closely associate with adult males.

When capturing *A. limifrons,* I noted that females "squirrel" and hide within the same vegetation cluster as originally sighted, whereas chased males commonly move several to many meters from the original sighting point. The inference is that females may have small defined territories, while males may have large loosely delineated territories.

Regarding reproduction, preliminary experiments by A. Stanley Rand (Smithsonian Tropical Research Institute) and Robin Andrews (Virginia

Polytechnic Institute and State University) have found that adult females can lay at least five fertile eggs without benefit of a male (pers. comm.). Initial copulation and apparently sperm storage are sufficient to provide an isolated female with a reproductive capacity for at least two months (period required to lay five eggs). Dr. Rand and his colleagues have also found that the average adult life expectancy of *A. limifrons* is about four months. This would mean older females do not need to rely upon a close association with males for reproduction.

Historically, if the most serious predation pressure has been applied by vertebrate species capable of forming a search image (i.e., birds), the strategy of dispersal would be quite understandable. That the common anoline mechanism for decreasing conspecific competition for food (body size and microhabitat differences between the sexes) appears absent in *A. limifrons,* indicates dispersal has been long-standing for this species.

Other Studies

Studies indirectly funded include the discovery that male *Anolis townsendi* of Cocos Island also has a large display repertoire of at least four distinct head-bob patterns (Jenssen and Rothblum, 1977). Jenssen (1975) has found that *Phenacosaurus heterodermus,* a member of one of the "anole" genera, has three display types: courtship, assertion, and challenge; this is one more than the modal number of head-bob patterns reported for repertoires of non-anoline iguanid lizards. The usual "assertive-challenge" pattern has been split into two distinct display types by *P. heterodermus.* Since *Phenacosaurus* appears to represent both a closely related taxon and an early divergence from *Anolis,* it is possible the large display repertoires of some anoline lizards were an early development in the anoles' behavioral evolution. The last study assisted by the Society's grant documented that an anolid lizard (*Anolis grahami*) could vocalize, and did so during aggressive encounters (Milton and Jenssen, 1979). This is the first report of an iguanid lizard using sounds in a social context.

REFERENCES

Bussjaeger, L.

1971. Phylogenetic significance of the comparative ethology of the *spinosus* group of *Sceloporus* (Iguanidae), 187 pp. Ph.D. thesis, University of Oklahoma, Norman, Oklahoma.

CARPENTER, CHARLES C.
1967. Aggression and social structure in iguanid lizards. Pp. 87-105 *in* "Lizard Ecology: A Symposium," W. Milstead, ed. University of Missouri Press, Columbia, Missouri.

GREENBERG, B., and NOBLE, GLADWYN K.
1944. Social behavior of the American chameleon (*Anolis carolinensis* Voigt). Physiol. Zool., vol. 17, pp. 392-439.

HOVER, EDWARD L., and JENSSEN, THOMAS A.
1976. Descriptive analysis and social correlates of agonistic displays of *Anolis limifrons* (Sauria: Iguanidae). Behaviour, vol. 18, nos. 3-4, pp. 173-191.

HUNSAKER, DON
1962. Ethological isolating mechanisms in the *Sceloporus torquatus* group of lizards. Evolution, vol. 17, pp. 62-74.

JENSSEN, THOMAS A.
1970. Female response to filmed displays of *Anolis nebulosus* (Sauria, Iguanidae). Anim. Behav., vol. 18, pp. 640-647.
1975. Display repertoire of a male *Phenacosaurus heterodermus* (Sauria: Iguanidae). Herpetologica, vol. 31, no. 1, pp. 48-55, illus.

JENSSEN, THOMAS A., and HOVER, EDWARD L.
1976. Display analysis of the signature display from *Anolis limifrons* (Sauria: Iguanidae). Behaviour, vol. 57, pp. 227-240, illus.

JENSSEN, THOMAS A., and ROTHBLUM, LINDA M.
1977. Display repertoire analysis of *Anolis townsendi* (Sauria: Iguanidae) from Cocos Island. Copeia, 1977, no. 1, pp. 103-109.

JENSSEN, THOMAS A., and SWENSON, BETTY
1974. An ecological correlate of critical flicker-fusion frequencies for some *Anolis* lizards. Vision Res., vol. 14, pp. 965-970.

MILTON, THOMAS H., and JENSSEN, THOMAS A.
1979. Description and significance of vocalizations by *Anolis grahami grahami* (Sauria: Iguanidae). Copeia, 1979, no. 3, pp. 481-489.

PYBURN, WILLIAM F.
1955. Species discrimination in two sympatric lizards, *Sceloporus olivaceus* and *S. poinsetti*. Texas Journ. Sci., vol. 7, pp. 312-315.

ROTHBLUM, LINDA M.; WATKINS, JEFFREY W.; and JENSSEN, THOMAS A.
1979. A learning paradigm and the behavioral demonstration of audition for the lizard *Anolis grahami*. Copeia, 1979, no. 3, pp. 490-494.

STAMPS, J., and BARLOW, G.
1973. Variation and stereotypy in the displays of *Anolis aeneus* (Sauria: Iguanidae). Behaviour, vol. 48, pp. 67-94.

THOMAS A. JENSSEN

Seamounts in the Austral Islands Region

Principal Investigator: Rockne H. Johnson, Hawaii Institute of Geophysics, University of Hawaii, Honolulu, Hawaii.

Grant No. 1035: In support of a study of volcanism in the Austral Islands.[1]

The discovery of an active submarine volcano to the southeast of the Austral Islands (Johnson, 1970; Johnson and Malahoff, 1971) has intensified the interest of geoscientists in this remote and otherwise inconspicuous island and seamount chain. While no extensive modern geological or geophysical studies have been made in the Austral region, the active Macdonald volcano serves as a benchmark for speculation on the role that this chain of volcanoes has played in the process of sea-floor spreading. Morgan (1972) has designated Macdonald volcano as the hot-spot overlying an upwelling plume of convecting mantle material. He traces previous manifestations of this plume along the Austral, Cook, Samoa, Ellice, Gilbert, and Marshall Islands. Menard (1973) has considered the remnants of ancient coral reefs, now elevated on many Austral and Cook Islands, and has interpreted these elevations in terms of an undulating asthenosphere. He compares the location of Macdonald volcano and those of other supposed Pacific hot-spots with features of the earth's gravity field. Also, Clague and Jarrard (1973) have remarked: "The active volcano Macdonald seamount serves as an anchor point for predicting ages along the Austral and Cook chains." These last authors have computed poles of rotation for the Pacific plate on the basis of trends of volcanic chains.

Herron (1972), taking a cautious exception to the hot-spot theory, suggests that the Tuamotu as well as the Austral chain "may have been partly formed by shearing during the temporary breakup of the Pacific . . . Plate." This breakup is related to an anomalously slow spreading rate, which she infers from magnetic lineations formed 5 to 10 million years ago.

Anticipating increased interest in the region, I conducted exploratory cruises through the Australs aboard my 63-foot ketch *Kawamee,* collecting

[1] The crew for the November-December 1973 cruise, during which most of the work was done, was noteworthy for its irrepressible enthusiasm. Members were Louis De Frank, Charles Schafer, Charles Poulos, Walter Reid, Jeffrey Watson, William Goodman, and Gaston Teihotaata. I thank David Handschumacher for the suggestion that the magnetometer sensor be placed at the masthead. Hawaii Institute of Geophysics Contribution no. 656.—R. H. J.

bathymetric and magnetic data. This report contains charts and profiles of a number of the seamounts that were encountered.

Method

The major cruise during which the data reported here were collected took place during November and December 1973. On that cruise both echo-sounder and magnetometer were operated continuously. Other cruises during which only bathymetric data were collected took place in July 1972 and July 1973. Figure 1 shows the locations of seamounts discussed in this report.

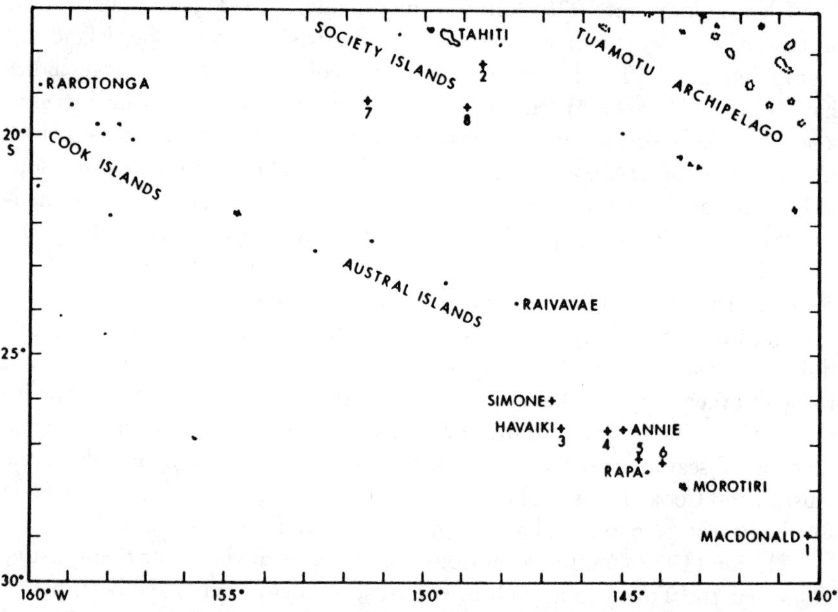

FIG. 1. The Austral Islands region. Seamounts in the order discussed in the text are 1, Macdonald volcano; 2, seamount southeast of Tahiti; 3, Havaiki guyot; 4, seamount west of Annie guyot; 5, seamount northwest of Rapa; 6, bank northeast of Rapa; 7, guyot southwest of Tahiti; 8, guyot south of Tahiti.

The echosounder used was the same 14-KHz Furuno model F-812-H carried aboard *Havaiki* (Johnson, 1970) during the discovery of Macdonald volcano. However, the receiver gain was enhanced, and the pulse timing was modified to provide continuous coverage, over 1,000-meter spans, to depths well beyond the 2,000-fathom designed limit. With the modifications, echoes were recorded from reflective bottoms under quiet conditions at depths in excess of 5,000 meters. Noise due to turbulence around the transducer limited reception at speeds above 5 knots. This situation was probably due to an unfavorable choice of transducer location abaft the widest section of the hull. As indicated depth is proportional to stylus speed, the powerline frequency that controls this speed was recorded at half-hourly intervals. The frequency was estimated, from a vibrating reed meter, to 1 part in 600.

The magnetometer used during the November-December 1973 cruise was a Geometrics model G-806 portable proton-precession magnetometer coupled to a Rustrack recorder. A novelty in the installation was the placement of the sensor on a plastic pipe 2½ feet above the vessel's aluminum mainmast, about 68 feet above the iron hull. The usual procedure is to tow the sensor some three ship lengths astern to avoid the influence of the hull upon the magnetic field (Bullard and Mason, 1961). However, the convenience and reliability of a fixed above-water installation outweighed the attraction of data free from artificial perturbations. A similar installation was successfully tested on the submarine *Aluminaut* (Higgs and Carroll, 1967). The error induced by *Kawamee*'s hull was measured at three locations in the Austral region by motoring on a series of courses (at 30° intervals) while over magnetically flat terrain and under light-weather conditions. The resulting heading-correction curves have a maximum span of about 180 gammas. Calibrations of the magnetic compass were, of course, obtained at the same time from observations of the sun's azimuth. The standard deviation of successive magnetometer readings while the vessel was moored in port (constant heading) was about 4 gammas. The standard deviation of a set of readings taken at sea while steering a compass course of 165° by autopilot was about 18 gammas. This scatter of readings while under way appeared to be a function of the ship's rolling and pitching motion as amplified at the masthead. As the rolling oscillations of a sailing vessel are not symmetrical about the level position, the magnetometer records probably contain heeling error as well as heading error. No convenient method was found for measuring the heeling error; however, it is probably on the order of the 18-gamma standard deviation observed at sea and therefore negligible for most purposes.

Navigation was primarily celestial. A clear day's observations would include about six stellar and planetary altitudes at morning twilight, solar altitudes at half-hourly intervals throughout the day, lunar altitudes at half-hourly intervals when available during the day, about six stellar and planetary altitudes at evening twilight, and, on nights with a bright moonlit horizon, perhaps nine or ten stellar and planetary altitudes after 2200 hours. After the cruise these data were prepared for computer processing and a track was estimated that provided a least-squares fit to the data. For this purpose the track was segmented so that a separate fit was obtained for the interval of each day's observations with the nighttime gaps bridged by dead reckoning.

Courses and speeds were read from the steering compass, which had a maximum deviation of 2°, and a Kenyon model KSO speedometer. The speedometer, purchased specifically for the Austral Islands work, proved unreliable; its odometer, which integrates speed and indicates distance run, failed twice within its first year. On the November-December 1973 cruise it failed just as the vessel departed Rarotonga to enter the Austral region. It was then necessary for the helmsman to estimate the average speed over each half-hourly interval for entry into the log. Computer-programmed comparisons of speedometer readings with the celestial observations later indicated that the speeds recorded were about 15 percent low. Accordingly a 15-percent correction was applied throughout.

Where the vessel's track repeatedly recrossed itself, as in a seamount survey, it is possible to improve upon the relative positioning of the track segments through a statistical analysis of the discrepancies in water depth and/or magnetic field as recorded at the crossing points (Johnson, 1971). This procedure, herein referred to as FUDGE (Fitting of Unacceptable Discrepancies in Geophysical Exploration), was used for two of the seamounts described in this report, both of which were guyots.

For the other seamounts, whose topographies are more rugged and whose shallow summits noticeably perturb the surface current, it was more convenient to determine the times of track crossing by constructing a graph of depth versus magnetic field strength along the track. In the absence of magnetic drift and with proper correction for heading and powerline frequency, each track crossing will have a corresponding crossing on the depth-magnetics graph. There will also usually be spurious crossings on the graph, but most of these can be rejected out of hand and from those crossings remaining a set can be chosen that is consistent with a nearly uniform current. Most seamounts are associated with steep magnetic gradients, which render the problem of drift and correction less critical. Also shallow seamounts and tidal variations will perturb the current, making some arbitrary adjustment of the track necessary to achieve agreement at the crossings.

For one seamount, Macdonald volcano, a radar-reflecting buoy was moored at the summit to serve as a navigational reference.

Seamounts

Although gross features of Macdonald volcano had been discovered during earlier visits by other vessels to this important seamount, no detailed survey had been obtained of the summit region. With the specific goal of exploring the summit, *Kawamee* approached Macdonald volcano in the early morning hours of December 1, 1973. The weather was quite pleasant, with a light breeze from the southeast sufficient to steady the vessel but not so strong as to inhibit maneuvering under power. It was desired to plant the navigational reference buoy at nearly the shallowest spot in order to minimize the scope of its mooring and thereby the variability in its position. After making the first turn at 0700 ship's time (ST; a ship's time 10 hours slow on Greenwich was used throughout the cruise), 2½ hours were spent searching the summit region for the 49-meter depth encountered by the *Argo* in 1969 (Johnson and Malahoff, 1971). The buoy was finally moored near a 70-meter sounding at 1000 ST. The vessel then lay-to for 2 hours to ascertain that the buoy was not dragging its anchor (two old storage batteries) and to fix the position during meridian passage of the sun. While it was alongside the buoy, 25 solar and 3 lunar altitudes were measured. The resulting fix at lat. 28° 59′S., long. 140° 16′W. was essentially in agreement with the satellite navigation of the *Argo*. A zigzag pattern, which remained within the 1,000-meter contour and returned to the buoy twice, was then motored for 3 hours. The buoy was recovered and *Kawamee* departed on a northerly course.

The summit bathymetry and the magnetics are shown in figure 2. Figure 3 is a reproduction of the echogram for two traverses of the summit. In this and following echograms there is a vertical exaggeration of about 14:1 depending on ship speed. (For further cautioning in interpreting echograms as topographic profiles, see Menard, 1964, p. 62.)

Menard (1964, p. 62) states that summit craters are common on submarine volcanoes. He gives typical dimensions of 300 to 1,000 meters diameter and 100-200 meters depth (below the surrounding lip). He shows as examples profiles of three seamounts at summit depths of 1,600 to 2,000 meters.

At shallow depths such as the summit of Macdonald volcano the problems of echogram interpretation are greatly simplified. However, there is no suggestion of a crater in either the bathymetric chart, figure 2, or the echograms, figure 3.

While the 1967 eruption of Macdonald volcano was explosive (Norris and Johnson, 1969) and probably produced tephra, such unconsolidated material would be very unlikely to form a crater lip in the presence of strong ocean currents. A more likely mechanism for crater formation would be collapse following the withdrawal of magma. This, apparently, has not occurred.

Neither is there evidence of a wave-cut shelf. Although there is a broadening of the contour spacing between 240 and 160 meters (fig. 2), the profiles (fig. 3) do not show the smoothness characteristic of wave-cut terraces. It is

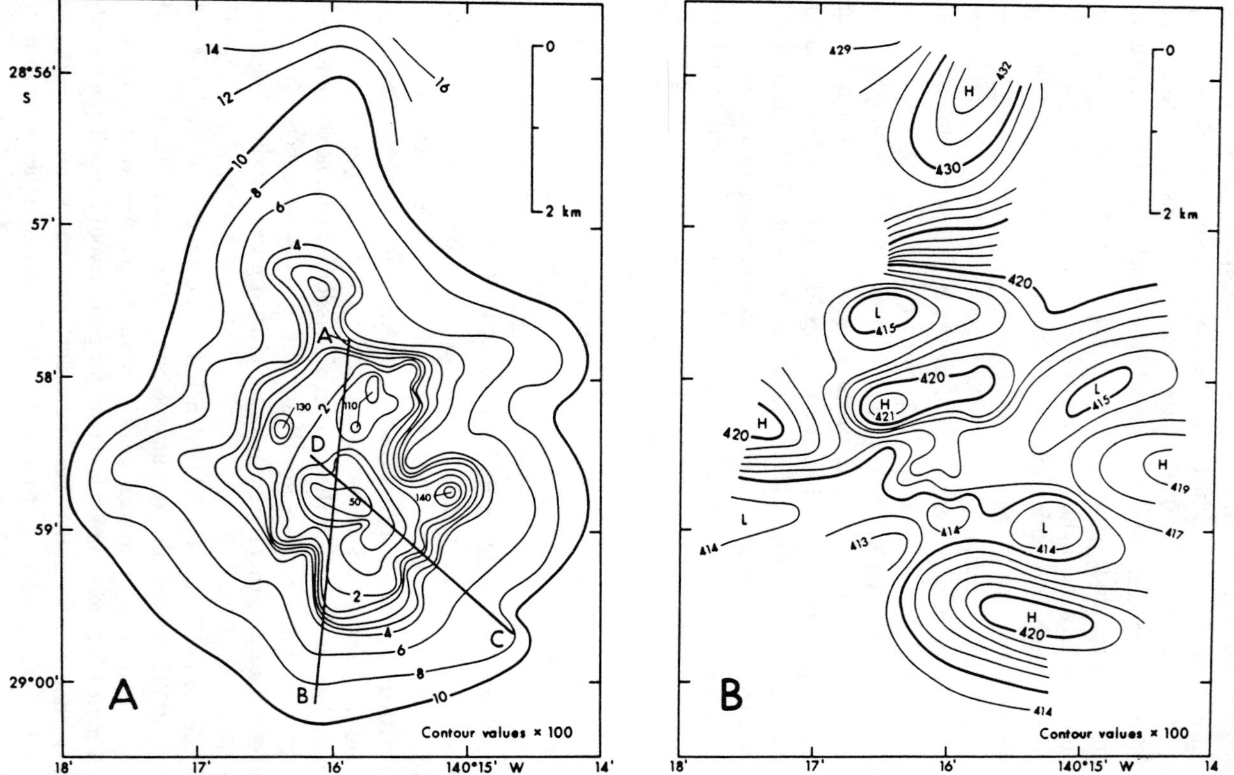

FIG. 2. A, Bathymetry of the summit region of Macdonald volcano; contours less than 400 meters are at 40-meter intervals. B, Total magnetic field intensity over the summit of Macdonald volcano; contours are at intervals of 100 gammas.

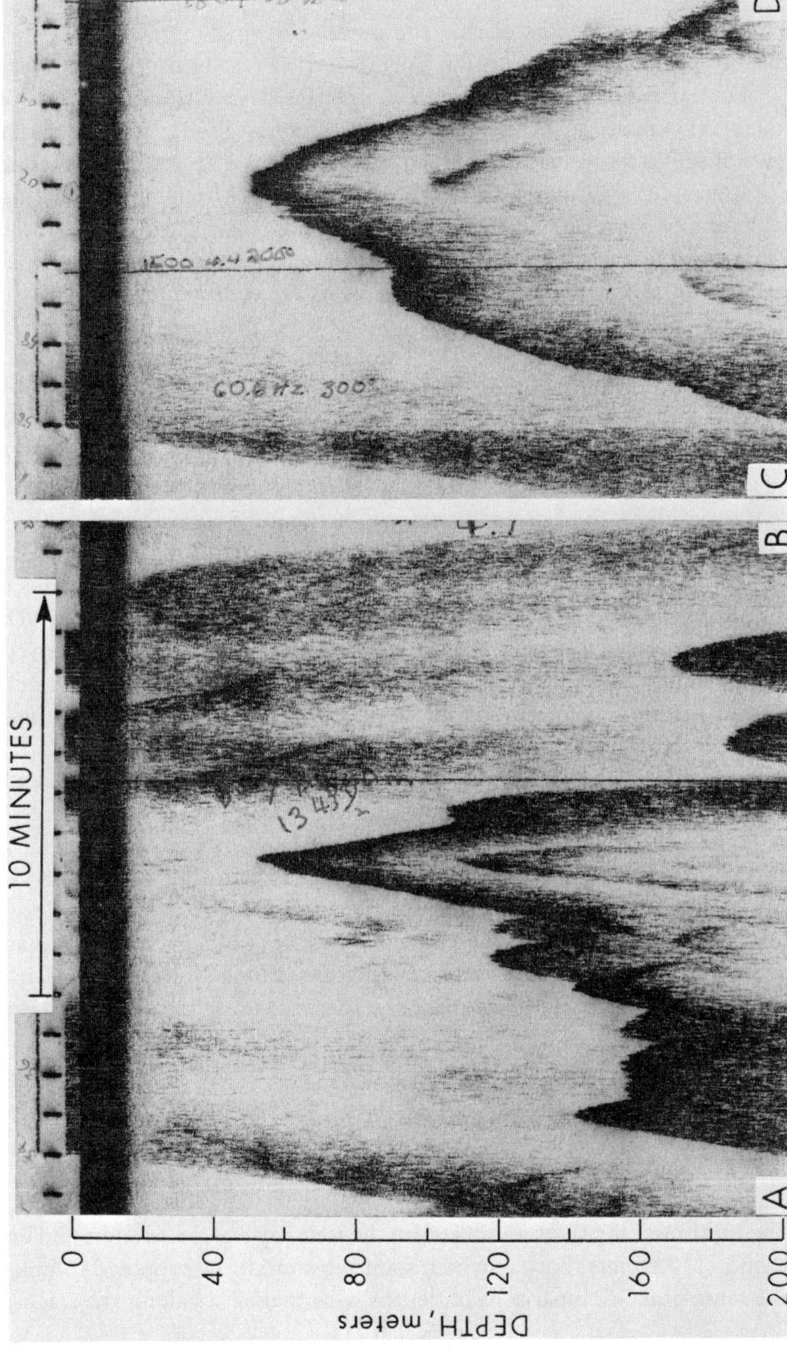

FIG. 3. Echograms generated while traversing the summit of Macdonald volcano.

more likely that the depths of this contour broadening represent an upper limitation of nonexplosive eruption during low glacioeustatic stands of sea level. The maximum Pleistocene regressions have been estimated at 130 to 160 meters (Donn et al., 1962; Milliman and Emory, 1968), which is about the level of the lesser pinnacles of Macdonald volcano (110-140 meters). The present summit at a 49-meter depth, then, has probably been built up during the Holocene transgression of the past 15,000 years.

Magnetic measurements taken aboard *Argo* in 1969 indicated the existence of strong reversely polarized anomalies in the summit region. The results of the detailed survey aboard *Kawamee* (fig. 2) show three reversely polarized anomalies all with wavelengths of about 1 kilometer and with amplitudes (crest to trough) ranging from 400 to 790 gammas. These are superimposed upon the broad (15-kilometer wavelength) normal anomaly found by *Argo.* The short wavelength anomalies show no strong relationship to surface features; the reversed anomalies probably indicate subterranean magma and adjacent rocks above the Curie temperature (hence not magnetized).

On the basis of the magnetic data previously collected, Johnson and Malahoff (1971) postulated the existence of an extensive magma chamber in the upper 2 kilometers of Macdonald volcano. The basis for this was not so much the observed reversed anomaly as it was the disparity between the observed major normal anomaly and the computed terrain effect. The extent to which the present detailed magnetic survey may require the alteration of previous computations remains to be determined.

Aligned with the two volcanoes that comprise the island of Tahiti, and 45 miles to the southeast, is charted a seamount with a least depth of 180 meters. Although not strictly within the Austral region, the seamount's position relative to the apparent trend of migration of volcanism in the Society Islands made it an interesting subject for study in the course of approaching and leaving Tahiti. If the age of Tahiti is comparable to that of Maui in the Hawaiian chain, as judged by the extent of erosion, then a continued southeastward migration of volcanic activity would place the site of any recent eruptions in the vicinity of the 180-meter seamount.

Kawamee visited the seamount on November 11 and 20, 1973, generating a simple crossing pattern the first day and a more extensive zigzag pattern the second day. The current on the first day was setting about 220° at 0.3 knot and on the second day about 250° at 0.5 knot. The bathymetry and the magnetics are shown in figure 4.

The minimum depth encountered on the first day was 180 meters and on the second, 175 meters; both of which soundings might be supposed to indicate the same peak. Comparisons of depths with magnetics along the tracks,

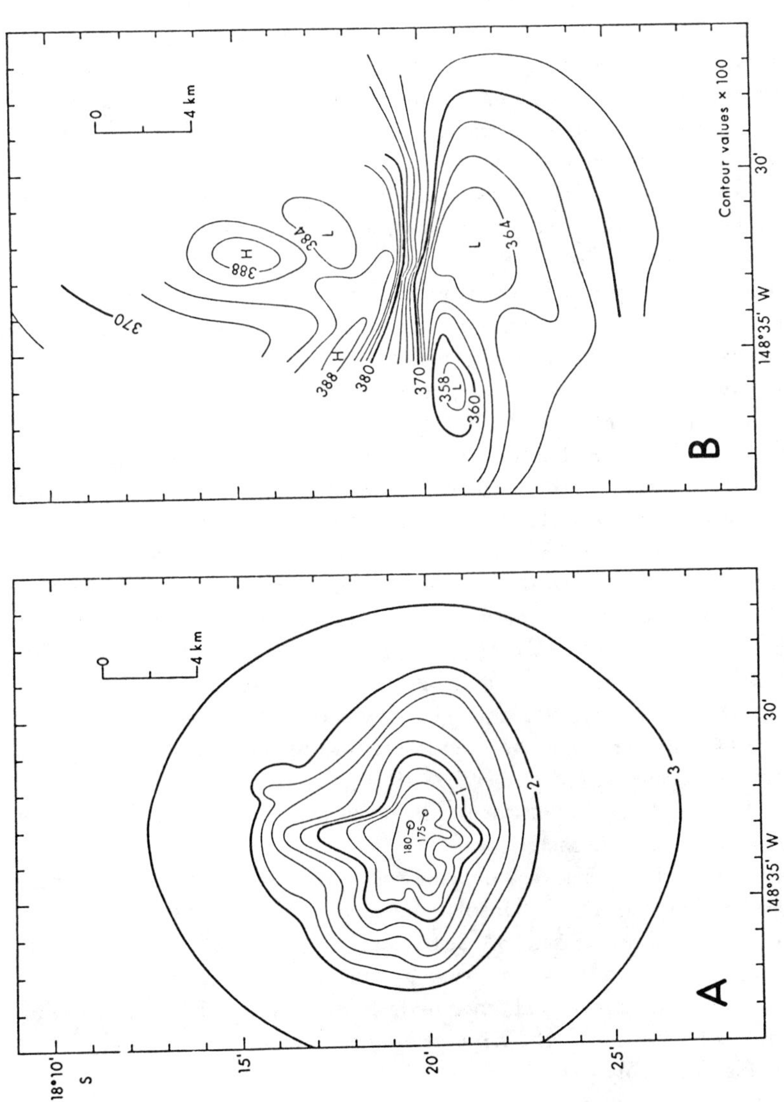

FIG. 4. A, Bathymetry of the seamount southeast of Tahiti; contours less than 2,000 meters are at 200-meter intervals. B, Total magnetic intensity over the seamount southeast of Tahiti; contours are at 200-gamma intervals.

however, indicate that they are horizontally separated about 800 meters and are probably two distinct pinnacles. No inference of the existence of a crater appears warranted.

Except for a depth that is greater by 130 meters, this seamount differs little in general size and shape from Macdonald volcano. The magnetic anomaly that it induces is strikingly different, however. It is normally polarized with a very steep gradient over the summit and a wavelength of about 4 kilometers such as might be computed for the terrain effect. It is unlikely, then, that the seamount has a hot core and is volcanically active.

Havaiki guyot was discovered by me in 1969 while enroute to the exploration for Macdonald volcano. At that time a single crossing was made with poor navigational control due to overcast sky. The unusual feature of this seamount is the many pinnacles distributed across its gently domed summit. In fact, to classify it as a guyot requires some modification of the usual definiton: a flat-topped seamount at a depth greater than 100 fathoms.

In order to fix its position better and to determine its extent, Havaiki guyot was visited by *Kawamee* on July 8-9, 1972. No operating magnetometer was aboard at the time. The summit was explored through the night by five traverses to the extent of the 1,800-meter contour. Evening and morning star sights, together with the FUDGE program, positioned the highest pinnacle at lat. 26° 38′S., long. 146° 31′W. about 7 miles west of the previously reported position. Figure 5 shows oval contours extending 22 miles NW-SE and 13 miles NE-SW at the 1,600-meter level. Figure 6 is the echogram for the major traverse. In all, about 15 pinnacles could be counted; the shallowest rises about 200 meters above its base to a depth of 800 meters.

The seamount west of Annie guyot was formerly charted as a 1,150-meter sounding near the western end of 1,600-meter-deep Annie guyot. A survey by *Kawamee* on November 25, 1973, showed it to be a separate seamount (fig. 7). A crossing of the saddle on December 5, 1973, found intervening depths of 2,520 meters.

Navigation for this survey utilized the FUDGE program with both magnetic and bathymetric data, four solar and nine planetary and stellar altitudes. The current was found to set 130° at 0.3 knot. The minimum depth encountered was 1,250 meters at a position 5 miles south of the position for the 1,150-meter depth shown on French hydrographic charts. The two soundings were probably taken over the same peak although the navigational discrepancy is unaccountably large.

The western seamount was apparently worn down to its present configuration by wave action at a time when it was at sea level. Its eroded summit has slopes of 6° to 9° similar to subbottom reflectors found on guyots in the Mid-

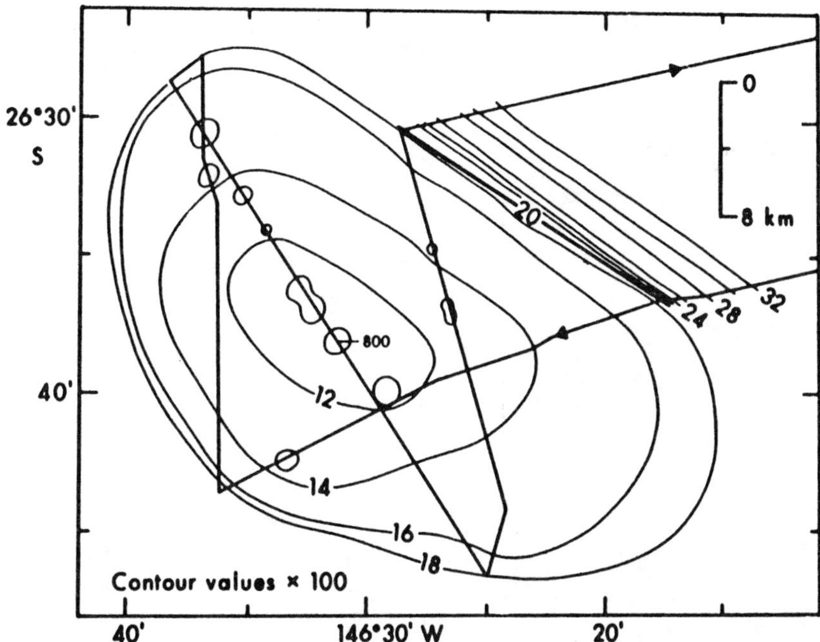

FIG. 5. Bathymetry of the top of Havaiki guyot with the track of *Kawamee.* Contours are at 200-meter intervals.

Pacific Mountains (Karig et al., 1970). Otherwise, the summit spans approximately the same depth range as Havaiki guyot. A few minor pinnacles were found near the shelf-break on the southeast side.

Annie guyot, although flat-topped, does not show as smooth a surface as neighboring Simone guyot (Johnson and Malahoff, 1971). One minor pinnacle was encountered on Annie guyot.

A seamount 20 miles northwest of the island of Rapa was surveyed out to the 1,000-meter contour on November 26, 1973. The minimum depth previously reported was 700 meters; a minimum depth of 330 meters was encountered by *Kawamee.* This volcano was probably built by the same migration of volcanism as Rapa. While the north slope of this seamount extends directly to the ocean floor, on the south it is built against a 1,200-meter-deep structure of possibly much greater age. The seamount's normally polarized magnetic anomaly pattern is not nearly as pronounced as that of Macdonald volcano or the seamount southeast of Tahiti. This may be due to part of its construction having taken place while the geomagnetic field was reversed.

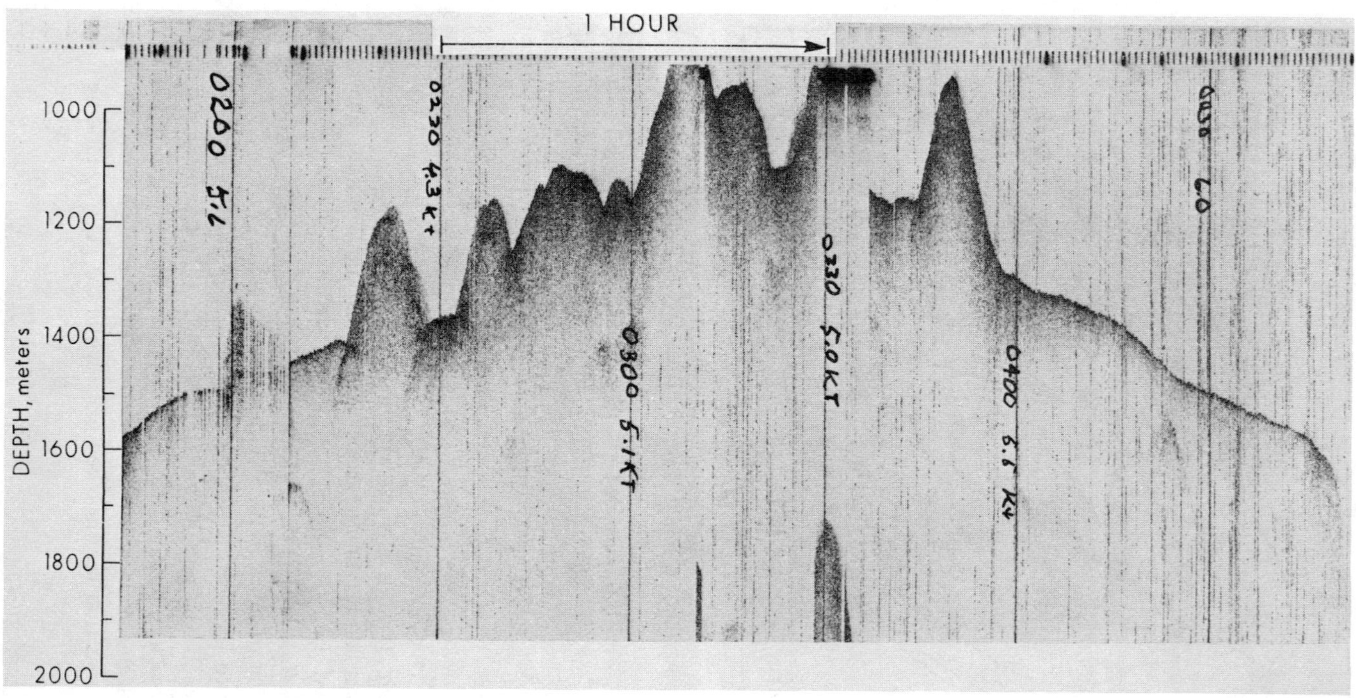

FIG. 6. Echogram of traverse of Havaiki guyot from northwest to southeast in figure 5.

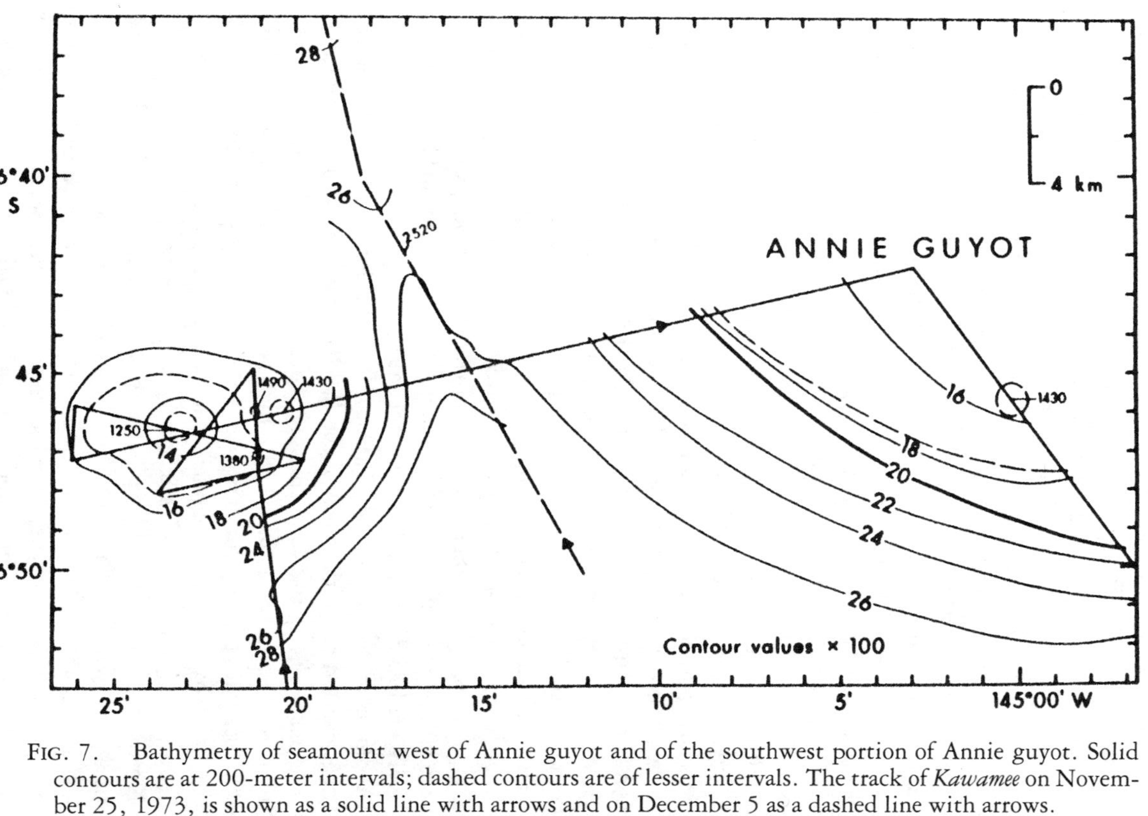

FIG. 7. Bathymetry of seamount west of Annie guyot and of the southwest portion of Annie guyot. Solid contours are at 200-meter intervals; dashed contours are of lesser intervals. The track of *Kawamee* on November 25, 1973, is shown as a solid line with arrows and on December 5 as a dashed line with arrows.

The bank northeast of Rapa, at a depth of 30 meters and about 2 miles across, was traversed twice by *Kawamee* on November 29, 1973. It and the seamount northwest of Rapa are on a line that approximately parallels the line formed by Nielson Reef, Rapa, Morotiri, and Macdonald volcano and is displaced from it by 30 kilometers. A prominent terrace is found at 100 meters, corresponding in depth to the Mamala shelf around Oahu (Brock and Chamberlain, 1968; Ruhe et al., 1965). This shelf was cut by repeated sea-level lowerings during the Pleistocene. It may be supposed that this seamount also was constructed as part of the Austral Islands migration of volcanism.

About 140 miles southwest of Tahiti, French chart 6036 shows a seamount at a depth of 300 meters. U. S. Navy Oceanographic chart 621 gives the depth as 164 fathoms, apparently a conversion from the metric measurement. *Kawamee* made several traverses of this seamount during the predawn hours of July 12, 1973, and found a guyot with a minimum depth of 510 meters (270 fathoms). The guyot was explored in search of a shallower pinnacle but none of significance could be found. A profile is shown in figure 8.

Most island and seamount chains on the Pacific plate are aligned along one of two basic trends, regarded as indicative of two consecutive directions of motion of the plate (Clague and Jarrard, 1973). One of these trends is that of the Austral, Society, and Hawaiian Islands, to name a few. The Ellice, Gilbert, and Marshall Islands, and the Emperor Seamount Chain, are examples of the other. The second group is comprised of older islands and seamounts. The alignment of the 270-fathom guyot southwest of Tahiti with Simone and Havaiki guyots roughly parallels the trend of the older islands, suggesting that they are all members of a genetically related chain. But the unnamed guyot's relatively shallow depth implies a younger age.

About 90 miles south of Tahiti at lat. 19° 21′S., long. 148° 56′ W. a seamount is charted along the track of the *Baird* on the Downwind expedition. *Kawamee* made nearly the same crossing, encountering a minimum depth of 1,200 meters versus the *Baird*'s 1,090 meters. The bathymetric profile identifies the seamount as a guyot. The seamount lies a little too far to the northeast to fit easily into the aforementioned alignment of guyots. However, further exploration may reveal other guyots aligned with it.

Noting that the 200-mile gap between Morotiri and Macdonald volcano is considerably wider than may be found elsewhere in seamount chains, Johnson and Malahoff (1971) speculated that there were other seamounts within the gap. With this possibility in mind, *Kawamee*'s path was directed along this gap both on approaching and leaving Macdonald volcano but no seamount was encountered. However, it was not a thorough search and the possibility cannot be ruled out completely.

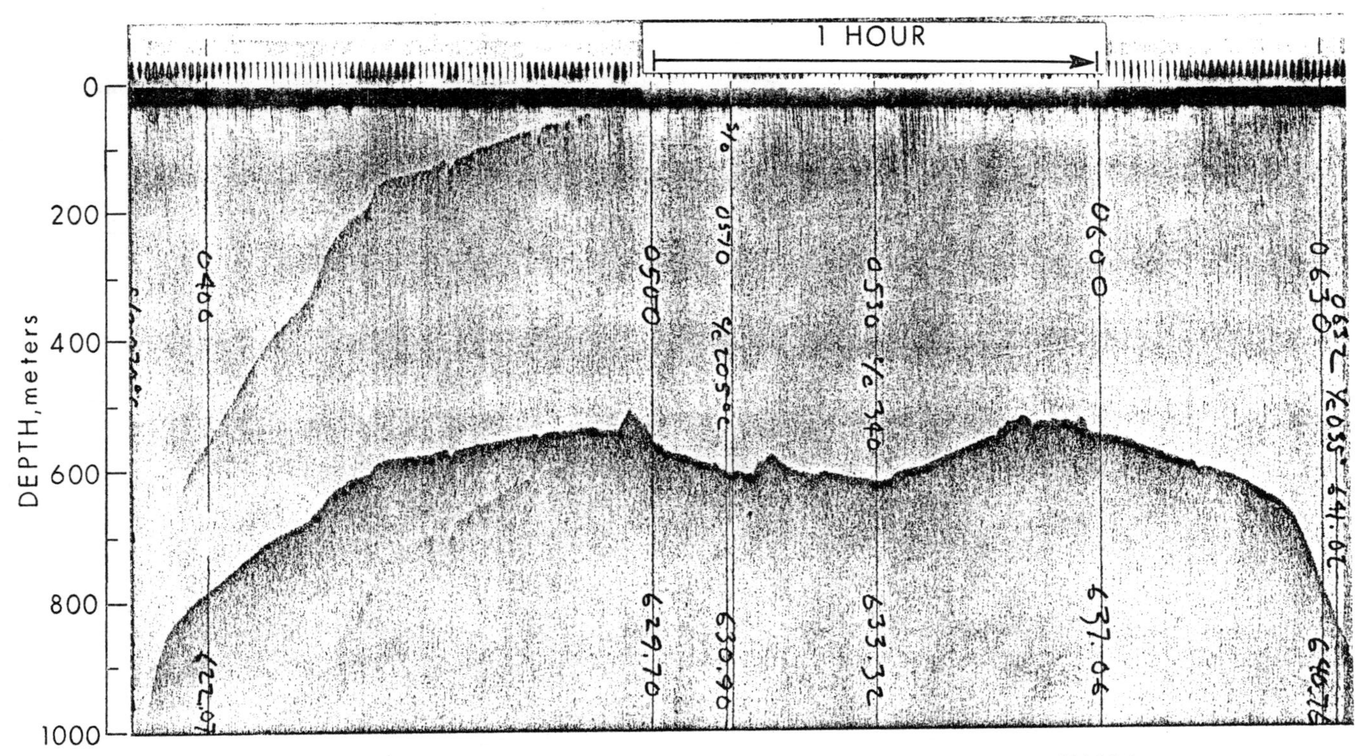

FIG. 8. Echogram of traverse (with two course changes) of guyot southwest of Tahiti.

Discussion

While this study does not resolve the question of whether the Austral chain was formed by ocean floor moving past a fixed hot-spot or by mechanisms involving distortion in the Pacific plate, a question can be raised with respect to the hot-spot hypothesis. Why should a mantle plume that produced the massive Society Islands chain be so short-lived while the relatively puny effects of the Austral hot-spot can be traced back as far as the even more massive Hawaiian chain? Such stability in a minor feature of the mantle circulation while sea-floor-spreading centers are shifting position at relatively short intervals (Herron, 1972) seems improbable.

On the other hand, Herron's (1972) observation of a spreading rate anomaly 5-10 million years ago may be related to the separation of the Australs into two en echelon chains. Tracing the migration of volcanism back from Macdonald volcano at a rate of 9 centimeters per year (Johnson and Malahoff, 1971) places the break in the chain within that time interval.

A feature that up to now has not been adequately treated in discussions of ancient island chains is the set of guyots that lie across the Austral trend. Havaiki, Simone, and Annie guyots were, at one time, major islands. It would be surprising if more members of that ancient island chain could not be found. The directions in which to look are indicated by the trends of older Pacific island and seamount chains.

The detailed survey of the summit of Macdonald volcano indicates that the 50-meter pinnacle is probably the site of recent eruptions rather than an erosional remnant. Exploration of the summit by SCUBA diving is feasible and could provide further insight into the nature of this stage of submarine volcanism and the question of submarine crater formation.

REFERENCES

BROCK, V. E., and CHAMBERLAIN, T. C.
1968. A geological and ecological reconnaissance off western Oahu, Hawaii, principally by means of the research submarine *Asherah.* Pacific Sci., vol. 22, pp. 373-394.

BULLARD, EDWARD C., and MASON, RONALD G.
1961. The magnetic field astern of a ship. Deep-Sea Res., vol. 8, pp. 20-27.

CLAGUE, DAVID A., and JARRARD, RICHARD D.
1973. Tertiary Pacific Plate motion deduced from the Hawaiian-Emperor chain. Bull. Geol. Soc. Amer., vol. 84, pp. 1135-1154.

DONN, WILLIAM L.; FARRAND, WILLIAM R.; and EWING, MAURICE
1962. Pleistocene ice volumes and sea-level lowering. Journ. Geol., vol. 70, pp. 206-214.

HERRON, ELLEN M.
1972. Sea-floor spreading and the Cenozoic history of the east-central Pacific. Bull. Geol. Soc. Amer., vol. 83, pp. 1671-1690.

HIGGS, R. H., and CARROLL, J. C.
1967. *Aluminaut* magnetometer operations, St. Croix, Virgin Islands, 1966. Naval Oceanogr. Office Informal Rpt. 67-33, 28 pp.

JOHNSON, ROCKNE H.
1970. Active submarine volcanism in the Austral Islands. Science, vol. 167, pp. 977-979.
1971. Reduction of discrepancies at crossing points in geophysical surveys. Journ. Geophys. Res., vol. 76, pp. 4892-4896.

JOHNSON, ROCKNE, and MALAHOFF, ALEXANDER
1971. Relation of Macdonald volcano to migration of volcanism along the Austral chain. Journ. Geophys. Res., vol. 76, pp. 3282-3290.

KARIG, DANIEL E.; PETERSON, MELVIN N. A.; and SHOR, GEORGE G.
1970. Sediment-capped guyots in the Mid-Pacific Mountains. Deep-Sea Res., vol. 17, pp. 373-378.

MENARD, HENRY W.
1964. Marine geology of the Pacific, 271 pp. McGraw-Hill Book Co., New York.
1973. Depth anomalies and the bobbing motion of drifting islands. Journ. Geophys. Res., vol. 78, pp. 5128-5137.

MILLIMAN, JOHN D., and EMORY, K. O.
1968. Sea levels during the past 35,000 years. Science, vol. 162, pp. 1121-1123.

MORGAN, WILLIAM J.
1972. Deep mantle convection plumes and plate motion. Bull. Amer. Assoc. Petrol. Geol., vol. 56, pp. 203-213.

NORRIS, R. A., and JOHNSON, ROCKNE H.
1969. Submarine volcanic eruptions recently located in the Pacific by sonar hydrophones. Journ. Geophys. Res., vol. 74, pp. 650-664.

RUHE, ROBERT V.; WILLIAMS, J. M.; and HILL, E. L.
1965. Shorelines and submarine shelves, Oahu, Hawaii. Journ. Geol., vol. 73, pp. 485-497.

ROCKNE H. JOHNSON

Population Ecology of the Flamingos of the World

Principal Investigator: M. Philip Kahl, International Council for Bird Preservation, Naples, Florida.

Grant Nos. 1022, 1108, 1316, 1412. To study the ecology and reproductive biology of flamingos.

From the fossil record we know that the flamingos (Phoenicopteridae) are an ancient avian group that was once widespread in Europe, North America, and Australia, as well as in the areas where they are found today (Brodkorb, 1963; Miller, 1963). They are now reduced to "relict" populations (Amadon, 1953) in isolated pockets, mostly in the tropics of America, Africa, and western Asia. Being highly specialized ecologically, flamingos are often superabundant in certain habitats and entirely absent in others.

Accurate censusing is difficult, owing to the large flocks and often inaccessible habitat. Since the meeting of the International Flamingo Symposium in 1973 (Kear and Duplaix-Hall, 1975), where previous population figures were compiled (Kahl, 1975), additional information suggests that some of the earlier figures were too high. Especially in the cases of the greater flamingo *(Phoenicopterus ruber roseus)* and the Chilean flamingo *(P. chilensis)* the estimates of total populations have been lowered somewhat. These estimates have been compiled from the observations of many observers and are subject to further revision in the future as some areas become better known. The most reliable figures are obtained from aerial surveys, combined with high-resolution photographs upon which birds and nests can be counted.

Surveys and Findings

Areas in which I personally conducted a survey, and the dates thereof, are listed below. Range maps depicting the current distribution of each population are given in Kahl (1975) and only a brief summary of ranges will be repeated here. The most intensive fieldwork was done during 1972-1974 under research grants from the National Geographic Society, New York Zoological Society, and International Council for Bird Preservation. To these organizations I express my sincere gratitude.

Americas:

Baharnas (Great Inagua)–Apr.-May 1972
Dominican Republic (Isla Saona)–Apr. 1975
Mexico (Yucatán)–Apr. 1972
Bonaire–Jan. 1972; June 1973
Ecuador (Galápagos Islands)–Mar.-Apr. 1972
Peru (southeastern)–Apr. 1973
Chile (northeastern)–Feb., Dec. 1972; May 1973
Bolivia (western)–Jan., Mar. 1972; Oct. 1972-May 1973
Argentina (northwestern)–Feb. 1972

Africa:

Kenya, Tanzania, Uganda–Nov. 1963-July 1967; Sept. 1972; Aug. 1973-Apr. 1974; Oct. 1976-Jan. 1977
Ethiopia (southern Rift Valley)–Apr. 1967
South West Africa (Etosha Pan; west coast)–Apr.-May 1974; Feb.-Mar. 1977
Mauritania (Banc d'Arguin; Aftout-es-Sahel)–May 1974
Tunisia–May 1974

Asia:

Turkey (south-central Anatolia)–June 1974
Israel (northern Sinai)–June 1974
Iran (L. Rezaiyeh; central Fars)–June-July 1974; July-Aug. 1975
Afghanistan (Ab-i-Istada; Dasht-i-Nawar)–July 1974
India (Great Rann of Kutch)–Nov. 1973

CARIBBEAN FLAMINGO *(Phoenicopterus ruber ruber)*

Range. Widespread in the Caribbean region, with largest numbers being found in the southern Bahamas and Greater Antilles; Bonaire, Netherlands Antilles, and the neighboring mainland of South America; and the Yucatán Peninsula, Mexico. A small, isolated population occurs in the Galápagos Islands, in the Pacific Ocean about 950 kilometers off the coast of Ecuador. Wanderers from the Caribbean have occurred as far away as Bermuda and the mouth of the Amazon. Most of the recent records from the North American Continent are probably escaped free-flying birds from Hialeah Park, Miami, and other captive collections.

Breeding. A number of former breeding sites, especially in the Bahamas and Greater Antilles, are no longer in use (Allen, 1956). At present, the major breeding locations are: Great Inagua Island, Bahamas (up to 20,000 birds in some years); Bonaire, Netherlands Antilles (4,000-6,000 birds); Río Lagartos, Yucatán, Mexico (up to 6,000 birds in some years); and southern Isabela Island, Galápagos (about 300-400 birds).

Numbers. Allen (1956) reviewed the history of the Caribbean flamingo and estimated that formerly there were approximately 95,000 birds. In 1956, he estimated that only 21,500 remained. Since then the population has apparently increased, and our knowledge has become more complete (Sprunt, 1975). Current estimates of population units are as follows:

Bahamas/Greater Antilles	38,000
Yucatán Peninsula	12,000
Southern Caribbean (Bonaire, etc.)	10,000
Galápagos Islands	500
Total estimated population	60,500

GREATER FLAMINGO *(Phoenicopterus ruber roseus)*

Range. The most widespread of all the flamingos, ranging from the Cape Verde Islands (23°W.) and West Africa eastward to southeast India and Ceylon (82°E.); and from Lake Tengiz, Kazakh S.S.R. (50°N.) southward to the Cape of Good Hope (35°S.). Within this range the greatest concentrations are found in the Great Rann of Kutch, India; the Middle East; the western Mediterranean and northwest Africa; South and South West Africa; and the Rift Valley of East Africa. Stragglers have occurred over much of northern Europe (reaching as far as Leningrad) and eastward into Siberia (as far as Lake Baikal).

Breeding. In recent years, nesting colonies have been active in all parts of the range. Major breeding populations are: Rann of Kutch, India (over 200,000 birds nesting in 1945 and twice that number in 1960; 36,000 in 1970; 15,000 in November 1973 and 30,000 in January 1974); Lake Rezaiyeh, Iran (40,000-50,000 in 1970, 1971, 1972; 58,650 in 1973; and 38,742 in 1974); Etosha Pan, South West Africa (27,000 in 1971; 10,000 in 1974); Lake Elmenteita, Kenya (20,000 in 1957; 17,000 in 1968); Sebkra de Sidi el Hani, Tunisia (20,000 in 1972); the Camargue, France (16,000 in 1960; 14,660 in 1969; 7,000 in 1974; and 10,000 in 1975); Lake Natron, Tanzania (14,000 in 1968); and Tuz gölu, Turkey (10,000 in 1970). Smaller colonies also occur irregularly in Spain, Morocco, Mauritania, South Africa, Israel/Egypt, Afghanistan, and Kazakh S.S.R.

Numbers. Probably the second most numerous of the flamingos of the world, but populations are difficult to assess because of the extensive range and interchange of birds between areas. Many census figures are available, but unfortunately they were often made in different seasons—or even different years—and it is not known how many birds may have been recounted or missed altogether. The largest uncertainty in our figures is the population in the Rann of Kutch, India, where hundreds of thousands were reported prior to 1960, but only tens of thousands during the 1970's. Owing to this apparent decline in the Indian population, the numbers in the Rann of Kutch are tentatively estimated at 200,000, pending further information.

Our best estimates are probably those based on counts during the breeding season and can be roughly tabulated as follows:

Region	Estimate
India (mainly Great Rann of Kutch)	200,000
Southern Africa (mainly Etosha Pan)	75,000
North-west Africa (Tunisia, Morocco, Mauritania)	60,000
East Africa (Rift Valley)	50,000
Iran (mainly Lake Rezaiyeh)	50,000
Turkey (mainly Tuz gölu, Kurbağa gölu)	25,000
Kazakh S.S.R. (mainly Lake Tengiz)	20,000
France and Spain (mainly the Camargue)	20,000
Afghanistan (Ab-i-Istada and Dasht-i-Nawar)	10,000
Israel/Egypt (Northwest Sinai)	2,000
Total estimated population	512,000

CHILEAN FLAMINGO *(Phoenicopterus chilensis)*

Range. Occurs mainly on salt lakes (up to 4,500 meters), from central Peru (Lago Junin: 11°S.) southward along the Andes to Tierra del Fuego (55°S.). Found also along both coasts of southern South America, mainly in the winter, and in the pampas of Argentina, where formerly more abundant. Nonbreeding birds are found in many localities in Argentina, Uruguay, Paraguay, and southern Brazil (Rio Grande do Sol Province); and stragglers have been reported on the Falkland Islands and at Río Tumbez in northern Peru, near the Ecuadorian border (Chapman, 1926).

Breeding. Today most breeding occurs at salt lakes in the Andes, from south-central Peru (Laguna Yauri-Viri: 14°S.) to extreme southern Chile (Puerto Natales: 52°S.) and southern Argentina. Recent breeding colonies have been found at the Salar de Surire, Chile (3,000-4,000 birds in May 1973); Salar de Uyuni, Bolivia (3,000-4,000 birds in February 1973); and east of Esquel, Chubut Province, Argentina (4,000-6,000 birds in summers of 1971-72 and 1972-73). Formerly, large colonies existed at low-altitude sites in Argentina: e.g., at Mar Chiquita (4,000 birds in 1941) and in Santa Fé Province (20,000 birds in 1936).

Numbers. Certainly the most numerous of the South American flamingos. Population estimates vary from 300,000 (Rooth, 1967; Cordier, 1965); 330,000 (Allen, 1956; Brown, 1959); 500,000 (Kahl, 1975); to 1,000,000 (Cordier, 1968, and personal communication). Numbers are difficult to assess, owing to the vastness and remoteness of much of the range.

My maximum counts have been 100,000 (Lago Poopó, Bolivia, in January 1972); 70,500 (Lago Poopó, Bolivia, in February 1973); 16,400 (Laguna Salinas, Peru, in April 1973); and 9,000 (Lago Uru Uru, Bolivia, in December 1972).

Approximately 12,000 were found wintering in Magallanes Province, southern Chile, in 1971 (Markham, 1971).

Total estimated population is 350,000.

LESSER FLAMINGO *(Phoeniconaias minor)*

Range. Primarily an African species, with an apparently sizable population in northwest India as well. The major concentrations are found on the soda lakes of the East African Rift Valley. Another large number exists in South West Africa and Botswana, and it is not known how much interchange may take place between this population and the one in East Africa. There is a small population in West Africa (Mauritania), and a straggler has occurred as far north as southern Spain (Bernis, 1966).

Breeding. Unrecorded until 1954, when discovered on Lake Natron, Tanzania (Brown, 1955). Since then fairly regular nesting has been reported from Lake Natron, and in 1962 a gigantic colony (an estimated 1,100,000 nests) occurred on nearby Lake Magadi, Kenya (Brown and Root, 1971). Large colonies have also been found in recent years on Etosha Pan, South West Africa (Berry, 1972). An apparently unsuccessful nesting was attempted east of Lake Mweru, Zambia, in 1955 (H. D. Brown, 1957), and in July 1965 a breeding colony of 1,600-1,800 birds was discovered in coastal southwest Mauritania, in West Africa (Naurois, 1965).

In January 1974, Ali and Shivrajkumar found a small number—estimated at 2,000-5,000 birds—breeding among greater flamingos in the Great Rann of Kutch, India. This is the first *breeding* record for this species outside of Africa (Ali, in press).

Numbers. By far the most numerous of all the flamingos. At least 3,000,000 must have been present at Lake Magadi, Kenya, in 1962, when over 1,000,000 pairs nested. Over 1,000,000 are often present at Lake Nakuru, Kenya; and Brown (1959) estimated 2,000,000 at Lake Hannington, Kenya, in March 1953. When J. Hopcraft, A. Root, and I made an aerial survey of Lake Hannington on September 4, 1972, we found an estimated

2,000,000 birds present. Brown (1975) estimates approximately 5,000,000 birds in the East African lakes, plus another 1,000,000 in South West Africa and Botswana.

The Indian population is uncertain but probably contains a few tens of thousands at least (Ali and Ripley, 1968).

Total estimated population is 6,000,000.

ANDEAN FLAMINGO *(Phoenicoparrus andinus)*

Range. Found mainly on salt lakes, above 2,500 meters in the Andes, from southern Peru (Laguna Salinas: 16°S.) southeastward along the altiplano to western Bolivia, north-central Chile (south to Salar de Maricunga: 27°S.), and northwest Argentina (south to near Tucumán: 27°S.).

This species has been collected by Hoy (pers. comm.) in northeast Salta Province, Argentina, at about 500 meters altitude (15-20 birds recorded in April 1956).

Breeding. The major and most regular breeding seems to be on the Salar de Atacama, northeast Chile. Also it has been found nesting on a number of other salt lakes in northeast Chile (e.g., Salars de Surire, Huasco, Coposa, and Ascotán), and at Laguna Colorada, southwest Bolivia (Johnson, 1965-67). Southernmost breeding reported in Aconquija mountains, west of Tucumán, Argentina, where Olrog (pers. comm.) has seen flightless young moving down a dry riverbed in the company of adults.

Numbers. Estimates have varied greatly, from 50,000-100,000 (Cordier, 1965); 100,000 (Rooth, 1967); 130,000 (Brown, 1959); 150,000 (Kahl, 1975); 250,000 (Cordier, pers. comm.); to 500,000 (Cordier, 1968).

The largest number I saw was an estimated 18,000 at Lago Uru Uru, Bolivia, on December 4, 1972. And at most other localities I have found this species less numerous than either *P. chilensis* or *jamesi.* Thus I feel that a population of about 150,000 is a reasonable estimate.

Total estimated population is 150,000.

JAMES FLAMINGO *(Phoenicoparrus jamesi)*

Range. Most restricted distribution of any flamingo. Found at salt lakes, mainly above 3,500 meters in the Andes, from southern Peru (Laguna Salinas, Lago Titicaca: 16°S.) southeastward along the altiplano to northeast Chile, western Bolivia, and northwest Argentina (Jujuy and Salta Provinces: 25°S.). In November 1972, two adults were observed and photographed near a breeding colony of Chilean flamingos by J. Muñoz, east of Esquel, Chubut Province, Argentina. This observation is approximately 2,000 kilometers south of the previously known range of this species. The photographs were shown at the International Flamingo Symposium in 1973, and it was unanimously agreed that the birds depicted were, indeed, *P. jamesi.*

This species has been collected by Hoy (pers. comm.) in the Oran region of northwest Argentina, at about 300 meters altitude (3 birds in July 1958; 2 birds in July 1966).

Breeding. Unrecorded until 1957, when discovered on Laguna Colorada, Bolivia (Johnson, Behn, and Millie, 1958). An estimated 5,000-7,000 birds were found nesting at Laguna Colorada in January 1958 (Peña, 1962), and 3,000-4,000 were nesting there in January 1960 (Conway, 1960). When I flew over Laguna Colorada in January 1972 and February 1973, I found no nesting flamingos (of any species); it is possible that they have shifted their breeding range northward since the early 1960's.

There was an unconfirmed report of large numbers of *P. jamesi* nesting at the southern end of Lago Poopó, Bolivia, in February 1968. Sixty-three small young were collected from this region for Sr. Cordier by Morato Indians, but, unfortunately, all the birds later died in captivity (Cordier, 1968, and pers. comm.).

Numbers. Most probably the least numerous of all flamingos. Estimates vary from 15,000 (Rooth, 1967; Brown, 1959) to 30,000-50,000 (Cordier, 1965, 1968, and pers. comm.). The largest reported single gathering was that of 10,000 at Laguna Colorada, Bolivia, in November 1965 (Morrison, 1972).

I favor the higher estimates, for between December 1972 and May 1973 I saw nearly 22,000 individuals, as follows:

Lago Uru Uru, Bolivia (Dec. 4, 1972)	3,000
Lago Poopó, Bolivia (Feb. 21, 1973)	8,000
Laguna Salinas, Peru (Apr. 19, 1973)	3,200
Laguna Sacabaya, Bolivia (May 11, 1973)	1,500
Salar de Surire, Chile (May 13, 1973)	6,000
	21,700

Total estimated population is 50,000.

Summary

This survey summarizes current knowledge on the ranges, breeding areas, and population numbers of the flamingos of the world.

Using figures compiled from my observations and those of many other workers, I estimate the populations of the six flamingos of the world as follows:

Caribbean flamingo	60,500
Greater flamingo	512,000
Chilean flamingo	350,000
Lesser flamingo	6,000,000
Andean flamingo	150,000
James flamingo	50,000
	7,122,500

REFERENCES

ALI, SÁLIM

———. Breeding of the lesser flamingo, *Phoeniconaias minor* (Geoffroy), in the Great Rann of Kutch. Journ. Bombay Nat. Hist. Soc. (In press.)

ALI, SÁLIM, and RIPLEY, S. DILLON

1968. Handbook of the birds of India and Pakistan, vol. 1, 380 pp., illus. Oxford University Press, London.

ALLEN, ROBERT P.

1956. The flamingos: Their life history and survival. Nat. Audubon Soc. Res. Rpt. no. 5, 285 pp., illus. New York.

AMADON, DEAN

1953. Migratory birds of relict distribution: Some inferences. Auk, vol. 70, no. 4, pp. 461-469.

BERNIS, F.

1966. Presencia de un flamenco enano, *Phoeniconaias minor,* en el Sur de España. Ardeola, vol. 12, p. 259.

BERRY, H. H.

1972. Flamingo breeding on the Etosha Pan, South West Africa, during 1971. Madoqua, ser. 1, no. 5, pp. 5-31.

BRODKORB, PIERCE

1963. Catalogue of fossil birds, pt. 1. Bull. Florida State Mus., vol. 7, no. 4, pp. 179-293.

BROWN, H. D.

1957. The breeding of the lesser flamingo in the Mweru Wantipa, northern Rhodesia. Ibis, vol. 99, no. 4, pp. 688-692.

BROWN, LESLIE H.

1955. The breeding of lesser and greater flamingos in East Africa. Journ. East. Afr. Nat. Hist. Soc., vol. 22, pp. 159-162.

1959. The mystery of the flamingos, 116 pp. Country Life, Ltd., London.

1975. East Africa. Pp. 38-48 *in* "Flamingos," J. Kear and N. Duplaix-Hall, eds. Poyser, London.

BROWN, LESLIE H., and ROOT, A.

1971. The breeding behaviour of the lesser flamingo, *Phoeniconaias minor.* Ibis, vol. 113, no. 2, pp. 147-172.

CHAPMAN, FRANK M.

1926. The distribution of bird-life in Ecuador; a contribution to a study of the origin of Andean bird-life. Bull. Amer. Mus. Nat. Hist., vol. 55, 784 pp., illus.

CONWAY, WILLIAM G.
1960. To the high Andes for the rarest flamingo. Anim. Kingdom, vol. 63, no. 2, pp. 34-50, illus.
CORDIER, C.
1965. À la recherche de flamants dans les hautes Andes. Zoo (Antwerp), vol. 30, no. 3, pp. 83-88.
1968. Flamingos in Bolivien. Freunde Kölner Zoo., vol. 11, no. 1, pp. 13-16.
JOHNSON, A. W.
1965, 1967. The birds of Chile and adjacent regions of Argentina, Bolivia and Peru, 2 vols., 397 and 477 pp., illus. Platt Establecimientos Gráficos S. A., Buenos Aires.
JOHNSON, A. W.; BEHN, FRANCISCO; and MILLIE, W. R.
1958. The South American flamingos. Condor, vol. 60, no. 5, pp. 289-299, illus.
KAHL, M. PHILIP
1975. Distribution and numbers—a summary. Pp. 93-102 *in* "Flamingos," J. Kear and N. Duplaix-Hall, eds. Poyser, London.
KEAR, J., and DUPLAIX-HALL, N., eds.
1975. Flamingos. Proc. Int. Flamingo Symposium, July 1973, 246 pp. Poyser, London.
MARKHAM, B. J.
1971. Censo invernal de cisnes y flamencos en Magallanes. An. Inst. Patagonia, vol. 2, nos. 1/2, pp. 146-157.
MILLER, ALDEN H.
1963. The fossil flamingos of Australia. Condor, vol. 65, no. 4, pp. 289-299.
MORRISON, T.
1972. The rarest flamingo. Oryx, vol. 11, no. 4, pp. 270-272.
NAUROIS, R. DE
1965. Une colonie réproductrice du petit flamant rosé, *Phoeniconaias minor* (Geoffroy), dans l'Aftout es Sahel (sud-ouest Mauritanien). Alauda, vol. 33, no. 3, pp. 166-176.
PEÑA, LUIS E.
1962. Notes on South American flamingos. Postilla, no. 69, pp. 1-8.
ROOTH, J.
1967. De soorten flamingo's en hun verspreiding. Vogeljaar, vol. 15, no. 2, pp. 304-309.
SPRUNT, ALEXANDER, 4TH
1975. The Caribbean. Pp. 65-74 *in* "Flamingos," J. Kear and N. Duplaix-Hall, eds. Poyser, London.

M. PHILIP KAHL

Conservation of the Kyrenia Ship, 1971-1972

Principal Investigator: Michael L. Katzev, Oberlin College, Oberlin, Ohio.

Grant No. 978: In further support of research on techniques for the preservation of the shipwreck near Kyrenia, Cyprus.[1]

Shortly after the time of Alexander the Great, a Greek merchantman sank to a watery grave off Kyrenia, Cyprus. Soon the ship became buried by sand and mud, and after more than 2,200 years only a portion of its cargo of amphoras stood above the flat seabed. This mound of wine jars, marking the shipwreck like a tombstone, was discovered by Andreas Cariolou, who in 1967 graciously presented the site to archeologists, and they undertook a survey that ascertained its size and date (Katzev, 1974a).

During two seasons of excavation, in the summers of 1968 and 1969, the material from the site was recovered (Katzev, 1970, 1973, 1975, 1976, 1978). The main cargo of the ship consisted of approximately 400 wine amphoras; these can be associated with ports of call at Samos and Rhodes. Almonds were another commodity carried in the ship, and over 10,000 were found by the excavators. Hopper-type grain-mill blocks, which together weigh about 1,650 kilograms, served as the ship's ballast. A variety of black-glazed plates, bowls, cups, and pitchers was raised, as well as numerous other articles used by the crew on this last voyage. Bronze coins, lost amid lead fishing weights, indicate that the ship went down about 300 B.C.

Most fortunately a large part of the merchantman's hull was also found. The port side was preserved, from the keel to above the waterline, for an extent

[1] With the permission and support of the Department of Antiquities of the Republic of Cyprus, work on the Kyrenia ship continued during 1971-1972 under the aegis of Oberlin College. In addition to that institution's sponsorship, financial aid was received from the National Endowment for the Humanities, Cyprus Mines Corporation, the John Brown Cook Foundation, the National Geographic Society, Ocean Search Incorporated, and the Dietrich Foundation. Cyprus Mines Corporation provided additional aid through its facilities on the island; and the staff of the United States Embassy in Cyprus rendered assistance in innumerable ways. Furthermore, an expression of gratitude is extended to the project's personnel, who have dedicated themselves to the successful preservation of the Kyrenia ship: Robin C. M. Piercy, assistant director; Frances M. Talbot, conservator; Laina Wylde Swiny, architect; J. Richard Steffy, ship reconstructor; Susan Womer Katzev, photographer and artist; Gay Donati Piercy, draftswoman.

of over 11 meters; the starboard side was only slightly less well preserved. In fact, approximately 70 percent of the ship still survived on the seabed. Each piece was labeled, recorded in situ, and then raised to the surface.

To prevent the waterlogged wood from cracking, warping, or shrinking caused by drying, the timbers were kept wet constantly. After preliminary washing they were placed in a fresh-water bath to begin leaching the salts from the wood. The water was changed regularly, and an antimicrobial agent—Dowicide A—was added to prevent bacterial growth.

Samples of wood, sent off to the United States Forest Products Laboratory for analyses, revealed that the keel, strakes, and frames were Aleppo pine; whereas the tenons, used in the shell-first method of constructing the Kyrenia ship, were oak. It was obvious to us that the timbers were thoroughly riddled by teredo (fig. 1); but through the analyses we learned also that there was a very considerable loss of cellulose in the wood, and the timbers were on a par with Pleistocene buried woods. We were advised that controlled, slow drying of the timbers would result in their great shrinkage and distortion.

Early in 1970 a series of experiments using polyethylene glycol (PEG) was begun in an effort to seek a method of preservation that would yield dimensionally stable wood. After a year of experimentation and another year of implementation, a program of treatment was followed that in 99 percent of the cases has maintained the dimensional integrity of the timbers.

Conservation

Each piece of wood was thoroughly cleaned with fresh water carefully directed by spray nozzles, as brushes were gently applied to the surfaces in order to sweep away mud, sand, and shells. The pieces were meticulously catalogued: over-all dimensions, location and size of nails or mortise and tenon joints, tool marks, and any other notable details were recorded. This description was supplemented by photographs of the pieces' surfaces. Also full-scale tracings of these surfaces were made on drafting film—Melinex 500 gauge; fine-tip felt pens were employed to produce these drawings, and different color inks were consistently used to detail different features, e.g., outline in brown, nails green, mortises red, lead sheathing blue, etc. This laborious process of documenting every piece of wood, completed by June 1972, insured against the loss of any information in case a timber suffered during preservation treatment.

The design of our treatment tanks was comparable to a double boiler. They were made locally with materials readily available. In all, eight tanks were operating at once; but the greater bulk, 3.5 cubic meters, of the wood

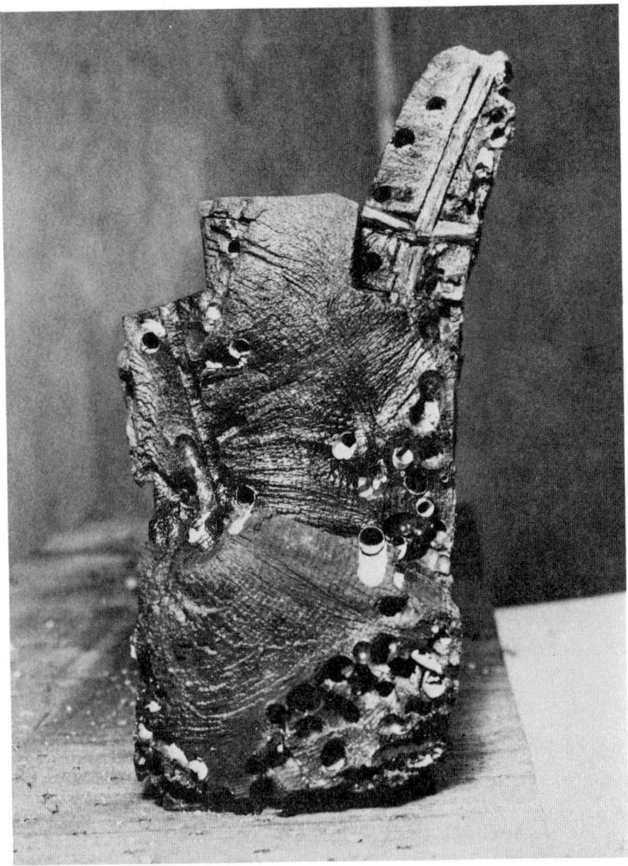

FIG. 1. Break in the keel reveals the extensive teredo penetration. Note a piece of the garboard joined to the keel by a tenon secured in its mortise by a peg. (Photo by Robin C. M. Piercy.)

was treated in two large tanks. These were boxlike in shape, measuring 3 meters in length, 1 meter wide, and 1.2 meters deep. Their sides and bottoms were made of galvanized steel, reinforced, with exterior jackets of Styrofoam for insulation; the top covers were wood. The interiors of the tanks were coated with fiberglass, to prevent any contamination of the PEG solution. The tanks were piped to a centrifugal pump to keep the PEG solution constantly recirculating. Lower chambers contained water, which was heated by several thermostatically regulated immersion heaters. Hence, through this double-boiler design, the temperature of the PEG solution above was controlled. Each of these large tanks went through two cycles of treatment before all the wood from the ship was preserved; and it should be noted that the PEG solution from the first cycle could be re-used in the second. The second cycle for each of these large tanks was begun during this grant period.

The pieces of wood were placed on trays made of marine plywood. These trays were 1.2 meters in length and 0.3 meter wide, and their depth varied, depending on the thickness of wood placed on them. The bottoms of the trays were drilled with holes, 0.006 meter in diameter, spaced approximately 0.03 meter apart; these holes facilitated the circulation of the PEG solution. The trays were set into the tanks two lengthwise and three across. As the trays were piled one atop another, a low concentration of PEG solution was added to the tanks to keep the wood constantly immersed. The loading of a tank took about one week, and when finished the preservation treatment was begun.

PEG of average molecular weight 4000 was added 6 days a week to increase gradually the concentration of the solution. The specific gravity of the solution was checked daily to follow precisely its rate of increase. And the temperature was also checked daily to control its slow rise. (As the concentration of the solution increased, the temperature had to be increased in order to maintain the fluidity of the solution.) Periodically pieces in each tank would be inspected (fig. 2) to be certain that the timbers were not shrinking or warping; also thin sections could be extracted and viewed with a binocular microscope to observe if the wood was satisfactorily absorbing the PEG solution. Below is an *average of schedules* used in preserving the wood of the Kyrenia ship.

Concentration range (pct.)	*Rate of increase (pct. per wk.)*	*Time (weeks)*	*Temperature range (deg. C.)*
0+-30	3	10	20-40
30	0	1	40
30 -45	1.5	10	40-50
45	0	2	50
45 -60	3	5	50-55
60	0	2	55
60 -75	3.75	4	55-60
75	0	2	60
75 -99	2	12	60-65
99	0	2	65

On the *average* it took 50 weeks to treat the timbers of the ship. But, of course, this time varied depending in part on the condition of the wood, the species,

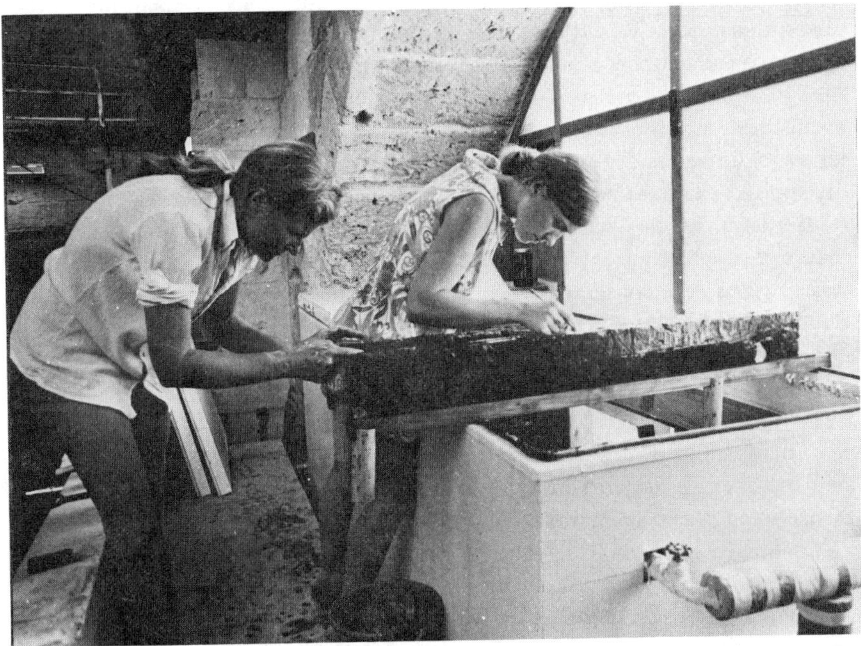

FIG. 2. During treatment the mast step is inspected to determine if it is suffering any dimensional distortion. (Photo by Robin C. M. Piercy.)

and particularly the cross-sectional dimensions of the timbers. For example, the thin ceiling planks (2-3 centimeters in thickness) were successfully preserved after 8-9 months of treatment; whereas the massive mast step (12 centimeters thick) required 24 months to treat.

Upon successful completion of a treatment, each piece was removed from the tank (fig. 3); and as it cooled to 55°C.—the melting point of PEG 4000—excess liquid PEG was quickly wiped away from the piece's surfaces with very slightly damp, hot sponges. The piece was then placed in a custom-sized polyethylene bag. This packaging partially insulated the piece to prevent further rapid heat loss; but one end of the bag was left unsealed to permit the escape of moisture evaporating from the timber. The piece was then stored on shelves encased with a curtain of polyethylene. These enclosed shelves were simple "drying ovens" where the temperature was controlled by electric heaters equipped with blowers to increase the air's circulation. By regulating these heaters the treated wood was "dried" of any residual moisture and slowly cooled at a rate of 1/2°C. per day down to room conditions. (Depending on the season this process would take from 50 to 80 days.)

Once the timbers had stabilized at ambient humidity and temperature, the PEG that had congealed on the wood's surfaces was removed by a variety of means: heat lamps to melt the waxlike compound, sponges dipped in hot water and squeezed as dry as possible, and hot-air blowers in tandem with almost dry sponges. This painstaking task had to be carried out on each piece; but the results rewarded us with more information on how the ship was built, as the marks of saws and adzes frequently came to light. Furthermore, when this job was finished, the conserved wood was at last ready to be used in the reconstruction of the Kyrenia ship.

Reconstruction

In our progress toward reassembling the ship using the original timbers a new member, J. Richard Steffy, joined the project, adding considerable experience in engineering, naval architecture, and the study in model form of ancient ships. Since January 1971 he has undertaken an exhaustive study of each fragment of the ship's hull. Working with copies of the full-scale tracings of the pieces, which were manually reduced to a more manageable 1:5 scale, he related these drawings to the in situ plan of the hull. During July and August he was present in Kyrenia examining the wood firsthand, making additional measurements, and gathering more detailed information. His meticulous analysis of this data will yield graphic projections of the ship's original contours. Indeed, such reconstructions of the ship's true lines in sheer, body, and half-breadth plans must be accurately developed before the actual reassembly of the ship can be confidently taken in hand. But already one significant discovery has been gleaned from Mr. Steffy's preliminary results. This 4th-century B.C. Greek merchantman had a rocker, or curved, keel, a most unexpected design feature.

Exhibition

During 1971 Kyrenia's Crusader Castle, including the temporary exhibit of finds from the Kyrenia ship and our conservation gallery, attracted 93,025 visitors, an increase of 34 percent over the preceding year. In the temporary museum a 1:20 scale sectional model of the ship's hull amidships—made by Mr. Steffy—was put on display. This model visibly contributed to the visitors' understanding of the ship's shell-first construction. And a slide set of 12

FIG. 3. Unloading of a large treatment tank. Two pieces of frames are visible. (Photo by Michael L. Katzev.)

color transparencies, illustrating the excavation and finds, was made available. This, judged by its sales, was also greatly appreciated by the visitors.

Extensive plans for the final exhibition of the ship and its contents were prepared. The Cypriot Department of Antiquities has allotted three adjoining galleries in Kyrenia Castle for the arrangement of these displays. The gallery, at present being used for the conservation of the wood, will be devoted to the reassembled ship; the middle gallery will contain a selection of finds from the ship: amphoras, millstones, crew's pottery, etc., and a full-scale sectional replica of the hull; the third gallery will have a series of photographs illustrating the excavation and a small theater for regular viewing of the 16-millimeter, color, documentary film covering the project from the ship's discovery through rebuilding. Footage for this film was shot focusing on the various phases of the wood's conservation. Currently the Department of Antiquities is working on the structural restoration of the latter two galleries: a collapsed groin vault in the middle gallery is being reconstructed (fig. 4, left); restoration of the partly destroyed arch dividing the third gallery has almost been completed (fig. 4, right); and the floors in both of these halls will soon be relaid.

Conclusion

Considering how uncertain is any process of conservation, this especially being true in such an experimental field as the treatment of waterlogged wood, we consider ourselves most fortunate to have been so successful in preserving the timbers of the Kyrenia ship. Now, as the final stages of conservation are approached, we confidently plan to undertake the actual reassembly of the ship using these preserved timbers, and to place this display on exhibit during 1973 so that the oldest seagoing hull yet excavated and reconstructed may be appreciated and studied by tourists and scholars for generations to come.

REFERENCES

KATZEV, MICHAEL L.

1970. Resurrecting the oldest known Greek ship. Nat. Geogr. Mag., vol. 137, no. 6, pp. 840-857, illus.

1973. Resurrecting a Greek ship 2,300 years old. Pp. 35-40 *in* "Men, Ships, and the Sea," by Alan Villiers, 436 pp., illus. National Geographic Society, Washington.

1974a. Cyprus underwater archeological search, 1967. Nat. Geogr. Soc. Res. Rpts., 1967 Projects, pp. 177-184, illus.

FIG. 4. *Left:* Reconstructing the groin vault of the middle gallery of the Kyrenia ship Museum complex. *Right:* The restored arch in the third gallery of the future Museum complex. (Photos by Susan Womer Katzev.)

KATZEV, MICHAEL L.—continued

1974b. Last port for the oldest ship. Nat. Geogr. Mag., vol. 146, no. 5, pp. 618-625, illus.

1975. Resurrecting an ancient Greek ship. Explorers Journ., vol. 53, no. 1, pp. 2-7, illus.

1976. Cyprus underwater archeological search, 1968. Nat. Geogr. Soc. Res. Rpts., 1968 Projects, pp. 177-188, illus.

1978. Cyprus underwater archeological search, 1969. Nat. Geogr. Soc. Res. Rpts., 1969 Projects, pp. 289-305, illus.

1979. Conservation of the Kyrenia ship, 1970-1971. Nat. Geogr. Soc. Res. Rpts., 1970 Projects, pp. 331-340, illus.

MICHAEL L. KATZEV

Reproductive Performance of Fish-eating Birds at Eagle Lake, California

Principal Investigator: James R. Koplin, Humboldt State University, Arcata, California.

Grant No. 970: In support of studies on reproduction of fish-eating birds.

In 1970 my associate David P. Garber and I initiated studies on the nesting ecology of ospreys (*Pandion haliaetus*) at two mesotrophic lakes, Eagle Lake and Lake Almanor, in Lassen and Plumas Counties, California (Garber, 1972; Garber and Koplin, 1972; Garber et al., 1974). My desire was to compare information from the mesotrophic lakes with that obtained previously from an oligotrophic lake (MacCarter, D. L., 1972; MacCarter, D. S., 1972; Koplin, 1978). Since both types of lakes contained similar concentration levels of pesticides, differences in reproductive performance of ospreys using the two types of lakes were attributed to differences in productivity of the two types of lakes (Koplin et al., 1977).

We learned in 1969, during a preliminary reconnaissance prior to initiating our studies on ospreys, that Eagle Lake is used by an unusual assemblage of 14 summer resident and 6 transient species of fish-eating birds; the diets of all 20 species, including ospreys, are composed totally or partially of one or more of 6 species of fishes in Eagle Lake. Consequently, because the reproductive performance of other species could reflect the influence of pesticide contamination and other forms of human disturbance in much the same way as does the reproductive performance of ospreys (Koplin, 1978; Garber, 1972), I initiated studies on the nesting ecology of fish-eating birds in addition to ospreys in 1970. My associate Gordon I. Gould conducted the bulk of the field studies (Gould, 1974).

Eagle Lake, at an elevation of 5,100 feet, is 10 miles north of Susanville at the interface of the Sierra Nevadas and the Great Basin. The lake is in a landlocked basin with no natural outlet. The major inlet, Pine Creek, originates in the Caribou Wilderness Area in Lassen National Forest adjacent to the east boundary of Lassen National Park and drains a watershed of approximately 500 square miles. Eagle Lake measures approximately 15 miles long by $1\frac{1}{2}$ to 5 miles wide, with about 25,500 surface acres of water. The northern two-thirds of the lake is divided into smaller inlets by the interdigitation of five rocky peninsulas of land. The northern one-third is relatively shallow, measuring a maximum of 25 to 40 feet deep depending on the amount of runoff from snowmelt following each winter. The southern two-thirds is relatively deeper, measuring a maximum of 105 to 120 feet deep.

Jeffrey pine *(Pinus jeffreyi)* dominates the vegetation around the southern shoreline of Eagle Lake, and big sagebrush *(Artemesia tridentata)* dominates the vegetation around the northern shoreline. Extensive shallow areas are along the northern shore. Rushes *(Juncus balticus)* are the dominant emergent plants in water less than 6 feet deep; the common tule *(Scirpus acutus)* predominates in water between 6 and 12 feet deep.

The fish fauna in Eagle Lake consists of two herbivores, the speckled dace *(Rhinichthys osculus)* and Lahontan redside *(Richardsonius egregius);* an omnivore, the Lahontan sucker *(Catostomus tahoensis);* and three carnivores, the brown bullhead *(Ictalurus nebulosus),* tui chub *(Siphateles bicolor),* and Eagle Lake trout *(Salmo gairdneri aquilarium).* All are abundant and all but the bullhead are native.

The fish-eating avifauna that are summer residents at Eagle Lake, in addition to ospreys, include: western grebes *(Aechmophorus occidentalis),* eared grebes *(Podiceps caspicus),* pied-billed grebes *(Podilymbus podiceps),* white pelicans *(Pelecanus erythrorhynchos),* double-crested cormorants *(Phalacrocorax auritus),* great blue herons *(Ardea herodias),* common mergansers *(Mergus merganser),* bald eagles *(Haliaeetus leucocephalus),* ring-billed gulls *(Larus delawarensis),* California gulls *(L. californicus),* Forster's terns *(Sterna forsteri),* black terns *(Chlidonias niger),* and belted kingfishers *(Megaceryle alcyon).* Transient species of fish-eating birds, those that migrate through the area in the spring and fall, include: the common loon *(Gavia immer),* horned grebe *(Podiceps auritus),* common egret *(Casmerodius albus),* snowy egret *(Leucophoyx thula),* black-crowned night heron *(Nycticorax nycticorax),* and red-breasted merganser *(Mergus serrator).* Out studies were restricted to summer residents. Of these, only populations of western, eared, and pied-billed grebes; double-crested cormorants; great blue herons; ospreys; and Forster's and black terns were sufficiently numerous for us to obtain quantitative measurements on reproductive success. Populations of white pelicans and the two species of gulls were sufficiently numerous for study, but none of the three species reproduced during the two summers of our study.

Results

Our studies in 1970 were devoted mainly to an extensive feasibility surveillance of the lake; i.e., location and description of nesting sites, determination of relative abundance of breeding populations, preliminary determination of breeding chronology, etc. Our studies in 1971 were devoted to estimating abundance of breeding populations and to measuring reproductive performance.

ABUNDANCE, BREEDING CHRONOLOGY, AND REPRODUCTIVE PERFORMANCE

Western Grebes. There were an estimated 1,400 to 1,900 pairs of western grebes on Eagle Lake in 1970 and 1971. The majority nested in colonies within emergent vegetation along shores in the northern one-third of the lake. Nests were constructed of reeds and were floating in water from 1½ to 12 feet deep. Nests ranged from 11 to 32 and averaged 19 inches in diameter, and the bottom of the nests averaged about 3 inches above the surface of the water.

Spring immigrants began to arrive at the lake in mid to late March and continued to arrive until late May. Courtship began within a week to 10 days after arrival and continued through mid-June. Nest construction began in mid to late May and continued through late July and early August. Incubation began in early June and continued through late September. Young began hatching in early July and continued to hatch through mid-September. Fall emigration from the lake began in early September and continued through early November.

Duration of incubation ranged from 21 to 29 days and averaged 22 to 23 days among 46 eggs for which incubation period was recorded. Bent (1919) reported an incubation period of 23 days, and Herman et al. (1968) reported an incubation period of 23 to 27 days.

Clutch size averaged 2.4 eggs per nest in 733 nests in which clutch size was recorded. Clutch size in one of the smallest colonies averaged 2.0 eggs per nest and in the largest colony 2.6 eggs per nest, indicating a direct relationship between colony size and clutch size. Hatching success, the percentage of nests in which at least one egg hatched, averaged 76 percent in 299 nests in which hatching success was recorded. The number of young hatched in the 299 nests averaged 1.0 chick per nest. Because grebes are precocial it was not possible to measure fledgling productivity. However, on the basis of ratios of chicks and adults, our best guess is that it averaged less than 1.0 and more than 0.5 fledgling per breeding pair of adults.

Eared Grebes. There were an estimated 1,750 to 1,925 pairs of eared grebes on Eagle Lake in 1970 and 1971. Eared grebes nested in emergent vegetation along the west shore in the northern one-third of the lake. Eared grebes nested on the periphery of western-grebe colonies in areas where the two species nested together.

Although smaller in size, nests of eared grebes were constructed of the same material and had the same general appearance as nests of western grebes.

Nests of eared grebes ranged from 5 to 32 and averaged 13 inches in diameter and were floating in water 16 to 53 inches deep. The bottom of the nests averaged about an inch above the surface of the water.

The arrival of spring immigrants began in mid to late March and continued through mid-May. Courtship began within a week to 10 days after arrival and continued through late June. Nest construction began in mid-June and continued through mid-August. Incubation began in mid-June and continued through early September. Young began to hatch in mid-July and continued to hatch through early September. Fall emigration from Eagle Lake commenced in late August or early September and continued through early November. In short, eared grebes immigrated into Eagle Lake at about the same time as did western grebes, but eared grebes began courtship and nesting activities later than did western grebes and their nesting activities were less prolonged than the nesting activities of western grebes.

Duration of incubation ranged from 18 to 25 days and averaged 20 days among 140 eggs for which incubation period was recorded. Bent (1919) reported that eared grebes incubate their eggs for approximately 3 weeks.

Clutch size averaged 2.8 eggs per nest in 1,634 nests in which clutch size was recorded. Clutch size averaged 2.6 eggs per nest in small colonies and 2.9 eggs per nest in larger colonies, indicating, as was the case in western grebes, a direct relationship between clutch and colony size. Hatching success averaged 87 percent in 715 nests in which hatching success was recorded. The number of young hatched in the 715 nests averaged 1.2 chicks per nest. Consideration of ratios of chicks to adults suggests that fledgling productivity was less than 1.2 and greater than 0.4 young per breeding pair.

Pied-billed Grebes. There were an estimated 200 to 275 pairs of pied-billed grebes on Eagle Lake in 1970 and 1971. Their nests were evenly distributed in emergent vegetation all along the west and east shores of the northern one-third of the lake. Pied-billed grebes were less colonial than western and eared grebes. Their nests were arranged linearly parallel to the shore, and the distance between adjacent nests averaged 175 feet, whereas nests of western and eared grebes were aggregated with arrangement of nests extending outward from the shore to the limits of nesting habitat, and the distance between adjacent nests averaged 16 and 10 feet, respectively.

All nests of pied-billed grebes were in *Juncus* because these grebes began to nest before *Scirpus* beds emerged. Their nests were similar in size and shape to nests of eared grebes; however, *Juncus* was the only nest material used, the nests were more closely woven, and the vegetation in the nests was more moist and decomposed than vegetation in nests of eared grebes. Most nests of pied-billed grebes were floating in water 10 to 46 inches deep.

Immigrating pied-billed grebes arrived and began courtship before the other species of grebes and before we began studies in the spring. However, immigrants continued to arrive until mid-April and to continue courtship until early May. Nest construction began in mid-April and continued through late May. Incubation began in early May and continued through mid-July. Young began hatching in late May and continued to hatch through late June. Fall emigration began in early September and terminated at some time prior to early November. Generally, the breeding chronology of pied-billed grebes was earlier than that of western and eared grebes.

Duration of incubation ranged from 21 to 26 and averaged 23 days among 42 eggs for which incubation period was recorded. Bent (1919) reported that pied-billed grebes incubate their eggs for 23 to 24 days.

Clutch size of 93 nests averaged 6.8 eggs per nest. Despite the fact that pied-billed grebes were less colonial than the other two grebes, clutch size ranged from 6.6 eggs per nest in areas where nests were most widely dispersed to 6.9 eggs per nest in areas where nests were more concentrated, indicating, as was the case in the other two species of grebes, a direct relationship between colony and clutch size. Hatching success averaged 91 percent in 57 nests in which hatching success was recorded. The number of young hatched in the 57 nests averaged 2.7 chicks per nest. Pied-billed grebes were so secretive that it was not possible to obtain ratios of adults and young; therefore we were unable to calculate fledgling productivity.

Double-crested Cormorants. Seven nests of double-crested cormorants were found on the ground of a small island in the center of Eagle Lake in 1970. No cormorant nests were found in 1971.

The nests were constructed of reed debris, were 4 to 12 inches high and 11 to 18 inches in diameter, and were spaced 2 to 7 feet apart. We visited the island too infrequently to obtain information on breeding chronology. The seven nests contained a maximum of 21 eggs. Only seven eggs in three of the nests hatched and only two of the seven chicks fledged.

Seventeen to 24 double-crested cormorants spent the summer of 1971 at Eagle Lake; as far as we know none of these birds reproduced. In 1971, a pair of Canada geese nested on one of the seven nests used by cormorants in 1970; the presence of the geese may have prevented the cormorants from nesting on the island in 1971. Apparently no other suitable nesting sites were available for cormorants at Eagle Lake.

Great Blue Herons. A great blue heronry with 37 nests was found in 1970 in a Jeffrey-pine woodland, approximately one-half mile inland from the central region of the west shore. The nests, located in five trees, were 55 to 95 feet above the ground.

The heronry was discovered on June 16, too late for information to be obtained on breeding chronology. At that time 36 chicks were found in 20 nests. Six dead young were found below nest trees at various times after June 16, suggesting a fledging rate of 0.8 young per breeding pair, on the assumption that each of the 37 nests was occupied by a breeding pair of birds earlier in the breeding season.

Herons began to nest in the same area in 1971, but the heronry was abandoned coincident with the construction of a fire lane. Work on the fire lane involved the felling of trees within 100 yards of the heronry.

Ospreys. There were an estimated 24 pairs of ospreys at Eagle Lake in 1970 and 1971. Seventeen (71 percent) of the 24 pairs nested on the tops of standing dead trees, three (13 percent) on the tops of living white firs *(Abies concolor),* one (4 percent) on the top of a living ponderosa pine *(Pinus ponderosa),* one (4 percent) on the top of a living incense cedar *(Libocedrus decurrens),* and one (4 percent) on the top of a power pole. Height of nests ranged from 7 to 120 and averaged 49 feet above the ground. Osprey nests were distributed from several yards to 4 miles inland from the lake shore all around the lake; however, most were concentrated from several yards to 1 mile inland from the central region of the west shore. Nests were constructed primarily of dead branches, were lined with grasses, and ranged from 3 to 4 feet in diameter and 1 to 2 feet in depth.

Each nesting territory had at least one perch site habitually used by the parent not in attendance at the nest site. Nests were visible from the perches in all territories. Eighty percent of the perches were in standing trees, 10 percent were on upright limbs of prostrate dead trees, and 10 percent were on power poles. Height of perches ranged from 7 to 160 and averaged 52 feet above the ground. The distance of perch to nest sites ranged from 5 to 300 and averaged 88 yards.

Immigrating ospreys began to arrive in late March and continued to arrive until early April. Courtship and nest construction began soon after arrival and continued through the end of April. Incubation began in late April and continued through early June. Young began to hatch in early June and continued to hatch through mid-June. Young began fledging in late July and continued to fledge through early August. Fall emigration occurred abruptly during the first week of October.

Duration of incubation ranged from 31 to 43 and averaged 38 days (Garber and Koplin, 1972). Bent (1937) and Ames (1964) reported incubation periods of 28 to 33 days for American ospreys. Dementiev and Gladkov (1951), England (1956), Bannerman (1956), and Brown and Waterston (1962) reported incubation periods of 35 to 38 days for Eurasian ospreys.

Clutch size of the 24 nests averaged 2.7 eggs per nest. Hatching success averaged 71 percent in 17 nests in which hatching success was recorded. The number of young hatched in the 17 nests averaged 1.7 chicks per nest. Fledgling productivity in the 17 nests averaged 1.2 young per nest.

Forster's Terns. There were an estimated 75 to 150 pairs of Forster's terns at Eagle Lake in 1970 and 1971. The nests were associated with colonies of western grebes. Forster's terns appeared to be territorial on an intraspecific basis but not an interspecific basis. The distance between tern nests averaged approximately 35 feet, whereas western-grebe nests frequently were within 15 feet of tern nests.

Nests were constructed of reeds and were roughly similar in size and shape to western-grebe nests. Tern nests were 8 to 10 inches in diameter and had a much deeper bowl than grebe nests. The bottom of the nest was 2 to 3 inches above the surface of the water.

Immigrating Forster's terns began to arrive in mid-April and continued to arrive until mid-May. Courtship began in late April and continued through mid-June. Nest construction began in early June and continued through mid-July. Incubation began in early June and continued through mid-August. Eggs began hatching in late July and continued through mid-August. Emigration from the lake began in early August and continued through late September.

Duration of incubation was obtained for only four eggs: one was incubated for 21 days, two for 22 days, and one for 23 days. Bent (1921) reported an incubation period of 23 days for Forster's terns.

Clutch size of 32 nests averaged 2.5 eggs per nest. Hatching success averaged 65 percent in 17 nests in which hatching success was recorded. The number of eggs hatching averaged 0.9 egg per nest in 12 nests in which hatching was recorded. No estimate of fledgling productivity was attempted.

Black Terns. There were an estimated 75 to 150 pairs of black terns at Eagle Lake in 1970 and 1971. They nested mainly along the southern portion of the northwest shore of the lake in emergent vegetation, frequently in shallow water. They did not nest in association with Forster's terns, nor with the grebes. No large concentrations of nests were found, but small colonies numbering 10 or fewer nests were found. Distance between nests in these colonies ranged from 12 to 100 and averaged 28 feet.

All nests of black terns were loosely constructed from *Juncus* fragments. In general apearance, the nests were relatively small, inconspicuous structures ranging from 3 to 8 and averaging 4 inches in diameter. All nests were on pre-existing, usually floating, substrate; of 40 nests closely examined, 13 were on floating boards or logs, 13 on muskrat rafts, 8 on abandoned grebe and Forster's-tern nests, and 6 on emergent plant debris. Depth of water beneath 45 nests ranged from 2 to 42 and averaged 25 inches.

Immigrating black terns began to arrive at Eagle Lake in late April and continued to arrive until late May. Nest construction began in mid-May and continued through late June. Incubation began in late May and continued through mid-July. Eggs began hatching in mid-June and continued hatching through mid-July and terminated in September. No information was obtained on chronology of courtship or on duration of incubation.

Clutch size of 24 nests averaged 2.8 eggs per nest. Hatching success of seven nests averaged 86 percent. The number of eggs hatching in the seven nests averaged 1.3 per nest. No estimate of fledgling productivity was attempted.

COMPARATIVE ABUNDANCE OF BREEDING POPULATIONS

Breeding populations of western and eared grebes at Eagle Lake in 1970 and 1971 were among the largest recorded in California and among the largest recorded in North America (Gould, 1974). Since 1971, however, the level of the lake has risen 15 feet, and breeding populations of western and eared grebes declined from 25 to 50 percent between 1970 and 1974 (Dawson, 1974; R. Lederer, pers. comm.). Breeding populations of the other species of fish-eating birds generally were similar to or smaller than other populations of the same species elsewhere in North America. Thus it might be concluded that breeding habitat at Eagle Lake in 1970 and 1971 was optimal for western and eared grebes and adequate or marginal for the other species studied.

COMPARATIVE REPRODUCTIVE PERFORMANCE

Clutch sizes of western and eared grebes at Eagle Lake averaged lower than clutch sizes of these grebes in other areas of North America (Gould, 1974). Clutch sizes of ospreys at Eagle Lake averaged similar to those in other areas of North America (Garber, 1972), and clutch sizes of pied-billed grebes and Forster's and black terns at Eagle Lake averaged higher than those in other areas of North America. Our data on reproductive performance of great blue herons and double-crested cormorants were too scanty for comparison with data from other areas.

Data on hatching success and fledgling productivity from other areas for comparison with our data were available only for ospreys (Garber, 1972). Hatching success and fledgling productivity of ospreys at Eagle Lake averaged lower than hatching success and fledgling productivity of ospreys in Florida and averaged approximately the same as hatching success and fledgling productivity of ospreys elsewhere in North America.

These considerations suggest that environmental conditions influencing reproductive success of the birds studied at Eagle Lake in 1970 and 1971 were most suitable for pied-billed grebes and Forster's and black terns; were less suitable for ospreys; and were least suitable for western and eared grebes.

FACTORS INFLUENCING REPRODUCTIVE SUCCESS

At least some of the variations in distribution, abundance, and reproductive success of fish-eating birds at Eagle Lake are identifiable. Human interference in the form of recreational activity was related to loss and avoidance of breeding habitat by grebes, avoidance of foraging habitat by western grebes, and abandonment of nests by ospreys and cormorants. Logging was related to the abandonment of the heronry by great blue herons and the loss of a clutch of osprey eggs. Pollutants in the form of DDT residues were implicated in reproductive impairment of western grebes and ospreys. Management of cattle grazing, frequency of use of a landing strip for small aircraft, real-estate development, and advertisement of Eagle Lake were viewed as potential threats to fish-eating birds. Predation, competition, seasonal shortage of food or disease, wind, decay of dead trees used by ospreys for nesting sites, accidents, and annual changes in depth of the lake also were identified as factors influencing distribution, abundance, and reproductive performance of fish-eating birds.

Predation. Several instances were noted of predation by Forster's and black terns and yellow-headed blackbirds *(Xanthocephalus xanthocephalus)* on eggs of western grebes, and one suspected instance was noted of predation by gulls on a clutch of osprey eggs. In all cases predation was associated with human disturbance. Eggs were preyed on while parents were off their nests in response to the presence of humans.

Competition. Competition for nesting habitat may have lowered the reproductive success of eared grebes. Western and eared grebes nested in similar habitat, but since western grebes nested earlier than eared grebes they presumably obtained the optimum nesting habitat; clutch size of eared grebes may have been reduced because they were forced to nest in suboptimal habitat. The protracted nesting season of western and eared grebes also may have been related to competition for nest sites. Apparently pied-billed grebes were affected little, if at all, by competition with the other grebes for nesting sites, since pied-billed grebes nested and completed their nesting activities before the other grebes began to nest.

Interspecific competition for food among the various species of fish-eating birds presumably was minimized or avoided by temporal and spatial differences in foraging behavior, by selection of different species of prey, and by selection of different size classes of the same prey species (Lack, 1973). Although these considerations were beyond the scope of our studies, certain differences were observed, and other differences could be deduced from the literature on food habits and the general tendency for different-sized predators to select different-sized prey. For example, grebes foraged beneath the surface of the water; western grebes foraged in open water to a larger extent than did eared and pied-billed grebes; and pied-billed grebes tended to forage closer to shore than did eared grebes. In addition, western grebes feed primarily on fish, pied-billed grebes feed on both fish and aquatic insects, and eared grebes feed primarily on aquatic insects and invertebrates (Palmer, 1962). Also, western grebes are considerably larger than the other grebes; presumably, therefore, western grebes select larger fish than pied-billed grebes. Similarly, terns foraged primarily on the surface of the water; Forster's terns feed primarily on small fish near the surface; whereas black terns feed primarily on aquatic insects in beds of emergent vegetation (Bent, 1921). Thus grebes and terns differ from each other in that grebes forage on relatively large to medium-sized fish and aquatic invertebrates captured beneath the surface of the water, whereas terns forage on small fish and aquatic invertebrates captured near the surface of the water. The three species of grebes differ from one another by foraging in different habitats on different prey and different-sized prey, and the two species of terns differ from each other by foraging in different habitats on different species of prey.

Ospreys foraged over open water and preyed on fish within several feet of the surface. Thus they partially avoid competition with western grebes by foraging nearer the surface than western grebes. In addition, ospreys capture fish ranging in size from 6 to 20 inches long, whereas western grebes capture fish ranging from 1 to 6 inches long. Furthermore, ospreys capture fish with their talons, whereas western grebes capture fish with their beaks.

It is possible that double-crested cormorants may compete for food resources with western grebes at Eagle Lake since they are both approximately the same size and they both forage on fish captured under water. However, cormorants may forage to greater depths than western grebes. More important, the abundance of cormorants was relatively much smaller than the abundance of western grebes at Eagle Lake in 1970 and 1971.

It is conceivable that white pelicans and ospreys may compete for food resources at Eagle Lake. Both pelicans and ospreys forage within several feet of the surface and both capture fish ranging from 6 to 20 inches long. However, they may forage in different subhabitats in the open water or they may forage primarily in different geographic regions of Eagle Lake. These are considerations requiring further study.

Starvation or Disease. Dead adult eared grebes were found washed up on shore during April in both years of the study. All were emaciated and had empty stomachs, indicating they starved. If food resources were sufficiently limited to result in starvation of eared grebes early in the breeding season, they could have been sufficiently limited to delay egg-laying and incubation. Limited food resources early in the breeding season, at the time of egg formation, also could account for the comparatively small average clutch size. However, numerous dead young pied-billed grebes also were found in June, suggesting the possibility of disease.

Wind. Apparently prevailing winds restricted grebe and tern nests to the lee sides of beds of emergent vegetation. Even so, nests on the windward sides of the beds of emergent vegetation occasionally were destroyed by wind. Wind was responsible also for the destruction of 8 osprey eggs out of 49 being closely monitored to measure reproductive performance. In addition, three nestling ospreys were killed when wind blew over the badly decayed tree containing the nest they were in; and two nestling ospreys flapping at the edge of their nests in preparation for fledging were blown from their nests by wind.

Accidents. Three nestlings in the 17 osprey nests being closely monitored for reproductive performance were killed accidentally. One died from wounds inflicted by porcupine quills on a porcupine hide used to line the nest. Also, two nestlings, one in each of two separate nests, apparently were smothered by their older siblings.

Depth of Eagle Lake. Increased precipitation over the past 30 years has caused an increase in the depth of Eagle Lake; the depth has increased 15 feet between 1971 and 1975 alone. Many of the beds of emergent vegetation along the west shore used by grebes and terns for nesting habitat in 1970 and 1971 have been inundated by water since 1972; existing vegetation along the west shore is too sparse for optimal nesting habitat. Consequently, as recently as 1975 breeding populations of grebes and terns have declined 30 to 50 percent in comparison to 1970-1971, and they have shifted some of their breeding sites to other areas around the lake (Dawson, 1974; pers. comm.).

Home sites, campgrounds, marinas, and the airstrip line the whole south shore, approximately one-fourth of the west shore, and approximately one-tenth of the east shore. In addition, cattle are grazed and watered along all but the south shore, and Eagle Lake is an important recreational fishing area (Gould, 1974).

Human Disturbance. Human activity destroyed some nesting habitat for grebes and terns along the northwest and south shores. Paths and boat ramps interrupted the continuity of beds of emergent vegetation in these areas. Also, paved areas in the two campgrounds and a marina on the south shore have been and are continuing to be inundated by the rising lake level; distribution of beds of emergent vegetation was restricted since the pavement overlies substrate required for growth of the vegetation. However, loss of vegetation is only secondary to the influence of the presence of humans in these areas. No grebe or tern nests were found within 100 yards of four boat ramps along the west and south shores; even the tolerant coots *(Fulica americana)* did not nest within 50 yards of the boat ramps. Also, human activities were so intensive in the campgrounds and the marina along the south shore that approximately 2.5 miles of habitat apparently suitable for nesting sites was avoided almost totally by grebes and terns. In addition, approximately 2.25 miles of similar habitat along the west shore was largely avoided by grebes and terns apparently in response to intensive human activities associated with housing tracts, campgrounds, and marinas.

Fishing and boating activities may have been responsible for the reproductive impairment of the cormorants in 1970. Grebes and terns did not appear to be bothered by fishermen and boaters entering beds of emergent vegetation. However, penetration of the beds of emergent vegetation by boaters and fishermen was fairly infrequent during our studies; more frequent use of the vegetation undoubtedly would cause avoidance of these areas in the same way that more frequented areas adjacent to boat ramps, marinas, etc., were avoided. Western grebes did not frequent areas of open water used heavily by boaters; since western grebes foraged in open water, intensive and sustained boating activity could account, at least in part, for the observed reproductive inhibition of western grebes. Eared grebes used open water only early and late in the breeding season, and pied-billed grebes continually remained in or near the beds of emergent vegetation; consequently these two species did not appear to be influenced by boating activity in open water.

Another threat to fish-eating birds is the loss of eggs to predators while parents are off their nests in response to the presence of humans. Several instances of predation by terns and blackbirds on eggs of western grebes took place when the grebes flushed from their nests during our investigations of the grebe colonies. In another instance, while campers parked near an osprey nest tree, the adults left the nest site, and indirect evidence indicated that gulls preyed on the clutch of four eggs during the absence of the adults. A second potential hazard of the presence of humans in the vicinity of osprey nests was identified during the course of our efforts to obtain fledgling counts. During these counts, 11 young ospreys flew from their nests, apparently for the first time. Two of these birds flew into Eagle Lake where they became entangled in aquatic vegetation, a third flew into and became entangled in a shrub, and a fourth landed in the bed of our pickup truck. The seven remaining chicks that made their maiden flights in response to our presence faired better than these four, which we rescued and replaced in their nests. However, this experience indicated the possibility that human-induced flights of juvenile ospreys not quite ready to fledge conceivably could amplify losses of these young birds to accidents and to predators.

Abandonment of the heronry by great blue herons coincident with felling of trees during construction of a fire lane has been mentioned. Loggers also felled a dead tree containing an osprey nest with a clutch of three eggs in 1970.

Livestock Disturbance. Late in the nesting season, during hot weather, cattle often waded into water up to 24 inches deep among the beds of emergent vegetation. Although we observed no deleterious effects of cattle on grebes or terns, it is conceivable that wading cattle could destroy eggs, nests, or both. The practice of placing salt licks within 50 feet of the shoreline aggravated this problem by concentrating cattle along the shoreline.

Chemical Contamination. Analysis of the eggs of western grebes and ospreys, and of fish from Eagle Lake, revealed the presence of DDT residues in the ecosystem (S. Herman, pers. comm.; Calif. Dept. Fish and Game). DDT residues in the eggs ranged from 2.5 to 12.4 ppm on a fresh-weight basis, whereas levels in the fish averaged approximately 0.2 ppm. Although the sample sizes were small, this information suggested that the levels of DDT residues in the eggs were too high to have been accumulated solely from the fish in Eagle Lake (J. Keith, pers. comm.). It is entirely possible that at least some of the DDT residues detected in the osprey eggs could have come from Central America where ospreys from Eagle Lake are known to spend the winter. We have band returns from Guatemala of ospreys banded at Eagle Lake; cotton farmers in Guatemala are known to have applied DDT on their crops as often as 70 times per growing season as recently as 1970 (S. Herman, pers. comm.). Since we do not know where western grebes from Eagle Lake spend the winter, we have no idea where they may obtain DDT during the winter. Wherever the predominant source of contamination, the levels of contamination in the eggs were sufficiently high to produce some reproductive impairment. Additional presumptive evidence of DDT-related reproductive impairment was the presence of near-term embryos in some of the unhatched eggs and thinner than normal eggshells of unhatched eggs. Thus DDT contamination could account at least partially for the observed reproductive impairment of western grebes and ospreys.

Aircraft Traffic. The influence of the airstrip on the west shore was difficult to evaluate. The airstrip was adjacent to the largest nesting colonies of both western and eared grebes. Ordinarily, cacophony in the grebe colonies was continuous; but all vocalizations stopped for about 30 seconds when an aircraft took off. This was the only observed influence on the birds. So few aircraft used the airstrip that the disruptions were very infrequent. It is possible that the birds would habituate to increased usage of the airstrip; it is also possible that increased usage of the airstrip could make this area of Eagle Lake unsuitable for nesting by grebes.

Future Threats. Perhaps the biggest human-related threat to this unique assemblage of fish-eating birds is continued real-estate development and advertisement of the virtues of Eagle Lake. Real-estate development and advertisement both will increase use of the lake by humans; as we see it, to the detriment of fish-eating birds of the lake.

Summary and Conclusions

Breeding populations of western, eared, and pied-billed grebes; double-crested cormorants; ospreys; great blue herons; and Forster's and black terns were studied at Eagle Lake, California, during the breeding seasons of 1970 and 1971. Populations of western and eared grebes were the largest of all populations of fish-eating birds breeding at Eagle Lake and among the largest, if not the largest, populations of western and eared grebes in North America.

Comparisons of reproductive parameters of fish-eating birds from Eagle Lake with similar reproductive parameters of these species from other areas in North America revealed that western and eared grebes at Eagle Lake were reproducing at depressed rates; and pied-billed grebes and Forster's and black terns were reproducing at inflated rates. The osprey population at Eagle Lake reproduced at a rate lower than populations in Florida, but at a comparable rate to other populations in North America. However, there is good evidence that osprey populations in Florida are reproducing at normal, not high, rates and that other osprey populations in North America, including the osprey population at Eagle Lake, are reproducing at depressed, not normal, rates. There is also good evidence that depressed reproductive rates of ospreys throughout much of North America are related to trophic magnification of DDT residues through the food chains whose apices are occupied by ospreys (Ogden, 1977).

Because western grebes occupy the same trophic position as ospreys, because eggs of western grebes from Eagle Lake are contaminated by DDT residues, and because we could discover no other factor to account for the depressed reproductive rate of western grebes at Eagle Lake, we tentatively concluded that DDT contamination was the primary factor responsible for reproductive inhibition of western grebes at Eagle Lake.

Limited food resources early in the breeding season and exclusion from optimal nesting habitat by western grebes were probably the two most important factors responsible for depressed reproductive performance of eared grebes. Contamination by DDT residues tentatively was ruled out because eared and pied-billed grebes occupy roughly similar trophic levels; the reproductive performance of pied-billed grebes at Eagle Lake was high, not low, in comparison to populations of pied-billed grebes in other areas of North America.

Existing and potential human disturbance in the form of recreation, real-estate development, and logging are viewed as the biggest potential threat to the unique assemblage of fish-eating birds at Eagle Lake.

Management Actions

Acting on these findings, the U. S. Forest Service and the California Department of Fish and Game established the Eagle Lake Osprey Management Area on federal lands along the west shore of Eagle Lake. All recreational and logging activities are prohibited in this area from March 15 to October 15. In addition, 20 sturdy cedar poles with platforms for nests were placed adjacent to 20 of the most decayed osprey nest trees in the fall of 1971; ospreys have used 12 to 13 of these "artificial" nest sites annually since 1972. Also, the beds of emergent vegetation used as nesting habitat by grebes and terns were chained off by the U. S. Forest Service to prevent use of these areas by boaters and fishermen.

REFERENCES

Ames, Peter L.
1964. Notes on the breeding behavior of the osprey. Atlantic Nat., vol. 19, pp. 15-27.

Bannerman, David A.
1956. The birds of the British Isles, vol. 5, 350 pp., illus. Oliver & Boyd, Edinburgh and London.

Bent, Arthur Cleveland
1919. Life histories of North American diving birds. U. S. Nat. Mus. Bull. 107, 245 pp., illus.
1921. Life histories of North American gulls and terns. U. S. Nat. Mus. Bull. 113, 245 pp., illus.
1937. Life histories of North American birds of prey, pt. 1. U. S. Nat. Mus. Bull. 167, 409 pp., illus.

Brown, Leslie H., and Amadon, Dean
1968. Eagles, hawks and falcons of the world, vol. 1, 414 pp., illus. McGraw-Hill Book Co., New York.

BROWN, P. E., and WATERSTON, G.
1962. The return of the osprey, 223 pp. Wm. Collins Sons & Co., London.

DAWSON, LORRIE J.
1974. Census of selected birds of Eagle Lake, 23 pp. Eagle Lake Field Station. (Mimeo rpt.)

DEMENTIEV, G. P., and GLADKOV, N. A., eds.
1951. Ptitsy Sovetskaya Sayoza, vol. 1, 652 pp. Moscow.

ENGLAND, M. D.
1956. Photographic studies of some less familiar birds, LXXVI: Osprey. Brit. Birds, vol. 49, pp. 489-492, illus.

GARBER, DAVID P.
1972. Osprey nesting ecology in Lassen and Plumas Counties, California, 59 pp. M.S. thesis, Humboldt State University, Arcata, California.

GARBER, DAVID P., and KOPLIN, JAMES R.
1972. Prolonged and bisexual incubation in California ospreys. Condor, vol. 74, no. 2, pp. 201-202.

GARBER, DAVID P.; KOPLIN, JAMES R.; and KAHL, JACK R.
1974. Osprey management on the Lassen National Forest, California. Proc. Conf. Raptor Conserv. Techniques, Raptor Res. Rpt., vol. 2, pp. 119-122.

GOULD, GORDON I., Jr.
1974. Breeding success of piscivorous birds at Eagle Lake, California, 94 pp. M.S. thesis, Humboldt State University, Arcata, California.

HERMAN, STEVE G.; GARRETT, RONALD L.; and RUDD, ROBERT L.
1968. Pesticides and the western grebe—a study of pesticide survival and trophic concentration at Clear Lake, Lake County, California. Pp. 24-53 *in* "Chemical Fallout," M. W. Miller, and G. G. Berg, eds. Charles C. Thomas Publishing Co., Springfield, Illinois.

KOPLIN, JAMES R.
1978. Reproductive performance of ospreys *(Pandion haliaetus)* at Flathead Lake, Montana. Nat. Geogr. Soc. Res. Rpts., 1969 Projects, pp. 323-332.

KOPLIN, JAMES R.; MACCARTER, DOUGLAS S.; GARBER, DAVID P.; and MACCARTER, DONALD L.
1977. Food resources and fledgling productivity of California and Montana ospreys. Pp. 205-214 *in* Trans. North. Amer. Osprey Conf.

LACK, DAVID
1971. Ecological isolation in birds, 404 pp. Harvard University Press.

MACCARTER, DONALD L.
1972. Reproductive and population trends of ospreys at Flathead Lake, Montana, 80 pp. M.S. thesis, Humboldt State University, Arcata, California.

MACCARTER, DOUGLAS S.
1972. Food habits of ospreys at Flathead Lake, Montana, 80 pp. M.S. thesis, Humboldt State University, Arcata, California.

OGDEN, J. C., Ed.
1977. Transactions of the North American Osprey Research Conference, 258 pp. U. S. Dept. Interior, Nat. Park Serv. Trans. and Proc., no. 2.

PALMER, RALPH S.
1962. Handbook of North American birds, vol. 1, 567 pp., illus. Yale University Press.

JAMES R. KOPLIN

Polar-bear Den Surveys in Svalbard, 1972 and 1973

Principal Investigator: Thor Larsen, Norsk Polarinstitutt, Oslo, Norway.

Grant No. 951: For polar-bear den surveys in Svalbard.

Surveys in 1972

An effort to estimate the abundance of polar-bear dens in Svalbard was made in 1972. Because most polar-bear females with cubs leave their dens over a relatively short period of time (Uspensky and Kistshchinski, 1972), large areas must be surveyed simultaneously. The purpose of the pilot study in 1972 was primarily to define the relative importance of various regions as denning areas, rather than to try to determine the absolute number of dens. Studies from other parts of the Arctic have demonstrated the feasibility of fixed-wing aircraft in polar-bear den surveys (op. cit.). These were used in Svalbard in 1972, both for den surveys and for the transport of field groups and supplies. With fuel depots established in Tjuvfjorden, Freemansundet, and Sorgfjorden, and with bases in Longyearbyen and in Ny-Ålesund, the aircraft were able to survey the entire archipelago (fig. 1). Two Cessna 185's with ski/wheels and cargo packs were used in the surveys. In addition to the pilot, each plane during surveys carried two observers, covering one side each. The cruising speed was between 130 and 150 kilometers per hour. Observations were made from altitudes between 70 and 100 meters. On most surveys the planes worked together. Either they searched one side of a fjord each, or a mountain at different altitudes, or one surveyed a shoreline while the other checked islands, riverbanks, etc. Some areas of particular importance were controlled repeatedly, while others were surveyed only once, because of great distances or bad weather conditions. About 200 hours were flown on surveys between March 25 and May 13. Field parties simultaneously searched possible denning localities on foot or on skis, using binoculars and spotting scopes frequently. If dens were discovered, efforts were made to determine whether it was a maternity or a temporary den, mainly on the basis of the tracks around it. During aerial surveys it was often difficult to classify dens. Tracks and other signs were studied through binoculars, and they were photographed, whenever possible, for later examination.

The islands Edgeøya and Barentsøya were surveyed several times during late March and throughout April. Not until April 27 and 28 did the aircraft

FIG. 1. Polar-bear dens recorded on Nordauslandet and Edgeøya, Svalbard, during aerial surveys in April and May 1972. X, fuel depots; o, single dens; O with number, concentration of dens.

find a group of eight and one single den in the eastern and northern part of Edgeøya. The northern coast of Nordaustlandet was surveyed from the air on April 8, 15, and 16. Prior to the last two surveys there had been more than a week of very calm weather on Nordaustlandet (E. Nyholm, pers. comm.). One could assume, therefore, that dens that had been opened during the first week of April would still be visible on the surveys. During 30 hours of effective flying (see fig. 1), 26 dens were located. On Kong Karls Land ground surveys were made between March 31 and April 18 by two field parties. The western massif of Kongsøya was surveyed by a 3-man group between March 31 and April 10, and 13 dens were found in four effective days, and an additional 9 were discovered during a 3-hour aerial survey on April 10. On Svenskøya, a 2-man field party found 21 dens in 6 effective days between April 12 and 18. Another 6 dens were found during a 2-hour aerial survey on April 18 (see fig. 2).

The northern and eastern coast of Spitsbergen were surveyed repeatedly, but no dens or evidence of denning was found. There was, however, a relatively high bear activity in some areas.

Of a total of 84 polar-bear dens found in Svalbard in 1972, 54 were spotted from the air, while 30 were found by the field groups. Air observations could not be proved to be more effective than ground surveys, or vice versa. Ground-observation success would depend upon topography and weather and light conditions. Drifting snow might fill up and cover dens shortly after they had been abandoned. By the use of aircraft, observation success was dependent upon cruising speed and altitude, light conditions, and the observer's skill and experience. The comparative air and ground counts on Kong Karls Land indicated that about 50 percent of the dens present in an area may be seen from the planes. Track observations and other signs indicated that about half the number of dens were maternity dens.

Surveys in 1973

The den studies in 1973 were concentrated on Kong Karls Land. The purpose was to try to determine the absolute number of dens on the islands, to distinguish between den types whenever possible, and to describe den sites and den constructions. Two field groups, each consisting of two men, carried out ground surveys on Kongsøya between March 15 and April 29 and on Svenskøya between March 17 and April 28. Each group surveyed the islands as often as possible in an effort to make absolute den counts. Each den found was marked with bamboo sticks and controlled repeatedly. Efforts were made to distinguish between maternity and temporary dens. When abandoned,

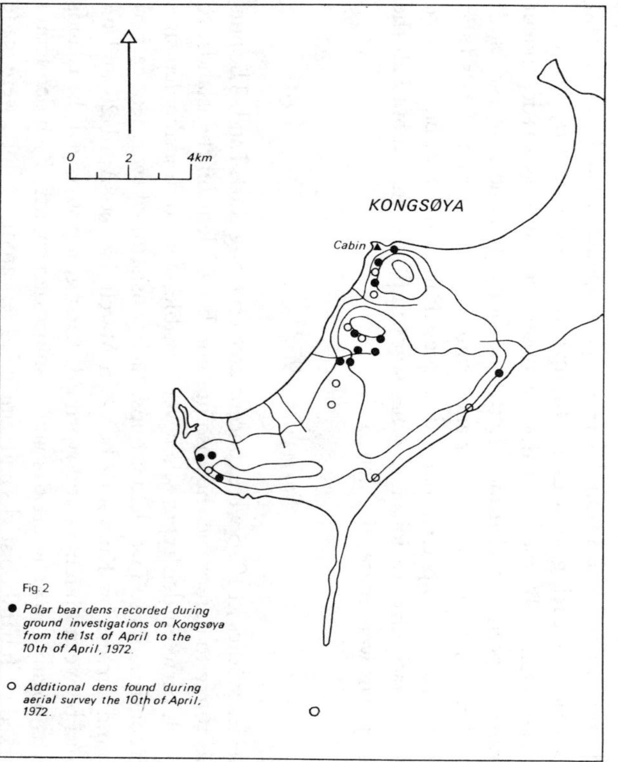

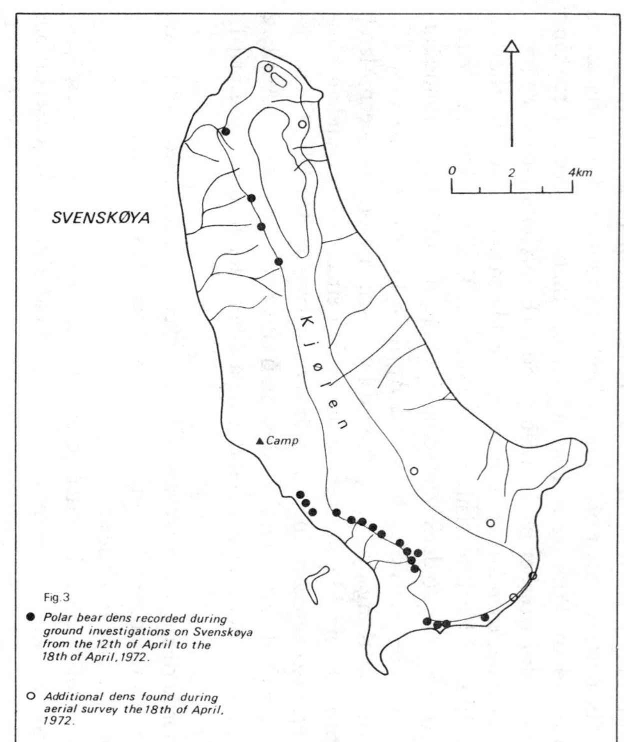

FIG. 2. Polar-bear dens recorded during ground and aerial surveys on Kongsøya (*left*) and Svenskøya (*right*), Svalbard, April 1972.

dens were in some cases dug out and described. The field groups also made observations of single bears and family groups and their activities. Bad weather conditions hampered the work for both groups. On Kongsøya, 26 days were effective for observations, during which 49 dens were found. Between March 16 and 26, 46 dens were found: 19 were classified as maternity dens, 6 as temporary dens, and of 24 the den type could not be determined. Of the unclassified dens, some were inaccessible, while others were filled and covered by snow during storms, so that they could not be found afterward. Five maternity dens and one temporary den were dug out and described. In most of the maternity dens the observers found that changes had taken place during the winter. In many cases the female had repeatedly dug out snow from the roof and packed it under her on the floor. Thus, tunnels and chambers could be drastically changed and elevated half a meter or more, sometimes necessitating a new tunnel to be dug out when the family was to emerge in the spring. When the floor of the dens was dug out, several layers of urine and much feces were often found. In some cases, two kilos or more of feces were found. In many cases, urine and feces were found in the vicinity of the den after it had been opened. Some dens were elaborate constructions, with two or more tunnels and several chambers or caves. Sometimes, digging had evidently been done by the cubs. A few maternity dens were rather simple, consisting of a tunnel and a chamber only. Most temporary dens consisted of a short tunnel, but in some cases there was also a chamber.

On Kongsøya, the majority of dens were oriented southward, between west and southeast. Altitudes varied between 30 and 250 meters above sea level, and the angle of the den site varied between 20° and 65°. The majority of the dens were located less than 1 kilometer from the coast. Most were abandoned shortly after they had been opened, and the female bear and her cubs headed straight out into the pack. Only in three cases did the families stay in their dens (for 12, 17, and 17 days), probably because the weather became bad shortly after they opened them for the first time. On Kongsøya, in addition to 5 females each with 1 cub, 3 females each with 2 cubs, and 2 females, each with 1 yearling, 13 single bears were observed.

On Svenskøya, there were 23 effective observation days; during these 16 dens were found, 10 between March 18 and 26. Of the 16, 2 were assumed to have been maternity dens, 6 to have been temporary, while of 8 the den type could not be determined. Eight dens were dug out and described. The changes that had taken place in some of the Kongsøya dens were also observed in some on Svenskøya. The majority of the dens were facing southwest, on the lee side of a ridge running northwest to southeast along the island. Altitudes varied between 40 and 150 meters, and the angle of the den site varied between 20° and 40°. On Svenskøya, in addition to 2 females, each with 1 yearling, 19 single bears were observed. Locations of the dens on Kongsøya and Svenskøya are shown on figure 3.

Discussion

The polar-bear den surveys in Svalbard in 1972 and 1973 show that Nordaustlandet and Kong Karls Land must be considered as particularly important denning areas. In Kong Karls Land there was 0.3 and 0.4 den per square kilometer in 1972 and 1973, respectively. On Kongsøya alone, in 1973, there were 1.5 dens per square kilometer of habitat suitable for denning. A marked difference in climate, temperatures, and ice conditions between northern and eastern Svalbard and the rest of the archipelago may explain the choices for den sites. There are also noticeable differences in the topography.

The location of den sites in 1972 and 1973 seemed to coincide with the amount of snow that had accumulated in various areas throughout the year. Most dens were found in slopes where they were protected from the prevailing north and northeast winds, and the den openings were normally facing away from the wind. Polar-bear dens in the Hudson Bay area are sometimes dug out in the earth as well as in the snow (Jonkel et al., 1972), but in Svalbard, earth dens were not found; this coincides with observations from other parts of the high Arctic (Harington, 1968; Uspensky and Kistshchinski, 1972).

Only 10 den sites occupied in 1972 on Kong Karls Land were used again in 1973. Of these, the sites of some may have been moved a hundred meters or more. Uspensky and Kistshchinski (1972) state that the same den sites are not necessarily used again every year in Wrangel Island. It is reasonable to assume that wind and precipitation may alter denning conditions in an area from one year to another, thus affecting the bears' choice of sites.

In Wrangel Island and in the Canadian high Arctic, most dens are found within 8 kilometers of the coast, but some are located as much as 25 kilometers inland (Harington, 1968; Uspensky and Kistshchinski, 1972). In the Hudson Bay area, two major den sites are located 20 and 70 kilometers inland (Jonkel et al., 1972). Most of the dens in Svalbard have been found less than 1 kilometer inland, partly because of the small sizes of the islands and peninsulas that may be suitable for denning.

Harington (1968) and Lønø (1972) state that polar bears depend upon the drift ice to get ashore and den. According to Vibe (1967), the drift ice is the major factor determining where and when polar bears will appear along the east Greenland coast. Lentfer (1972) states that unfavorable ice conditions

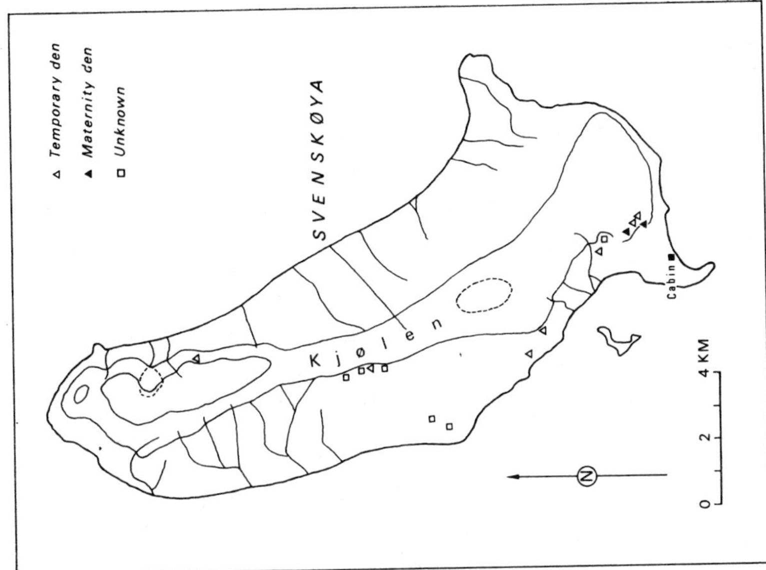

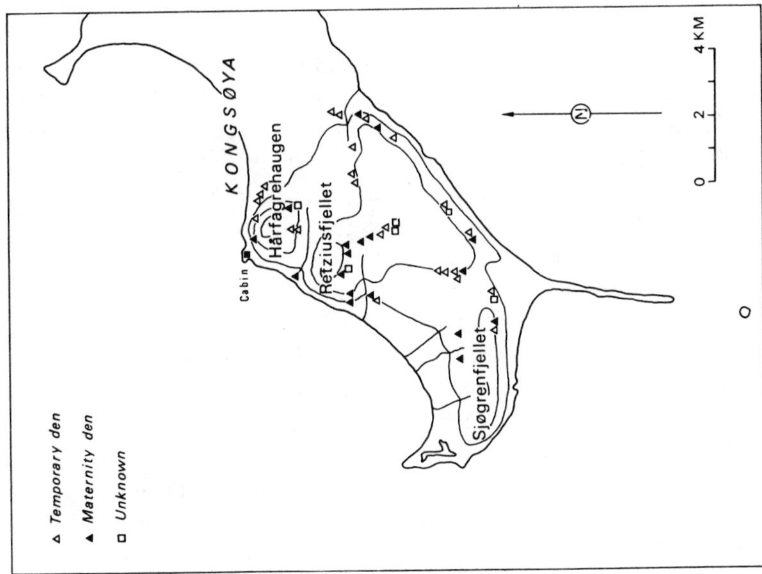

FIG. 3. Polar-bear dens recorded during ground surveys on Kongsøya (*left*) and Svenskøya (*right*), Svalbard, March and April 1973.

may prevent the female bears from coming ashore, so that they sometimes are forced to den on the sea ice. On Wrangel Island, female polar bears will come ashore to den from mid-September onward, and in years with normal ice conditions the majority will den up during October (Uspensky and Cernjavskij, 1965). According to Parovshchikov (1964), female polar bears on Franz Josef Land will den during October and November. In 1971, northern Svalbard and Kong Karls Land were embraced by the ice by early October. The ice edge probably reached Barentsøya and Edgeøya by the end of October (Vinje, 1973 and pers. comm.). Compared with information from other parts of the Arctic, the ice conditions should not, therefore, have prevented the female bears from going ashore in any of these areas to dig their dens. In 1968, the ice surrounded Edgeøya and Barentsøya even earlier in the autumn (Larsen, 1971). But very few signs of denning were found on those two islands in 1969 and in 1972, in spite of relatively intense surveys both springs. It is unlikely, therefore, that the ice conditions account for the lack of dens on Barentsøya and Edgeøya. In 1972, the edge of the loose ice (i.e., about 3/10 ice cover) was found at Kvitøya, 200 kilometers north of Kong Karls Land, by late October. By November 4, the loose ice had reached Kong Karls Land, while the more consolidated ice did not reach the islands before mid-November (Vinje, 1974 and pers. comm.). Polar-bear dens were as abundant on Kong Karls Land in 1973 as they had been in 1972. If we assume that the drift ice determines when polar bears may come ashore, they cannot have reached Kong Karls Land before the first week of November at best, in 1972.

Lønø (1970) states that most polar-bear family groups leave their dens in Svalbard between April 10 and 25. But the observations from Nordaustlandet and Kong Karls Land in 1972 indicated that most of the dens had been opened and abandoned before mid-April, and in 1973 most of the dens on Kong Karls Land were abandoned before April 1. Some females with cubs stay in their dens well after that date. When our data disagree with Lønø's findings, it may be explained by the fact that most of his information was based upon observations of family groups that were out and that may have abandoned their dens some time before the records were made.

The den surveys in Kong Karls Land in 1973 were quite extensive, and probably few dens were overlooked by the field parties. Almost four-fifths of the dens found on Kongsøya, which were controlled, were maternity dens. But probably only one-fourth of the controlled dens on Svenskøya were maternity dens. The data from 1972 and 1973 indicate that about 40 maternity dens can be found on Kong Karls Land in a normal year. The comparative air and ground counts from Kong Karls Land in 1972 indicate that about 50 percent of the dens were overlooked from the air. Thus, an evaluation of the observations from Nordaustlandet indicate that an estimated 20 to 30 maternity dens may be found there every winter. It is most probable that the total number of maternity dens in Svalbard in a normal year is well below 100.

It is questionable whether den counts can serve as a basis for accurate population estimates of polar bears. The accuracy of both ground and air surveys is limited by several factors. Ground surveys require a massive effort over a relatively short period of time. Data by different observers cannot immediately be compared, as observation techniques and efficiency vary. Establishing an exact ratio between maternity and temporary dens requires close examination of almost every den found, which is impossible because some of them are inaccessible and because such inspection is time consuming. But information about the relative abundance of dens can be obtained through repeated counts over several years, and this may reveal changes in polar-bear abundance and population composition. Combined air and ground surveys will probably give the best results, and the use of helicopters will probably be more effective than fixed wing aircrafts. Surveys must be extensive during the period when the majority of polar-bear females with cubs leave their dens. In Svalbard, surveys and den counts may be easier than in many other areas, because so many of the dens are concentrated close to the coast.

Acknowledgments

The polar-bear den surveys in Svalbard in 1972 were sponsored by the National Geographic Society, NATO Research Grants Program, Miljøverndepartementet, World Wildlife Fund International, and World Wildlife Fund in Norway. NTNF Avdeling for Romforskning (Department of Space Research) helped us with housing facilities in Ny-Ålesund, Svalbard. For their keen interest and assistance, I thank the members of the expedition: Lars Flemming Jørgensen, Jon Storm Mathisen, Eirik Nesse, Ole Swang, and Bjørn Wold. I also thank the pilots Stig Lennart Frank, Rolf Mortensson, and Endre Røvang and the engineer Leif Wenneberg. And my special thanks go to Olav Hjeljord and Ivars Silis, who helped to plan and conduct the study.

The 1973 den surveys were made possible by funds from Miljøverndepartementet, Roald Amundsens Minnefond, and World Wildlife Fund in Norway. I wish to thank Jens Angard, Jan Bakkerud, Svein Ingvaldsen, and Claus Sande for their great interest and efforts while carrying out the fieldwork.

REFERENCES

Harington, Charles R.
1968. Denning habits of the polar bear. Can. Wildlife Serv. Rpt. Ser., no. 5 30 pp.

JONKEL, CHARLES J.; KOLENOSKY, G. B.; ROBERTSON, R. J.; and RUSSELL, R. H.
1972. Further notes on polar bear denning habits. IUCN Publ., new ser., no. 23, pp. 142-164.

LARSEN, THOR
1971. Polar bear investigations in Svalbard, 1968 to 1969: A progress report II. Norsk Polarinst. Årbok 1969, pp. 94-100.
1972. Air and ship census of polar bears in Svalbard. Journ. Wildlife Management, vol. 36, no. 2, pp. 562-570.

LENTFER, JACK W.
1972. Polar bear–sea ice relationships. IUCN Publ., new ser., no. 23, pp. 155-171.

LØNØ, O.
1970. The polar bear in the Svalbard area. Norsk Polarinst. Skrift., vol. 149, 103 pp.
1972. Isbjørnhiene på Hopen. Polarboken 1971-1972, pp. 93-98.

PAROVSHCHIKOV, V. JA.
1964. A study of the population of the polar bear in Franz Josef Land. Acta Soc. Zool. Bohemoslov, vol. 28, no. 2, pp. 167-177.

USPENSKY, SAVVA M., and CERNJAVSKIJ, F. B.
1965. Material on the ecology, distribution and protection of the polar bear in the Soviet Arctic. Pp. 215-228 *in* "Game Animals: Biology and Economic Exploitation." Rossel'khozizdat, Moscow.

USPENSKY, SAVVA M., and KISTSHCHINSKI, A. A.
1972. New data on the winter ecology of the polar bear in Wrangel Island. IUCN Publ., new ser., no. 23, pp. 181-197.

VIBE, CHRISTIAN
1967. Arctic animals in relation to climatic fluctuations. Medd. om Grønland, vol. 170, no. 5, 227 pp.

VINJE, T.
1973. Sea ice and drift speed observations in 1971. Norsk Polarinst. Årbok 1971, pp. 81-85.
1974. Sea ice and drift speed observations in 1972. Norsk Polarinst. Årbok 1972, pp. 140-145.

THOR LARSEN

Demographic and Social-Anthropological Study of the Hambukushu of Botswana

Principal Investigator: Thomas John Larson, Northern Virginia Community College, Annandale, Virginia.

Grant No. 1026: For a demographic survey of Ngamiland peoples along the Okavango River and Delta, Botswana.

The purpose of the field research was to obtain additional information about the Hambukushu of Ngamiland, Botswana. I had made a preliminary ethnographic study of them from September 1950 to January of 1951, and while lecturer for the department of social anthropology of the University of the Witwatersrand from 1968 to 1970 I carried out four short field trips to study the Hambukushu during the university holidays. From the research of 1950 I wrote an M.A. thesis for American University and a B. Litt. thesis for Oxford University. These and other scientific papers and articles resulting from the 1968, 1969, 1970, and 1972 field studies of the Hambukushu are listed in the references.

After preparations and travel the expedition members[1] reached Shakawe along the Okavango River on June 28, 1972. From Shakawe our equipment and supplies were transported by primitive sand sled as we visited the communities of Royeyi, Nxumakao, Shamakwakwa, and Mohembo on the border of the Caprivi Strip of Namibia. There I conducted studies of the rural economy, demography, and social customs of the river peoples. Also ethnographic artifacts were collected and photographs taken for teaching and lecture purposes. Recordings were made of dances and ceremonies at Mohembo.

On July 3, Harry Latta had to return to his government job in Washington, D. C. On July 4 we crossed the Okavango River in dugout canoes to set up camp at East Mohembo community. Here music was recorded and I carried out a demographic study of the community.

[1] David Breedon, of Charlottesville, Virginia, was my administrative assistant; Michelle Anderson, of Reston, Virginia, the artist-anthropologist assistant; Robin Lance, of Annandale, Virginia, the musicologist-anthropology student; John Jankowski, of San Francisco, camp assistant; and Harry Latta, of the U. S. Office of Transportation (now graduate student in anthropology, Catholic University), in charge of supplies.

On July 5 we journeyed to the community of Kxaugwe, consisting of 35 extended household villages. David Breeden was put in charge of the construction of a camp of native huts and a *utara* (shelter). This was to be the base of operations for all our studies.

From July 5 to August 22 I carried out intensive studies of the demography of Kxaugwe, of the rural economy of the Hambukushu, and of witchcraft, sorcery, religion, social organization, political structure, cosmology, and other aspects of Hambukushu culture. Recordings were made by Robin Lance of the music and of the numerous religious dances and other ceremonies. A study was made of the *Hathimo* ceremonies I observed during our stay. Other studies were made of the *Mandengure* ceremony and both ceremonies were filmed and recorded.

The Hambukushu live in extended household villages in communities along the extensive flood plain on the edge of the sand belt of the Okavango River, which is in the Central Kalahari. Originally a small Bantu-speaking tribe of the great Barotse Empire, the tribe emigrated to the Okavango River islands near Popa Falls, which now is located in the Caprivi Strip of Namibia. Soon they outgrew the islands and migrated southward into Ngamiland of Botswana along the Okavango River.

Though primarily primitive agriculturalists raising mostly millet, corn, beans, peanuts, squashes, and melons, they also are pastoralists in that they raise some cattle, goats, donkeys, and horses. They hunt and fish and collect the wild food products of the flood plain and the Kalahari wilderness.

The Hambukushu are especially famous because their traditional chiefs are great rainmakers. Tribesmen from neighboring regions paid these chiefs yearly tribute. Today the Hambukushu of Ngamiland number roughly 15,000, with a recent influx of approximately 3,000 more Hambukushu refugees from the southeastern part of Angola. The Hambukushu of Ngamiland have been under the rule of the patrilineal Tawana, the ruling tribe of Ngamiland. The Hambukushu are matrilineal and originally came from the Congo, following the Zambezi River and then settling along the Kwando and Okavango rivers.

My investigation is a broad general ethnographic study of the Hambukushu with special emphasis upon their ecological adaptation to their riverine environment. These people still maintain their skill in practicing their traditional crafts of blacksmithing, pottery-making, woodworking, canoe-making, basketry, and bead- and jewelry-making. They are great rivermen and trade up and down the river and through the Okavango Delta to Maun. They are the best farmers of Botswana and will become more important to the economy of the country as the Okavango Delta becomes developed.

Of special interest are the matrilineal clans and lineage system. There are today approximately ten clans with totems. A person is not supposed to marry another person of his own clan. Polygyny is common and residence is generally patrilocal. A person takes the clan and lineage of his own mother. The deceased elder lineage members become spirits who haunt their kinsmen in their dreams and force them to give them gifts of food and beverages and carry out their wishes. In this way tradition and tribal customs are reinforced.

Though the tribe in Ngamiland comes under the rule of the Tawana headman at Shakawe and the Tawana Chief at Maun, the scattered communities along the Okavango River come under the jurisdiction of appointed *nduna* or headmen. Below this level are the *whiheto* or heads of individual villages. Today all Botswana people are considered equal *Motswana* under the new republic.

The research grant contributed by the National Geographic Society greatly added to the knowledge of the Hambukushu which I am endeavoring to put into published form as soon as time permits. No other anthropologist has studied the Hambukushu of Ngamiland. I hope to be able to return to the Okavango country to carry on additional studies of the Hambukushu and other river peoples.

REFERENCES

LARSON, THOMAS JOHN

1961. The ecological adaptation of the Mbukushu, a Bantu tribe of Ngamiland. Unpublished M.A. thesis, American University, Washington, D. C. University Microfilms, Inc., Ann Arbor, Mich.

1962. Rainmakers of the Okavango. Explorers Journal, vol. 40, no. 2, pp. 44-47.

1963. Epic tales of the Mbukushu. African Studies, vol. 22, pp. 176-189.

1965. The political structure of the Ngamiland Mbukushu under the rule of the Tawana. Anthropos, St. Augustin, Germany, vol. 60, pp. 164-176.

1966. The significance of rainmaking for the Mbukushu. African Studies, vol. 25, no. 1, pp. 23-36.

1968. A preliminary ethnographic survey of the Mbukushu of Ngamiland, 214 pages. B. Litt. thesis for the University of Oxford.

1970. The Hambukushu of Ngamiland. Botswana Notes and Record, vol. 2, pp. 29-44.

1971. The Hambukushu migrations to Ngamiland. African Social Research, vol. 2, no. 11, June, pp. 27-49.

1971. The spirits of the ancestors and the mandengure ceremony of the Hambukushu of Ngamiland. Anthropos, vol. 66, pp. 52-70.

1972. Tales from the Okavango, 118 pp. Howard Timmins, Cape Town.

1972. Verhale van die Okavango, 112 pp. John Malherbe, Cape Town.

1972. Hambukushu of the Okavango. Explorers Journal, vol. 50, no. 1, pp. 30-48.

1973. Ancestor worship and group therapy of the Hambukushu of Ngamiland, Virginia Social Science Journal, vol. 8, no. 2, pp. 1-8.

1975. Craftwork of the Hambukushu of Botswana. Botswana Notes and Records, vol. 7, pp. 109-120.

1976. Expedition to South West Africa. Explorers Journal, vol. 54, no. 2, pp. 84-89.

1978. Kinship terminology of the Hambukushu of Ngamiland. Botswana Notes and Record, vol. 9, pp. 85-89.

1978. The Hambukushu of Ngamiland, ecology and settlement patterns of a riverine people, 274 pp. Unpublished Ph.D. thesis, University of Virginia.

THOMAS JOHN LARSON

Early Man Research in East Africa, 1971

Principal Investigators: Louis S. B. Leakey[1] and Mary D. Leakey, Centre for Prehistory and Palaeontology, Nairobi, Kenya.

Grant Nos. 932, 933, 941, 1016. In further support of the Leakeys' archeological and paleontological excavations in Olduvai Gorge, Tanzania, and in aid of the Centre for Prehistory and Palaeontology, Nairobi.

Research

Excavations. During 1971 a major excavation was carried out at Site SC in the upper part of Bed II, where a hominid arm bone had been found in January. The bone appeared likely to belong to *Homo erectus,* and it was hoped that further parts of the skeleton might be recovered. This project proved unsuccessful, but a particularly massive upper molar tooth of *Australopithecus boisei (Zinjanthropus)* was found at the same level, confirming that the robust *Australopithecus* survived at Olduvai into upper Bed II and was contemporary with *Homo erectus.* Plentiful faunal remains and some artifacts were also found at this site.

Bed IV. Recent observations in the field by Dr. F. H. Brown (who has been largely responsible for establishing the geologic sequence in the Omo Valley, Ethiopia) and further laboratory work by Dr. R. L. Hay have gone a long way toward elucidating the chronologic sequence of the Acheulean sites excavated in Bed IV during 1970. Some additional fieldwork remains to be done by Dr. Hay, but it is now possible to correlate the two principal areas where archeological material was found in stratigraphic succession, i.e., HEB and WK.

In addition to work on Beds III and IV a number of geological test pits were sunk at the request of Dr. Hay in order to clarify certain parts of the Olduvai sequence that were nowhere exposed by natural erosion.

Dating. Very interesting results were obtained on oriented samples from various beds at Olduvai submitted for paleomagnetic readings. This research was carried out by Dr. A. Brock, of the Physics Department, University of Nairobi, to whom I am most grateful.

It was found that a number of the deposits at Olduvai are magnetic, particularly the red beds. These have given results that can be correlated with the

[1] Dr. Leakey died on October 1, 1972.

known changes of the earth's magnetic field, based on sequences of dated deep-sea cores. Samples from upper Bed II through to upper Bed III have given reversed polarity (i.e., when the magnetic pole was in the south), and these can be assigned to the closing stages of the last major epoch of reversal. This is known as the Matuyama Epoch and came to an end approximately 700,000 years ago. Further samples from a red bed in Bed IV have normal polarity and can reasonably be considered to lie within the Brunhes Normal Epoch, which succeeded the Matuyama Epoch. On this basis Acheulean sites in the lower part of Bed IV can be dated to between 600,000 and 500,000 years. (Note: Reversed samples have now been collected from within lower Bed IV, indicating that it is earlier than considered in 1971.)

Carbon-14 dates have also been obtained for a living site belonging to the Late Stone Age that is within the Gorge at the Second Fault. This site is in the Naisiusiu Beds and has yielded a microlithic industry with small geometric tools of a type formerly attributed to the Kenya Capsian. Two separate dates have been obtained, based respectively on the bone collagen and ostrich eggshell. Both have given figures of between 17,000 and 17,500 B.P.

The Olduvai Museum

The Museum was finally opened to the public in January 1971. Financial assistance for the exhibits was obtained from the Tanzania Antiquities Department and the Wallace Genetics Foundation, Washington, D. C. The National Museum at Dar es Salaam provided technicians to carry out some of the basic work in preparing the exhibits, and Miss Irene Sedgwick and Mrs. Judith Shackleton voluntarily dedicated many weeks to preparing the exhibits with me.

The museum is small but has proved very popular and enables visitors to see and understand some of the more important discoveries made at Olduvai. Parties of students from the Universities of Nairobi and Dar es Salaam have substantially increased since it was opened.

The two principal exhibits in the museum are mounted on a large central panel, back to back. One side shows a section through the deposits exposed in the gorge, with samples of the more important beds and explanatory labels on the geology by Dr. R. L. Hay. The opposite side of the panel shows a section through the gorge with the different beds shown in distinctive colors. Panels to the right and left, painted in matching colors, show the stone industries and principal hominid discoveries from each bed. Casts of the more important fossil animals are mounted on a large wall panel with copies of the paintings by J. Matternes depicting the reconstructed animals facing them.

There are also wall panels showing the sequence of faulting, the distribution of raw materials used for making stone tools, as well as the ground plans of two living floors in Bed I. Enlarged photographs supplied by the National Geographic Society of the personnel and the vehicles of the 1931 expedition to Olduvai are a most popular exhibit.

Visitors

During 1971, 17,581 people visited the Gorge. Donations to the Research Fund amounted to $861 and sales of books, postcards, etc., to $4,400, of which approximately half can be counted as profit (the National Geographic Society book by L. S. B. Leakey, *Animals of East Africa,* proved the most profitable item). Entrance fees were raised by the Antiquities Department from 3/- to 5/- for non-citizens of Tanzania and amounted to $10,000. This money is now administered by the Conservator of Antiquities on behalf of the Ministry of Education. It has been agreed that the costs of visitors' facilities, guides' salaries, maintenance, and upkeep of the museum and protected sites will be met from this money.

Ngorongoro Conservation Unit

My warm thanks are due to Mr. Mgina, the Acting Conservator, who has rendered most valuable help to the Olduvai project. Whenever possible, he arranged for water to be brought to the camp by the Ngorongoro water truck. He has also supplied graders to improve the roads and has seconded Conservation masons and carpenters to erect a stone building over the hut circle at Site DK.

Vehicles

A new Bedford 3-ton truck has been purchased, as the 1966 truck was no longer roadworthy and entailed very heavy running costs. The Land Rover purchased during 1970 was wrecked by the camp driver and has not yet been replaced owing to difficulties with the National Insurance Corporation of Tanzania who wish to settle the claim for Shs. 12,000 instead of Shs. 19,000 for which the vehicle was insured.

Publications

Volume 3 of the Olduvai monographs was finally on sale on December 30th, priced at £10. Papers have also been published in *Nature* during July and August 1971 on the hominid skull from Bed I (H.24) and on the hominid remains from Bed IV (H.28). These two papers were written by myself in joint authorship with L. S. B. Leakey and Dr. M. H. Day. A paper on the Late Stone Age site in the Naisiusiu Beds is due to appear in *World Archaeology* in February 1972. Dr. R. L. Hay and I are joint authors.

MARY D. LEAKEY

Domestic Architecture and Village Layout in Mainland Greece, About 2200-800 B.C.

Principal Investigator: William A. McDonald, University of Minnesota, Minneapolis, Minnesota.

Grant No. 1032: In partial support of a study of domestic architecture and village layout in mainland Greece, 2200-800 B.C.

This research project was begun in the fall of 1972 under the direction of Dr. William A. McDonald with the assistance of Dr. Stanley E. Aschenbrenner, a research associate of the Nichoria project. As of this writing the study is continuing, and the detailed results will be incorporated in volume 4 of the final publication of the excavations conducted by the Minnesota Messenia Expedition (MME) at Nichoria in Messenia (extreme southwest Greece). The time spread of the study here reported includes the Middle and Late Bronze Age, called Middle Helladic (MH) and Late Helladic (LH) in mainland Greece, and the Early Iron (EI) Age. The somewhat arbitrary division between MH and LH is usually placed about 1600 B.C., and that between LH and EI about 1100 B.C.

The project objectives may be summarized as follows:

1. To identify the common characteristics as well as the contrasts between habitation sites where important evidence has been uncovered on domestic architecture and village layout.
2. To formulate simple generalizations about single characteristics of domestic architecture in and between the major time periods.
3. To formulate more complex generalizations involving relationships or combinations of such characteristics.
4. To describe in detail "typical" houses according to construction techniques, plan, and period.
5. To suggest for future excavators what kinds of sites, periods of occupation, and excavation techniques would be most likely to produce evidence needed to close serious gaps in our present knowledge of domestic architecture and village layout.
6. To provide a reasonably comprehensive index to specify at what sites and in what houses within these sites important evidence was discovered on relevant features such as the techniques used in the construction of foundations and superstructure, hearths, chimneys, roof supports, and second floor (if any).

The major motivation for the study was our growing awareness during the Nichoria excavation (1969-73) of the relative uncertainty in the discipline about chronological developments and regional differences in architecture versus other artifactual indicators; for example, ceramics. The senior collaborator carried out library research and corresponded with or personally discussed their results with excavators in the United States, Britain, and Greece. On this basis he compiled a list of 36 sites where significant building remains have been interpreted as private homes or associated structures. Buildings identified as "palaces," sanctuaries, and tombs were excluded, except as their location is relevant to village or town layout. The literature was combed for plans and descriptions of individual buildings and building complexes, as well as for previous attempts at synthesis and classification.

In spring of 1973 the two collaborators, often accompanied by Roger Howell, visited 25 of the 36 sites (see map, fig. 1) and made careful observations and measurements. With the aid of a 12-page checklist, it was possible to conduct a systematic review of the published data and sometimes to include additional information from our own inspection. As for the sites we did not visit, either the advance knowledge of the collaborators or more up-to-date information from colleagues certified that there is now nothing worth seeing of an architectural nature. Plans to visit several sites in the Aegean islands for purposes of comparison with the mainland data were revised, mainly for the same reason. Only two sites on islands close to the coast of Attica (i.e., Euboea and Aegina) were actually studied.

The following are the major groupings of the information entered in our set of check-sheets. Items 2 through 5 are further subdivided chronologically, i.e., Middle Helladic (MH), Late Helladic (LH), Early Iron (EI):

1. Siting.
2. Settlement plan.
3. Ground plans of individual buildings.
4. Arrangement and function(s) of individual rooms.
5. Techniques of construction.

The fieldwork included also careful observation and intensive discussion of the precepts and practice concerning domestic architecture in Greek villages of the late 19th and early 20th centuries A.D. In spring 1973 we visited with several of the oldest surviving builders living in the town of Langadia in Arkadia and studied construction techniques in older houses in their village. Men from Langadia were specialists in stone masonry and constructed buildings all over southern Greece, including the vicinity of our own excavation site. There is a tradition that their ancestors came from a famous Byzantine area whence they may have derived their celebrated technical skill. We spent considerable time also in the town of Messini (a few kilometers east of our own

FIG. 1. Map showing sites studied in Greece.

site) where all the older buildings are of mud-brick (without wooden frame) on stone foundations. Here too we interviewed local builders who practiced this technique in their younger years. With a retired stonemason now living in Kalamata we inspected a village in which the majority of the stone houses are over a century old and most are abandoned and in various stages of disintegration. We also carried out a small trial excavation on one of the oldest

REGISTER OF SITES

acr. - acropolis
comp. - complex
cont. - controlled
E - excellent
EI - Early Iron Age
env. - environs
F - fair

G - good
int. - intersection
LH - Late Helladic
med. - medium
MH - Middle Helladic
obsc. - obscured
P - poor

pen. - peninsula
pt. - part, partial
riv. - river
sev. - several
spr. - spring
str. - stream
term. - terminus

Name of site	*Periods of habitation*	*Status of remains*	*Physical description*	*Communications*	*Agricultural resources*	*Water supply*	*Fortifications*	*Extramural cemetery*	*Intramural burials*	*Complete or restorable house plans*
Aigina	MH	obsc.	low	main	F	P	MH	LH	MH?	MH(comp.)
	LH EI?		acr.	isl. harbor						LH(2)
Argos (Aspis)	MH? LH?	obsc.	high acr.	harbor route int.	E	F (riv.)	MH?	LH	?	MH?(4) LH?(2)
Asea	MH	very obsc.	high acr.	on main route	G	G (strs., spr.)	?	?	MH	MH(7)
Asine	MH LT EI?	obsc.	acr. slope & env.	harbor? coast road	G	P	?	MH? LH EI	MH	MH(sev.) LH(sev.)

Aghios Kosmas	LH	very obsc.	low pen.	harbor on coast route	F	P	LH	?	LH	LH(3)
Berbati	MH LH	fair	acr. slopes	on main route	G	E (str., spr.)	?	?	?	LH(block?)
Brauron	MH LH	obsc.	med. acr.	harbor? route int.	F	G (str., spr.)	MH?	LH	MH	MH(1) LH
Eleusis	MH LH EI?	obsc.	acr. slopes	harbor? on main route	E	G?	MH? LH?	MH LH	LH	LH(2)?
Eutresis	MH LH	fair	med. acr.	on main route	E	G (riv., spr.)	LH	?	MH	MH(10) LH(4)
Kirrha	MH LH	not visible	low mound	harbor route term.	G	P?	?	?	MH LH	MH(4)? LH(3)?
Korakou	MH LH	very obsc.	end of med.e ridge	harbor? on main route	G	?	LH?	?	?	MH(2) LH(5)
Koukounara	LH	obsc.	low hill in narrow ridge	on main? route	G	G (riv.)	?	LH	?	LH(1)

REGISTER OF SITES—CONTINUED

acr. - acropolis
comp. - complex
cont. - controlled
E - excellent
EI - Early Iron Age
env. - environs
F - fair
G - good
int. - intersection
LH - Late Helladic
med. - medium
MH - Middle Helladic
obsc. - obscured
P - poor
pen. - peninsula
pt. - part, partial
riv. - river
sev. - several
spr. - spring
str. - stream
term. - terminus

Name of site	*Periods of habitation*	*Status of remains*	*Physical description*	*Communications*	*Agricultural resources*	*Water supply*	*Fortifications*	*Extramural cemetery*	*Intramural burials*	*Complete or restorable house plans*
Krisa	MH LH	very obsc.	end of high ridge	cont. main route	G?	F?	LH	?	MH	MH(4)? LH(3)?
Lerna	MH LH	good	med. mound	harbor? on main route	G	E (spr.)	?	?	MH LH	MH (sev.)
Lefkandi	MH LH EI	F	med. acr.	harbor on main isl. route	G	?	?	EI	LH	MH (1, pt.) LH (comp.)
Malthi	MH LH	F	high acr.	cont. main routes	E	E (riv., spr.)	MH LH	LH	MH	MH (many) LH (many)
Mycenae	MH LH EI?	G	high acr. & slopes	cont. main routes	G	F (spr.)	LH	MH LH	?	MH(1) LH(many) EI(1)?

Nichoria	MH LH EI	G	high ridge	harbor route int.	E	G (riv., sprs.)	?	LH EI	LH	MH(1) LH(many) EI(3)
Olympia	MH LH EI	F	valley floor	on main route	G	G (rivs.)	?	LH	MH	MH(5)
Peristeria	MH LH	obsc.	high acr.	cont. main route	F	G? (riv.)	LH	MH LH	LH	MH(1, pt.) LH(2)?
Pefkakia	MH LH	G	low acr.	harbor? on main route	F	?	?	?	MH?	MH(2)
Thermon	MH? LH EI	G	valley floor	on isolated route	G	E (sprs.)	?	?	?	LH(8)?
Thorikos	MH LH EI	G	high acr.	harbor on coast route	G	?	?	LH EI	MH	MH(pt.) LH(pt.) EI(pt.)
Tiryns	MH LH EI	G	med. acr. & slopes	on main route(s)	E	F (str., wells?	LH	LH EI	?	LH(sev.)
Zygouries	MH LH	very obsc.	med. mound	on main route	G	?	?	MH LH	MH	LH(sev.) LH(1)

abandoned stone houses in Karpofora, the modern village nearest to our excavation site, to verify what the builders tell us about width and depth of stone foundations below floor level (in relation to the height of walls), width of construction trench, and other features not observable above ground.

At this writing we are still testing the applicability of all the above-mentioned data to the architectural remains from our own excavation. As for the results of the study, we shall record here only the "hard" facts assembled in the Register of Sites (pp. 466-469), plus the following tentative generalizations:

1. There is at present disappointingly little solid information about village layout at any point in the time range covered by our study. Malthi (no. 16) is the only site where the area excavated even remotely coincides with the original extent of the settlement, and there is no reason to believe that its layout (clearest for late MH) is "typical." A few other sites have yielded the complete plan of up to ten buildings at least roughly contemporary with one another, as well as some idea of their related streets and alleys. Monumental surround walls are relatively rare at any period. At our site of Nichoria a far larger than average area (about 5,000 square meters) has been excavated to varying depths; but we have had to leave untouched more than 80 percent of the area that seems to have been inhabited, at least in some periods within the time covered by this study. And even in the excavated sections it is going to be difficult to reconstruct anything approaching a dependable "town plan" for any given period because of the disappearance of vital information through erosion, cultivation, repairs, and remodeling, as well as re-use of the building materials and foundations.

2. Although in the past Greek archeologists have devoted a disproportionate amount of attention to palatial and near-palatial complexes of Late Helladic times, it appears that this kind of information sheds relatively little useful light on ordinary domestic architecture in the same time range.

3. In terms of construction techniques, it looks as if there was at least as much variation in domestic architecture between different sites at the same period as there was on the same site in different periods. If true, this phenomenon is possibly due in large part to varying availability of certain types of construction materials. It would also fit in with the pattern of developing evidence for the persistence of many culture traits from MH to LH, and even into the Early Iron Age.

4. On the long-debated question of flat versus pitched roofs in developed MH and LH contexts, it is virtually certain (if we accept the excavators' judgment that burnt-clay fragments showing wood impressions are actually from roofs and not from walls) that a sloping roof of any considerable pitch is

excluded. Furthermore, there is absolutely no reliable evidence for the use of terra-cotta roof-tiles within the time span under review.

The Register of Sites includes *only* information on towns and villages where excavation (major or minor) has revealed relatively important evidence on domestic architecture that can be dated in our time range (2200-800 B.C.). It should be noted that some of these sites have also yielded useful evidence on periods both earlier and later than our chosen parameters. Readers may be puzzled by the categories of information we have included and excluded. For instance, there is no heading "Town Planning," partly because the available evidence is so sparse and partly because most of the existing information seemed impossible to summarize in chart form (at least at this stage of our study). Such headings as "Fortifications" and "Extramural Cemetery(ies)" do, however, have a bearing on town layout. On the other hand, several headings like "Physical Description," "Communications," "Agricultural Resources," and "Water Supply" call attention, in our opinion, to the kind of background information without which one should not approach more specific problems concerning domestic architecture.

WILLIAM A. MCDONALD
STANLEY E. ASCHENBRENNER

An Eocene Flamingo Nesting Area, Sweetwater County, Wyoming

Principal Investigator: Paul O. McGrew, University of Wyoming, Laramie, Wyoming.

Grant No. 981: For an investigation of an Eocene flamingo nesting area in Wyoming.

During the summer of 1970 Faroy Simnacher, then a graduate student of the University of Wyoming, while conducting stratigraphic studies for a graduate thesis discovered a concentration of fossil bird bones. A block of matrix from the site measuring approximately 2 by 3 feet and 6 inches thick was collected and upon preparation in the University of Wyoming laboratory proved to contain 109 bones, all belonging to an extinct species of flamingo. In addition, there were a number of fragments of eggshell. It seemed obvious that Mr. Simnacher had made the rare discovery of a nesting site of this bird.

Because of the unique importance of the discovery a grant was provided by the National Geographic Society to excavate the site and to travel to East Africa to study the ecology of the modern counterpart of the fossil flamingo. The summers of 1971 and 1972 were spent excavating the bird concentration and studying the stratigraphic relationships of the area (fig. 1). During the winter of 1972-73, with Dr. Alan Feduccia of the University of North Carolina, I made a trip to Kenya to study Lake Nakuru and Lake Hannington, where there were major concentrations of flamingos.

The bird site is located in SE 1/2, sec. 24, T. 25 N., R. 102 W., Sweetwater County, which is in a remote and desolate part of Wyoming (fig. 2). The stratigraphic section in the area consists of an intertonguing sequence of fluvial and lacustrine sediments. The fluvial sediments are referred to the Cathedral Bluffs member of the Wasatch formation and the lacustrine sediments to the Wilkins Peak member of the Green River formation. A few fossil mammals found near the bird concentration indicate that the sediments are early Middle Eocene in age, or about 45 million years old.

To the south of the locality was the main body of a very large lake known as Lake Gosiute. It is believed that the fossil flamingos concentrated and nested along the shore of this lake. As the lake expanded from time to time it flooded forested areas and killed the trees. In the flamingo quarry were many algal-encrusted logs and branches. These were oriented, presumably parallel

FIG. 1. The fossil-bird quarry, showing grid established before excavation was started.

FIG. 2. Panoramic view of the quarry-site locale in remote area of Sweetwater County, Wyoming. In the lower left is the camp; in the lower right is the bird quarry.

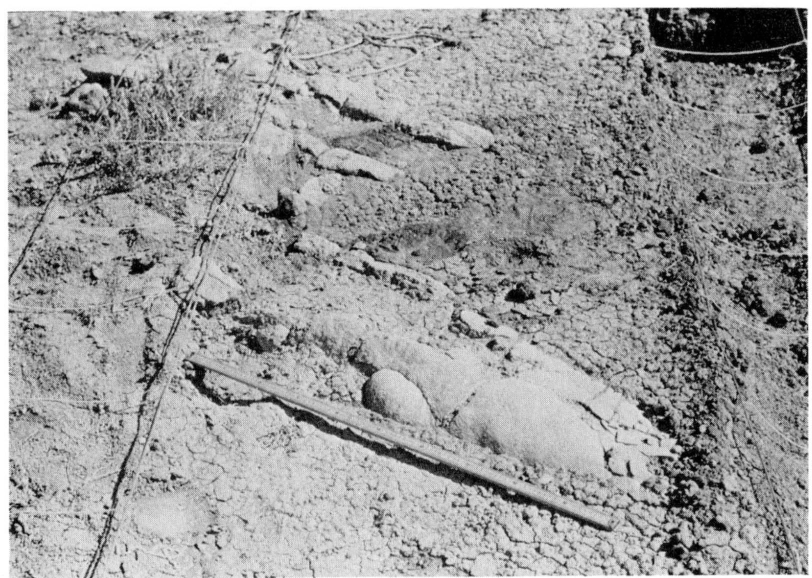

FIG. 3. Alga-encrusted logs occurring with the flamingo bones, presumably oriented parallel to the shore of the ancient lake.

with the shore line of the lake (fig. 3). Many fish bones, fragments of aquatic turtle shells, and crocodile bones attest to the aquatic environment. A very similar situation exists today around the shore of Lake Nakuru, in Kenya, where hundreds of thousands of flamingos concentrate (fig. 4).

The several hundred bones derived from the quarry provide adequate material for skeletal reconstruction of the Eocene flamingo (fig. 5). Although basically like the modern representatives of the family there are a number of important differences. Perhaps the most obvious one is that the extinct form did not have the decurved bill so typical of modern flamingos. In general form the bill was very much like that of a duck. The difference between the bill of the modern and extinct forms doubtless reflects a difference in feeding habits. Modern flamingos are primarily filter feeders, and the main diet consists of algae and microorganisms obtained from the water and bottom muds. Occasionally, however, flamingos will take a variety of small mollusks, crustaceans, worms, and small fishes. Stomach contents usually include an abundance of organic muds. The matrix in which the fossil bird bones are included contain literally thousands of tiny bone fragments of small fishes. It is difficult to relate these bones to the diet of the flamingos because fish bones

FIG. 4. Lake Nakuru, Kenya, with tree drowned by expanding waters. At the time we visited the lake it hosted an estimated 2 million flamingos.

are usually completely ingested by birds that include fish in their diets. It is possible that these bones remained from partially digested or regurgitated food. Many living fish-eating birds (e.g., herons, ibises) regurgitate food on their nest sites to feed the young, and many dead fish may be observed on the ground surrounding the nest sites. It is not improbable that similar habits of the Eocene flamingo may account for the numerous fragments of fish bones.

An unexpected and still unexplained result of the fieldwork was the discovery of hundreds of small coprolites, or fossil excrement. These were first interpreted as the excrement of small mammals that may have raided the nesting site to feed on eggs or chicks. It is now believed that the pellets came from the flamingos themselves. On Lake Nakuru, in Kenya, almost exactly similar pellets were found abundantly where flamingos concentrate. The feces of most birds consist almost exclusively of uric acid and would not be preserved in the fossil record, and we have been unable to find any record that flamingos differ in this respect. We are working on the theory that undigestable organic *muds* that are found in the stomach contents of modern flamingos may well have become concentrated and expelled as these pellets. Geochemical and other studies are now in progress that may solve this interesting puzzle.

FIG. 5. A reconstruction of the Eocene flamingo-like bird.

Dr. Feduccia is studying the taxonomic relationships of the Green River flamingo and has determined that it is closely related to a bird of approximately the same age from Argentina originally described by Howard (1955) as *Telmabrates antiquus*. Nomenclatorial complications, however, require that the generic name be changed to *Presbyornis,* a form from the Green River formation of Utah, described by Dr. Alexander Wetmore in 1926.

REFERENCES

FEDUCCIA, ALAN

1978. *Presbyornis* and the evolution of ducks and flamingos. Amer. Scientist, vol. 66, pp. 298-304.

FEDUCCIA, ALAN, and MCGREW, PAUL O.

1974. Flamingos from the Eocene of the Green River formation of Wyoming. Contr. Geol. Univ. Wyoming, vol. 13, pp. 49-61.

McGrew, Paul O., and Feduccia, Alan
1973. A preliminary report on a nesting colony of Eocene birds. Wyoming Geol. Assoc. 25th Field Conf., pp. 163-164.
Wetmore, Alexander
1926. Fossil birds from the Green River deposits of eastern Utah. Ann. Carnegie Mus., vol. 16, pp. 391-402.

Paul O. McGrew

Behavior of the Reef Sharks of Rangiroa, French Polynesia

Principal Investigator: Donald R. Nelson, California State University, Long Beach, California.

Co-investigator: Richard H. Johnson, S.E.A. Institute, Inc., Papeete, Tahiti.

Grant Nos. 950, 1051, 1273. In support of a comparative behavioral study of tropical Pacific reef sharks.[1]

Between October 1972 and January 1975 we conducted a boat-based expedition to French Polynesia for the purpose of a comparative behavioral study of the sharks of a tropical Pacific coral-reef habitat. The research was broad in scope, aimed at establishing baseline information on the reef species and assessing potential for future studies of a more specific nature.

Previous insights on how sharks behave in natural underwater environment, especially toward divers, were provided by the early experiences of Eibl-Eibesfeldt and Hass (1959), Limbaugh (1963), and Cousteau and Cousteau (1970). In-the-water studies of specific behaviors included Hobson's (1963) comparative study of feeding behavior (i.e., responses to test food presentations), Nelson and Johnson's (1970a) study of diel activity rhythms, and Johnson and Nelson's (1973) study of agonistic display toward divers. A number of field studies have dealt with acoustic attractions of sharks and are

[1] This report summarizes expedition results, especially comparisons between species. Detailed findings regarding individual species or behaviors are published elsewhere (see References). A comprehensive treatment of the sharks of Polynesia has been published in book form (Johnson, 1978), partly as a result of this expedition.

Besides the primary expedition support from the National Geographic Society, we acknowledge the assistance of the Office of Naval Research (through contract N00014-68-C-0318, under project NR-104-062) and, after January 1975, of the S.E.A. Institute, Inc. We thank the many persons who participated in the expedition, especially J. Ewald, C. Johnson, B. Lundberg, H. Loew, R. McKenzie, J. McKibben, D. Mosher, V. Nelson, T. Sciarrotta, W. Smith, K. Wright, and G. Zimmerman. We are grateful also to those representatives of the government of French Polynesia who helped the expedition, especially M. Danoir, S. Stein, and C. Tokoragi.

discussed by Myrberg et al. (1972, 1976) and Nelson and Johnson (1972, 1976).

These studies, while of unquestioned value, involved mainly sharks that had been *attracted* to within the observer's view by "opportunistic" feeding stimuli (sounds, odors) or by the presence of the divers themselves. As discussed by Nelson (1977a), they provide relatively little information on what sharks do in the absence of the above "artificial" influences, i.e., their normal patterns of activity, space utilization, predation, and social interaction. It was to these aspects of behavior that the present study was primarily aimed.

Study Area. The research was conducted at Rangiroa, largest atoll in the Tuamotu Archipelago, located at lat. 15° 00′S., long. 147° 40′W., approximately 300 kilometers northeast of Tahiti (fig. 1). The Rangiroa lagoon measures about 80 kilometers long and 32 kilometers wide and has a maximum depth of 34 meters. It possesses two major deep-water connections to the ocean, Avatoru and Tiputa Passes, located 9 kilometers apart on the northern rim of the atoll. Most of the expedition work occurred in these passes, on adjoining ocean and lagoon reefs, and on the ocean reef at Maherehonae (northwest corner of atoll).

Rangiroa has a population of about 1,000 persons, most of whom live in the two villages bordering the passes. Many of the residents are expert fishermen and divers and possess considerable knowledge of local sharks. Some of the divers make their living by spearfishing and, in doing so, come into frequent conflict with sharks. Several divers bear scars from shark attack.

The expedition was based aboard the research vessel *Søkende Hai,*[2] a 12-meter diesel-auxillary ketch, which was sailed to French Polynesia from California. When on site, *Søkende Hai* was usually moored in Avatoru Pass, near the village wharf, and daily work on nearby reefs was conducted from a 5-meter Avon inflatable outboard boat.

Rangiroa has been the site of several previous shark studies, including the acoustic-attraction experiments of Nelson and Johnson (1970b) and Brown (1973). The well-known shark film "The Predators" was filmed in Tiputa Pass in 1966 by Al Giddings and Dewey Bergman.

[2] Presently owned by R. H. Johnson and renamed the *S.E.A. Quest.*

FIG. 1. Rangiroa, Tuamotu Archipelago, French Polynesia. Enlarged map shows the study areas where most of the research was conducted. Another study area, Maherehonae, lies 15 kilometers west of Avatoru Pass at the NW corner of the atoll.

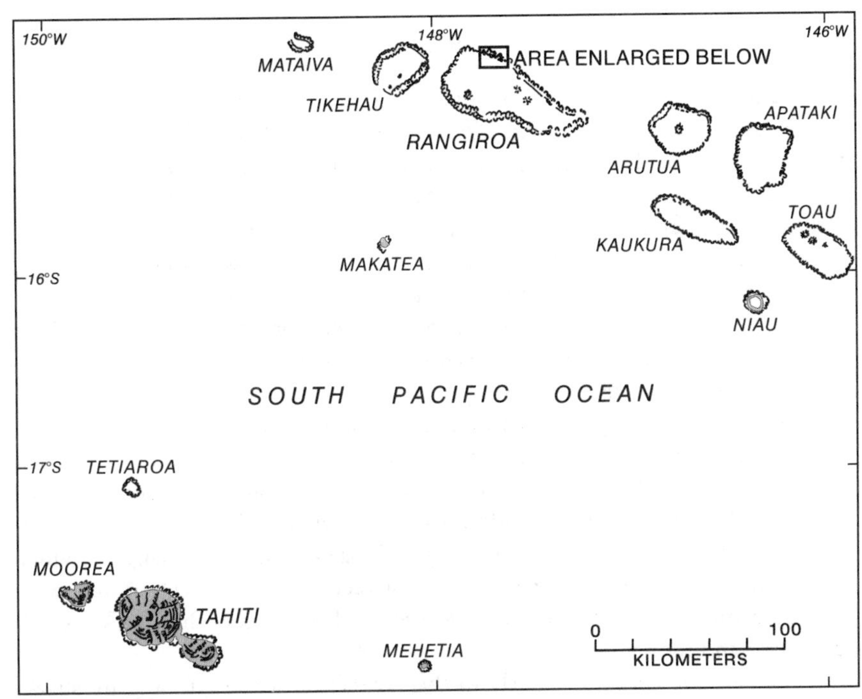
150°W
148°W
146°W
AREA ENLARGED BELOW
MATAIVA
TIKEHAU
RANGIROA
APATAKI
ARUTUA
TOAU
KAUKURA
MAKATEA
16°S
NIAU
SOUTH PACIFIC OCEAN
17°S
TETIAROA
MOOREA
TAHITI
MEHETIA
0
100
KILOMETERS

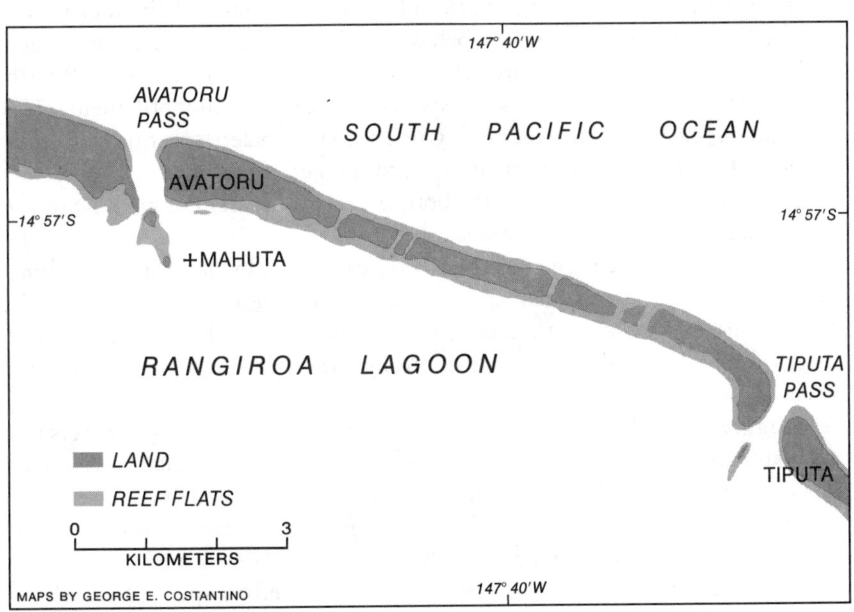
147° 40'W
AVATORU PASS
SOUTH PACIFIC OCEAN
AVATORU
14° 57'S
14° 57'S
+MAHUTA
RANGIROA LAGOON
TIPUTA PASS
TIPUTA
LAND
REEF FLATS
0
3
KILOMETERS
147° 40'W
MAPS BY GEORGE E. COSTANTINO

Methods

Direct Observation. Most data were gathered visually by observers in the water, usually by surface-swimming or free-diving (breath-holding). SCUBA was used occasionally, when greater depths or bottom times were desired, or for underwater photography. Visibility ranged from about 30-50 meters in clear water (ocean reefs, flood tides in passes) to about 10-15 meters in turbid water (ebb tides in passes). During turbid conditions we often had to dive partway to the bottom for useful observation. In the vicinity of the passes currents were strong (several knots). During full ebb or flood it was difficult or impossible to hold position by swimming. At such times we often used drift-through observation techniques.

Baiting. Although we were primarily interested in "natural" behaviors, it was necessary to bait-attract sharks to facilitate tagging them or to implant telemetry transmitters. We also conducted standard baiting sessions to count sharks and to identify tagged individuals for long-term home-range and population studies. These sessions usually involved on-site spearfishing, in which both sounds and odors contributed to attractiveness. Fishes speared were mainly abundant reef species, e.g., surgeonfishes, parrotfishes, jacks, small groupers, and moray eels.

Conventional Tagging. Early in the expedition we began tagging sharks in preparation for continuing studies of population sizes, individual movements, home ranges, and social behaviors. Most sharks were spear-tagged under water with modified Floy FH69 stainless-steel dart tags (fig. 2) with color-coded plastic streamers (vinyl spaghetti over nylon monofilament). Using a rubber-powered Hawaiian-sling or Tahitian-arbalete speargun, the diver normally approached from above and tagged the shark while it was preoccupied with bait placed on the bottom. It was usually not possible to get within tagging range of unbaited sharks.

Some sharks were tagged in the boat after capture by hook and hand line. We caught most by an underwater angling technique in which a diver held the line and set the hook; then people in the boat pulled in the catch. These sharks were measured, then tagged through the dorsal fin with numbered yellow-plastic rototags.

Tagging served to facilitate recognition of individual sharks by divers under water. Both types of tags were coded by streamer length and color pattern as well as placement site on the shark's body. The color code was readable at distances up to 10-15 meters. Effective tag life, however, was limited by (1) obscuring of the colors by algae and other growths and (2) damage or shedding of the tag. In general, we found that tags on cave-dwelling species (reef whitetip sharks) stayed relatively unobscured as long as 6-12 months but were more prone to damage from contact with coral. Tags on sharks inhabiting shallow open water (blackfin reef, some gray reef sharks) became algae-obscured much sooner but could often still be identified by tag length and placement site.

Ultrasonic Telemetry. In the spring of 1973 we initiated telemetry trackings at Rangiroa for the purpose of (1) obtaining continuous, round-the-clock data on activity, movements, and home ranges and (2) facilitating diver interception of telemetered individuals for direct observations. The instrumentation and techniques used were similar to those described in detail by Ferrel et al. (1974) and Nelson (1974). The transmitters operated at discrete frequencies near 40 kHz, were pulse-rate encoded (most with depth sensors), had a useful range of 2-3 kilometers, and a life of several days to several weeks (depending on battery).

We found that the best application method was to allow free-swimming sharks to self-ingest the transmitter concealed in bait. This method was completely atraumatic and had no noticeable effect on the shark's behavior. Some such stomach implantations resulted in regurgitation of the transmitter several days later, allowing its recovery and reuse. Some initial trackings utilized external attachment via a barbed dart (Floy FH69), but these were suspected of having caused abnormal movements because of the trauma resulting from capture and/or dart attachment.

Results

Species Present. Twelve species of sharks were observed under water or captured by expedition personnel, and two or three additional were confirmed by local reports (table 1; figs. 2-4). While most of the research was on the gray reef shark (most social, most aggressive to man) and the reef whitetip (most readily observed), specific studies involved also the blackfin reef shark, the blacktip shark, and the silvertip shark. Information on the remaining species came from incidental observations, captures, and local reports.

New Records. Three of the species we encountered were apparently first records from French Polynesia, i.e., not listed by either Bagnis et al. (1972) or Randall (1973). Both the silky shark and the great hammerhead, although seen on several occasions during the expedition, had not been previously reported. The capture of a single specimen of bull shark was an unexpected event, as this species is normally associated with coastal waters of relatively large landmasses.

Somewhat surprisingly, we did not encounter the scalloped hammerhead, *Sphyrna lewini,* in Rangiroa, although it is reported as well known in Tahiti.

FIG. 2. Reef whitetip sharks, *Triaenodon obesus,* with color-coded dart tags. Above: With clean, readable tags, swimming above reef. Opposite, top: With older tag, obscured by algae. Center: resting in open cave. Bottom: tagging apparatus, consisting of Hawaiian sling, spear with applicator, and dart. (Photos by R. McKenzie; R. Johnson, bottom, right.)

However, there were persistent reports (and one possible sighting by R. Johnson) of another large hammerhead (3-meters TL) at Rangiroa. Natives call this shark the *Ma'o afata* (box-head shark) and describe it as having a relatively square-shaped hammer, about as long as wide. If this description is accurate, it must be a new species.

Habitat Preference. In the areas we dived, the sharks most frequently encountered were the gray reef, blackfin reef, and reef whitetip. These are the three species most commonly seen by divers in clear-water coral areas throughout the tropical central Pacific. Aspects of their biology have been treated by Wass (1971), Randall and Helfman (1973), and Randall (1977). The distinct habitat partitioning described by Hobson (1963) for these species at Enewetak also occurs at Rangiroa.

Each of the species we regularly observed had its own particular *daytime* habitat preference in terms of depth, bottom type, and water clarity. No two species had identical distributions, although there was considerable overlap. In terms of mean preferred depth, the blackfin reef shark was shallowest, rarely over 10-15 meters deep, and sometimes was in less than 1 meter of water, e.g., over the ocean reef flat shoreward of the surf. The reef whitetip was

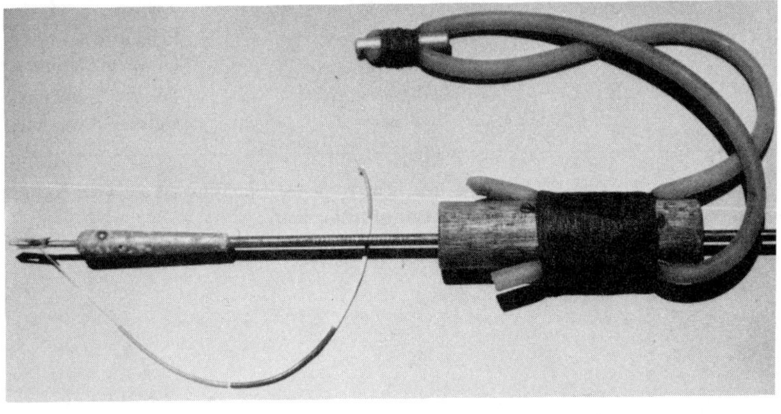

generally seen at medium depths (10-30 meters), while the gray reef shark was typically deeper (20-100 meters), but with a wider over-all depth range. The silvertip was deepest (30 meters +), seen only at the outer edge of the ocean reef when attracted up from below the drop-off (except for a few juveniles in the lagoon).

TABLE 1. Species of Sharks at Rangiroa, French Polynesia

First 12 species confirmed by direct sighting or capture by expedition personnel; last 3 species from reliable local reports. Habitat code: L, Lagoon; P, Passes; O, Ocean reef; s, shallow (0-10 meters); m, medium depths (10-30 meters); d, deep (30+ meters).

Local name [1]	*American name*	*Species*	*Remarks* [2]
Raira	Gray reef	*Carcharhinus amblyrhynchos* (= *C. menisorrah*)	Common (L,P,O,m,d)
Mauri	Blackfin reef (Blacktip reef)	*C. melanopterus*	Common (L,P,O,s)
Oihe	Blacktip	*C. limbatus*	Uncommon (L,P,m)
Tapete	Silvertip	*C. albimarginatus*	Uncommon (O,d)
Tautukau	Silky	*C. falciformis* [3]	Pelagic (see text)
Parata	Oceanic whitetip	*C. longimanus* (= *C. maou*)	Pelagic (see text)
(None)	Bull	*C. leucas* [3]	Rare (single specimen caught on Ocean reef)
Torire	Reef whitetip	*Triaenodon obesus*	Common (L,P,O,m)
Arava	Lemon	*Negaprion acutidens*	Uncommon (L,O,m)
Nohipiri	Nurse	*Ginglymostoma ferrugineum* (= *Nebrius concolor*)	Uncommon (L,O,m)
Ruhia	Tiger	*Galeocerdo cuvieri*	Uncommon (L,O,d)
Tamataroa	Great hammerhead	*Sphyrna mokarran* [3]	Uncommon (L,P,O,m)
Afata	"Squarehead"	*Sphyrna* sp.	New species? (see text)
A'ahi	Shortfin mako	*Isurus oxyrinchus*	Pelagic (dead specimen found on Ocean reef)
(None)	Whale	*Rhiniodon typus*	Pelagic, Rare (one sighted in Lagoon

[1] The common name used in Rangiroa. The name used in Tahiti is sometimes different. Names often prefaced by "Ma'o," the general name for shark.

[2] Apparent abundance and typical daytime habitats, based on sightings and captures by expedition personnel in study area, or by local reports.

[3] New record from French Polynesia.

The lemon shark, nurse shark, and great hammerhead were seen only infrequently, usually in medium depths. Tiger sharks were never seen free-swimming (except in company with another hooked tiger), although they could be caught at night by a set line on the ocean reef (15-meter depth). They are apparently too deep to be seen by divers during the daytime.

In terms of bottom topography, the two cave-dwelling species (reef whitetip and nurse) were the most restricted to areas of high coral relief with caves and crevices. It is probably this factor, even more so than depth, that primarily determines their distribution.

At the opposite habitat extreme were the silky shark and the oceanic whitetip, both pelagic species not normally associated with reefs. Only one oceanic whitetip was seen at Rangiroa, an individual that appeared over the ocean reef during an acoustic playback experiment, apparently attracted in from the open sea. Silky sharks were seen several times near the surface a few hundred meters off the mouth of Tiputa Pass (one captured for identification). They might occasionally come within sight of the ocean reef.

In terms of water clarity, the blacktip shark appeared the most restricted to turbid-water conditions. We encountered it regularly at ebb or low tide in Avatoru Pass off the village wharf, where it regularly appeared in search of fish scraps sometimes discarded there. When the clear water arrived shortly after the start of flood tide, these sharks retreated with the turbid water back into the lagoon (determined by telemetry). Gray, whitetip, and blackfin sharks were commonly seen in both clear and turbid waters, although adult gray sharks of lagoon areas usually preferred the turbid side of clear/turbid interfaces. Silvertip sharks appeared the most restricted to clear water, as exists on the deep ocean reef; indeed their conspicuous white fin tips are very visible in this clear, deep-blue environment, and seem likely to have some signaling function.

Although considerable overlap exists in the normal habitats of the above species, opportunistic feeding situations, such as baiting or sound playback, can temporarily create a greater-than-normal overlap. For instance, when baiting (spearfishing) at a medium depth on the ocean reef, we found that the accumulated group of sharks could include blackfins (attracted down from shallower areas), whitetips (attracted laterally), and grays and an occasional silvertip (attracted up from deeper water).

Area Preference. We did most of the conventional tagging and telemetry on two species, the gray reef shark and the reef whitetip. Work was concentrated at several specific study areas (subareas) within the over-all expedition area (fig. 1). As summarized in table 2, a relatively high percentage of tagged

TABLE 2. Summary of Data from Conventional Tagging and Reobservation of Sharks at Rangiroa

Species	*Number of sharks tagged*	*Number of sharks reobserved, (percent of number tagged)*	*Number of reobservations* [1]	*Percent of reobservations in original tagging area*	*Maximum time from tagging to last reobservation*
Reef whitetip	113	78 (69%)	1,106	98.8	3 years, 4 months
Gray reef	65	28 (43%)	66	100.	4 years, 2 months
Blackfin reef [2]	40	11 (27%)	24	87.5	3 months, 15 days
Silvertip [2]	3	2 (67%)	2	100.	10 days

[1] Maximum of one observation/day counted for each individual.
[2] Data through 5/15/73, after which tagging work on these species was discontinued.

individuals were later reobserved. Results indicated that both species have strong, long-term home-area attachments, with probably little interchange between areas.

The gray reef sharks we studied were separated into at least five relatively distinct area-associated groups or subpopulations. Their home areas were: Avatoru Lagoon (Mahuta), Avatoru Pass, Tiputa Lagoon, Tiputa Pass, and Maherehonae Ocean Reef. Of the 28 tagged individuals reobserved (66 total resightings), all were in the original areas of tagging—evidence for relatively little interchange between groups. Since many of these resightings were months to years after tagging, it seems that such home-area preferences can be quite long term. Some interchange does occur, however, as shown by one tracked individual (bait implanted without trauma) that moved from the Mahuta area to Tiputa Pass.

One adult gray reef shark resident at Mahuta was translocated (by boat) to a site on the ocean reef west of Avatoru Pass. Although it did not return to Mahuta for at least 24 hours (determined by telemetry), it was resighted again at Mahuta on two occasions, 8 and 9 months later.

Most of our tagging/reobservation work with reef whitetip sharks was at Mahuta Reef in the Avatoru Lagoon area. In this limited area, measuring roughly 450 meters long, 120 meters wide (0.05 square kilometer), we tagged 75 individuals, of which 64 (85.3 percent) were resighted. Of these 64 individuals, only 8 were ever sighted beyond Mahuta, and of these 8 only 2 were sighted elsewhere. Most of these beyond-Mahuta sightings, however, were at sites relatively close (1-3 kilometers). Of the 1,106 total resightings of all tagged whitetips from all areas, only 2 (0.2 percent) represented a move of considerable distance—one Mahuta-tagged shark seen in Tiputa Pass (9 kilometers away) and one Tiputa-tagged shark seen at Mahuta.

A further indication of the stability of the Mahuta whitetip population came from counts of the tagged/untagged ratios during baiting sessions. At the end of the tagging period in December 1973, the Mahuta population was about 95 percent tagged. By January 1975, about 75 percent of the sharks were still tagged. In March 1976 an estimated 50 percent still carried visible tags, tag fragments, or tagging scars. By April 1977 this estimate had dropped to 40 percent.

Diel Behavior/Home Range. We determined shark activities for the full diel cycle by tracking telemetered individuals as continuously as possible throughout the day and night. Altogether, we conducted 17 successful, mostly multiday trackings—9 gray reef sharks, 5 reef whitetips, 2 blacktips, and 1 blackfin reef shark. All sharks tracked exhibited a basically nocturnal activity pattern, i.e., they were wider ranging and had greater rates of movement at night.

The gray reef shark, like the other species of *Carcharhinus,* appeared to swim continuously throughout the diel cycle. During the day, however, gray sharks typically swam slowly in groups (packs), milling about in one limited "core area" in a relatively deep part of their home range. At dusk they moved away from the core area and ranged widely, presumably foraging, over a variety of areas generally much shallower than the daytime core area. Tracking data suggested also that individuals were more dispersed at night, although this could not be confirmed by direct observation. If so, the gray shark pattern would be an example of the space-utilization behavior known as "refuging," as discussed by Hamilton and Watt (1970) and suggested for sharks by Barlow (1974).

Gray sharks from different area groups showed diel patterns that were fundamentally similar but different in detail. These routines were quite regular from day to day and, once determined, were quite predictable. For instance, the daytime area for Avatoru Lagoon grays was over the deeper edge of Mahuta Reef, whereas the nighttime areas included the shallower parts of Mahuta, the reefs bordering lagoon islets, and Avatoru Pass itself all the way to the ocean. In contrast, sharks from Tiputa Pass spent the days quite deep off the mouth of the pass, then moved through the pass into the lagoon in early evening. These sharks spent the night ranging over shallow lagoon reefs—the pass itself, and along the shallow ocean reef near the surf zone. For one Tiputa Pass individual tracked continuously for 72 hours, the home range (maximum polygon of plotted positions) was about 2.0 kilometers long, with an area of approximately 0.83 square kilometer.

The daily routines of gray reef sharks (and of blacktip sharks) were markedly influenced by the tidal cycle, at least in areas of strong tidal currents and water-clarity fluctuations. For example, central Tiputa Pass was usually devoid of gray sharks during the clear flood or high tides, but was regularly visited by these sharks just after the start of ebb tide. Telemetered individuals from beyond the mouth of the pass also made temporary movements into the pass at this time.

Reef whitetip sharks exhibited a distinctly nocturnal pattern, remaining inactive in a limited area by day, then ranging much beyond this at night. Typical daytime behavior of Mahuta whitetips was to rest in particular caves, sometimes coming out at slack tides or in response to attractive stimuli such as produced by spearfishing. At dusk these sharks departed their caves and ranged over relatively shallow reefs well beyond the limits of their daytime core area. At dawn, the sharks returned to Mahuta and entered their home caves. During the days Mahuta whitetips apparently stayed within the central Mahuta area of roughly 0.05 square kilometer, while at night they collectively ranged over an area of about 1.0 square kilometer.

A number of sand-floored, coral caves in the Mahuta area were utilized by whitetips as home caves, i.e., caves to which the same individuals would return for at least several days in succession. Home-cave data were obtained both from telemetry trackings and from daily diver examinations of these caves for tagged individuals. We found that a given shark usually used a particular cave daily for several days to several weeks. One individual was seen in the same cave regularly for three weeks, up until the time we ceased examining caves. When we looked into this cave 11 months later, the same shark was present. Sometimes a shark would switch home caves after several days of observation, but this behavior may have been an artifact in response to the diver.

Response to Feeding Stimuli. The increased activity exhibited by sharks at night suggests that most normal searching for food occurs then, but we were unable to witness natural nocturnal predation because of the difficulties of observing unbaited sharks after dark. Some natural feeding also takes place during the day, especially if a good opportunity arises. We witnessed a few instances of natural or seminatural predation, e.g., a blackfin shark chasing and capturing an uninjured surgeonfish, several whitetips seizing spear-wounded, free-swimming surgeonfish.

It is well known that sharks will readily respond during the daytime to opportunistic feeding stimuli such as fish odors and struggling sounds. Nearly every day we observed such behavior while spearfishing. As originally reported by Hobson (1963), the commonly observed species show distinct differences in this situation. Gray sharks usually approached rapidly and excitedly and were very adept at seizing exposed prey, apparently employing vision to orient their final attack. They would attack a struggling fish on a spear at any level in the water column but would not enter very far into coral caves. In contrast, reef whitetips were reluctant to swim very far off the bottom but would pursue prey deeply into caves and crevices. We suspected that in doing this they used mainly olfaction and/or electroreception.

Blackfin sharks and other reef *Carcharhinus* behaved more like gray sharks but seemed more cautious in final approach, possibly owing to the observer's presence. During interspecific competition for exposed bait, gray sharks were normally the most successful, but if bait was placed deep within the reef, only the whitetips (and nurse sharks) had a chance at it.

We conducted one controlled sound-playback experiment and made a variety of incidental observations of acoustic-attraction behavior. These results are published elsewhere (Nelson and Johnson, 1976). One significant observation involved a situation similar to that which undoubtedly occurs during natural predation. A large surgeonfish, which had just been seized by a whitetip, began struggling (vibrating) in the shark's jaws. This struggling immediately triggered a rapid, excited approach by several nearby whitetips, which were obviously trying to benefit from this feeding opportunity.

Social Behavior. Of the species we observed at Rangiroa, the gray reef shark was the most organized into groups, both as juveniles and adults. Blacktip sharks appeared to be at least loosely gregarious, based on our limited observations of this species off the Avatoru wharf. Blackfin reef sharks were predominantly solitary but were occasionally seen in loose groups of three or four. Silvertips were seen singly or in twos, but since they appeared in response to attractive stimuli, true social grouping could not be confirmed.

Except for the very few instances noted below, reef whitetip sharks did not socially group when swimming. When at rest, however, they showed a distinct preference for being near others—especially in caves, but also to a certain degree on the open bottom. On any given day their distribution among suitable home caves was clumped, i.e., most caves empty, a few with many sharks—and these favored caves occasionally changed.

Gray reef sharks formed true social groups, i.e., those maintained by biosocial attraction, not just fortuitous aggregation about attractive stimuli such as bait. Lone grays were sometimes seen, especially along the ocean reef, but most were in groups or packs of as many as 50 sharks. These packs were usually in the form of relatively polarized (parallel swimming) schools with inter-individual distances of from several to less than one-half body lengths. Packs of first-year juveniles (fig. 3) were usually in areas adjacent to, but shallower than, the areas of adult packs. In the central Mahuta area, the juvenile group could usually be seen from the surface in clear water. The larger grays maintained their daytime pack farther back into the lagoon in deeper, more turbid water where they could not be seen from the surface. We were able to free dive and intercept this pack if one of its members carried a telemetry transmitter.

In addition to grouping per se, gray sharks exhibited certain specific motor patterns such as follow-formations (close, single-file swimming), turn-backs, and circular milling. These patterns resembled some of those described by Myrberg and Gruber (1974) from a colony of captive bonnethead sharks, *Sphyrna tiburo.* Such behaviors were much rarer in reef whitetip sharks, but on one occasion a prolonged five-shark follow-formation was observed at Mahuta. The most frequent interaction involving swimming whitetips was the give-way, in which two individuals happened to approach on a collision course; then one (usually the smaller) gave way by altering course and sometimes accelerating away. When such behavior occurred between grays and white-tips, it was always the whitetip that gave way.

In general, gray reef sharks were bolder than the other species and appeared to be dominant over them in competitive situations. Several grays often competed intraspecifically for large pieces of bait, but such "fights" were decidely nonagonistic, i.e., no apparent threats or attacks directed towards competitors, just vigorous efforts to bite the bait itself.

Several observations were made of possible courtship or pair formation. In both blackfin reef sharks and reef whitetips a close-following behavior was seen in which the female led in a tail-up attitude, while the male followed closely, generally orienting its snout to the female's vent. In the blackfin shark, the lead shark was also seen to swim in a slow, sinuous manner, unusually close to the sand. The initial approach path of the following shark indicated that olfactory orientation was involved, possibly to a sex-attractant pheromone. These observations are detailed elsewhere (Johnson and Nelson, 1978) along with a description of copulation in blackfin sharks as related by several Tahitian witnesses.

FIG. 3. Gray reef sharks, *Carcharhinus amblyrhynchos.* Top: Adult female on ocean reef (diver in mobile cage in background); center: group of juveniles at Mahuta Reef (Avatoru Lagoon area); bottom: juvenile of about 1 meter total length. (Photos by R. Johnson; D. Mosher, center.)

FIG. 4. Sharks of Rangiroa. Above: Silvertip shark, *Carcharhinus albimarginatus.* Opposite, top: Blackfin reef shark (blacktip reef shark), *C. melanopterus;* center: blacktip shark, *C. limbatus;* bottom: great hammerhead shark, *Sphyrna mokarran.* (Photos by R. Johnson; R. McKenzie, opposite, center.)

Symbioses. Several species of symbiotic fishes associated with the reef sharks at Rangiroa. Both gray reef and whitetip sharks commonly carried remoras, *Echeneis naucrates.* Whitetips were occasionally accompanied by young yellow jacks, *Gnathanodon speciosus,* a fish whose juvenile-only piloting behavior has been previously described (Hobson, 1963b). These fish usually rode just in front of the shark's snout or close to the body farther posterior, and sometimes remained with the shark even when it rested in caves or on the open bottom. At such times we noticed them occasionally picking at the shark's skin, in a manner suggesting cleaning symbiosis. Several times we observed the cleaner wrasse, *Labroides dimidiatus,* servicing the body surface of a whitetip shark in a cave.

Diver-shark Interactions. For years, Rangiroa has been the site of much traditional native diving and spearfishing. In certain favored areas, e.g., Mahuta, Tiputa Pass, spearfishermen interact almost daily with sharks. Spearfishing provides an opportunistic feeding situation for the sharks, which regularly compete for wounded fish that break off spears. Sharks, especially grays, will also attack struggling fish on the spear, and the divers must work quickly to pull the fish in before this happens. If shark interference becomes

too great, divers sometimes fire spears at the sharks to drive them away. Thus, while human activity provides a feeding opportunity for these sharks, it provides also a reason for them to be shy of divers.

Certain species of sharks are regarded as dangerous by native divers and are treated accordingly. Several spearfishermen have been bitten by gray reef sharks, one by a blacktip. Reef whitetips, however, are regarded with little or no concern. Large lemon sharks are treated as quite dangerous, especially if wounded by being speared. During the expedition a recently captured gray reef shark attacked R. Johnson after it was released from the boat. He successfully held off the shark, receiving only a minor cut on his thumb. The shark then bit the boat and a nearby buoy.

In general, we found the reef sharks in the study area to be shy of divers, unless highly excited by feeding stimuli. This shyness might be due in part to previous experiences with native divers. In more remote areas rarely visited by divers, the sharks (especially grays) were noticeably bolder, at least initially. In general, blackfin and blacktip sharks were the most shy, while the whitetip was more indifferent to divers. The gray reef shark was more variable, depending on the situation, sometimes shy, sometimes bold. They also made occasional "investigative" approaches to divers in the absence of normal feeding stimuli, but this behavior was notably less in the study area than at some other locations, e.g., Enewetak, Marshall Islands.

We noticed a distinct habituation to divers in the Mahuta population of reef whitetip sharks. When we began tagging in late 1972, individuals were difficult to approach closely enough for tagging, even when baited. Toward the end of the main tagging/reobservation work one year later they were much easier to approach, some being tame enough to touch by hand without alarm. During the year's work at Mahuta these sharks had much exposure to divers—we made many dives close to individual sharks (in order to read tags), never harming or frightening them, except for the initial tag application.

Agonistic display of gray reef sharks toward divers was observed on a number of occasions. As described previously (Johnson and Nelson, 1973), this display can be released by rapid diver approach and under such circumstances is thought to represent defensive threat. It consists of laterally exaggerated swimming, sometimes with rolling or looping, accompanied by (1) lifting of the snout, (2) dropping of the pectoral fins, (3) arching of the back, and (4) lateral bending of the body. In at least several past incidents this display has prefaced rapid, direct attack on divers under circumstances suggesting an agonistic rather than a feeding motivation.

Evidence from the present study further supports a nonfeeding motivation for the display. We made observations during diver-shark interactions in feeding situations (e.g., shark approaching or circling bait) and in nonfeeding situations (e.g., shark making an "investigative" approach to a diver in the absence of bait). Results showed that rapid diver approach in nonfeeding situations was much more likely to release display than the same diver approach during feeding situations. We saw no unequivocal instance of display directed toward another shark, but it is logical to assume that this behavior does have some place in the animal's natural ethogram.

The precise function of the exaggerated-swimming display remains uncertain, and there have been various hypotheses advanced for its function and origin, including those of Barlow (1974) and of Johnson (1978). There is a popular belief that this display is used in territorial behavior, i.e., defense of an area against intruders, but actual support for this is scanty. The only real evidence comes from Enewetak—several cases of sharks approaching and displaying to stationary divers (McNair, 1975; Nelson, 1977b). During the present study, however, none of the instances of display or other observed behaviors could be considered evidence for territoriality.

REFERENCES

BAGNIS, RAYMOND; MAZELLIER, PHILIPPE; BENNET, JACK; and CHRISTIAN, ERWIN
1972. Fishes of Polynesia, 368 pp. illus. Editions du Pacifique, Papeete, Tahiti.

BARLOW, GEORGE W.
1974. Derivation of threat display in the gray reef shark. Mar. Behav. Physiol., vol. 3, pp. 71-81.

BROWN, THEO W.
1973. Sharks—the search for a repellent, 134 pp., illus. Angus & Robertson, Sydney.

COUSTEAU, JACQUES-YVES, and COUSTEAU, PHILIPPE
1970. The shark: Splendid savage of the sea, 277 pp., illus. Doubleday & Co., New York.

EIBL-EIBESFELDT, IRENAUS, and HASS, HANS
1959. Erfahrungen mit Haien. Zeitschr. Tierpsychol., vol. 16, pp. 733-746.

FERREL, DONALD W.; NELSON, DONALD R.; SCIARROTTA, TERRY C.; STANDORA, EDWARD A.; CARTER. HOWARD C.
1974. A multichannel ultrasonic biotelemetry system for monitoring marine animal behavior at sea. Trans. Instr. Soc. Amer., vol. 13, no. 2, pp. 120-131.

HAMILTON, WILLIAM J., and WATT, KENNETH E. F.
1970. Refuging. Ann. Rev. Ecol. Systemat., vol. 1, pp. 263-287.

HOBSON, EDMUND S.
1963a. Feeding behavior in three species of sharks. Pac. Sci., vol. 17, pp. 171-194.

HOBSON, EDMUND S.—continued

1963b. Notes on "piloting" behavior in young yellow jacks. Underwater Nat., vol. 1, no. 4, pp. 10-13.

JOHNSON, RICHARD H.

1978. Sharks of Polynesia, 170 pp., illus. Editions du Pacifique, Papeete, Tahiti.

JOHNSON, RICHARD H., and NELSON, DONALD R.

1973. Agonistic display in the gray reef shark, *Carcharhinus menisorrah,* and its relationship to attacks on man. Copeia, 1973, pp. 76-84.

——. Behavior of the gray reef shark at Rangiroa, French Polynesia. (In prep.).

1978. Copulation and possible olfaction-mediated pair formation in two species of carcharhinid sharks. Copeia, 1978, pp. 539-542.

LIMBAUGH, CONRAD

1963. Field notes on sharks. Pp. 64-69 *in* "Sharks and Survival," P. W. Gilbert, ed. D. C. Heath & Co., Boston.

MCNAIR, RHETT

1975. Sharks I have known. Skin Diver Mag., vol. 24, pp. 52-57.

MYRBERG, ARTHUR A., JR.; HA, SAMUEL J.; WALEWSKI, S.; and BANBURY, J.

1972. Effectiveness of acoustic signals in attracting epipelagic sharks to an underwater sound source. Bull. Mar. Sci., vol. 22, pp. 926-949.

MYRBERG, ARTHUR A., JR.; GORDON, CHARLES R.; and KLIMLEY, A. PETER

1976. Attraction of free ranging sharks by low frequency sound, with comments on its biological significance. Pp. 205-228 *in* "Sound Reception in Fish," A. Schuijf and A. D. Hawkins, eds., Elsevier, Amsterdam.

MYRBERG, ARTHUR A., JR., and GRUBER, SAMUEL H.

1974. The behavior of the bonnethead shark, *Sphyrna tiburo.* Copeia, 1974, pp. 358-374.

NELSON, DONALD R.

1974. Ultrasonic telemetry of shark behavior. Naval Res. Rev., vol. 27, no. 12, pp. 1-21.

1977a. On the field study of shark behavior. Amer. Zool., vol. 17, pp. 501-507.

1977b. Home range and food habits of Pacific reef sharks. *In* Annual Report FY 1976, Mid-Pacific Marine Laboratory, Enewetak, Marshall Islands.

NELSON, DONALD R., and JOHNSON, RICHARD H.

1970a. Diel activity rhythms in the nocturnal, bottom-dwelling sharks, *Heterodontus francisci* and *Cephaloscyllium ventriosum.* Copeia, 1970, pp. 732-739.

1970b. Acoustic studies on sharks, Rangiroa Atoll, July 1969. (Unpublished Technical Report No. 2, Office of Naval Research, 16 pp.).

1972. Acoustic attraction of Pacific reef sharks: effect of pulse intermittency and variability. Comp. Biochem. Physiol., vol. 42A, pp. 85-96.

1976. Some recent observations on acoustic attraction of Pacific reef sharks. Pp. 229-239 *in* "Sound Reception in Fish," A. Schuijf and A. D. Hawkins, eds., Elsevier, Amsterdam.

NELSON, DONALD R., and JOHNSON, RICHARD H.—continued

_____. Behavior of the reef whitetip shark at Rangiroa, French Polynesia. (In prep.)

RANDALL, JOHN E.

1973. Tahitian fish names and a preliminary checklist of the fishes of the Society Islands. Occ. Pap., B. P. Bishop Mus., vol. 24, no. 11, pp. 167-214.

1977. Contribution to the biology of the whitetip reef shark *(Triaenodon obesus).* Pacific Science, vol. 31, pp. 143-164.

RANDALL, JOHN E., and HELFMAN, GENE S.

1973. Attacks on humans by the blacktip reef shark *(Carcharhinus melanopterus).* Pac. Sci., vol. 27, pp. 226-238.

WASS, RICHARD C.

1971. A comparative study of the life history, distribution, and ecology of the sandbar shark and the gray reef shark in Hawaii, 219 pp., illus. Ph.D. thesis, University of Hawaii.

DONALD R. NELSON
RICHARD H. JOHNSON

Volcanic-Gas and Petrologic Investigations of Galápagos Islands Calderas

Principal Investigator: Bert E. Nordlie, Iowa State University, Ames, Iowa.

Grant No. 1020: For a study of volcanic gas and petrology of Galápagos Islands calderas.

The present grant made possible a continuation during the summer of 1972 of studies of active volcanoes of the western Galápagos Islands begun two seasons before. As principal investigator of the project I was at that time chief scientist of the Laboratory of Experimental Petrology and associate professor of the Department of Geosciences at the University of Arizona. Involved also in the research were Wayne E. Colony, John R. Delaney, Terrence M. Gerlach, and Edmund Mathez, all graduate students in the Department of Geosciences.

Workers prior to 1956 gave only passing attention to the two western islands of the Galápagos. In 1956, Banfield et al. reported on a reconnaissance of Isabela Island and gave a general summary of the volcanoes. McBirney and Williams (1969) included some brief examinations of certain areas of the two western islands in their work and gave a summary of the existing knowledge of the volcanoes. Simkin and Howard (1970) described the 1968 caldera collapse in Fernandina, and Simkin (1972) made comparisons between the shapes of the western volcanoes and guyots.

Although the Galápagos have been characterized as one of the most active volcanic areas in the world (Williams and McBirney, 1968), very little was known about the most active area in the Galápagos, the islands of Isabela and Fernandina. Six active volcanoes form these islands; our research was carried out on five of the volcanoes: Cerro Azul, Wolf, Fernandina, Alcedo, and Sierra Negra. The main objectives of the research included: (1) characterization of the geology, including similarities and differences, (2) determination of histories of development and the mechanism of formation of calderas, (3) determination of the petrology of the basalts, (4) examination of the large-scale structures associated with the volcanoes. Our long-standing interest in volcanic gases led to studies of two fumarole areas: Volcán Azufre in the Sierra Negra caldera and the "geyser" of Volcán Alcedo.

The extremely difficult logistics of field research required that only key areas be studied in detail. Traverses to volcano summits provided information

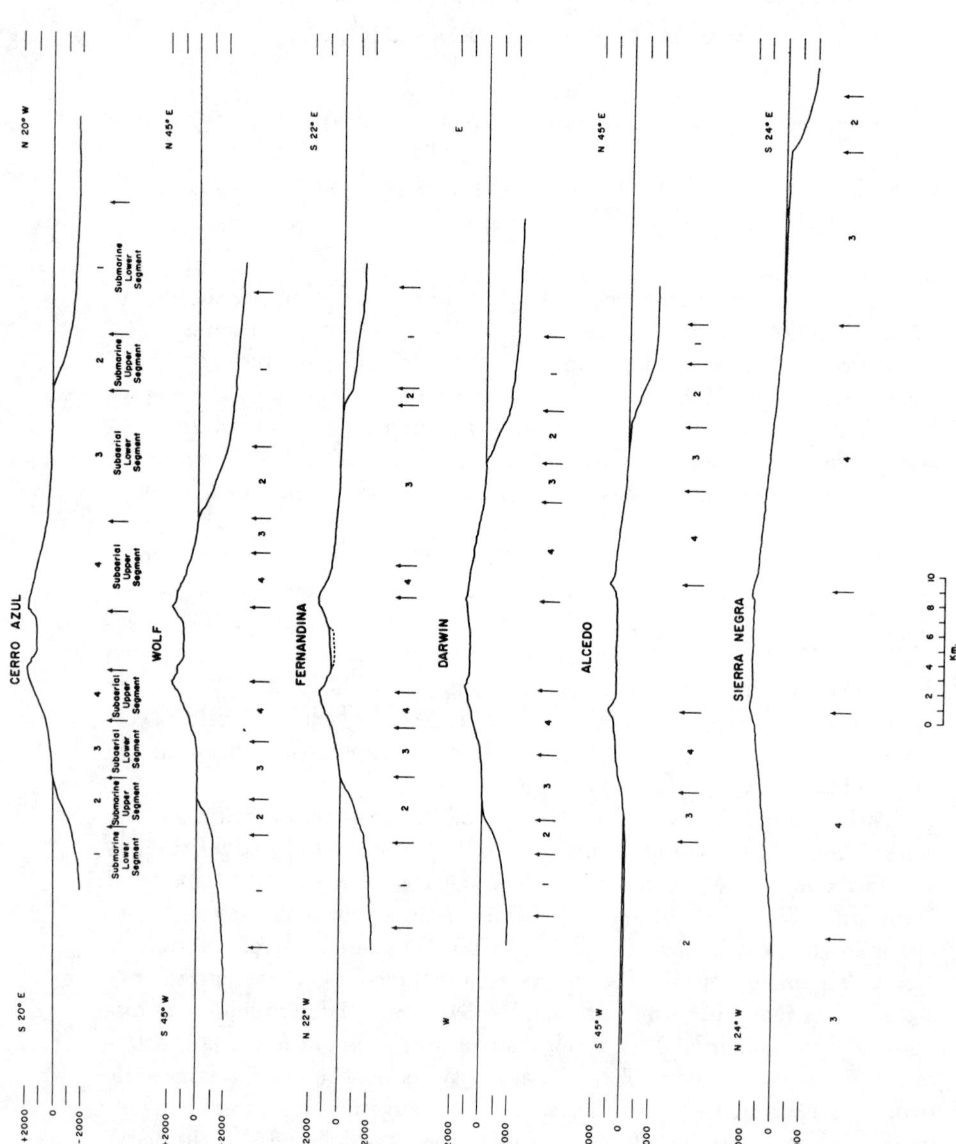
CERRO AZUL
S 20° E
N 20° W
Submarine Lower Segment
Submarine Upper Segment
Subaerial Lower Segment
Subaerial Upper Segment
WOLF
S 45° W
N 45° E
FERNANDINA
N 22° W
S 22° E
DARWIN
W
E
ALCEDO
S 45° W
N 45° E
SIERRA NEGRA
N 24° W
S 24° E
+2000
0
-2000
0 2 4 6 8 10
Km.
No vertical exaggeration

on general features. Detailed mapping of recent eruption areas and of three calderas provided in-depth information. Mapping was done on enlarged aerial photographs. Samples were obtained from all surface flows traversed and detailed sampling and section measuring were accomplished on caldera walls. Fumarole and geyser studies involved detailed mapping, temperature measurements, semiquantitative gas analyses and sampling for laboratory analysis.

Subsequent laboratory work included: (1) petrographic and chemical analyses of the basalts and fumarole deposits, (2) chemical analyses of waters and gases, (3) K-Ar dating of selected basalt samples, (4) Sr isotope and trace element analyses of basalts, (5) construction of diagrams showing volcano profiles, caldera features, and large scale structures, using aerial photographs and U. S. Hydrographic Office charts.

Brief summaries of the results of our investigations are presented here. The reader is referred to the following publications for more details: Nordlie (1973), Delaney et al. (1973), Nordlie and Colony (1973), Colony and Nordlie (1973).

Morphology and Structure of the Western Galápagos Volcanoes

All six volcanoes exhibit the same large-scale morphology in profile. They rest on the sea floor, the general depth of which is 2,400 to 3,400 meters below sea level. Each volcano has four distinct slope segments, which extend from the sea floor to the volcano rim. The slope segments are separated by three very short transitions or slope elements (fig. 1).

Submarine Lower Segment (Submarine Base). This segment is the initial rise of a volcano from the sea floor at the outer limits of its flanks. The angle is less than 10° from horizontal, and the length is usually the greatest of the four segments.

Submarine Upper Segment. This segment is much shorter than the submarine lower segment and has a high angle, ranging between 20° and 26°. The segment ends precisely at sea level for the younger volcanoes and ends less than 200 meters below sea level on parts of the older volcanoes.

FIG. 1. Profiles of the western Galápagos volcanoes. These profiles are oriented approximately perpendicular to dominant fissure zones connecting volcanoes. Slope-segment limits are indicated by arrows and identifying names are given for Cerro Azul; segments for other volcanoes are given by numbers. The submarine segments are absent where coalescence of adjacent volcanoes has occurred.

Subaerial Lower Segment. This segment begins at sea level and extends inland part way up the visible flank of the volcano. The angle is less than 10°; the length varies with the particular volcano and with the position on a volcano.

Subaerial Upper Segment. This segment extends from the subaerial lower segment to the top of the volcano. The angle is high and the length is relatively short. Both the angle and length are important indicators of the evolutionary stage of the volcano.

Each volcano has a flat top in profile. The caldera covers most of the summit area, although a wide flat rim surrounds the caldera on the younger volcanoes.

There are variations on the scheme described above that provide evidence for the mechanisms by which the volcanoes developed. Profiles were drawn to scale along many orientations through the center of each volcano. Differences in the profiles of an individual volcano cannot be explained by erosion; they are constructional features. Also, major eruption centers are centrally located or are concentrically arranged around the calderas so that constructions on the different profiles have similar source areas near the summit.

The subaerial upper segment is a sensitive indicator of the differences between over-all volcano profiles. Length and angle data for this segment from several profiles for a volcano can be plotted to show that these parameters change by downslope lengthening. As additional lava flows down the volcano from the summit the subaerial upper segment lengthens and assumes a lower angle. More mature slopes have lower angles and longer lengths due to more lava accumulation along that direction. More mature slopes had the steeper angles and shorter lengths of less mature slopes at an earlier time; conversely, less mature slopes will become more mature as future eruptions add lava along these directions.

Each volcano has a limited range of profile characteristics, most easily shown by examining the variations in the subaerial upper segment. Comparison shows that the range of characteristics for one volcano differs from the range for another volcano. For example, the subaerial upper segment for Volcán Wolf is short (4.5–6.5 kilometers) and has a high angle (17°–27°) in all directions from the volcano center; conversely, this segment is long (7–11 kilometers) and has a low angle (8°–16°) in all directions on Volcán Alcedo. The ranges in these parameters for the two volcanoes do not overlap. Since accumulation of lava causes greater slope maturity (flattening and lengthening) each volcano will develop more mature profiles in all directions as its age increases. The long, low angle slopes of Alcedo are interpreted as indicating its greater age in comparison with Volcán Wolf. By comparing all six volcanoes their relative ages, based upon profile maturity, can be determined. Figure 1 has been arranged in this age sequence, which is, from youngest to oldest: Cerro Azul, Wolf, Fernandina, Darwin, Alcedo, and Sierra Negra. Other evidence to be discussed supports this age sequence.

The submarine upper segment has a remarkably constant angle, and the upper limit is so closely related to sea level that a genetic relationship seems required. It is proposed that this segment is simply the submarine extension of subaerial flows which entered the sea. A more rapid cooling caused the formation of a steeper slope; the different "angle of repose" is a function of the difference in interface with the lava (air versus water).

The submarine lower segment varies in angle and in depth to its upper limit. A comparison of all profiles reveals a distinct correlation: as the depth to the upper limit of the segment increases, the horizontal distance to the upper limit from the caldera center decreases, and the segment angle increases. An important result of this correlation is that if the submarine lower segment in any direction is extrapolated to the center of the volcano, it almost always reaches an elevation of about 1,000 meters above sea level.

The submarine lower segment is interpreted as being the early, dominantly submarine construction of the volcano. Originally, this *submarine base* extended to the central portion of the volcano; later, other slope segments were superimposed upon it. Figure 2 shows how the submarine base is overridden. The superimposed profiles of this figure show stages of growth with the inner profile indicating the volcano morphology when it was less mature.

Figure 2 shows how profiles with differing maturities appear in relation to one another as parts of a building mechanism. The subaerial segments are modified by lava addition such that their angles decrease and their lengths increase with time. Apparently, little accumulation occurs high on the slopes; subaerial accumulation is at low elevations. Significantly, on the average, flows reach the sea and deposit most of their material below sea level. The submarine volume of accumulated material is much greater than the subaerial volume.

Comparing the three parts of figure 2 shows the influence of the type of submarine bases upon which building occurs. Although the building process is the same in both cases a deep, high-angle base leads to a different over-all morphology than a shoal, low-angle base. With less submarine filling required on a shoal, low-angle base, the volcano is able to build horizontally more rapidly with corresponding influences on the subaerial segment parameters.

Three major influences on the large-scale morphology can be defined from profile comparisons. First, the nature of the early-formed submarine base will

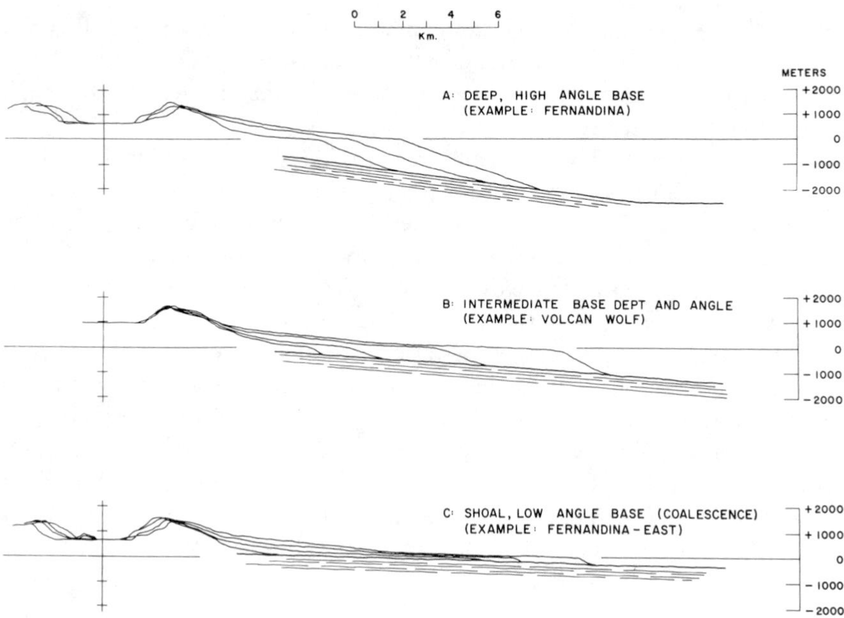

FIG. 2. Superimposed half-profiles having the same submarine base (submarine lower segment) parameters, except for the depth to the upper limit. Caldera centers are aligned. The mechanism of volcano growth can be seen in each part of the figure and shows that lava flows move far down the volcano to the subaerial lower and submarine segments; increasing profile maturity flattens the subaerial profile. The influence of the early-formed submarine base can be seen by comparing parts A, B, and C.

exert a strong influence on the parameters of the other slope segments throughout much of the history of the volcano. Second, on a single volcano, differing slope maturities (amounts of building) can be determined along different profile directions. Third, gross differences in relative volcano ages affect profile parameters; this causes the above variations to span different ranges of values. The discussion indicates that each volcano formerly had a morphology much like the volcano that precedes it in the age sequence.

The submarine slope segments cover the depth range of the large topographic swell known as the "Galápagos Platform." Because of this, the Galápagos Platform is considered to be volcanogenic. For the most part, the Galápagos Platform must be formed by submarine flows deposited early in the history of each volcano.

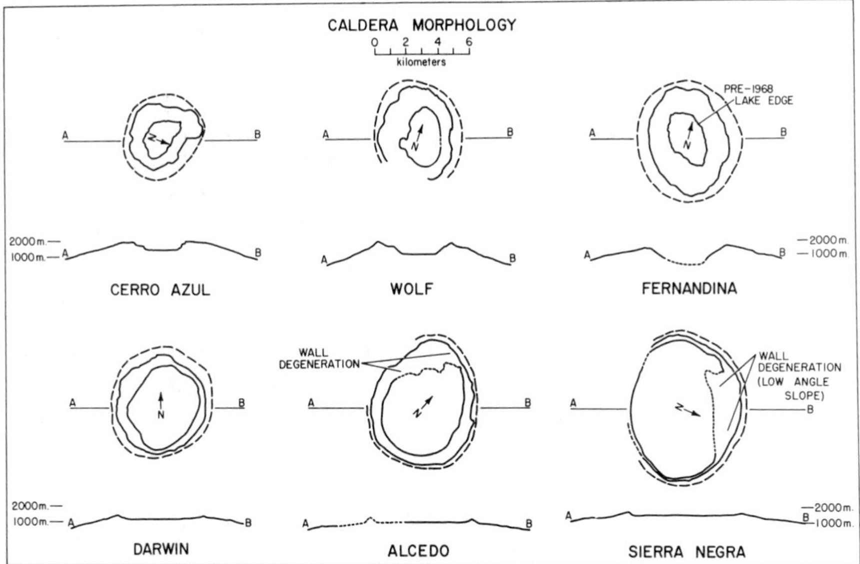

FIG. 3. Plan shows outlines of lowermost floors, edges of rims, and upper limits of subaerial upper segments (dashed). Depths, diameters, and directions of elongation are also shown. Volcanoes are arranged in the order of their relative ages as indicated by profiles and also suggested by caldera characteristics. Note gradations in the following features: (1) depth, (2) diameter, (3) circularity, (4) elevation, (5) loss of subaerial upper segment, and (6) loss of "flat" crown around caldera (distance between dashed contour and edge-of-rim outline).

The broad, flat tops of the volcanoes are, for the most part, calderas; their plan views and profiles are shown in figure 3. These are arranged in the age sequence inferred from the profile analysis; this sequence is in agreement with variations in caldera features and is further delineated by them. Within the sequence, the calderas fall into two distinct groups: the first includes Cerro Azul, Volcán Wolf, and Fernandina; the second comprises the other three.

The noteworthy features which change sequentially from Cerro Azul through Sierra Negra are:

1. Rim diameters increase from 3 to 4 kilometers at Cerro Azul to 9 kilometers at Sierra Negra. Floor diameters increase from 1 to 2 kilometers to more than 8 kilometers.

2. Caldera depths depend upon where measurements are made, but Cerro Azul, Wolf, and Fernandina are quite deep, and the last three are much shallower.

3. The maximum elevations of the first three volcanoes are the greatest; those of the second group are as much as 630 meters lower. This is a particularly significant distinction in that it is a result of the way in which the calderas are formed.

4. Plan views of maximum rim-elevation contours are all roughly circular. Caldera-rim outlines grade from the considerably elongated, irregular shape of Cerro Azul to nearly circular shapes for Darwin, Alcedo, and Sierra Negra. The trend in circularity is even more notable in the outline of the caldera floors.

5. Benches on the walls (evidence of incomplete collapse) are more common and complex in the first group than in the second. At least five benches are present in Cerro Azul; several benches are present in Wolf and Fernandina. One or two benches are clearly visible in Darwin and Alcedo. Sierra Negra contains no well-defined benches.

6. The lowermost floors of Cerro Azul, Wolf, and Fernandina are covered by recent volcanic deposits so that no large structural features are visible. In contrast, the older floor covers of both Alcedo and Sierra Negra indicate differential movement of parts of their floors. The western floor of Sierra Negra contains an unusual, north-trending, sinuous ridge, which may indicate a rotation of part of the floor.

Compared with other volcanoes, those of the Galápagos Islands have a greater tendency to form a flat crown around the caldera; this is best shown on the younger three, where the rim areas are almost level and several hundred meters wide. Sierra Negra and Alcedo, and to some extent Darwin, drop off quickly into the caldera from the maximum elevation of the rim, indicating that the enlarging of the caldera has consumed the flat crown.

An outstanding feature of the younger volcanoes is the system of fissures radiating from the central caldera. These fissures are marked by lines of parasitic cones on the volcano slopes and are the sources of small flank eruptions. This radial pattern is clearly visible in aerial photographs, and many were examined in the field. Sierra Negra has linear groupings of fissures and cones which are essentially normal to the caldera on the west and northeast; however, a well-developed radial pattern is not visible. A radial pattern is also not distinguishable on Alcedo.

There is a distinct lower limit to the surficial expression of the radial fissures on the younger volcanoes. This termination of fissures corresponds closely with the change from the subaerial upper segment to the subaerial lower segment. The restriction of the radial fissures to the subaerial upper segment is one of the most significant features displayed by them.

Aerial photographs show that there is a significant increase in the concentration of cones that dot the volcano slopes along fissure lines connecting the volcano centers. Unlike the radial fissures, these linking fissure zones extend below the subaerial upper segment to the seashore or through the areas between volcanoes on Isabela.

These linking fissures roughly parallel the long dimensions of the calderas; this coincidence is well developed on Cerro Azul, Wolf, and Fernandina. Most of the fissures produced limited flows; some, however, have been the sources of extensive flows, such as that between Cerro Azul and Sierra Negra, which spans the island from north to south.

Another type of fissure pattern has a circumferential orientation with respect to the caldera. These fissures are located at the volcano summit, in close proximity to the caldera, and are the loci of numerous small cones. They are the major sources of the large flows which have covered the volcano slopes. Circumferential fissures are visible in classic form in Cerro Azul, Wolf, and Fernandina. Up to four concentric sets of fissures occur in some places, with the outermost being about two kilometers from the caldera rim. In other places only a single fissure set is visible.

On Cerro Azul, Wolf, and Fernandina the fissures linking the volcanoes and extending up to the calderas coalesce with the circumferential fissures. The general arrangement is reminiscent of the foliation around the "eye" in an augen gneiss. The circumferential fissures parallel the shape of the caldera around both sides. Then, as they approach either end of the elongated caldera, they change from rim parallelism and coalesce into a single fissure zone coincident with the direction of the linking fissure zones.

On the older volcanoes (Alcedo and Sierra Negra) the circumferential pattern appears to have degenerated into a broad band of fissures and cones bending around the caldera. Here the linking fissure zone is dominant across the volcano summit and a circumferential pattern is no longer well defined.

Darwin suggested that there are two major directions of alignment of the Galápagos Islands. Banfield et al. (1956) suggested that these directions correspond to larger, major fissure directions and that the "deeper vents are controlled by fissure intersections." Intersecting Darwinian trends were identified for Wolf, Darwin, and Alcedo. The present work supports this earlier work and provides evidence for additional lineaments, which cross near the centers of Cerro Azul, Sierra Negra, and Fernandina. In addition, one lineament is defined as "dominant" with the other being "subordinate" at each volcano.

Dominant lineaments are expressed by (1) orientation of the coalescence of circumferential and linking fissure zones, (2) elongation of the caldera, and

(3) abundance of recent eruption centers on the volcano flanks, extending below the subaerial upper segment. These lineaments are designated as dominant because of their influence on the morphology and structural features of the volcanoes. On Wolf, Darwin, and Alcedo the dominant lineaments correspond with previously proposed Darwinian trends with a north-northwest orientation. The dominant lineament for Cerro Azul and Sierra Negra passes through both volcanoes in an east-northeast direction.

Subordinate lineaments are much less obvious. They are inferred from minor fracture zones and localized eruption sites, as well as by the alignment of the volcanoes. Two of the subordinate lineaments are newly proposed Darwinian trends and pass through Cerro Azul and Sierra Negra.

The dominant and subordinate lineaments form a grid, and the newly defined lineaments extend this grid to the west. The six volcanoes are located at the junction of a dominant lineament with a subordinate one. Apparently, either lineament direction in the grid can be dominant and the major features of the volcano will be oriented accordingly. A single lineament can be dominant for one volcano and subordinate for another; this is true for the lineament that passes through Fernandina (dominant) and Sierra Negra (subordinate). Not all lineament junctions are presently the loci of a volcano. This may be because both lineaments have subordinate characteristics at the junction, and the more limited activity associated with both lineaments does not allow a major volcanic center to develop.

Model for the Origin of the Western Galápagos Volcanoes

The western Galápagos Islands provide a unique opportunity to study the development of basaltic volcanoes, especially the mechanisms by which calderas form. The six volcanoes are closely related in space and time and all are still very active. They have marked similarities, but gradational differences arrange them in a sequence such that an order by age is implied. The previous descriptions give evidence for five distinct stages of development. All the

---

FIG. 4. Development of the western Galápagos volcanoes. Figure sequence summarizes the proposed model for the development of the western Galápagos volcanoes. The true profiles of the volcanoes were used in those parts which correspond to the present state of each volcano. Building by flows is based upon the earlier figure. Random-dashed dikes indicate a radial orientation; black-lined dikes indicate a circumferential orientation. Note especially the loss of the subaerial upper segment portion of the volcano and the elevation decrease with increasing age and caldera diameter.

SUBMARINE BASE CONSTRUCTION

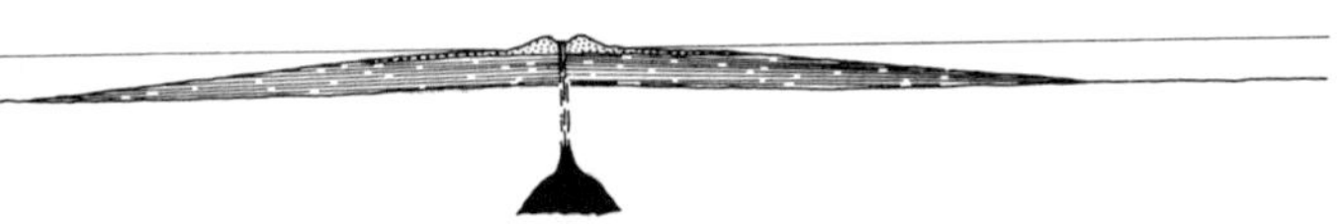

SUBAERIAL CONSTRUCTION

TUMESCENCE: EARLY

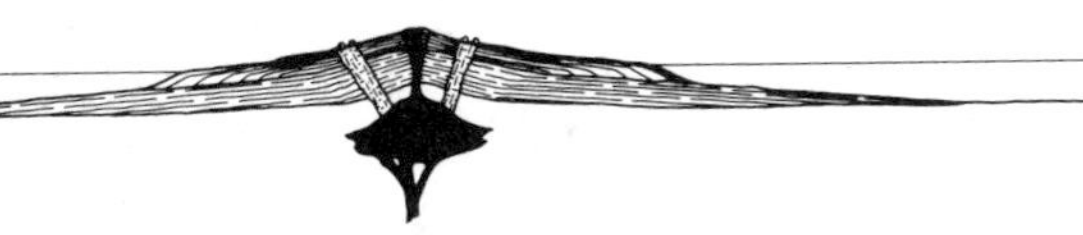

CALDERA DEVELOPMENT: EARLY
CERRO AZUL

CALDERA DEVELOPMENT
WOLF, FERNANDINA

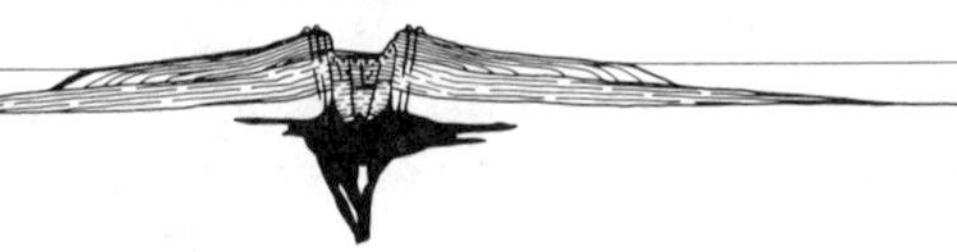

MORPHOLOGICAL DECLINE
DARWIN

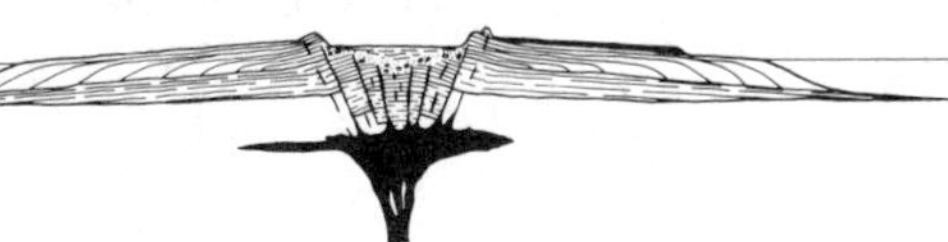

MORPHOLOGICAL DECLINE
ALCEDO, SIERRA NEGRA

volcanoes have passed through the first three stages and they are now in various parts of the fourth and fifth stages. Figure 4 summarizes these stages and has been drawn using the actual profiles where they apply. The figure should be correlated with the following discussion.

Initially, a volcanic center develops at the junction of two major fissure zones (Darwinian trends). The earliest growth of the volcano results from a series of submarine flows that cover a wide area of the sea floor. A gently sloped submarine shield is formed, part of which presently forms the submarine lower segment of a volcano. Submarine valleys and ridges exist, and this irregular topography influences the profiles developed during later building; i.e., at a given distance from the volcanic center the submarine base is at different depths in different directions. Submarine base construction continues until the top of the growing volcano extends a few hundred meters above sea level.

Once subaerial flows can exist, subaerial construction continues rapidly. Flows are expelled from a central eruption area and the altitude of the volcano reaches to some 1,000 meters. Many flows reach the sea, enlarging the island, and then extend for some distance below sea level. The accelerated cooling of lavas in the sea forms the submarine upper slope; subaerial construction forms the subaerial lower segment, such that the visible profile is that of a low angle shield. Radial and circumferential fracturing are absent or unimportant during this period. Most eruptions are from a limited central vent area, although eruptions may occur along the throughgoing fissure zones that link the volcanoes.

The third stage is characterized by tumescence or swelling of the upper part of the volcano. Magma may migrate upward into the building conical form of the volcanic pile and lift the upper portion of the developing shield. Regardless of the precise cause of tumescence, the major characteristics of tumescence are the development of radial fissures because of the expansion and a steepening of the upper slopes of the volcano. This steepening causes the formation of the subaerial upper segment, which eventually may be many degrees steeper than the subaerial lower segment. Eruptions from the central vent area, as well as from the radial fissures, build the volcano as tumescence continues.

The filling of the radial fissures by dikes aids in the expansion and ultimately supports the swollen volcano. This type of fissure filling would tend to create a self-supporting dome, which could retain its expanded form, even after magma withdrawal. The magnitude of the tumescence required to form present-day profiles and the number of dike-filled radial fissures needed can be calculated. Field observations show that the required number of dikes do exist on the younger volcanoes; the yearly rate of tumescence is well within expected amounts.

At the top of the volcano, tumescence is expressed by a spreading apart of the generally parallel fissures of the throughgoing "dominant" linking fissure zone around the central eruption area. This forms the first incipient circumferential fissures. Successive cycles of tumescence, radial fracturing and dike filling, and magma withdrawal eventually create a dome that is under compression over-all but which has a central portion that is unsupported and under tension. Ultimately, this central portion will collapse; this sets the stage for caldera development.

Tumescence grades into and initiates the following stage in which collapse creates a caldera. The most notable feature of caldera development is the formation of circumferential fractures ringing the caldera. Initial collapse may be controlled by the spreading linking fissures at the summit and an elongate, or grabenlike, depression may be formed. As tumescence continues collapse will increase and the unsupported central portion of the dome will form its own circumferential fissures along lines of tension.

Eruptions from the radial fissures will continue, but they would decrease in importance as a transition of activity to the circumferential fissures takes place. The tensional nature of the circumferential fissures favors the localization of eruptions along them. Once they are well developed and circumferential fissures can release magmatic pressure more readily, radial fracturing by tumescence decreases in importance. Radial fissures become less distinct as they are covered by flows from the circumferential fissures near the summit. As radial diking ceases the elevation increase caused by tumescence ceases and the volcano has reached its maximum height.

The caldera stage involves maximum caldera depth, maximum volcano height, maximum tumescence and formation of the subaerial upper segment, and a transition from radial to circumferential fracturing. During the next stage these morphological extremes become subdued. During this stage the swollen upper portion of the volcano is largely consumed by caldera collapse along circumferential fissures. As the rim is consumed, the elevation of the volcano decreases. Collapse and lava filling decrease the caldera depth. The morphology exhibited by the younger volcanoes of the western islands evolves to that of the older volcanoes, Alcedo and Sierra Negra.

Collapse will become less important as the swollen dome becomes consumed. With the formation of new circumferential fissures decreased, the influence of the linking fissure zone which crosses the volcano may become more important. As on Sierra Negra, a wide complex fissure zone crosses the volcano; although it bends around the caldera, taking advantage of those circumferential fissures that are present, the linking fissures crossing the entire volcano are well expressed.

As a final step in the morphological decline the central caldera may become obliterated by filling and cone formation within the crater. As is the case for the older Galápagos Islands, a gentle shield profile dotted by many scoria cones on the slopes and the summit plateau will represent the end result of this process.

Studies of Two Fumarole Areas

Volcán Azufre, located in the Sierra Negra caldera, is the most active fumarolic area in the Galápagos Islands. Large areas are covered with nearly 1 meter of deposits, and active vents are depositing crystalline sulphur and are pervasively leaching and altering the basalt talus on which the fumaroles are located. Cones and ridges of crystalline sulphur are built over the vents at temperatures below 113°C.; primary sulphur deposition at higher temperatures was not observed.

Small pockets of liquid sulphur were observed near a few vents, and sulphur stalactites occur within some of the cones. This liquid is formed by the melting of sublimated deposits. Several sulphur flows were found, with the largest measuring 225 meters in length. The characteristics of the flows indicate that they are a recurring phenomenon at Azufre. Sand cones formed by sand-fountaining "sand pots" occur over high-temperature vents (175-235°C.), but liquid sulphur is notably deficient in these sand deposits.

Field analyses of the gases show that they contain a large percentage of gases other than water and air; this is largely due to the dry climate and the collecting technique. C/S and SO_2/H_2S values indicate that the gases are closely related to a magmatic source. Thermal gradients show that solid sulphur could be stable only to very shallow depths and that the vaporization temperature of sulphur may be reached at depths of several meters.

Equilibrium calculations were used to estimate the importance of various sulphur-depositing mechanisms. The gases are not oxidized and may represent a partially quenched, high-temperature composition. Below 170°C. sulphur could be deposited from SO_2, H_2S, and sulphur gas. Oxidizing reactions will cause sulphur deposition once the gases contact the atmosphere. In the light of the field data, the oxidizing reactions prove to be the dominant and controlling mechanism for sulphur deposition; condensation of liquid sulphur from the gases is, at best, a minor process.

Liquid sulphur, including the sulphur flows, is apparently formed by melting of the crystalline deposits during fluctuations in the thermal gradient. A cyclic sulphur budget is suggested, and the presence of liquid sulphur at greater depths is considered probable.

A water fountain and three associated pools are perched on the wall of the Volcán Alcedo caldera, at the end of a line of active fumaroles. In July 1970, the lower basin was dry and the overflow pool was partially filled; the fountain pool was nearly full and was at the boiling temperature. Gases forcefully pumped from a vent caused a continuous fountaining and abundant steam. Opal shoreline deposits and "mushrooms" mark former maximum water levels, during which the overflow pool level is controlled by a spillway to the lower basin. A levee between the fountain and overflow pools causes their separation when the water level drops. Reports show that the pools were full in August 1968, became completely dry by October 1970, and partially refilled in 1971. Throughout the cycle, sulphurous steam flowed from the vent.

The water chemistry of the fountain and overflow pools shows an increase in dissolved constituents in the latter; both are high in boron. Calculations indicate that the water of the overflow pool is not in equilibrium with its deposits but is equilibrated with the atmosphere. The fountain pool shows the opposite conditions. Silica content and the location of geyserite deposits indicate that opal saturation occurs as the water cools and circulates through the overflow pool.

Strata in the levee show cycles of mud, opal, and sand deposition, which correspond to periods of maximum filling, partial filling, and dryness, respectively. Subaerial deposition of the sand is shown by its high physical maturity (rounding and frosting) and lack of chemical alteration. Sand fountaining and the formation of a sand cone, associated with a high-pressure fumarole, were observed at another area in the Galápagos. The physical nature of this sand is nearly identical to that of the levee around the Alcedo vent. The same process is proposed for the formation of the levee deposits; this subaerially formed cone is modified during periods of pool filling.

A turbulent gas flow velocity of about 6 meters per second would account for the position and size of the levee sand grains. A very small driving force at depth would be required. Gas analyses from fumaroles north of the fountain have a relatively high magmatic component and favor the stability of magnetite. A similar gas, with periods of slight oxidation, would be compatible with the chemistry of the levee sand. The source of water in the pools is largely meteoric; the fountain and overflow pools depend more upon subsurface flow, while the lower basin receives surface water from the caldera wall.

REFERENCES

BANFIELD, ARMINE F.; BEHRE, CHARLES H.; and ST. CLAIR, D.
1956. Geology of Isabela (Albemarle) Island, Archipélago de Colón (Galápagos). Geol. Soc. Amer. Bull., vol. 67, pp. 215-234.

COLONY, WAYNE E., and NORDLIE, BERT E.
1973. Liquid sulfur on Volcán Azufre, Galápagos Islands. Econ. Geol., vol. 68, no. 3, pp. 371-380.

DELANEY, JOHN R.; COLONY, WAYNE E.; GERLACH, TERRENCE M.; and NORDLIE, BERT E.
1973. Geology of the Volcán Chico area on Sierra Negra Volcano, Galápagos Islands. Geol. Soc. Amer. Bull., vol. 84, pp. 2455-2470.

MCBIRNEY, ALEXANDER R., and WILLIAMS, HOWEL
1969. Geology and petrology of the Galápagos Islands. Geol. Soc. Amer. Mem. 118, 197 pp.

NORDLIE, BERT E.
1973. Morphology and structure of the western Galápagos volcanoes and a model for their origin. Geol. Soc. Amer. Bull., vol. 84, pp. 2931-2956.

NORDLIE, BERT E., and COLONY, WAYNE E.
1973. Fumarole with periodic water fountaining, Volcán Alcedo, Galápagos Islands. Geol. Soc. Amer. Bull., vol. 84, pp. 1709-1720.

SIMKIN, TOM
1972. Origin of some flat-topped volcanoes and guyots. Pp. 183-193 *in* "Studies in Earth and Space Sciences," R. Shagam et al., eds. Geol. Soc. Amer. Mem. 132.

SIMKIN, TOM, and HOWARD, KEITH A.
1970. Caldera collapse in the Galápagos Islands, 1968. Science, vol. 169, pp. 429-437.

WILLIAMS, HOWEL, and MCBIRNEY, ALEXANDER R.
1968. An investigation of volcanic depressions, pt. 1: Geologic and geophysical features of calderas, 87 pp. Progress report, NASA Manned Spacecraft Center, Houston, Texas.

BERT E. NORDLIE

The Tlapanec Indians of Tlacoapa, Guerrero, Mexico

Principal Investigators: Marion Oettinger, Jr., and Patricia Amanda Parsons, Cornell University, Ithaca, New York.

Grant No. 958: For an ethnographic study of the Tlapanec Indians of Tlacoapa, Mexico.

The approximately 50,000 Tlapanec Indians of the State of Guerrero are among the most enigmatic groups in Mexico. Geographical isolation and a completely unfounded reputation for violence are among the factors that have contributed to the mystery surrounding their heritage.

In an effort to understand some of the historical and contemporary social structure of the Tlapanecs and to predict the kind of impact this might have on their future, we began a one-year ethnographic research program in the Tlapanec community of Tlacoapa and its environs. Of the 12 Mexican *municipios* (counties) with a large Tlapanec population, Tlacoapa has the highest concentration of Tlapanecs and, therefore, seemed likely to provide us with unique and traditional cultural information. Our expectations were realized. One year in the field indicated the importance of the Tlapanecs. This report, submitted in 1974, emphasizes the necessity for continued study to unlock further mysteries that were merely touched. Our year's research was sponsored jointly by the National Geographic Society and the National Science Foundation, for which we are very grateful.

Goals of Research

In our Tlapanec research we first sought to establish a baseline ethnographic study of Tlacoapa from which other studies could be drawn. This was especially important since there were no previously published reports on Tlacoapa, and primary Tlapanec information was limited to Schultze-Jena (1938) and Lemley (1949). Second, we hoped to collect and preserve for future generations of Tlapanecs as much of their traditional culture as possible, including religion, social organization, folklore, and material culture. In addition, we each conducted more intensive research on topics of a larger theoretical interest to the discipline of anthropology.

P. Parsons Oettinger worked on the unusual socialization patterns affecting Tlacoapa's children. Her findings are recorded in her master's thesis entitled *A Village of Children: Multiple Socialization Influences and the Problem of a New Cultural Identity in a Tlapanec Indian Village* (1973).

Marion Oettinger, Jr., concentrated his theoretical considerations on Tlacoapa's manifestations and maintenance of social boundaries: those unique foci that make Tlacoapeños define themselves as Tlacoapeños even when pressures for change might encourage them to include themselves within the larger cultural context of "outside" Mexican society. His work was submitted as a doctoral dissertation, *The Voice of the Neighbors: A Study of Tlapanec Community Boundaries and Their Maintenance* (1974).

Since both of the above-mentioned works are available in thesis and dissertation form, we will concentrate this report on the more general nature of our ethnographic research and the methodology employed.

Introduction to the Tlapanecs

The Tlapanec Indians live in the rugged Sierra Madre del Sur mountain range of southern Mexico (see map, fig. 1). Although in the same state as the popular and cosmopolitan seaside resort of Acapulco, the Tlapanecs around Tlacoapa form a cultural and geographic isolate, accessible only by a strenuous mountain hike from the nearest road, which ends 15 hours away.

It is an easy area in which to find oneself lost, and this has led to stories and legends about the perils of venturing into the mountains of the Sierra Madre del Sur. Such fame has discouraged further settlement and development of the area and has encouraged some unlawful activity, which adds potence to the infamous reputation. The area around Tlacoapa, however, is extremely peaceful, and, although its inhabitants must struggle to subsist within the environment, they pride themselves on their nonviolence. Their strong social organization, the variety of vegetation in the area, and the diverse ecological niches that have traditionally been exploited serve to sustain the Tlapanecs. They remain a relatively tranquil group surrounded by the rough, majestic beauty of the mountains, which both support them and define the physical limits of their lives.

The name Tlapanec presently refers to those who speak the Tlapanec language. Originally it was the name given them by the Aztecs to designate the people who "painted themselves with red ochre, and because the name of their god was Toltec, the red Tezcatlipoca" (Sahagún, 1961, p. 187). Among themselves, however, they are known as *mépa*.

The Tlapanec language is placed by most linguists in the Hokan family of linguistic origin. It is most closely related to the now-extinct Subtiaba language of Nicaragua, Tequixtlatec Chontal of the coast of Oaxaca, and the Seri

FIG. 1. Sketch map of the Tlapanec area.

of the State of Sonora. The full significance of this linguistic heritage and its possible significance for migratory patterns and early culture contact are still to be determined, but the linguistic isolation of the people reinforces their geographical and cultural isolation and further underlines their uniqueness. Tlapanecs have retained their language. In fact, over 65 percent of the total population of Tlacoapa speak nothing but Tlapanec. This is the highest degree of monolingualism in Mexico (Marino Flores, 1967, p. 22). In the past

15 years intensified efforts by the schools and Catholic Church have increased the amount of Spanish spoken. This increases the rate of culture change and accelerates the urgency for anthropologists to collect traditional information before it is lost to acculturation.

Tlacoapa, which is Nahuatl (Aztec) for "place between two rivers," is located at the point where two streams have meandered out of their mountain sources into a confluence whose force, during the height of the rainy season, can move boulders and drag with it anyone foolish enough to brave crossing its impermeable flow. Its power is used also to bring fertility, through irrigation, to dry lands in the valley of Tlacoapa.

The two rivers and valley bring Tlacoapeños together into communal work forces and also create an ideal location for a village, Tlacoapa, which provides a ritual focus, a meeting and marketplace, and a political, social, and religious center in which the mountain Tlapanecs can gather. The community does not consist of a set of full-time inhabitants. It is what is called an "empty town center." Although the village has almost 200 houses, these are second houses of the Tlacoapeños who live, most of the time, in one of the ten *rancherías* (hamlets) that surround Tlacoapa. The village, therefore, lacks a constant population and is "empty" except for a rotating group of public officials doing community service, schoolchildren, large gatherings for special occasions, and the non-Tlapanecs who run the mission and the school.

This type of settlement pattern with widely scattered farms and a ritual center has resulted in an interesting economic, political, and social organization, the study of which required a precise methodology. Gaining an accurate perspective on a community such as this one necessitated accurate observation and careful defining of the community and the theoretical problems that seemed most important.

Methodology

We arrived in the village of Tlacoapa in mid-August 1971 and remained there until July 6, 1972. We were thus able to record a yearly cycle of events. We worked in the mountains of Tlacoapa for periods of 6 weeks at a time with intervening 10-day visits to Mexico City to study migration patterns and historical documents and to resupply ourselves with food and equipment.

Our primary methodology was participant observation, which enabled us to get a general understanding of the community without interfering. We kept journals and recorded our data each evening. Data were initially gathered on a very informal basis through questioning randomly selected individuals.

After December we also established formal work sessions with paid informants.

Maps made of the village of Tlacoapa, the surrounding *rancherías,* and the *municipio* were variously used to designate house construction, population distribution, and political composition of a particular area. The houses in the village were mapped according to ownership to determine if patterns of village residence corresponded with patterns of mountain residence. These maps indicated patterns, the implications of which could be explored later.

A household census designed to determine household composition, age distribution, infant mortality rate, linguistic patterns, occupation, traveling habits, out-migration rate, and type of residency pattern was conducted with 100 families. This represents 20 percent of the households in the community of Tlacoapa. In addition, its information indicated some of the relationships between residents of the *rancherías* and the empty town center of Tlacoapa.

The same sort of census (35 households) was conducted in Totomixtlahuaca, a Tlapanec village located 5 hours to the south of Tlacoapa. Data from this census will be compared with those from the similar census made in Tlacoapa.

Formal interviews were conducted with all leaders of both political and religious organizations of the community. Such interviews were designed to show the responsibilities of each officeholder and the steps necessary to achieve their current status.

Life histories were recorded from all five *principales* (community elders who have passed all stages of the civil-religious service). Since all are elderly men, often with as much as 40 years of service, these life histories provided a diachronic view of Tlapanec life. Because most of the *principales* were monolingual in Tlapanec, recordings were made in that language and were later translated and transcribed into Spanish by a bilingual assistant.

We took over 3,000 photographs during our stay in Tlacoapa. Tlapanec material culture was rigorously and thoroughly recorded on film. In addition, nonmaterial aspects of Tlapanec life were photographed with special attention paid to religious festivals and the more ritualistic aspects of Tlapanec life. While photography was employed mainly for documentation, it will be used eventually as a tool in the analysis of spacing, market composition, and other aspects of sociometrics.

Projective testing was used on a limited scale to indicate possibilities for future tests. Over 100 children were asked to draw on paper a man, a woman, a tree, and a house. All were from kindergarten or first and second grades of the primary school located in Tlacoapa. This test was administered primarily to see how children reared in a three-dimensional society are able to cope with two-dimensional forms or symbols. In addition, such a test, while of no use for comparative purposes, is of great importance in revealing a child's perception of his family and society.

Three genealogies were gathered during our field session. Such a method is useful in determining kinship terminology, extent of reckoned kin, marriage laws, and movements of population. Genealogies of fictive kin (godparenthood) were also gathered.

An urban census of 50 individuals from the community of Tlacoapa who now live in Mexico City was conducted. This can indicate reasons why they had left the Tlapanec region, how they found help upon arriving in Mexico City, and what problems they encountered upon arrival in an urban setting.

Using information gathered from these sources, we are able to make some general conclusions about the economic, religious, and social makeup of the Tlapanecs, especially in Tlacoapa. This is used as a basis for our more theoretical considerations and will be useful in future investigations.

Cultural Patterns

Economy. The vast majority of the Tlapanec people are subsistence-level agriculturalists who grow little for export and produce most of what they consume. As in most areas of Mexico, corn, beans, and squash, the "trinity of Mesoamerica," serve as staples. Corn is by far the most important crop and all Tlapanec life revolves around its planting, growing, and harvesting.

Because of the ecological variation of the Tlapanec region, Tlapanecs are able to grow a wide variety of corn. Altitudes in the community of Tlacoapa range from 1,000 to 2,600 meters, and this allows the Tlapanecs to exploit three basic eco-environments: low lands, middle mountain lands, and high mountain lands. Each of these areas has its own planting schedule, its own particular weather patterns, and its own peculiar suitability for certain crops. The same variation in environment also yields a tremendously diverse supply of wild vegetables and fruits. Many people in the Tlapanec region exploit all three ecological environments and consequently are busy in their fields all year.

Most farming depends upon seasonal rains, but frequently river waters are diverted in the valleys during the height of the dry season (November to March). Irrigation systems are cooperative efforts involving as many as 5 or 10 families who own or work lands near the irrigation ditches.

Tlapanecs also maintain herds of animals. Although many families keep a cow or a bull, most maintain only sheep and goats. Sheep are used for wool, and both sheep and goats are sometimes slaughtered for meat on festive occasions. One of the primary functions of animal herding is for the economic gain realized. Several times a year animal buyers pass through the Tlapanec region, purchasing great quantities of sheep and goats as they go. Herds, therefore, can be considered Tlapanec "bank accounts."

Sheep's wool is woven into blankets and *gabanes* (serape-like garments), which are diagnostic of the Tlapanec people. Most of the weaving is done by women, who take particular pride in executing their craft well. Weavings are generally made for home use, but occasionally a family will save extra garments and take them to Tlapa for sale.

Sunday markets are fairly common in the Tlapanec region. Tlacoapa, partly because of its importance as a religious center, is one of the most active markets in the area. Each Sunday, especially during the dry season, Tlacoapa's plaza hums with people from surrounding hamlets and communities, some selling their wares, some exchanging certain goods and produce for other items, and others simply strolling around visiting with people they have not seen in a long time. In addition to their economic import to the community, Sunday markets serve also to integrate the community by bringing people together on a weekly basis.

Since Tlapanecs produce practically everything they consume, there is very little reason to go to outside markets. Salt, the one essential item that is unavailable locally, prompts most heads of households to make at least one trip a year to a large market in Tlapa, Chilapa, Acapulco, or San Luis Acatlán, all major trips for Tlapanecs. Such trips are remembered and talked about for months after the return of the traveler.

Religion. Tlapanec religion is an interesting blend of Colonial Period Catholicism and an earlier indigenous religion, which was basically animistic and polytheistic. The arrival of the Catholic mission in Tlacoapa in 1960 put an end to overt traditional religious practices and forced local *mesos* (shamans) to conduct their ceremonies in sub-rosa fashion.

The principal deities of the Tlapanecs are those associated with natural phenomena directly affecting the lives of the people. *Akun iya,* the rain god, is the most important deity in the Tlapanec pantheon and is celebrated widely on the 24th and 25th of April each year. On these days people gather and make sacrifices of animals and flowers to *Akun iya* in hopes that he will send rain to the area. In past years communal sacrifices were made by local leaders on behalf of the community. Today, sacrifices are made by individuals who conduct their ceremonies privately, high in the mountains and far from the watchful eyes of Catholic priests. The fire god, *Akun Mbatsu,* is also very important and is celebrated in both myth and legend.

With the exception of a very small group of Protestants, all Tlapanecs are nominally Roman Catholic. The church is inevitably the center of activity in all Tlapanec communities, and many families maintain small family altars in their homes, usually adorned with pictures of favorite saints.

Catholic religious worship is manifested most vividly through the celebration of *mayordomias* (religious fiesta stewardships). Tlacoapa, for example, has eight such days throughout the year. Each saint's day fiesta brings people in from the outlying hamlets for several days of music, ritual, and socializing. At the head of each *mayordomia* is the *mayordomo* who is in charge of making all the arrangements for the fiesta. *Mayordomos* do not work alone, however; each has a group of men who share in the work and expenses of the occasion.

Each community has its patron saint, and it is the celebration of this saint's day that is most elaborate and costly. For those living in Tlacoapa the patron saint is San Pedro. Festivities pertaining to the celebration of San Pedro in Tlacoapa usually last for about a week. During this period masses and countless prayers are made, beseeching San Pedro to bestow upon the inhabitants of the community good health and abundant harvests. Candles and incense are burned, flowers are offered, and musicians are brought in to play for hours on end.

The most colorful aspect of *mayordomias* are the dances. For major *mayordomias,* members of the community, usually males, don brightly colored costumes and dance masks and dance as groups for several days, stopping only to eat and nap (fig. 2). Most of the dances performed are clearly of European origin, depicting, for example, struggles between Christians and Moors (the Christians always win). Some dances, however, are more aboriginal in theme and form and suggest a pre-Hispanic origin.

Although most Tlapanecs actively attend Catholic church services, they do not do so at the expense of their older beliefs. Both systems of worship are acknowledged and when possible blended to produce a Christo-pagan religion, unique to each community. Traditional Tlapanec shamans and Catholic priests are both considered important and their function for Tlapanec society deemed equal.

Social Organization. Tlapanecs have no sense of tribal unity; rather they consider themselves members of communal land units. Each unit is a social community and each has its own civil and religious governments. All male members of the community must share in the responsibility of running the political and religious systems, and they do so by serving *cargos,* hierarchically arranged offices served in rotating fashion. All must share in the expenses and labor of keeping the community viable and autonomous.

FIG. 2. Masked figure for the dance of the Chorreos.

The minimal unit of organization within the community is the family (fig. 3). Through the family, children are reared and initially socialized to the ways of the Tlapanec world. While the influences of the family are great, many often give way to new forces represented by the church and the school once the child is old enough to mix with others outside of his extended family.

Family life is based upon cooperation rather than competition. When important decisions are made, husbands and wives make them jointly. Such cooperation is necessary in societies such as those characteristic of the Tlapanec region in which subsistence is so delicately balanced.

Marriage, out of which family life evolves, is one of the strongest institutions in the Tlapanec area. Although there are variations from area to area, Tlapanec marriage involves four basic steps before consecration is realized. First, a bride quest takes place involving four late-night visits by the boy, his father, and a matchmaker to the home of the prospective bride. Next, the wedding takes place and involves a gathering at the girl's home of the extended families of the boy and the girl. The wedding is followed by a period of bride service in which the couple resides matrilocally and the boy works for his in-laws. The length of bride service ranges from several months to a lifetime, but the average length of time spent in service for one's in-laws in Tlacoapa is 3 years. Civil and Catholic ceremonies are usually performed rather unceremoniously during this period of the marriage process.

The final and most colorful step in marriage is called the Burning of the Firewood ceremony. This ancient ceremony, which lasts two days and two nights, is perhaps the most traditional ceremony among the Tlapanec today. It involves the ritual joining of two families through joint sacrifice and suffering. Burning of the Firewood ceremonies are officiated by shamans who, during the course of the ceremony, offer over 40,000 items in sacrifice to traditional Tlapanec deities. Upon termination of this ceremony the couple is considered married by all tenets of Tlapanec society. A detailed description and analysis of this ceremony can be found in a recent publication of the Sociedad Mexicana de Antropología (Oettinger and Oettinger, 1973).

Tlapanec marriages tend to be endogamous at a community level. In Tlacoapa over 90 percent of all marriages took place between persons from within the boundaries of the communal land area, i.e., the community. The usual result of such a high degree of endogamy is the lacing together of a dispersed population within the community through the multiple ties of marriage.

Conclusion

The future of Tlapanec society is uncertain. Improved transportation and better educational facilities offer new alternatives never dreamed possible by

FIG. 3. A Tlapanec family.

Tlapanecs of earlier generations. The availability of these alternatives is at times upsetting. P. Parsons Oettinger (1973) has described Tlapanecs of Tlacoapa as being "anxious"—uncertain at present which route to take and frightened by the uncertainties of whatever new choices might be made.

Migration of Tlapanecs to large urban areas such as Mexico City is taking its toll on traditional lifestyles. In some instances communal spirit is giving way to individual attitudes which are characteristic of urban environments. This will undoubtedly affect attitudes toward the maintenance of communal land boundaries. Once these lands are lost, traditional Tlapanec life will be lost also.

REFERENCES

LEMLEY, H. V.

1949. Three Tlapanec stories from Tlacoapa, Guerrero. Tlalocan, vol. 3, pp. 76-82.

MARINO FLORES, ANSELMO

1967. Indian population and its identification. Handbook of Middle American Indians, vol. 6, pp. 12-25. University of Texas Press, Austin, Texas.

OETTINGER, MARION, JR.

1974. The voice of the neighbors: A study of Tlapanec community boundaries and their maintenance. Unpublished doctoral dissertation, University of North Carolina at Chapel Hill.

OETTINGER, MARION, JR., and OETTINGER, P. PARSONS

1973. The Burning of the Firewood ceremony: Final consecration of marriage in the Tlapanec community of Tlacoapa, Guerrero. Balance y perspectiva de la antropología de Mesoamerica y el norte de México. XIII Mesa Redonda de la Sociedad Mexicana de Antropología, pp. 195-205. Jalapa, Mexico.

OETTINGER, P. PARSONS

1973. A village of children: Multiple socialization influences and the problem of a new cultural identity in a Tlapanec Indian village. Unpublished M. A. thesis, University of North Carolina at Chapel Hill.

SAHAGÚN, BERNARDINO DE

1961. Florentine codex: General history of the things of New Spain: Book 10—The people; pt. 11, 197 pp. Translated from the Aztec into English by Charles E. Dibble and Arthur J. O. Anderson. School of American Research, Santa Fe, New Mexico, and University of Utah.

SCHULTZE-JENA, L. S.

1938. Bei den Azteken, Mixteken, und Tlapanaken der Sierra Madre del Sur von Mexiko. Indiana, vol. 3. Gustav Fisher, Jena.

MARION OETTINGER, JR.
PATRICIA AMANDA PARSONS

Field Investigations of Yak in the Nepal Himalaya

Principal Investigator: Richard P. Palmieri, Mary Washington College, Fredericksburg, Virginia.

Grants Nos. 1031, 1162. In support of a study of yak and yak hybrids, considered ecologically, functionally, and in culture history.

The domestication and role of animals in human culture are important themes of research in a number of disciplines, most notably zoology, anthropology, and geography. Numerous persons in these disciplines have conducted much research on a wide variety of animals, but it has been the many species of bovines, especially those of South Asia, that have attracted the most attention of late. Cattle not only have played an important role in the culture history of Asia, but also today they supply to much of the population of this part of the world great quantities of food, directly in the form of meat, milk, and milk products, and indirectly in the form of traction for pulling plows.

One of the principal bovine resources of Asia is the yak, *Bos (Poëphagus) grunniens* Linnaeus. But, despite the recent interest in domesticated animals in general and bovines in particular, there has been little systematic study of the yak or of the yak's position in culture history, economy, and ecology. Though Matthias Hermanns's *Die Nomaden von Tibet* (1949), the study by James F. Downs and Robert B. Ekvall entitled "Animals and Social Types in the Exploitation of the Tibetan Plateau" (1965), and Ekvall's *Fields on the Hoof: Nexus of Tibetan Pastoral Nomadism* (1968) have dealt with certain aspects of the problem, primarily among the pastoral nomads of Inner Asia, much remains to be done. It was this need that prompted our initial investigations.

Preliminary research in major American libraries, conducted over four years, uncovered abundant, though scattered, information on the position of the yak in the cultures, economies, and diets of a number of Asian peoples. This information, collected from regional and ethnographic studies and the accounts of missionaries, travelers, and explorers, was subsequently organized and formed the basis of a thesis submitted to the University of Texas (Palmieri, 1970). But, because the observations varied considerably in date and quality, the conclusions drawn in that study were tentative. Therefore, a field investigation, to be carried out in the Nepal Himalaya, was proposed which had as its core four primary goals: (1) An examination of the functional role of yak in the economies of the Nepal Himalaya and Tibet; (2) an examination of the geographic distribution of yak and yak hybrids and the mechanics of breeding and hybridization; (3) an investigation of the position of yak in the cultural life of Nepalese and Tibetan folk, especially the role of yak in religion; and (4) an examination of the evidence, cultural and ecological, bearing on the question of means and motives of yak domestication.

With support from the National Geographic Society, and the generous cooperation of the Nepal Studies Institute of Tribhuvan University and the Royal Government of Nepal, field investigations were conducted during 1972-73 among Sherpa and Bhotia folk of Solukhumbu and the Langtang-Trisuli valleys in eastern and central Nepal, and Thakali and Bhotia folk of the Kali Gandaki Valley in western Nepal. At the same time, numerous Tibetan settlements were visited where recent arrivals from Tibet were questioned at length in an attempt to reconstruct the role yak and hybrids played in the plateau and valley regions north of the Himalaya. Empirical observations were made and coupled, whenever possible, with information collected from individuals in the field. Photographic documentation was also carried out, as were simple cartographic assignments.

Functional Role of Yak and Yak Hybrids in Economy

Yak-keeping inhabitants of the Nepal Himalaya and Tibet often employ a tripartite classification system, based upon seasonal patterns of primary economic activity and the character of exploited environments, to describe their communities and lifeways. At the heart of this system is the role played by yak and yak hybrids in economy. The Tibetan terminology for the three divisions—*rongpa, yulmadrog,* and *drogpa*—seems especially valid since it focuses our attention on the ecology and economy of these three groups.

Rongpa are the inhabitants of the *rong,* the deep river valleys found in southern and eastern Tibet and which trend southward from the crest of the Himalaya. In general conversation, however, the term *rong* has come to mean those areas which are arable or which are actually under cultivation. Hence, *rongpa* are persons whose main occupation is farming. The care of livestock is restricted almost entirely to those animals—cattle—which are necessary in agriculture, for pulling plows, producing manure, trampling out grains, and transporting foodstuffs. Such animals are grazed during daylight hours on pastures located beyond the village fields. At night the cattle are returned to the village where they are housed in stables located beneath the houses.

Yulmadrog, as their Tibetan name implies, are seminomadic. An important portion of their activity is devoted to the cultivation of foodcrops in a village environment (Tib. *yul).* Unlike the *rongpa* who generally inhabit areas of lower elevation, however, *yulmadrog* devote a significant amount of energy to the care and breeding of cattle in a pastureland environment (Tib. *drog).* Such pastures are located at the heads of valleys, in areas too high for profitable cultivation, often seven or eight days away from the *yulmadrog* village. Herds of yak and yak hybrids are grazed in these Himalayan meadows in one of two ways, depending on the region and peoples involved.

One of the *yulmadrog* grazing systems is similar to that so familiar in the European alpine situation. Known as transhumance, the system involves the annual abandonment, in late spring, of the agricultural village by most families. Only a few persons remain behind to tend crops. The cattle are herded to higher pastures in summer and are returned to lower elevations in autumn, to pastures located just beyond the village fields. The other *yulmadrog* system functions differently. The herds are maintained throughout the year on pastures distant from the village by herders assigned to the task. Only occasionally do such persons visit the village, to transport butter, cheese, and other products for sale, trade, or family consumption.

The *drogpa* are the inhabitants of the *drog,* the extensive, treeless pastureland environment of Central Asia. *Drogpa* do not cultivate. They look with disdain on those who till the earth, focusing their attention instead almost exclusively on the care and breeding of livestock. *Drogpa* keep their yak on pastures throughout the year; they themselves inhabit tents, which they shift seasonally from pasture to pasture. In winter, *drogpa* drive their herds of yak into lower, more sheltered regions and make their winter quarters there. In earlier times, the *drogpa* of southern Tibet often pitched their winter camps in the Nepal Himalaya.

Though living in different environments and pursuing different lifeways, *rongpa, yulmadrog,* and *drogpa* have close relationships. For example, a substantial trade in foodstuffs takes place in winter between pastoral nomads and agricultural communities. It is a trade that results in a diet more balanced in protein and carbohydrates for both groups. The *drogpa* receives starches that he adds to his protein-rich meals, while the farmer receives a welcome supply of meat and milk products in return.

Mention should be made of the dynamic characteristics of the various economic communities described above. For a variety of reasons, both ecological and cultural, members of each group have on occasion found it beneficial to shift environments and occupation. Thus, after a particularly devastating occurrence of rinderpest, *drogpa* are known to have become tenant farmers in the *rong.* And *yulmadrog* who have capitalized on their peculiarly advantageous ecological and economic position are known to give up the plow entirely for the life of tent and *drog.*

Distribution and Hybridization of Yak

Domesticated yak are descendants of wild yak, *Bos (Poëphagus) mutus* Przhevalski, found now only in very high and unpopulated regions of central Asia. Like their ancestors, domesticated yak prefer cold, inhospitable regions and are seldom found below about 10,000 feet above sea level. If kept in lower elevations for long periods of time, yak do not do well, are said to lose their reproductive capability, and may succumb to high temperatures. Tibetan and Himalayan breeders have, however, through hybridization of yak with common cattle *(Bos taurus* and *Bos indicus),* produced animals that can survive lower elevations and warmer temperatures while preserving, even improving upon, most of the desired qualities of pure yak. Such hybrids can produce more milk than yak, for example, and can carry heavier loads.

Two major difficulties are associated with the hybridization of yak, however. First, while hybrid cows are fertile, male hybrids are sterile. This requires that constant hybridization be carried out to replace old, useless, and dead animals. And, second, hybrids can be produced only in those restricted regions—in certain areas of the Himalaya, for example, or along the margins of the Tibetan Plateau—where environmental conditions can be tolerated by both yak and common cattle. These difficulties have led to a flourishing trade in hybrids from areas where they can be produced to regions that do not embrace the ecological limits of both yak and common cattle.

Another factor that influences trade and distribution of hybrids is parentage. The progeny of a bull/yak cow cross is said to survive better in colder environments than the hybrid of yak bull/common cow parentage. The latter is believed to be better suited to lower and warmer elevations. These beliefs concerning parentage result in hybrids being traded among peoples inhabiting different elevations. Backcrosses are traded also, to various areas where they are thought to do better than pure yak or first generation hybrids.

The variety of hybrid types and backcrosses produced for specific ecological conditions by Tibetan and Himalayan folk has led to a complex nomenclature for hybrids. Tibetan in origin, this nomenclature is based upon parental combinations and relative genetic contribution. While a detailed analysis of hybrid nomenclature is beyond the scope of this report, it does imply a sophisticated approach to the problem of providing animal resources to persons inhabiting varying environmental situations.

The Role of Yak in Religion

The predominant religion among yak-herding folk of Tibet and the Nepal Himalaya is Lamaism, a form of Tantric Buddhism that is superimposed on an indigenous shamanist and animist tradition. For lamaists, the religious functions of yak are varied, but principal among them is use of the animals in iconography, ritual, and as a source of ceremonial substances. In iconography, for example, yak assume the role of vehicles or mounts for some gods who, in a manner reminiscent of ancient storm gods of the Near East, are depicted seated or standing on them. In some cases, that of *Yama,* the Tibetan god of death and ruler of the underworld, for example, the association between yak and gods can be traced to India where similar gods employ common cattle as their vehicles. But there is also evidence which suggests that at least some god/yak associations represent indigenous, pre-Buddhist conceptions as well.

Rituals that make use of yak include scapegoat observances, liberation, and sacrificial ceremonies. Scapegoat observances are performed from time to time to rid a community of sin. A yak is chosen to assume responsibility for the collective sin of a community and is then driven off. Liberation ceremonies can also be performed for the benefit of an entire community but, more commonly, it is the act of an individual as an expression of personal devotion. In liberation ceremonies, a yak is selected and donated to the gods. The animal should be without blemish and is allowed to range freely. After dedication to the gods, no economic use can be made of liberated yak. Finally, the occasional sacrifice of yak is conducted, despite the teachings of Buddha, for two reasons: to bind oaths and to ensure fertility of man, animals, and crops.

Associated with the ritual functions of yak are certain ceremonial materials deriving from them. One of the most important of these materials is butter, used to anoint objects in religious observances, and burned in huge quantities in votive lamps. Moreover, yak butter, colored with vegetable dyes, is the basic component of the impressive Lamaist bas-relief and free-standing iconographic sculptures used in various ceremonies. Another ritual item derived from yak is the *chowery,* a yak tail mounted on a handle and used as a ceremonial wand and religious insignia. Yak tails are traded over much of Asia where they also are an emblem of noble position and military rank.

Domestication

Because archeological and historical evidence is not yet available, we are still uncertain of the motives that may have prompted man to domesticate yak. Various theories of cattle domestication are recognized, however, and their usefulness should be considered within the present context. First is the ecological theory argued by Frederick Zeuner (1963) that domestication was the result of relationships, often symbiotic, between man and animals living in the same habitat. Then, there is the theory—a popular one—that animals were domesticated to satisfy some economic need. Proponents of the economic theory often hold, for example, that cattle were domesticated to ensure a constant supply of milk and/or meat. While such theories, when applied to the yak, are attractive, they are not supported by empirical evidence and remain unconvincing.

A third theory, originally proposed by Eduard Hahn (1896), is the controversial idea that noneconomic and religious motives may have prompted man to domesticate certain animals, including common cattle. Though Hahn wrote in the 19th century, recent studies (Hoffpauir, 1968; Simoons, 1968) of other bovine species—water buffalo *(Bubalus bubalis)* and mithan *(Bos frontalis)*—seem to confirm his hypothesis. With some basic modifications in the theory, the evidence bearing on the question of yak domestication is not in conflict with Hahn's view. That is, noneconomic and religious motives may have been decisive elements in the domestication of yak.

REFERENCES

DOWNS, JAMES F., and EKVALL, ROBERT B.
1965. Animals and social types in the exploitation of the Tibetan Plateau. Pp. 199-184 *in* "Man, Culture, and Animals," Anthony Leeds and Andrew P. Vayda, eds. Amer. Assoc. Adv. Sci. Publ. 78, 304 pp.

EKVALL, ROBERT B.
1968. Fields on the hoof: Nexus of Tibetan pastoral nomadism, xii + 100 pp. Holt, Rinehart & Winston, New York.

HAHN, EDUARD
1896. Die Haustiere und ihre Beziehungen zur Wirtschaft des Menschen, 581 pp. Duncker & Humblot, Leipzig.

HERMANNS, MATTHIAS
1949. Die Nomaden von Tibet, xvi + 325 pp., illus., 4 folded maps. Herold, Vienna.

HOFFPAUIR, ROBERT
1968. The domesticated buffalo in India and Pakistan. Thesis, Department of Geography, University of Wisconsin.

PALMIERI, RICHARD P.
1970. The yak in Tibet and adjoining areas: Its economic uses, social interrelationships, and religious functions. Master's thesis, University of Texas.

SIMOONS, FREDERICK J.
1968. A ceremonial ox of India: The mithan in nature, culture, and history with notes on the domestication of common cattle, xv + 323 pp. University of Wisconsin Press, Madison.

ZEUNER, FREDERICK J.
1963. A history of domesticated animals, 560 pp., illus. Harper & Row, New York.

RICHARD P. PALMIERI

Geographic Variation in the Frequency of Spontaneous Tumors in Fern Gametophytes

Principal Investigator: Carl R. Partanen, University of Pittsburgh, Pennsylvania.[1]

Grant No. 1004: To study normal and abnormal development of bracken fern gametophytes.

The plant that we commonly recognize as "fern" is the sporophyte (diploid) phase of the life cycle. During its reproductive cycle, this sporophyte ("spore bearer") produces spores, which have a reduced (haploid) chromosome number. The spore grows into a small, inconspicuous plant, the gametophyte ("gamete bearer"), which has the function of producing egg cells and sperm. When these combine in fertilization, a new sporophyte is initiated.

Gametophytes, readily grown from spores, are useful laboratory objects for various kinds of biological studies, especially developmental. They can be grown in the laboratory under aseptic conditions, on chemically defined media. Their developmental patterns are responsive to changes in the controlled environmental conditions under which they are grown. This demonstrates the influence of exogenous (extrinsic) factors upon the process. Endogenous (intrinsic) factors also play a role in the process, and the developmental pattern is a consequence of the interaction of these two categories of factors. To analyze the role of either of these, one must be held within a constant pattern (defined as "normal"), while the other is varied. Our primary interest has been in the endogenous, heritable factors. Although we can enhance the genetic variability in a population of spores by exposing them to X-rays, ultraviolet irradiation, or certain chemicals (Partanen and Steeves, 1956; Partanen and Nelson, 1961; Partanen and Shin, unpublished), our concern in the present study has been with spontaneous developmental abnormalities, that is, those which occur in untreated spore populations. These are the results of changes that have occurred within the genetic information of the cells. Although there are a variety of such abnormalities, some of them relatively subtle at the morphologi-

[1] I am grateful for the assistance of several persons during the course of this study: Professor R. Brown, Department of Botany, University of Edinburgh, who placed the resources and facilities of his laboratories at my disposal during the period in Scotland; and Ms. C. Muirhead and H. Paul of the Royal Botanic Gardens, Dr. R. Kirkwood of the University of Strathclyde, and Dr. D. J. Martin of the West of Scotland Agricultural College, who assisted with the spore collections.

cal level, our studies have centered on one type that is extremely obvious and therefore readily detectable in cultures containing tens of thousands of normal gametophytes. This is a gross abnormality, completely devoid of any structural organization, that we have termed "tumor" (Partanen, 1956; Partanen, 1972). (See fig. 1 for comparison of normal and tumorous gametophytes.)

Earlier studies showed that tumors occur spontaneously at a very low frequency, in the range of less than one event per million spores (Partanen, 1958). We had accepted this as a plausible range for a haploid organism, and it has been predictive for many spore populations that have been sampled. However, some studies in our laboratory have indicated much higher frequencies in other spore collections (Dickinson, 1971). A number of plausible explanations could be invoked. However, the most obvious difference between the spore collections was that they were from different geographic localities.

Since no other information was available on variation in the developmental aspects of fern spores with respect to their geographic origins, the present study was undertaken. The objective was to make more numerous collections of spores of the bracken fern *(Pteridium aquilinum)* and subsequently to test these under uniformly controlled laboratory growth conditions. Since earlier data were based on pooled spore collections from relatively wide areas, e.g., a square mile or more, there was no way to determine whether such a collection contained a heterogeneity of subpopulations with varying degrees of tumor incidence, or whether they were uniform in that respect. This consideration led us to a broad geographic area, Scotland, where bracken fern was abundant both for wide and local sampling.

In this study the separate spore collections were very localized, to the extent that many of the collections were clonal. This is made possible by the extensive vegetative growth that a single sporophyte of *Pteridium* can undergo over a number of years. Annually, there is extensive growth of the underground stem, the rhizome, giving in successive years an ever increasing stand of fern in which all the "plants" are, in fact, parts of the same plant. Thus samples of assumed clonal spores, collected over a relatively small area, could be compared with similar collections from widely different areas.

The spores, once collected, were stored in sealed vials in the freezer. The individual spore lots were then assayed quantitatively for the frequency of spontaneous tumors, in aseptic culture. The experiments were designed to test a million spores per collection. In some cases, when the number of spores in the collection was limiting or when part of the cultures were lost through contamination, less were used. Where there was a sufficient number of spores in a potentially interesting lot, more were assayed. Although none of these

FIG. 1. Top: Normal gametophytes of *Pteridium aquilinum,* as grown aseptically in vitro. They are essentially a sheet of cells, primarily one cell in thickness except in the central portion. Bottom: A tumor isolated from a culture of *Pteridium aquilinum* gametophytes. Tumors are 3-dimensional masses of cells, growing in all directions, with no over-all organization. They can be continued indefinitely in aseptic culture, with no reversion to normal growth. Both figures were photographed at the same magnification; the scale shown between them is in millimeters.

sample sizes would be considered adequate for making fine distinctions in the range of rare events occurring, e.g., at the frequency of one in a million, the differences being sought in this study were those of a substantially higher frequency. These sites could then be studied at a later date in an attempt to determine causal factors.

Results

The results of the spore assays conducted to date are summarized in table 1. Tumors were scored after at least two months of culture subsequent to the spores being sown. These were scored on the basis of established criteria of morphology and minimum size (2 millimeter diameter). The final determination was made under a stereo microscope at 50× magnification. The accuracy of visible scoring was tested by isolating putative tumors into a separate culture and making subsequent observations of their growth. These "spot checks" of scoring accuracy show a reliability of over 95 percent. Since varying

TABLE 1. Results of Spore Assays

Collection sites are indicated within 100 meters by the grid references, which refer to the British Ordnance Survey grid maps in the One-inch Series (one inch = 1 statute mile).

Spores		*Tumors*		
Lot	*Assayed*	*Total*	*Per 10^6 spores*	*Collection site*
CP 71.2	1,000,000	1	1	NT 204 747 (Edinburgh)
CP 71.6	1,000,000	4	4	NT 203 746 (Edinburgh)
CP 71.7	500,000	0	0	NT 202 612 (Penicuick)
CP 71.8	1,750,000	0	0	NT 198 613 (Penicuick)
CP 71.9	950,000	0	0	NT 199 615 (Penicuick)
CP 71.11	1,650,000	19	11.5	NT 204 747 (Edinburgh)
CP 71.15	1,000,000	22	22	— (Invermoriston)
HP 71.2	950,000	3	3.2	NT 175 567 (Glencoe)
CM 71.12	1,800,000	7	3.9	NY 388 782 (Dumfriesshire)
CM 71.14	1,800,000	8	4.4	NT 402 365 (Peebles)
CM 71.15	1,750,000	4	2.3	NT 382 377 (Peebles)

numbers of spores were assayed, the tumor frequency is expressed on the basis of numbers per million spores for purposes of direct comparison. The collection sites are located in the table to within 100 meters by grid coordinates. The more definitive description and location of the site is noted in the field data.

These data suggest that there is a variation in the frequency of spontaneous tumors in discrete populations of *Pteridium aquilinum* spores. Although many of the spore samples fall within the expected low range, at least two (CP 71.11 and CP 71.15) are in the next order of magnitude, and therefore quite probably are significantly higher.

An analysis of the field data suggest no obvious correlative factors in the environment. If one attempts to apply relatively broad geographic interpretation to these data, then one can draw a comparison between CP 71.2, 6, and 11 (all collected on Corstorphine Hill, Edinburgh) and CP 71.7, 8, and 9 (all collected in the Pentland Hills, near Penicuick). The latter show no tendency toward this abnormality, whereas the former show a detectable and variable tendency. Thus, there may be some general factor(s) at play. However, upon finer dissection of the locale, one can find essentially the same range of variability expressed within a range of about 200 meters (CP 71.2, 6, and 11). This would suggest that there may also be some rather specific local factors in the immediate vicinity of the plants.

Conclusions

The primary objective of this study has been fulfilled. The data obtained indicate that there is geographic variability in the frequency of spontaneous developmental abnormalities in the gametophytes of *Pteridium aquilinum.* The questions of degree of variability, and possible causal factors, remain to be answered. These can best be approached by more intensive study of selected sites from the present study, those of markedly low and high frequency. These studies should include massive spore collections, for subsequent laboratory testing, and detailed ecological studies of the specific collection sites.

REFERENCES

DICKINSON, W.

1971. L-methionine and the development of the gametophyte of *Pteridium aquilinum.* Ph.D. thesis, University of Pittsburgh.

PARTANEN, CARL R.

1956. Comparative microphotometric determinations of deoxyribonucleic acid in normal and tumorous growth of fern prothalli. Cancer Res., vol. 16, pp. 300-305.

PARTANEN, CARL R.—continued

1958. Quantitative technique for analysis of radiation-induced tumorization in fern prothalli. Science, vol. 128, pp. 1006-1007.

1972. Comparison of gametophytic callus and tumor tissues of *Pteridium aquilinum.* Bot. Gaz., vol. 133, pp. 287-292.

PARTANEN, CARL R., and NELSON, J.

1961. Induction of plant tumors by ultraviolet radiation. Proc. Nat. Acad. Sci., vol. 47, pp. 1165-1169.

PARTANEN, CARL R., and STEEVES, T. A.

1956. The production of tumorous abnormalities in fern prothalli by ionizing radiations. Proc. Nat. Acad. Sci., vol. 42, pp. 906-909.

CARL R. PARTANEN

Behavior, Songs, and Populations of Parasitic Finches

Principal Investigator: Robert B. Payne, Museum of Zoology, University of Michigan, Ann Arbor, Michigan.

Grant No. 1005: For a study of the behavior of indigobirds in the field in Africa.

In January 1972 I began a study of song behavior in parasitic finches in order to use the songs of birds as population markers and to find how the songs are related to the biology of the birds. With the support of the National Science Foundation and the National Geographic Society, I studied populations where I had tape-recorded birds in 1967. I also began a long-term study of behavior in a population where individual birds were marked for recognition.

The village indigobird *(Vidua chalybeata)* lives in much of the bush country of Africa. Females lay their eggs in the nests of red-billed firefinches *(Lagonosticta senegala),* common birds in the traditional thatch-roofed huts and villages of the rural country. The young indigos are reared by the adult firefinches and learn their songs. Later when they are grown the indigos learn the songs of older indigos that mimic the same kind of firefinch. In the areas with more than one kind of indigo, each kind parasitizes a different species of firefinch, and so by copying only the older indigos having songs like their own foster parents the singing indigos maintain their own song traditions. These traditions include not only the mimetic songs but also some distinctive songs that only indigos have. In any local population all the indigos of a species share all, or nearly all, their songs with one another, but these songs are all distinct from those of other populations that may be only a few miles apart.

The local song differences, or dialects, define local populations of indigos. By using the songs as behavioral markers of populations, I hoped to determine the numbers of birds in a population and the dispersal of birds between different populations. I also hoped to find the songs useful in determining how populations graded into one another over distance.

Stability and Change in Populations and in Songs

In 1972 I looked for indigos in five of the localities where I had tape-recorded them in 1967. Indigos were still alive and well and singing in all these localities, and I recorded 100 to 300 songs of most of the singing birds for comparisons in terms of time and distance.

The first study area was the confluence of the Olifants and Eland Rivers east of Marble Hall, Transvaal. I tape-recorded *Vidua chalybeata* there on January 8 and 9. One indigo was singing in the same call-site tree where I had recorded songs of an indigo in 1967. The birds seem to have long-time traditions and a strongly developed sense of certain places.

From January 13 to 29 I lived along the Klein Letaba River in Transvaal, basing my work at Gert Roux's farm "Kondowe." Here about 45 kilometers downstream from Tzaneen I tape-recorded 52 singing *Vidua chalybeata* in a 24-kilometer stretch of river bush and citrus orchards near the Hans Merensky Wildlife Reserve, where giraffe are reared for restocking wildlife farms. The Letaba River sample also gave a census complete enough to let us determine how the song dialects grade into neighboring populations. Analysis of the songs shared between birds in this area showed the occurrence of seven distinct song populations, the longest one extending 5 kilometers along the river. Nearly all birds shared songs with their neighbors on one or both sides. In addition to the birds sharing songs with their neighbors there were 6 birds that shared songs with birds from other populations recorded along the 24-kilometer stretch—4 of these had evidently dispersed from one song population into the neighboring population and two others had leapfrogged over one population into a more remote population. Of these 6, 3 were bilingual and also sang the songs of their neighbors. Also discovered were 3 birds each singing a completely unique set of songs. These birds were probably immigrants from song populations outside the 24-kilometer study area. The occurrence of these birds singing songs characteristic of remote populations indicates considerable movement of birds between populations. The song populations appear to exchange individuals with each other to an extent not known before in any other kind of bird with local song dialects.

Also along the Letaba River I recorded songs of two other indigo species, *Vidua purpurascens* in the Merensky-Kondowe area and *V. funerea* 6 and 10 miles east of Tzaneen. These songs were compared to the 1967 samples from the same populations.

The fifth population revisited was the one in Maun, Botswana, along the acacia-lined Thamalakane, a river that flows either east or west depending on local rains at the edge of the Kalahari Desert. *Vidua chalybeata* were singing in the same areas as in 1967, though none were found in exactly the same trees February 8 to 18, 1972. Recordings of 15 birds along 13 kilometers of river showed three distinct song populations. Only one bird had a high proportion of songs that did not match its neighbors' songs. It had a larger song repertoire than any other Maun birds, and half (12 of 23) its distinct song types were unique. The other songs were shared with its neighbors. This bird, a

FIG. 1. A village indigobird singing on its call-site perch at Maun, Botswana.

male, was likely an immigrant from a remote population that found a call-site in Maun and that was bilingual at least at the time when I recorded it, singing its old songs as well as having become familiar with the local dialect. It had frequent female visitors who did not seem reluctant to approach it in spite of its alien songs.

Analysis of more than 4,000 songs of indigos from these 1972 samples with those of songs recorded in 1967 showed, surprisingly, that not a single song type was the same over this 5-year period. Most individual indigos have a song repertoire of about 18 song types, yet none of these types could be matched with any assurance with the presumably corresponding song type of five years earlier. Each song had changed in at least three complex notes. This song change is probably not due to a complete exodus or extinction of one population and its replacement by a new set of birds from elsewhere; at least there were no obvious signs or records of indigobird population catastrophies at Maun, and we know from the continuous bird observations of Dr. Peter Jones, who lived in Maun, that indigos sang there in 1969, 1970, and 1971. The most likely explanation, one that developed through our later work, seems to be that individual birds in all these areas had changed their songs over the intervening years, and that other birds (probably younger birds) had copied these changed songs and introduced their own copying mistakes.

Behavior in a Local Population

During the past three years we have monitored the songs of the population and of the longer-lived males in it at Lochinvar National Park, Zambia. Color-ringing and behavior observations were begun in January 1972 by University of Michigan student Dale Lewis and have been continued by him for three breeding seasons, by Billie Chipeta (a Zambian wildlife biologist), by Karen Payne (a birding housewife), and by myself. We have also followed the mating success of individual males at their call-sites and the mating pattern in the population to find which males mate with which females. It has been possible to relate song changes to the differences in mating success of the different males in the population in this study.

Lochinvar National Park includes about 260 square kilometers of river flood-plain, grassland, and woodland. Up to 10 years earlier it had been a private cattle ranch, and the large predators of Africa had been severely reduced in number, but most of the woodland was protected and wildlife was encourged to live together with the cattle. The rare lechwe *(Kobus leche)* occurs in its largest numbers here, and other large animals include zebra, buffalo, eland, and kudu. The area outside the park has many people living in villages, with the woodland cleared for maize cultivation and cattle grazing. The sanctuary of the park is visible from 500 kilometers above the earth (fig. 2). Indigos were common locally both along the edge of the woodland and around the villages and dams. Firefinches nested in many of the huts in the villages and indigos laid their eggs in their nests. We found dozens of firefinch nests by looking in the thatch roofs, but none in the grass or bush of Lochinvar Park, though surely the firefinches nested there as well.

Tape recordings of indigos at Lochinvar in 1972 showed within the woodland area of the park two distinct song populations, each largely in *Acacia nilotica* woodland, where their favorite grasses *Echinochloa* and *Setaria* are abundant. A third dialect population lives just south of the park in the more

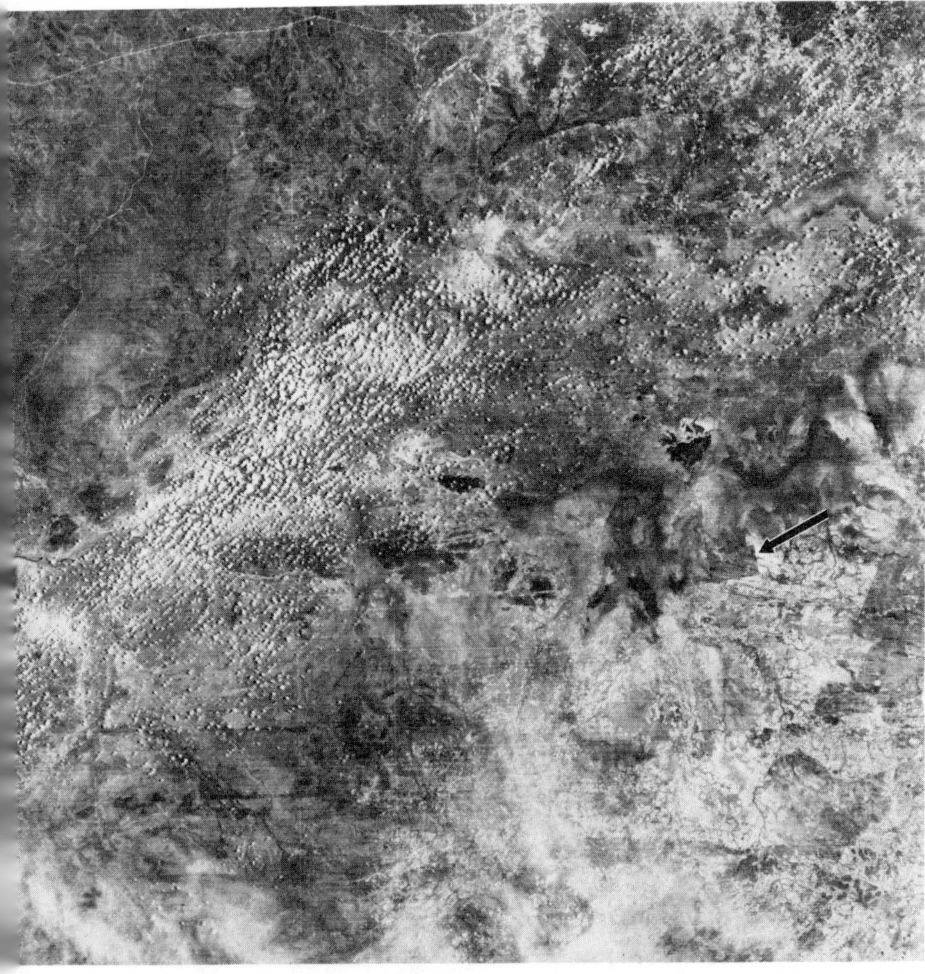

FIG. 2. Study area south of the Kafue River in southern Zambia as seen from EROS satellite. The southeastern corner of Lochinvar National Park borders the cultivated area of the heavily populated villages. Left side of the photo is north. The arrow points to the eastern edge of the park; the border here is 5.5 kilometers long.

heavily grazed village area, and other dialect populations were found within 10 kilometers of the park. Tape recordings made in 1973 and 1974 showed that these song populations were stable, though a boundary area shifted from one dialect to the other in 1973. By counting the number of singing males within 20 square kilometers of the park and neighboring area and by netting, color-ringing, releasing, and recapturing males and females, we found that about 20 males and 20 females live within each song population area. Not all males have singing places, and some males begin to sing only when the established older males are removed from their call-sites.

MATING SYSTEMS

Earlier studies of indigos had shown that several females may visit a singing male and that at least four females may mate with him. The color-banded population at Lochinvar allowed us to identify males and females as individuals and to see if there was a tendency for individual females to prefer certain males to others. During more than 700 hours of observation of males at their call-sites in 1973 we found that individual females visited several males on a single day. Because the singing males are usually more than 200 meters from their nearest neighbors we were able to follow individual females only through a combination of fast footwork along the roads linking call-sites and a team of two or three observers each at a different call-site. Several individual females were seen to visit at least three males in a row, being courted by each one in turn. On one occasion we saw a female RYRY return and mate with a male RYRB she had visited an hour earlier. The females appear to be trap-lining several males in the population, perhaps comparing the songs or behavioral responses of each male, and then selecting one of the males as a mate.

The dispersion of the male singing places is reminiscent of that of the species of birds of paradise in New Guinea, where males are scattered nearly out of hearing range of each other. Tom Gilliard (1969) regarded these social systems as "exploded leks" derived from the communal display grounds of males where females can visit and compare individual males at once. Certainly the females respond to the dispersed singing males very much as grouse or ruff females respond to the communal displaying males of their species, by comparing the position in the group and the behavior of the different males and then as a group mating with one of the males in preference to the others. We found 53 percent of the matings in the most closely observed population of indigos at Lochinvar to be completed by a single male (RYRB) at his call-site, "junction." RYRB together with two other males (RYYG and RGRG) accounted for 86 percent of all of the matings in the population of about 20 males. Altogether 6 males accounted for all the observed matings.

Recordings of color-ringed birds showed that a few males have minor song idiosyncrasies, i.e., one or two odd syllables in songs that otherwise match the songs of their neighbors. All these odd singers had zero mating success. On the other hand, every time the males with several matings to their credit changed their song, the other males in the population did likewise. These changes, usually involving only a few notes in the entire song repertoire, were quickly passed around the entire population of singing males. The accumulation of these song changes within and between breeding seasons is sufficiently great that some of the songs recorded early in 1972 had, by the middle of the 1974 season, changed enough to be no longer recognizably the same song types. It appears that the song changes observed between 1967 and 1972 in the indigo populations in Transvaal and Botswana were simply the effects of two more years of song differentiation in the repertoires of individual birds and their copiers or "mimics."

During 1972 and 1974, but especially in 1973, we accumulated over 1,000 hours of observations of individual males at their mating sites to compare differences in breeding success of these males with any differences in their song behavior or their local habitat. Songs were very similar between individual males and usually birds had no songs that distinguished them from their neighbors, apparently because songs of the more successful birds are so quickly copied by the others. The displays of males given in courtship were documented by 16-millimeter cinematography, but it turned out that the successful breeding birds and the unsuccessful males did their displays in very much the same way. Photographic records also aided in the comparisons of habitat quality of the different males.

The variables among the males that have been examined so far do not give a single answer to the question of how females choose a mate, but several variables are strongly associated with the mating success of the males. RYRB and RYYG were among the most centrally located males in the local pattern of the population in being close to the weighted geometric mean of the area. Other males were often found for a few weeks around RYRB, near the same central-tendency location, but females were never seen to mate with these newcomers and could apparently distinguish RYRB from other birds nearby. Mating success in the population was related to the closeness of a watering site and the males such as RYRB that sang within 100 meters of a water place were able to exclude other males from the place. Females often feed with the male after courtship near his call-site, both after they have mated and also (and more often) when the male has courted her but she is not immediately receptive to him, and there appears to be some correlation of male mating success with the relative abundance of the favored seeds of *Echinochloa* and *Setaria* grasses near the sites, but we do not have sufficient plant census data to establish convincingly this tendency. Behavioral variables that appear to be related to mating success include the number of minutes in each hour that the male is on his call-site tree and the total number of songs he sings in that period.

Males frequently visit one another's sites and either hop into its site tree if the resident male is away, or, more often, since he is usually on his site, they perch concealed in a nearby bush or thicket for about three minutes, which is just about the time required for a singing male to run through most of his song repertoire. Males visit other males daily at their call-sites. Most likely this is the time they can hear the song changes of their neighbors; they may also move into a superior call-site if they find it unoccupied, or they may occasionally steal a mating, though we never observed an interloper to mate successfully with a female visiting the resident male. At any rate, males recognizable by their color-bands as the singers at their own call-sites (as well as males without call-sites) visit other males in the dialect population. We never saw a male visit outside his usual song neighborhood. The distances over which a song dialect extends are likely close to the economic limits of the travel time and effort of individual birds in comparing songs of their neighbors.

SONG LABILITY

We recorded one individual male in 1972 shortly after he was ringed near the center of one dialect area and then established a singing site at the edge of the next dialect area. He was bilingual, having the song types of both his old and new populations. Later in the season he had dropped most of the old song types and was singing more of the song types of his new population. This bird was not resighted the next year, but two other birds in the same area (on "buffalo" and "edam" call-sites) were bilingual.

Males do not always change their song when moving into a new neighborhood. An unringed male succeeded two other males on the buffalo call-site late in the 1973 season and had no song types in common with any other indigos in any of the tape-recorded populations around Lochinvar. In 1974 another bird at buffalo was bilingual and had the song types of one of the same neighbor birds as the 1973 buffalo birds, but the other repertoire was of a population south of the park. He was seen to mate in 1974. Again the local females appeared to accept him even though some of his songs were unusual. Whether or not males acquire the songs of their neighbors appears to be related to their social position and mating success.

Experimental studies in our lab generally support the interpretation of some song learning after dispersal as seen in the field. Several young indigos (both *Vidua chalybeata* and *V. purpurascens),* captured as young dispersing birds in the field and caged with singing older indigos but otherwise isolated from the sound of all other birds, copied the songs of the older birds. On the other hand, a bird reared in captivity with his father to the age of 45 days and

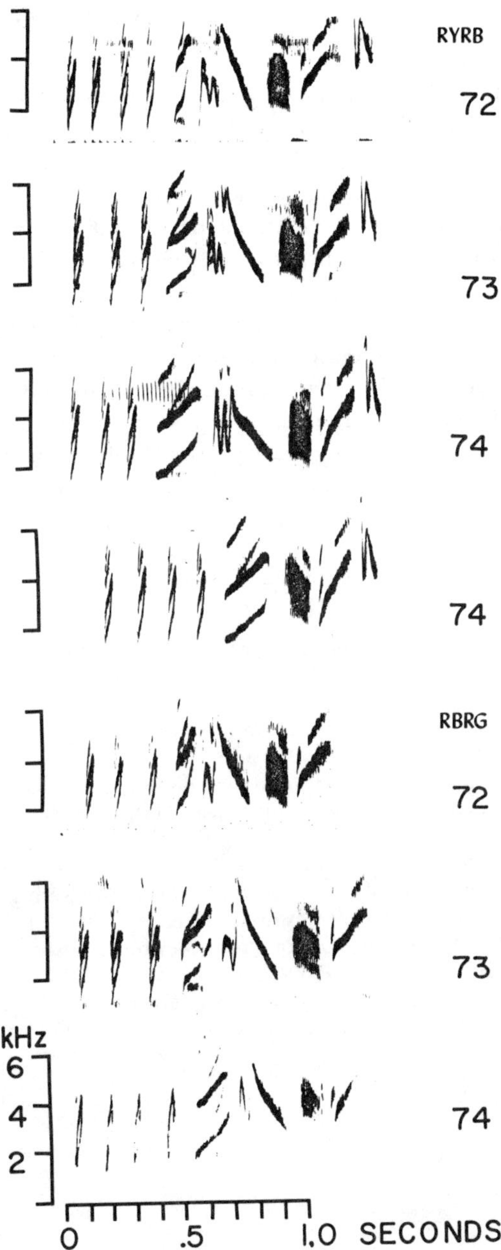

FIG. 3. Audiospectrographs of the songs of two color-ringed *Vidua chalybeata* living in the field at Lochinvar Park. All birds in the population adjust their songs within and between breeding seasons to each other, particularly to the local stud RYRB.

then acoustically isolated did not sing the song types of his father, but rather improvised and crystallized his own idiosyncratic song through a process of subsong. Indigos can also copy the songs of their host species even when the host comes from a remote area, as one captive first-year *V. chalybeata* from Zambia copied the song of a west African firefinch that he first heard when he was a few months old and of dispersal age. He also has continued to sing his native songs.

We hope to continue observations of the change of songs at Lochinvar and to relate the song changes to the mating success of individual birds. This information may be helpful in determining the ecology and evolution of song learning in birds and, by some extension, in solving the problem of the evolution of learning in general. Songs have proved helpful in the size and structure of populations of these birds, and they may be equally helpful in determining the history of learning behavior in animals.

REFERENCES

GILLIARD, E. THOMAS

1969. Birds of paradise and bower birds, 485 pp., illus. Weidenfeld and Nicolson, London.

PAYNE, ROBERT B.

1972. A place in Africa called Lochinvar. Goldeneye, vol. 11, no. 5, pp. 1, 2, 8.

1973. Behavior, mimetic songs and song dialects, and relationships of the parasitic indigobirds *(Vidua)* of Africa. Ornithol. Monogr., vol. 11, 333 pp.

1979. Population structure and social behavior: models for testing the ecological significance of song dialects in birds. *In* "Natural Selection and Social Behavior: Recent Research and New Theory," R. D. Alexander and D. W. Tinkle, eds. Chiron Press, Newton, Massachusetts.

PAYNE, ROBERT B., and KAREN PAYNE

1977. Social organization and mating success in local song populations of village indigobirds, *Vidua chalybeata*. Zeitschr. f. Tierpsychol., vol. 45, pp. 113-173.

ROBERT B. PAYNE

Research on the Behavior of Various Species of Whales

Principal Investigator: Roger S. Payne, New York Zoological Society and Rockefeller University, New York City.[1]

Grant Nos. 987, 1100, 1246, 1366, 1685. In aid of continuing studies of the vocalization and behavior of the right, humpback, and other species of whales.

Although many plants and animals have been brought to extinction at the hands of man, they have always been species that occupied a limited habitat: an island or single continent. We have never completely wiped out any species with a worldwide range. I suspect the closest we have come may be with the right whale *(Eubalaena glacialis)*, a truly cosmopolitan species, which formerly occurred off the coasts of all continents and is now rare throughout its entire range.

We are entering a critical stage in our escalating problems of living in balance with the natural world—a point in our history when we can fear extinction even of cosmopolitan species. To avoid making the irretrievable error with right whales, we need to know much more about them. In spite of 30 years of nominal protection, they have not undergone the rapid recovery in numbers that gray whales have (Rice, 1971). We have no idea why this may be so, so little is known about the basic biology of this species. Our aim in the research reported here was to study the basic biology of the right whale and to develop estimates of its population by new methods that would not rely on killing whales. The final phase of the work was to apply what we had learned to preserving the species.

In 1970 we found an excellent place for studying this species—the waters surrounding Península Valdés on the Argentine coast (fig. 1). Here, for the first time we could hope to make a comprehensive study of the behavior of a free-ranging baleen whale. This report covers the first seven years (1971-1978) of our study, which is ongoing (1979).

[1] Scientific personnel of these studies included: Katharine B. Payne, James Gould (now of Princeton University Biology Department), Bernd Würsig (University of California at Santa Cruz), Christopher Clark (graduate student at the State University of New York at Stony Brook), and Peter Tyack (graduate fellow, Rockefeller University).

History and Description of the Project

A one-month reconnaissance expedition in 1970 convinced us that Península Valdés was the right place for our study of right whales: it had a major concentration of easily observable individuals living close to shore. We discovered also that in this species a series of unique white markings (called callosities) on the tops of the whales' heads makes it possible to identify individuals, since the placement, number, size, and shape of the white markings are different in every whale. These are illustrated in figure 2. Heretofore it had not been possible to identify individuals in herds of wild whales.

Encouraged by the results of our first trip, we returned in 1971 with grants from both the National Geographic Society and the New York Zoological Society and accompanied by James Gould (then a graduate fellow from Rockefeller University) for a longer (3½-month) study. The results of that expedition were so filled with promise that we returned to Península Valdés in 1972, again sponsored by the National Geographic Society and the New York Zoological Society, and stayed for 20 months. Two graduate students of the State University of New York at Stony Brook, Christopher Clark and Bernd Würsig, assisted in our study during the fall of 1972, thanks to a further grant from the National Geographic Society as well as funding from the University. Both have since returned for separate stays of two years each to collect material for their Ph.D. theses—Clark concentrating on right-whale vocalizations, and Würsig on two porpoise species, the dusky dolphins *(Lagenorhynchus obscurus)* and the bottlenose dolphin *(Turbiops* sp.), which live in the same area and interact with the whales.

Scientific Results

We find from repeated air census flights that from mid-May to late November there are about 150 right whales located in three well-defined areas along the Península Valdés coast (at other seasons the herds are presumedly feeding far to the southeast in sub-Antarctic waters). These areas are separated by about 75 miles of coastline. Individuals, particularly males, move between them freely. In about 60 complete aerial censuses during the whole season we *always* saw whales in these three areas (see fig. 1) and it was rare to see any elsewhere.

The functions of the three regions differ. Golfo San José appears to be principally a nursery for growing subadults, a mating ground and a home for three small groups of mothers and calves, which utilize the area for calf raising. At Punta Norte the population consists almost entirely of females accom-

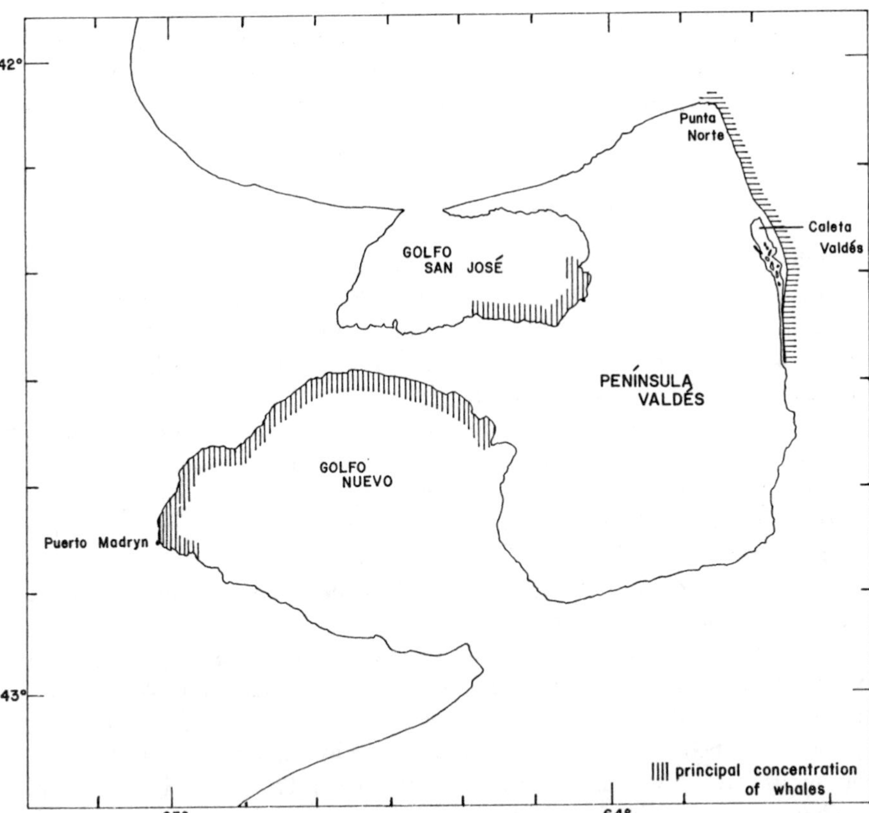

FIG. 1. Península Valdés, on the east coast of Argentina. Shaded areas represent regions of the bay frequented by whales. Oddly enough, right whales are only rarely seen outside these areas, even though to human senses adjacent areas would seem identical.

panied by newborn calves, with males staying around for only short periods and most other whales transient. A majority of the females return to these two areas at 3-year intervals to bear calves. The Golfo Nuevo population consists mainly of adult whales, but their main activities are not yet clear, except for the fact this area is obviously of minor importance for calf raising. Our work has been centered at the edge of Golfo San José at a field station built by the New York Zoological Society in a place where we are seldom out of sight of whales during their sojourn in the area. At many times the whales are within 200 yards of shore. The whales show no response to an observer on the beach walking near them. They also allow close approach or even touching by swimmers and boats, particularly when they are engaged in mating activities, and they are unbothered by a plane circling over them as long as it is at altitudes above a few hundred feet.

Acoustics and Behavior

Recent research has advanced the knowledge about the behavior of baleen whales through studies of their vocalizations. (For reviews see Tavolga, 1965; Schevill, 1964; Schevill and Watkins, 1962; and Backus, 1958.) Much of my own work has been in this area, particularly with humpback whales (Payne and McVay, 1971; Payne and Webb, 1971).

A great weakness in research on baleen-whale vocalizations is the almost total lack of data concerning the behavior that accompanies the sounds and of data on the responses, if any, either acoustic or non-acoustic, of other whales. Even rudimentary observations such as what sex or age group makes which sounds are not available. Thus the field is still somewhat stymied in the collecting and cataloguing phase, where much is known about variety of sounds but little about behavioral context or meaning.

Our research in Argentina has made a start at filling this gap. In 1971 we were able to get well over 100 hours of tape of their sounds, some of which can be associated with detailed observations by an aerial observer (in a circling plane) of the behavior of the groups responsible for these sounds. The variety of sounds uttered by this species is large (Payne and Payne, 1971). However, we found no indication that right whales produce "songs" (long, repeated patterns of sounds such as are known for the humpback whale *Megaptera novaeangliae,* Payne and McVay, 1971), though others (Cummings and Phillipi, et al., 1970) have reported this.

Starting in 1972, Christopher Clark has worked at correlating sounds with behavior. The problem he particularly addressed himself to is that often too many whales are heard at one time over our submerged hydrophone array for us to determine unambiguously which whale is vocalizing at any given moment. Since we use 3 or 4 hydrophones, each being simultaneously recorded on one channel of a four-channel tape recorder, we can later analyze the tape to reveal the location of the sound source. But this analysis after the fact does not help us correlate the vocalization with the behavior of a particular whale since at the time one needs to know which whale to watch. To determine which whale is vocalizing one needs instantaneous analysis in "real time." Only with this sort of information is it possible to understand the significance of the rich variety of sounds these whales make. Clark's particular interest in

1973 was to use a device he had developed to do this analysis based on time-delays or phase differences between hydrophones. This allowed him to make extensive recordings of known whales engaged in known behaviors. In this way it was possible, particularly in his later work, to decode for the first time important aspects of the whales' communication system. That work is currently under analysis.

In addition to sound recordings, we made observations of whales from a variety of places and viewpoints and with varied objectives. For example, one of our most valuable techniques was to make repeated air census flights identifying and plotting locations for every whale we encountered. We also made observations from shore (or from a small boat near the whales) and from directly overhead (of whales immediately beneath an observer seated on a cliff, or of any whale in the bay, from a small plane circling above it), and we observed whales at close range underwater by diving with them. From the cliffs we made a weekly census (later a daily one) of behavior patterns of whales in the region. In favorable circumstances we were able to obtain age, sex, and identity of the whales we were watching. We took over 12,500 photographs of whales engaged in typical activities. The unique callosity patterns on their heads when photographed from above allowed us to put together a catalogue (sort of a rogues' gallery) of all head patterns in the area, which we used to identify individuals. Thus in every airflight and every observation session we gathered information not only on the behavior patterns characteristic of this species but also on the lives of specific individuals in the herd; from day to day and year to year we could follow their changing activities, note with whom they consorted, how that varied with time of day and with the season, where they went, etc. From month to month and year to year we noted the ratio of familiar heads to new heads which gave us a way to estimate population size. We also noted the appearance of new calves, and disappearance of other individuals from the herd: information upon which we are now basing a study of the population dynamics within this herd.

We were able to measure for the first time the growth rate of young right whales by a technique that we invented and that others are now adopting. By motoring near a whale in a boat bearing a board on which was painted a circle 1 meter in diameter, while an observer in a plane overhead photographed both whale and boat simultaneously, we could determine the length of the whale

---

FIG. 2. (See following pages.) Aerial photographs of right whale heads showing the great variety in patterns of callosities (white markings on whale's head). The number in the top right-hand corner is the individual whale number—bottom right is the year that photograph was taken.

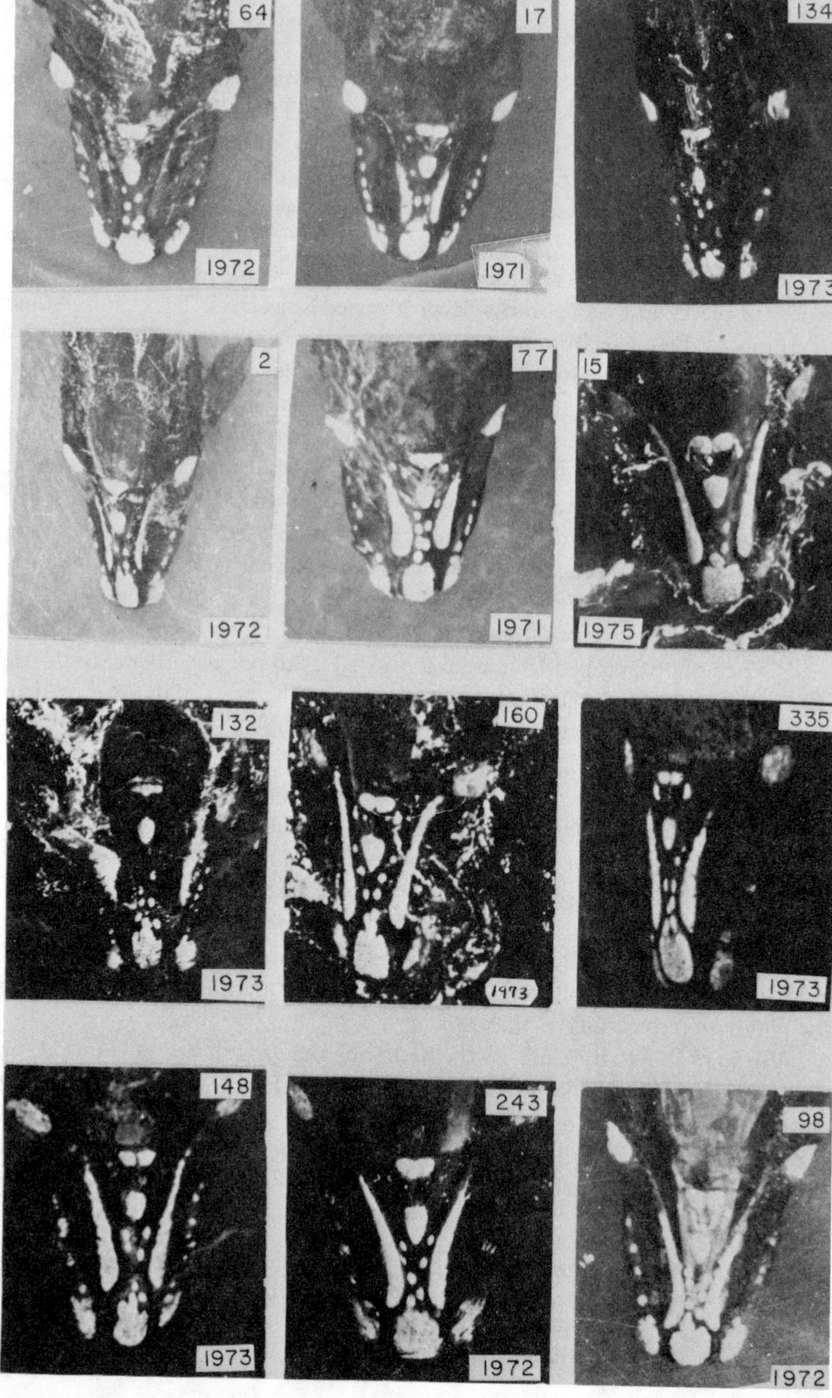
64
1972
17
1971
134
1973
2
1972
77
1971
15
1975
132
1973
160
1973
335
1973
148
1973
243
1972
98
1972

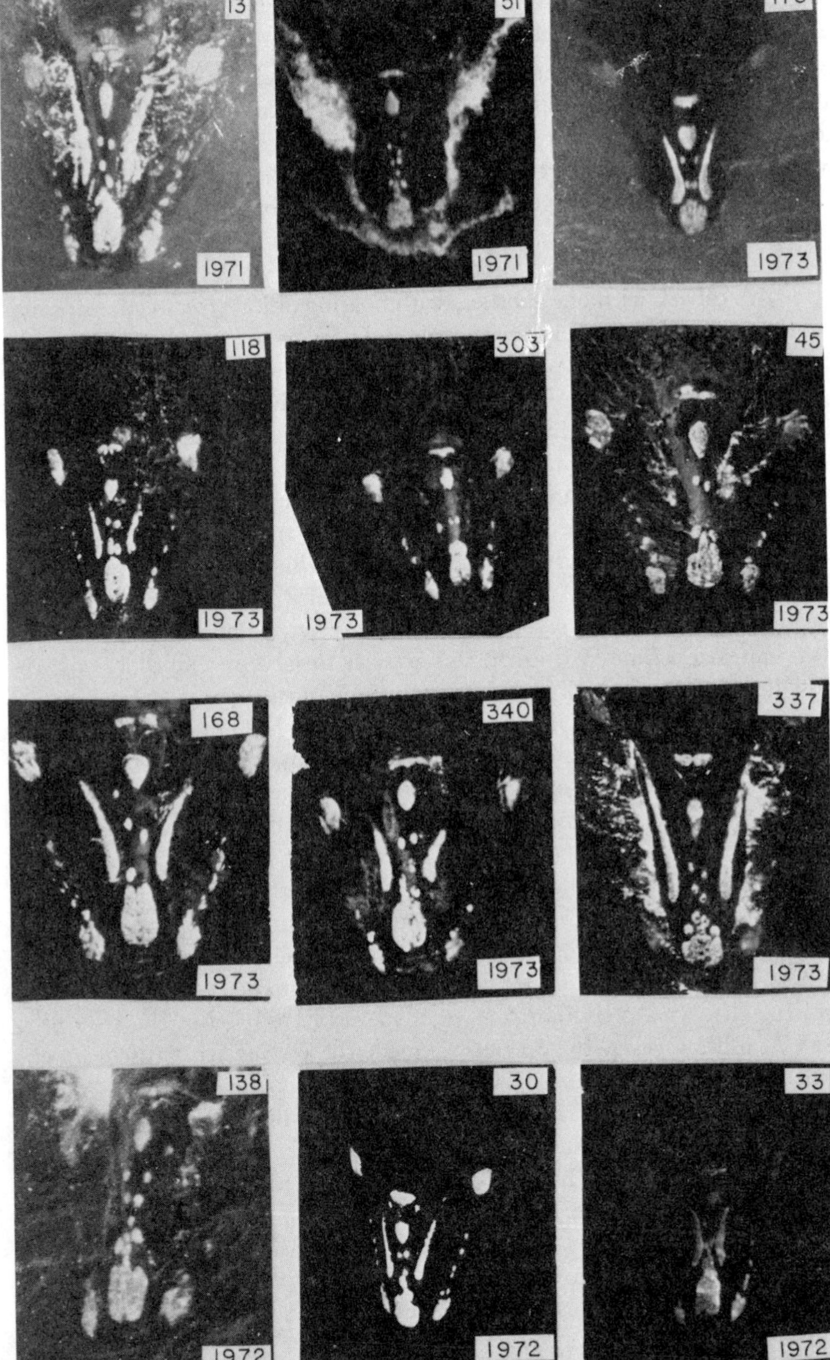
13
1971
51
1971
178
1973
118
1973
303
1973
45
1973
168
1973
340
1973
337
1973
138
1972
30
1972
33
1972

by using the diameter of the circle as a measuring stick. When a whale we had already measured pulled alongside a whale of unknown length the second could be measured against the first. By comparing the size of young whales with their mothers we watched the growth rate of the young during the time they were present. We are currently building our information into an estimate of population (Whitehead and Payne, in press).

We found that play is a prominent activity of whales in the area. They play with calves, with one another, with floating objects (seaweed, our sonobuoys, anchored boats), even with seals and porpoises.

There seems to be no part taken by the male in raising young, and mating appears to be totally promiscuous, there being no observed pair bond. For example, we witnessed one male mate with two females and one of those females with another male—all in an afternoon. The activities preceding and accompanying mating are complex and become more interesting as we continue with the analysis of our results.

We witnessed a peculiar form of behavior which other observers (Cummings et al., 1972, 1974) believed was feeding in which a whale holds the entire tail as well as the last several feet of its body motionless in the air for up to 20 minutes at a time. We found this activity to serve several functions, the most interesting of which seems to be sailing—not, apparently, as a way to get around but as a form of play.

During the southern summer (December-May) of 1972-73, when the whales had migrated out of our study area, we worked on three projects:

(1) A survey of the fossil whale remains in the cliffs surrounding Península Valdés, and a study of the recent cetacean corpses and bones found on the beaches in the area. During this phase of the expedition, James G. Mead, curator of marine mammals at the Smithsonian Institution, joined us. We found extensive representation of fossil baleen whales, including two complete cetothere skulls and several nearly whole skeletons from the Tertiary period, indicating that whales similar to modern species have lived in the area for at least 20 million years. In addition we made the very exciting discovery of a little-known whale species, *Tasmacetus shepherdi,* found dead on a remote beach. This was the first time a whole specimen of this species had ever been dissected and the first time the species had ever been seen in the Atlantic Ocean—other specimens having been found only in the New Zealand-Tasman Sea area (Mead and Payne, 1975).

(2) We made an intensive search for evidence that the Península Valdés right whales migrate along the coast on their way to or from southern feeding grounds. The areas we searched included the Beagle Channel between

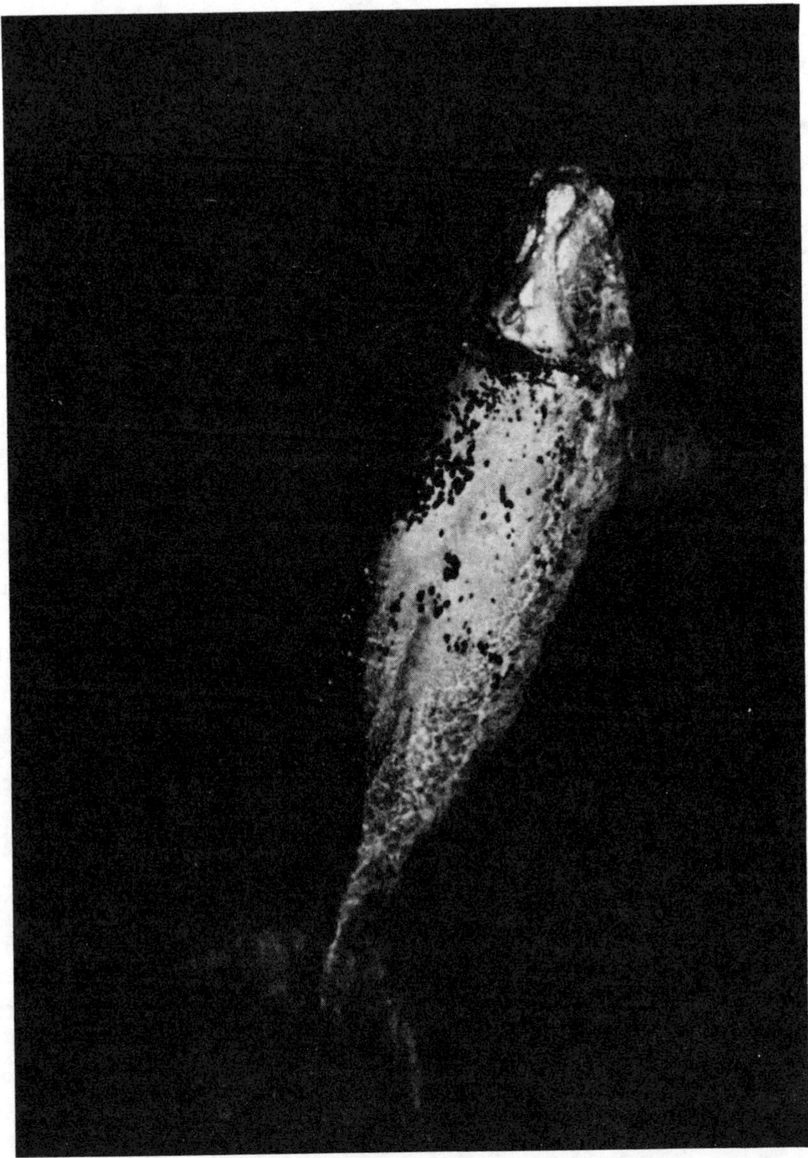

FIG. 3. A rare, partial albino right whale. This individual has been studied intensively over a 7-year period. A record of its growth over the years constitutes the first direct measurements ever made of growth rates of large whales in their natural state.

Ushuaia and Punta Arenas (thanks to the National Science Foundation research vessel *Hero)* as well as the waters near Palmer Peninsula in Antarctica (thanks to the *Lindblad Explorer)* and the Falkland Islands. Our hope was to encounter at least one of the whales we can recognize from our catalogue of the individuals in the herd. But not only did we fail to find a single live right whale; also we had no sign of any dead ones on the dozens of beaches we searched in aerial surveys of the Falklands and Fuegian canals, and no reports of whales in the last quarter century from many residents of the estancias and outposts along the coast with whom we talked. (Since this fruitless search, however, we believe we may have obtained evidence for a more eastward, mid-ocean migratory path. We are anxious to follow this up in the future.)

(3) Graduate student Bernd Würsig started a study of the behavior and biology of the dusky dolphin *(Lagenorhynchus obscurus),* as revealed by radio tracking. He also characterized a small herd of *Tursiops* sp. photographically; these, he found, could be recognized and followed as individuals on the basis of idiosyncrasies of their dorsal fins. This enabled him to describe the degree of stability of the herd over a 4-year period. Würsig has recently completed his thesis and has already published a report on the findings in these two studies (Würsig, 1976; Würsig and Würsig, 1977).

The following outline gives the over-all picture of the present form of the right whale study as we finish analyzing our data from Argentina:

All the studies started during the grant period 1971-1973 are ongoing in 1978 with a number of popular articles and several definitive scientific papers on our results now behind us and half a dozen papers and two books (one technical, one popular) in preparation.

Our study has also been featured in a number of hour television specials including one by the National Geographic Society, Survival Anglia (2 films), BBC-TV, and the Canadian Broadcasting system. The total audience for these 5 films exceeds 150 million. R. Payne has also lectured at several major universities on this work, starting with an NGS lecture in Constitution Hall. There are many indications that the publication of two major articles on the whales of the Península Valdés in the *National Geographic* had a great deal to do with a decision in 1974 by the Province of Chubut in Argentina to declare San José Bay on Península Valdés (the prime whale habitat) a nonexploitable marine reserve for all time. The whole Valdés Península is now under consideration as a national park.

FIG. 4. This spectacular activity is called breaching and serves several functions. One is a primitive means of communication—the signal being the sound of the whale hitting the water.

Humpback Whales

Grant No. 1685 enabled us to follow up on observations by Katharine Payne demonstrating that the elaborate springtime vocalizations (the so-called "songs") of humpback whales *(Megaptera novaeangliae)* change every year. From our work in Bermuda we know that each singer keeps pace with the annual changes so that its song is like the song of that year (Payne and Payne, in press). The grant allowed us to extend this work to the humpback whales near Hawaii. Because high volcanic islands lining the Hawaiian chain cast a wind shadow, the waters near the islands are calm enough to allow daily study. With Rockefeller University graduate fellow Peter Tyack, we recorded throughout the 1976-77 season and analyzed the changes in the song that occurred. We found that the songs change constantly, that although there are different songs (dialects) in Bermuda and Hawaii the laws upon which the songs are based are the same; meaning that the laws for constructing songs are inherited and the whales improvise within these laws. Whether the inheritance of the laws for these songs in two such isolated areas is genetic or cultural remains to be seen.

Part of this research program was carried out with Dr. Sylvia Earle and Al Giddings, both highly skilled divers of broad experience. On several occasions they were able to observe whales that were singing. These observations revealed that, while singing, humpbacks are relatively still and maintain a depth of about 100 feet. They do not release air during the production of sounds but apparently generate their sounds internally. On one occasion the observers saw a peculiar stretching behavior following each phrase in one of the themes of the song. This suggests that there may be a visual display associated with singing in humpbacks.

A useful outcome of our research is that the County of Maui in Hawaii has now designated the entire area of ocean surrounding the islands of Maui, Lanai, Kahoolawe, and Molokai as a park for humpback whales during the time they are in the area. This appears to be the first time a local United States government established a program to protect an endangered species.

We are grateful to the National Geographic Society for their continued support of our whale studies and for the direct contribution that they have made to conservation of whales by giving them so much coverage in the magazine. It is this kind of exposure that makes it possible to gain local support for parks that will protect whales forever.

Another outcome of the humpback-whale research is the publication of a second record album, "Deep Voices," featuring humpback and right whale sounds. These in turn have led to numerous "serious" and popular musical compositions. It is a welcome result to see whales being so broadly adopted.

REFERENCES

BACKUS, R. H.
1958. Sound production by marine animals. Journ. Underwater Acoust., vol. 8, pp. 191-202.

CUMMINGS, W. C.; FISH, J. F.; and THOMPSON, P. O.
1972. Sound production and other behavior of southern right whales, *Eubalaena glacialis.* Trans. San Diego Soc. Nat. Hist., vol. 17, no. 1, pp. 1-14

CUMMINGS, W. C., and PHILIPPI, L. A.
1970. Whale phonations in repetitive stanzas. Naval Undersea Research and Development Center, San Diego, Techn. Publ. NUC TP 196, 8 pp.

CUMMINGS, W. C.; THOMPSON, P. O.; and FISH, J. F.
1974. Behavior of southern right whales: R/V *Hero* cruise 72-3. Antarctic Journ. of U. S., vol. 9, no. 2, pp. 33-38.

MEAD, JAMES G., and PAYNE, ROGER S.
1975. A specimen of the Tasman beaked whale, *Tasmacetus shepherdi,* from Argentina. Journ. Mamm., vol. 56, pp. 213-218.

PAYNE, ROGER S.
1971. Whales and the endangered species conservation act. The Sciences, vol. 11, p. 18.
1972a. The whale fund manual, 33 pp. New York Zool. Soc.
1972b. Swimming with Patagonia's right whales. Nat. Geogr. Mag., vol. 142, no. 4, pp. 576-587.
1972c. Report from Patagonia: The right whales. New York Zool. Soc. Spring Newsletter, 6 pp.
1972d. The song of the whale. Pp. 144-167 *in* "Marvels of Animal Behavior," P. Marler, ed. Nat. Geogr. Soc.
1974. A playground for whales. Animal Kingdom, vol. 77, pp. 7-12.
1976. At home with right whales. Nat. Geogr. Mag., vol. 149, no. 3, pp. 322-341, illus.
1978. Behavior and vocalizations of humpback whales *(Megaptera* sp.), and A note on harassment. Appendices 8 (13 pp.) and 13 (2 pp.) *in* "Report of a Workshop on Problems Related to Humpback Whales *(Megaptera novaeangliae)* in Hawaii, July 1977," Kenneth S. Norris and Randall R. Reeves, eds. PB-280 794. Report no. MMC-77/03. Springfield, Va. (Prepared for the U. S. Marine Mammal Commission.)

PAYNE, ROGER S., and MCVAY, S.
1971. Songs of humpback whales. Science, vol. 173, pp. 587-597.

PAYNE, ROGER S., and PAYNE, KATHERINE B.
1971. Underwater sounds of southern right whales. Zoologica, vol. 56, no. 4, pp. 159-165.

PAYNE, ROGER S., and WEBB, D.
1971. Orientation by means of long-range acoustic signaling in baleen whales. *In* "Orientation: Sensory Basis," H. E. Adler, ed. Ann. New York Acad. Sci., vol. 188, pp. 110-141.

RICE, D. W., and WOLMAN, A. A.
1971. The life history and ecology of the gray whale *(Eschrichtius robustus).* Amer. Soc. Mammal., Spec. Publ. 3, 142 pp.

SCHEVILL, W. E.
1964. Underwater sounds of cetaceans. Pp. 307-316 *in* "Marine Bio-Acoustics," W. N. Tavolga, ed. Pergamon Press, Oxford.

SCHEVILL, W. E., and WATKINS, W. A.
1962. Whale and porpoise voices. Woods Hole Ocean. Inst., Contr. 1320, 24 pp. (includes a phonograph record).

TAVOLGA, W. N.
1965. Review of marine bio-acoustics, state of the art: 1964. Techn. Rep. (1964) NAVTRADEVCEN 1212-1 (U. S. Naval Training Device Center, Port Washington, N.Y.), 100 pp.

WHITEHEAD, H., and PAYNE, ROGER S.
1976. New techniques for assessing a population of right whales without killing them. *In* "Proceedings of the Scientific Consultation of Marine Mammals," United Nations Food and Agricultural Organization, ACMRR/MM/SC/79.

WÜRSIG, BERND
1976. Radio tracking of dusky porpoises *(Lagenorhynchus obscurus)* in the South Atlantic, a preliminary analysis. *In* Proceedings of the Scientific Consultation of Marine Mammals. Publ. Food and Agr. Org. United Nations, ACMRR/MM/SC/83.

WÜRSIG, BERND, and WÜRSIG, MELANY
1977. The photographic determination of group size, composition, and stability of coastal porpoises *(Tursiops truncatus).* Science, vol. 198, pp. 755-756, illus.

Records by Roger S. Payne

1977. Deep Voices. Capitol Records ST-11598.
1970. Songs of the Humpback whale. Capitol Records ST-620

Motion Pictures by Roger S. Payne

1971. The Right Whale at Home. New York Zoological Society.
1975. Magnificent Monsters of the Deep. Survival Anglia (television).
1976. Portrait of a Whale. National Geographic Society Educational Film.
1976. The Right Whale: an Endangered Species. National Geographic Society Educational Film.
1976. The Right Whale. National Geographic Society Lecture Film.
1977. Gentle Giants of the Pacific. Survival Anglia (television).

ROGER S. PAYNE

Ethnographic Research on *Afkodre*, Surinam

Principal Investigator: B. Edward Pierce, SUNY College at New Paltz, New Paltz, New York.

Grant No. 974: To make an ethnographic investigation of *afkodre:* magic and religion among Surinamese Creoles.

This research embraced the gathering of ethnographic data on *afkodre,* the Afro-Caribbean magico-religious complex of lower status Creoles or *Nengre* in Paramaribo, Surinam, during the summer of 1971. Hector V. Hidalgo, a graduate student in anthropology at Florida State University, accompanied me to Surinam as a research assistant but was forced to return to the United States before the field research was completed. Hermine Zaalman was employed to help with the transcription of tapes.

Traditionally oriented *Nengre* refer to their Afro-Caribbean magico-religious possession complex as *afkodre* or *winti. Afkodre* is a Surinamese Creole term derived from the Dutch *afgoderij* (heathenism). *Winti* is the generic name for possessing spirit. While some Surinamese Creole nationalists who consider *winti* possession as the quintessential expression of Creole ethnicity object to the term *afkodre* because of the negative connotations of the Dutch cognate, those who are most heavily involved in the complex use the term freely with no negative connotations. I have retained the term *afkodre* in this and several other papers as the reflection of the fact that the complex is distinctively Afro-Caribbean and consists of belief and ritual systems that include but are not limited to *winti.*

I originally became interested in *afkodre* as a result of reading *Suriname Folk-Lore,* the only source on *Nengre* supernaturalism published in English (Herskovits and Herskovits, 1936). Between 1967 and 1969, when I was involved in field research on the family organization of *Nengre* in Paramaribo, I attended several public *winti* ceremonies and made initial attempts to gather information on the *afkodre* complex. Preliminary research indicated that most *Nengre,* including those who are actively involved in *afkodre,* do not have a comprehensive and systemic view of its belief and ritual systems and that the significance of the complex is much greater than the publicly manifest singing, dancing, and drumming would lead one to suspect. It became apparent that an adequate ethnographic analysis of the *afkodre* complex would have to be based on ethnographic interviewing and observation of a *bonuman* or specialist in *afkodre.*

The research period covered 10 weeks, from the third week of June through the end of August. During this period I spent approximately 40 hours in interviews and 60 hours in the observation of rituals with a *bonuman* informant whose anonymity must be preserved. The interviews were tape recorded and transcribed, and field notes were taken during periods of observation. Research was carried out exclusively in *Sranan,* the Surinamese Creole language that is utilized by *Nengre* in traditional contexts and particularly in discussing *afkodre.*

The field data have provided the basis for three papers presented at professional meetings (Pierce, 1972a, 1972b, 1973), and one paper based on historical data gathered from Surinamese libraries during the research period supported by the National Geographic Society grant has been accepted for publication (Pierce, 1974).

A summary description of the *afkodre* complex follows. While the description is based on data gathered from a single informant during a relatively brief period, I am confident that it is a reasonably accurate and complete representation of sociocultural reality.

The Afkodre *Complex*

Principal Focus of Afkodre. *Afkodre* consists of loosely structured systems of belief and ritual associated with a considerable variety of supernatural beings and with supernatural power in general. Precise definition of *afkodre* in terms of its parameters or components is impossible, but the complex can be approached in terms of what evidence suggests is its central focus. The central focus of *afkodre* is *bonu* or the curing of one of two general categories of disease according to the *Nengre* world view.

At the most general level, *Nengre* classify diseases as *gado siki* "God sickness" or *Nengre siki* "Nengro-sickness." *Gado siki* is due to the will of God and, if it can be cured, is amenable to Western European medical treatment. *Nengre siki* is disease or misfortune caused by non-Christian supernatural power.

A person who suffers persistent physical or mental maladies initially visits one or more doctors with the expectation that he will be cured. If the doctors' cures remove or appear to remove the symptoms, the patient assumes that he was suffering from a *gado siki.* If the disease is not cured after visits to several doctors, the patient will probably reach the conclusion that he is suffering from *Nengre siki.* Persistent misfortune or tragedy that is unwarranted and unnaturally severe is also classified as *Nengre siki.* When *Nengre siki* is suspected, a *bonuman* is consulted on the basis of past experience or on the advice of elders who are considered to be knowledgeable in *afkodre.*

The specific causes of *Nengre siki* are infinite in number but can be subsumed within six general categories: (1) *Kunu* or retribution for evil actions by ancestors, (2) *wisi* or evil magic by other human beings, (3) failure to observe *trefu* or patrilineally inherited food taboos, (4) *fiofio* or disease caused by apparently friendly social interaction between individuals who harbor repressed feelings of anger toward each other, (5) *ogri ai* or evil eye, which is caused by the glance of an envious individual, and (6) anger or malevolence by ancestral *yorka* (ghosts) and *winti.* If the data provided by the *bonuman* informant are representative, category 6 is the cause of most cases of *Nengre siki.*

Basic Categories of Supernatural Beings. Numerous types of supernatural beings are differentiated by the *Nengre.* The categories that are most important insofar as *afkodre* is concerned are *yorka* (ghosts) and *winti* (possessing spirits).

Some *yorka* are considered to be malevolent in that they wander by night and attack victims or are controlled by human beings who use them for evil magic. Other *yorka* are attached to cognatic descent groups. Ancestral *yorka* may possess their descendants and give them warnings and advice, but if not properly cared for they can cause *Nengre siki.* While traditional *Nengre* families still serve their ancestral *yorka,* the importance of these is apparently declining.

Winti, the most important supernatural beings in *afkodre,* are possessing spirits that are similar to *loa* of Haitian *vodun* and *orisha* of Brazilian *candomble.* They manifest themselves in mediums who are sometimes referred to as *asi* (horses). *Winti* usually mount their mediums in response to particular drum rhythms and songs, or at the urging of a *bonuman.* However, if a *winti* is extremely angry at its medium, unexpected and unsolicited possession can occur.

Each *winti* has particular behavior patterns that their mediums manifest when possessed. In addition, *winti* have specific preferences in ornamentation, clothing, food, drink, and entertainment, and they demand that these be given to them in various types of sacrifices, feasts, and public celebrations. If *winti* are properly served, they give their mediums knowledge and useful skills, but if their desires are ignored they cause *Nengre siki.*

Each *winti* is either male or female, and *winti* of either sex possess mediums of the same or opposite sex. Each *winti* is associated with a significant part of the Surinamese environment. Several of the important dimensions of contrast are *Nengre Kondre* (Negro Country, or African) as opposed to an unnamed category of indigenous Surinamese *winti; tapu* ("sky"); *gron* ("earth"); *watra* ("water"); *busi* ("bush"); *pranassi* (plantation); and *foto* ("city"). These environmental categories are combined with a changing set of categories that appear to reflect segments of Surinamese society to produce a tremendously complex system of classification. An attempted formal analysis of the *winti* classificatory system suggests that it encapsulates a folk geography and folk history and that it is generative rather than taxonomic (Pierce, 1973).

Winti become attached to mediums in three ways: (1) Inheritance through the mother or father; (2) acquisition from the place at which the medium was conceived, and (3) personal attraction felt by a *winti* for a particular individual. All human beings are considered to have at least four and many have six *oso* (house) or permanent *winti.* Those with weak personalities may be possessed by additional *winti* on a temporary basis.

Components of Individuals' Souls. All human beings are considered by *Nengre* to have a "soul" that consists of two components, the *kra* and the *djodjo,* and each of these has a masculine and feminine aspect. The male and female aspects of the *kra* and *djodjo* are associated with *winti* of the appropriate sex. On ceremonial occasions the masculine and feminine aspects of the *kra* and *djodjo* may be addressed by day names that are derived from Akan languages of West Africa, but they are usually referred to and addressed by the names of the *winti* with which they are associated. Male and female *kra winti* are inherited through the father or mother and endow their medium with knowledge and foresight. Male and female *djodjo winti* are acquired by an individual from the location at which his parents conceived him, and endow him with skills and talents. *Kra winti* are considered to fill the role of parents toward the medium, and *djodjo winti* to occupy roles analogous to those of foster parents who nurture and nourish him. In addition to *kra* and *djodjo winti,* an individual may be born with *pepe* and *nene* (godfather and godmother) *winti,* but ideas concerning the manner in which they are acquired are vague. *Kra, djodjo,* and possibly *pepe* and *nene winti* remain with an individual throughout life and are referred to as *oso winti* or house *winti.* If an individual's house *winti* are weak and ineffectual, other *winti* who feel a personal attraction to him may possess him temporarily; and in such cases the individual is continually troubled because of the changing and contradictory demands that his *winti* make. The dominant *kra* and *djodjo winti* of a male are feminine *winti;* and the dominant *kra* and *djodjo winti* of a female are masculine.

The Bonuman *and* Bonu *Rituals.* The *bonuman,* who may be either a male or a female, has a *kra winti* that is especially adept at foreseeing or divining and a *djodjo winti* that is adept in the performance of *bonu* cures. In addition to his ritualistic and magical skills, the *bonuman* should be able to talk eloquently and politely so that he can converse persuasively with *winti* and *yorka*.

The *bonuman* who served as the informant for this study insisted on several occasions that while he performed *bonu* cures in the way that his *winti* instructed him, other *bonuman* performed during rituals differently. While I attended public *winti* ceremonies presided over by several *bonuman,* I did not have the opportunity to observe their performance of private rituals and ceremonies. However, on the basis of observations of rituals performed by the principal informant, and general verification through casual interviewing of others who are actively involved in *afkodre,* it can be provisionally suggested that the following ritual sequence is general.

When an individual consults a *bonuman* for the first time, his male and female day names, ancestral plantation, place of conception, and *winti* must be determined. The *bonuman* establishes these facts through divination with a fetish that belongs to the *kra winti* on which his power of divination depends. This initial divinatory session is referred to as *firi* ("feeling") or *luku* ("looking"); and the fetish that is utilized is a *firi* or *luku obia*.

After the patient's soul components have been identified, the *bonuman* can converse directly with the *winti* in a ritual referred to as *kari kra* (calling of the *kra*). In this ritual the patient holds a cup of water containing an egg, cowrie shells, and various other objects in his outstretched palm. The *bonuman* summons and questions the patient's *winti* with the aim of determining whether the malady or misfortune is due to *Nengre siki* and, if so, how to remedy it. Only questions requiring a positive or negative response are asked. The *winti* that is being questioned indicates an affirmative answer by making the medium's hand tremble so as to spill water forward. If water is spilled to the rear, *yorka* are possessing the individual and must be questioned.

If the patient is suffering from a *Nengre siki* one or several of the following may be required: (1) *Wasi* or bathing with teas in which key ingredients are various types of leaves, spices, perfumes, and alcoholic beverages; (2) *skin paiman* (body sacrifices) of jewelry requested by the *winti* that are to be worn by the medium; (3) *pranassi paiman* (plantation sacrifices) offerings of food, beverages, and useful items such as cloth, thread, scissors, and knives to be placed at the habitation site of the *winti* (usually the ancestral plantation or patient's place of conception); (4) *kra tafra* or *yorka tafra* or ceremonial feasts at which *winti* or *yorka* are given their favorite food and drink; and (5) *winti pre* or *yorka pre* or public entertainments for *winti* or *yorka* during which their favorite music is played and they possess their mediums and dance.

The ceremonies enumerated in the preceding paragraph are arranged in order of increasing elaborateness and expenditure. *Winti* and *yorka pre* may last for a week and involve lavish contributions of food, liquor, and money by large numbers of family members. A *pre* is usually accompanied by *kra* and/or *yorka tafra, skin* and *pranassi paiman,* and *wasi.* A *kra tafra* may involve seven elaborate feasts that extend through a week and are accompanied by *skin* and *paranassi paiman* and *wasi.* No cases were observed in which *pranassi paiman, skin paiman,* or *wasi* was the culmination of the ritual sequence. It is doubtful that *winti* or *yorka* that were dissatisfied enough to cause *Nengre siki* would require such minor placation.

It is important to note that all the rituals mentioned above are expensive and time consuming and that most *Nengre* are economically marginal subsistence wage earners. They are not performed unless and until it becomes absolutely necessary, and seldom occur more than once in five or ten years. In some cases, those who are obligated to give feasts and/or entertainments try to postpone them until *bigi yari* (big year) or fifth birthdays which should be celebrated with dancing, feasting, and other forms of conspicuous consumption. This discussion does not exhaustively cover all rituals that are important in the *afkodre* complex, but it provides the reader with a general idea of the types of ceremonies that occur most frequently.

Conclusions

Most of the ethnographic literature that has appeared on Afro-Caribbean possession cults has followed the lead of Herskovitz (1937) in conceiving of pantheons of possessing deities in terms of the retention of African gods in the New World and the synchretic merging of the characteristics of these gods and Roman Catholic saints. Numerous African deities have survived in one form or another in *afkodre,* but unlike the cults that developed in Hispanic and French areas of the Caribbean in which the metropolitan religion was Catholicism, the identities of *winti* are never merged with those of Catholic saints or any other Christian supernatural beings. Furthermore, it is extremely important to note that large numbers of *winti,* and as a matter of fact the general system for classifying *winti,* are not African or Christian, but Afro-Caribbean. This suggests that *afkodre,* and presumably other Afro-Caribbean possession cults as well, might be conceived of as adaptive responses to Creole environments.

Afro-Caribbean possession cults have generally been described as if their members form relatively formally organized congregations, which gather at regular intervals at a place of worship that is presided over by a "priest" or "priestess." This is definitely not the case with *afkodre. Afkodre* rituals always occur on the basis of a *bonuman*-patient relationship. Varying numbers of kinsmen and nonfamilial members of the patient's personal network may attend, and those who are gathered are associated on a temporary basis. The patient may reject the *bonuman*'s services at any time, for any reason, and he is perfectly free to seek the advice of another specialist.

The heterogeneity of the belief and ritual systems of *afkodre* has been noted. This heterogeneity, and the extreme fluidity of its social organization, suggest that the *afkodre* complex is characterized by a high degree of adaptive flexibility. It has provided answers and remedies to questions and problems that Afro-Caribbeans in Surinam have faced from the Period of Slavery until the present in rural areas as well as the urban environment.

REFERENCES

HERSKOVITS, MELVILLE J.

1937. African gods and Catholic saints in New World Negro belief. Amer. Anthrop., vol. 39, pp. 635-643.

HERSKOVITS, MELVILLE J., and HERSKOVITS, FRANCES S.

1936. Suriname folk-lore, 766 pp. Columbia University Press, New York.

PIERCE, B. EDWARD

1972a. The synthesis of Christian and non-Christian elements in Afkodre: Synchretism in the folk religion of lower status Creoles in Paramaribo, Surinam. Paper presented at 12th annual meeting of Northwestern Anthropological Association, Buffalo, New York, April 21, 1972.

1972b. The social organization of Afkodre. Paper presented at 71st annual meeting of American Anthropological Association, Toronto, Canada, December 1, 1972.

1973. The expression of world view in winti classification. Paper presented at symposium on Afro-American expressive culture, Southern Anthropological Society, Wrightsville Beach, North Carolina, March 8, 1973.

1977. The historical context of Nengre kinship and residence: Ethnohistory of the family organization of lower status Creoles in Paramaribo. Pp. 107-131 *in* "Old Roots in New Lands: Historical and Anthropological Perspectives on Black Experiences in the Americas," Ann M. Pescatello, ed. Greenwood Press, Westport, Conn.

WOODING, C. J.

1972. Winti: Een Afroamerikaanse Godsdient in Suriname, 565 pp. Krips Reprob. v., Meppel, Holland.

B. EDWARD PIERCE

Ecology of the Golden-rumped Elephant-shrew (*Rhynchocyon chrysopygus*) of Kenya

Principal Investigator: Galen B. Rathbun, Department of Zoology, University of Nairobi, Kenya.

Grant No. 989: For a study of the golden-rumped elephant-shrew in the coastal forests of Kenya.

The elephant-shrews (Macroscelididae), seldom-seen and little-known insectivores endemic to Africa, occupy a wide range of habitats. Although the family has been taxonomically revised (Corbet and Hanks, 1968), it has been largely neglected behaviorally and ecologically except for some recent short-term work on *Macroscelides* in the Namib Desert of southwest Africa (Sauer, 1973). Of the four elephant-shrew genera, *Rhynchocyon* is probably the most specialized and least known. *R. chrysopygus,* one of three species in the genus, is large for an insectivore, weighing over 500 grams and having a body length of approximately 270 millimeters (fig. 1). Its distribution is restricted to the coastal forests of Kenya from Mombasa north through the Boni Forest.

FIG. 1. The golden-rumped elephant-shrew, *Rhynchocyon chrysopygus.*

I carried out a field study of this elephant-shrew (in press) at Gedi Historical Monument, Malindi, Kenya, between April 1971 and December 1972. The monument is a 44-hectare area containing 13th-century Arab ruins that have been totally overgrown with lowland, dry, semi-deciduous forest and scrub. The forest floor was continually covered with dry leaf litter and small patches of sedge and grass. Visibility beyond 10 meters was usually poor because of the vegetation. The ruins were surrounded by small farms and thus could be considered an island in terms of elephant-shrew movements. A system of trails was maintained in the forest for tourists, and in addition a network of small paths was constructed in the southern third of the forest, which formed the principal study area.

I captured elephant-shrews by means of nylon fishing nets strung loosely along the trails and paths. Before being released, captured animals were sexed, aged, and marked on both rear legs above the ankles with colored plastic bird rings. By slowly and cautiously walking the trail and path network with binoculars it was possible to resight and observe the elephant-shrews. During the study period specimens were collected monthly about 5 kilometers from Gedi in the Sokoke-Arabuko Forest. Data on feeding and reproduction were gathered from these specimens.

Population Structure and Social Behavior

The mean monthly density at Gedi was 1.6 elephant-shrews per hectare. The adult sex ratio was equal. The litter size was always one and the minimum observed breeding interval was approximately 36 days, which was probably the result of a postpartum estrus. The elephant-shrews bred throughout the year. The theoretical maximum fecundity was thus 10 young per female per year, but the actual observed fecundity was 4 or 5 young per female per year. The gestation period is unknown, but it is probably about 42 days. The location of the precocial birth and the period of time the young is restricted to the nest are also unknown, but it is estimated that first emergence from the nest occurs about 2 weeks after birth. By the time the young emerged from the nest it was weaned, and in approximately 5 more days it was independent of its mother, although it remained on her home range for a highly variable period.

The elephant-shrews were distributed as pairs on contiguous territories that were stable and fairly consistent in size. The mean territory size for 11 individuals was 1.7 hectares, with a range of 1.4 to 2.0 hectares. Of the total sightings (1,826) for these same individuals, 8.3 percent were outside of their territories. During the 21-month study no permanent boundary changes were observed, although on three occasions territories were temporarily combined when a resident male disappeared and a nearby resident male moved in and occupied both territories. This condition was unstable, and in all cases the original boundaries were re-established when the vacated territory was occupied by a nonterritorial male. The females maintained their boundaries during these temporary shifts.

Both sexes scent-marked with a caudal gland, which was periodically rubbed on the leaf litter or fallen branches while the animal foraged or walked along. No evidence of scent, urine, or dung posts was observed. Of the total sightings for 8 territorial animals, 6.3 percent included marking behavior.

Both sexes defended their territories sex-specifically; males most often chased males and females most often chased females. In a chase sequence a resident would assume a low, crouched position with its head low, ears forward, and nose waving about in the air as it cautiously approached an intruder. Warning slaps of the resident's tail on the leaf litter would occur every 1 to 3 seconds as the gap between the animals closed. When approximately 3 meters apart the two animals would break into a high-speed chase, one behind the other, in zigzags and wide circles through the forest. A chase would continue until the intruder was driven from the territory. Territorial aggression was restricted to chasing with occasional physical contact. Males were more intensely territorial, marking and chasing more often than females (Rathbun, 1978).

It is very likely that the distinctive rump patch in *R. chrysopygus,* which shows no sexual dimorphism, is related to the animal's territorial behavior. Both sexes have well-developed canines, although the male's are larger, that do not appear to be specially adapted for feeding. When dermal scars, as might be inflicted by these canines during conspecific territorial chases, were cumulatively plotted from 84 study skins a concentration was found on the rump patch. In addition, both sexes have a dermal thickening under the rump patch. In the males it is most highly developed and the rump skin can be three times thicker than the skin on the middle of the back. Considering the animal's territorial behavior and its morphology I speculate that the rump patch may serve as a conspecific target organ, and thus during territorial chases any aggressive blows would be directed toward the region of the body that is morphologically adapted to receive them (Rathbun, 1978).

Although the animals were permanently paired, the pair bond appeared to be relatively weak. Pairs spent little time together, and, when possible, resident males would attempt to mate with intruding females and intruding males would attempt to mate with resident females. Of the total sightings for three territorial females 21 percent included the male close-by. While a pair moved through their territory the male always followed the female. On many occasions males were observed to follow the exact course a female had foraged along some 5 to 10 minutes before. The characteristic musky odor of *Rhynchocyon* and the periodic scent marking were probably important in intrapair communication. Observations of pair greetings were few and consisted of nose-nose and nose-side contacts and vocal chattering, and in more intensive encounters the female would attempt to crawl under the male. Males, while following females, would often come up and make nose-anus and nose-genital contact and then attempt to mount, but successful copulation was not observed as the females always walked away.

Young normally did not participate in defending the parents' territory, nor were they observed to be chased off of their parents' territory. One young left its parents' territory and occupied a vacant one only 32 days after nest emergence, while at the other extreme a "young" animal was still resident on its parents' territory 27 weeks after emergence, when fieldwork was terminated. It appears that the young were able to remain indefinitely on their parents' territory while they made occasional excursions in search of unoccupied territories. They eventually either found a vacancy or disappeared, presumably to predators. Scent-marking by territorial animals may have been important in communicating occupancy to these nonterritorial young elephant-shrews. Animals violating territories were behaviorally obvious and probably at a considerable disadvantage by not being familiar with the area. Only territorial animals were observed to breed. Emigration was probably not successful because of the island nature of the study area. Of the 17 young produced by four territorial pairs in 12 months, 3 were successful in obtaining their own territories, 3 were still on their parents' territories when fieldwork was terminated, 1 was known to have been taken by a bird of prey, and the remaining 10 disappeared, presumably to predators. During the same period on the same territories 5 territorial adults disappeared. It is estimated that once a territory is obtained an elephant-shrew may live to 3 to 4 years of age.

Individual Behavior

R. chrysopygus was found to be diurnal, spending nearly the entire day foraging in the leaf litter. It occasionally was observed resting at midday either on the forest floor or rarely in a nest.

Dry leaf nests were periodically constructed on the forest floor during the early morning. A typical nest was built in approximately 2 hours. The animal dragged dry leaves from the immediate area using stiffly outstretched forelegs while lurching backward, thus accumulating a pile of leaves under the chest and abdomen. It then carefully arranged the leaves in a shallow excavation in the soil using the forefeet and occasionally the mouth. A finished nest appeared as an indistinct mound of leaves, a half meter in diameter, on the forest floor. At dusk a lone individual would very cautiously approach a nest and slip under the leaves for the night. Different nests were used every night or every few nights.

Elephant-shrews were never seen to burrow or climb, and there was no evidence of bipedal locomotion. They were very alert and when disturbed they were prone to swift escape into the undergrowth where they froze for 1 to 5 minutes or until the disturbance ceased. *R. chrysopygus* did not normally construct or use trails as do other macroscelidids.

Allogrooming was never observed and autogrooming was composed of frequent scratching using the rear legs. Face washing, as in many insectivores and rodents, was never observed.

Vocalizations appeared to be restricted to a low-intensity, high-pitched chatter between individuals and a loud, high-pitched rabbitlike cry from captured adults and young in distress.

Feeding Habits

The elephant-shrews foraged nearly continuously all day for invertebrates by slowly walking along probing under leaves, fallen branches, and stones with their long mobile noses. They used their forefeet to excavate leaves and to dig small conical holes in the soil. Analyses of 21 stomachs indicate that the elephant-shrews were feeding only on invertebrates. No plant or vertebrate remains were found. In addition, monthly leaf-litter faunal samples were collected over one year to determine food availability. The variables involved in both the stomach analyses and the availability samples make it difficult to make meaningful correlations, but it appears that *R. chrysopygus* was feeding on nearly all those invertebrates that were available and approximately in proportion to their availability. No significant seasonal variation was found (Rathbun, 1976).

The elephant-shrews ingested whole most small-prey species, such as spiders and insects, using a flick of the tongue, which can be extended a few millimeters beyond the nose. Larger-prey species, such as millipedes and earthworms, were held either to the ground with the forefeet and gnawed apart or in the mouth and clawed apart with the forefeet. No food storage or hoarding behavior was seen.

A commensal feeding relationship between *R. chrysopygus* and the red-capped robin-chat, *Cossypha natalensis,* was discovered. The robin-chat employed two techniques in gathering invertebrate prey in relation to the elephant-shrews. Firstly, it participated actively by hawking flying or hopping invertebrates that the elephant-shrew flushed as a result of its foraging and nest-building activities. Secondly, the robin-chat often foraged in the leaf litter that the elephant-shrew had recently disturbed. In the months of September, October, and November 1971, 7.6 percent of the total elephant-shrew sightings included a robin-chat within 1 meter. The relationship is considered commensal, for there was no evidence that the presence of the robin-chat was of any advantage or disadvantage to the elephant-shrew.

REFERENCES

CORBET, G. B., and HANKS, J.

1968. A revision of the elephant-shrews (Macroscelididae). Bull. Brit. Mus. Nat. Hist. (Zool.), vol. 16, pp. 47-112.

RATHBUN, G. B.

1973a. Territoriality in the golden-rumped elephant-shrew. E. African Wildl. Journ., vol. 11, p. 405.

1973b. The golden-rumped elephant-shrew. East African Wildlife Leadership Foundation, "News," vol. 8, no. 3, pp. 3-7.

1976. The ecology and social structure of the elephant-shrews *Rhynchocyon chrysopygus* Günther and *Elephantulus rufescens* Peters. Ph.D. Thesis, Department of Zoology, University of Nairobi, Nairobi, Kenya.

1978. Evolution of the rump patch in the golden-rumped elephant-shrew. Bull. Carnegie Mus. Nat. Hist. vol. 6, pp. 11-19.

——. The ecology and social structure of elephant-shrews. Zeitschr. Tierpsychol., Advances in Ethology Supplement no. 200. (In press.)

——. *Rhynchocyon chrysopygus.* Mammalian Species no. 120. (In press.)

SAUER, E.G.F.

1973. Zum Sozialverhalten der Kurzorigen Elefantenspitzmaus, *Macroscelides proboscideus.* Zeitschr. für Saugetierk., vol. 38, pp. 65-97.

GALEN B. RATHBUN

Livelihood Mobility and Economic Diversity in Three Villages of Trinidad

Principal Investigator: Bonham C. Richardson, Virginia Polytechnic Institute and State University, Blacksburg, Virginia.

Grant No. 940: For a spatial analysis of peasant livelihood behavior in Trinidad.

From June to September 1971 I did field research on the island of Trinidad in the southern Caribbean, testing some ideas I had developed from earlier work in coastal Guyana. In the latter country in 1968-69 I had found that inhabitants of rural areas displayed a high degree of mobility from their villages of residence, seeking different kinds of employment on both a daily and seasonal basis.[1] This livelihood mobility was encouraged by the presence of a paved coastal highway that linked together almost all villages of Guyana. Historically, the coastal highway of Guyana facilitated the movement of villagers to nearby plantations. Rural Guyanese still divide their time between doing extravillage wage work and farming local community lands.

In Trinidad, the economic history of which is similar to that of Guyana, I sought to determine if there were similar livelihood characteristics among the rural populace. My research was therefore directed to determining the degree of mobility of rural Trinidadians past and present, the part-time nature of their economic activities, and whether their behavior was influenced also by a plantation-biased transportation network. In a broader sense, I wanted to determine how subsistence and market activities were combined by Trinidad villagers to comprise total livelihood.

Trinidad is the larger in the two-island state of Trinidad and Tobago that received independence from England in 1962. Trinidad is the southernmost of the Lesser Antilles and geologically related to Venezuela whose shoreline is less than 10 miles across the Gulf of Paria from the southwestern tip of the island. Lying at lat. 11°N., Trinidad receives most of its rain from June to December, the highest totals occurring in the three ranges of hills and mountains that run generally east-west across the island. The natural vegetation is mainly rain forest, and it still dominates all but the west-central part of Trinidad.

[1] Bonham C. Richardson, "Spatial Determinants of Rural Livelihood in Coastal Guyana." *Professional Geogr.*, vol. 25, no. 4 (November 1973), pp. 363-368.

In the latter area, forest zones were first cleared under Spanish supervision in the late 16th century. This calm leeward side of the island was an attractive zone for sugarcane plantations as Trinidad passed from Spanish into British hands in the late 18th century. Western Trinidad continues to be the most densely populated area of the island and the locus of most of its economic activity.

The population of Trinidad is roughly 1,200,000, divided between the two principal ethnic groups, Negro descendants of former African plantation slaves and Indian descendants of former indentured plantation workers. Blacks and "mixed" peoples (about 600,000) dominate Trinidad urban areas while Indians (approximately 480,000), locally called "East Indians," are numerically superior in rural parts of the island.[2]

As in Guyana, I worked mainly with the Indian ethnic group in Trinidad's rural areas. Indentured Indian workers were first imported to the Caribbean in 1838 after freed slaves had proved an unreliable labor source according to plantation owners. The importation of Indians to the Caribbean ended in 1917. During the 80-year period of emigration, almost 400,000 Indians had arrived from the recruiting terminals at Calcutta and Madras.[3] About 240,000 had gone to British Guiana (Guyana), 140,000 to Trinidad, and lesser numbers to Grenada, Jamaica, and St. Vincent. Indians usually served for five years on plantations. After that either they were repatriated to India or they settled in local Caribbean village settlements as small-scale farmers and part-time estate workers. Descendants of these ex-indentured Indians, and a few of the original and now elderly emigrants from India, remain the dominant ethnic group in the rural zones of Guyana and Trinidad.

Scholarly interest in Indians of the English-speaking Caribbean has usually centered around the persistence or dissolution of cultural traits originating in India.[4] The presence of an Asian minority and African majority in the southern Caribbean has also inspired a number of studies dealing with racial, cultural, and political pluralism in the region. Although I was interested in learning about these aspects of culture and society while doing village field-

---

[2] Estimates are based upon Government of Trinidad and Tobago, *Annual Statistical Digest, 1969* (Central Statistical Office, 1971). As of early 1974 the most recent official population census for Trinidad and Tobago was that for 1960.

[3] See Dwarka Nath, *A History of Indians in British Guiana* (London: Thomas Nelson & Sons, 1950), and Judith Ann Weller, *The East Indian Indenture in Trinidad* (Río Piedras, Puerto Rico: Institute of Caribbean Studies, 1968).

[4] A good example is Morton Klass, *East Indians in Trinidad* (New York: Columbia University Press, 1961).

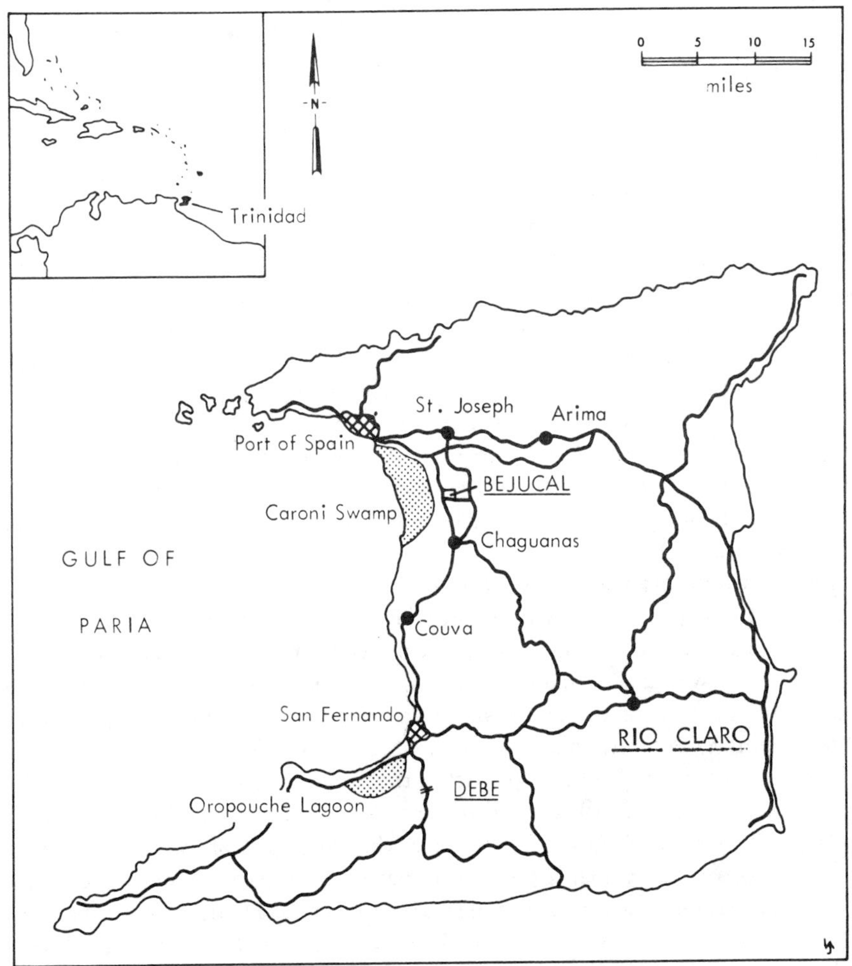

FIG. 1. Trinidad, showing study areas.

work in Trinidad, I was more concerned with the villagers' economic behavior.

When I first arrived in Trinidad in June 1971, I made contact with several of the national and local government agencies concerned with rural settlement, planning, and agriculture as well as the Trinidad Islandwide Cane Farmers' Association. Officials from this organization, an independent body whose constituency is the small-scale sugarcane farmers of the island, were very helpful in providing introductions to village leaders in various areas of Trinidad. After a general reconnaissance of about three weeks, I selected three village areas for more intensive study, Bejucal (about 2,500 population), Debe (about 3,500) in western Trinidad, and Rio Claro (about 3,500) in the southeastern part of the island (see map). The first two village zones are located on the open plain of western Trinidad adjacent to large-scale sugar estates. Their populations are overwhelmingly Indian, exclusively so in Debe. Rio Claro is racially mixed, and its surroundings are mainly in forest. I spent the better part of a month interviewing people in each of the three villages. In using these village areas as sample communities, I was able to interview and observe at the level of the individual and also obtain data reflecting Trinidad's rural area in general during a relatively short field period.

In the three settlement areas I observed village activities and surrounding lands although most of my information came from personal interviews. I sought out older men in the village areas who remembered early community histories, none of which had ever been recorded or has appeared in national yearbooks or archives. Some of the old men could remember almost to the beginnings of their settlements in the late 19th century. For contemporary livelihood data I systematically interviewed 75 heads of households in each of the three village areas. I identified three different zones in each settlement area and interviewed 25 household heads as "subgroups" in each so that I would not have a sample of all cane farmers or all rice farmers, for instance, from interviewing exclusively in one part of a village area. Distances of up to 3 miles sometimes separated subgroups within the same settlement zone.

I supplemented village field research with archival study while I was in Trinidad. The West Indian Collection at the University of the West Indies in St. Augustine was valuable for over-all perspective. Early plantation and settlement maps were available at the Lands and Surveys Department at the main government house in Port of Spain. The Port of Spain library has annual yearbooks of Trinidad that go back well into the 19th century, and each yearbook has economic reports about the various districts of the island. Since returning from Trinidad I have done additional historical research about Trinidad at the New York Public Library.

Historical evidence from both village interviews and archives was a fundamental part of my research findings in rural Trinidad. None of the villages are yet a century old, and it was instructive to learn how each settlement area had evolved partially as an economic adjunct of nearby estates.

In both the Bejucal and Debe areas, the first ex-indentured Indians built huts in about 1890. The two villages were ecologically typical of most of the first settlements for ex-indentured plantation workers in Trinidad. Zones in the extreme west-central portion of the island were set aside for Indian village settlements as early as 1869. Such lands were invariably on low elevations and marginal to large-scale cane estates. Seasonal flooding was therefore a hazard associated with subsistence agriculture in Bejucal and Debe as it was with all other early settlements of ex-indentured workers.

Wet rice was the main village crop in both communities. Padi apparently first came to Trinidad as rations for the indentured estate workers. Village padi planting technology changed in both villages between 1890 and 1910 from hand broadcasting to hand transplanting. The latter type of planting involves both higher labor inputs and higher grain outputs than in broadcasting and was apparently an adaptation to growing village populations. Independent village communities of Trinidad had grown rapidly in the late 1800's because of natural increases and also as more Indians moved away from plantations upon the expiration of their indenture periods. Vegetable crops supplemented padi cultivation in both communities. All village agriculture was susceptible to flooding in the rainy seasons. In these periods fishing and the collecting of both fresh- and salt-water crabs provided important sources of protein for the Indian villagers.

The ecological uncertainties associated with subsistence agriculture plus the proximity of sugarcane estates reinforced the need for part-time plantation work. Every male Indian in Debe and Bejucal, in the years around 1900, worked on nearby plantations. This work provided insurance for Indians against the possible failure of village crops. Moreover, it was convenient for nearby estates to have a ready reservoir of cheap labor in neighboring villagers for seasonal harvesting work. Indians from both Debe and Bejucal provided such labor from January to March. Familiarity with sugarcane led eventually to individual cane farming by villagers on better-drained village lands. Roads and trails from the settlement areas to plantations have been continually improved since that time, reinforcing the symbiotic nature of plantation and village.

In an article describing the livelihood activities in Debe and Bejucal in 1900 I have posited a series of microenvironmental zones common to both village areas that were exploited by the Indians living there.[5] Food collecting took place in brackish coastal swamps. Subsistence agriculture was in low-lying village lands. Wages were available in better-drained plantation areas. The varying subsistence and wage components of total livelihood were spread out over several miles. Settlement areas of Debe and Bejucal were located in

---

[5] Bonham C. Richardson, "Livelihood in Rural Trinidad in 1900." Annals Assoc. Amer. Geogr., vol. 65, no. 2 (June 1975), pp. 240-251.

the subsistence agriculture zones, and village residents exhibited a great deal of livelihood mobility from one small ecological zone to another. These movements reinforced livelihood diversity and not the exploitation of a single economic niche. Debe and Bejucal therefore evolved as interdependent entities with nearby plantations, the large estates and small communities linked by villagers' movements.

Rio Claro also grew up in the vicinity of large agricultural estates although its environment was quite different from the other two villages. Eastern Trinidad is forested. The open, cut-over plain in which Debe, Bejucal, and most of the other Indian villages were first located is different from the Rio Claro area. The forest zone in the eastern two-thirds of the island never supported a large peasant population. This area's local ecosystem is incapable of supporting sustained subsistence agriculture without drastic modification.

Cacao plantations, which never required the large number of Indians that western sugar estates did, have traditionally dominated the agriculture of central and eastern Trinidad. The island railway arrived in Rio Claro in 1913 mainly to transport cacao beans to Port of Spain, although there are records of roads and trails in the region in the 1880's. By 1915 there were a "few" indentured Indians in the vicinity. In the next few years a small-scale farming class evolved in the Rio Claro district. Individuals were granted virgin estate lands for a 3- to 5-year period during which they cleared the forest, replacing it with cacao seedlings as well as their own corn and hill rice. They eventually moved on, leaving young cacao trees for the use of the estate owners. Both blacks and Indians engaged in this "contract system." The descendants of each group remain in Rio Claro.

Original village settlement patterns have persisted in all three communities. The layouts of roads and houses in each place, first brought about by mutual needs between estates and individual villages, were spatial manifestations of livelihood activities of local residents. In the early days of each community, huts and houses were usually arranged in linear patterns along roads so that villagers could easily commute back and forth to part-time plantation work. Settlement linearity persists in rural Trinidad, and it reinforces the back-and-forth livelihood mobility to extra-village jobs by people in Debe, Bejucal, Rio Claro, and most other rural areas of the island. Several observers have commented that long-distance travel in Trinidad is often easier than traveling short distances to village lands. The effects of such a road system have obvious implications for agricultural development schemes or other programs that would emphasize an intensity of local labor inputs.[6]

[6] Bonham C. Richardson, "Plantation Infrastructure and Labor Mobility in Guyana and Trinidad," pp. 205-224 *in* "Migration and Development," Helen Safa and Brian duToit, eds. (The Hague: Mouton Publishers, 1975).

In conjunction with settlement linearity, I gathered data on contemporary livelihood mobility during my house-to-house interviews in the three village areas. All but 40 of the 225 household heads interviewed had at least one member of the household working at some nonagrarian job. Such work usually took the person away from the village. Labor migration from each settlement area is facilitated by all-weather asphalt highways. In 125 cases persons commuted 5 miles or less to extravillage wage jobs. Sixty traveled 5 to 10 miles. In Bejucal village, 36 traveled to work daily to Port of Spain, a distance of almost 15 miles. There was a great variety of extravillage jobs held by residents of the three settlement areas. They were canecutters, clerks, market retailers, truck drivers, carpenters, seamstresses, mechanics, teachers, policemen, secretaries, and government officials. These workers all represent active links between the villages and the island-wide economy. Therefore we can in no way refer to rural areas of Trinidad as being occupied by a traditional peasantry whose activities are confined to local village lands. Laborers were imported to the Caribbean for three centuries to serve on plantations oriented toward the production of tropical staples for metropolitan markets. Descendants of these laborers continue to be closely tied economically to towns, cities, and plantations.

Combinations of contemporary agricultural and nonagricultural elements of livelihood from the three villages were revealing. Among the households covered in the survey, many were devoid of major elements of agriculture. Sixty-seven households had neither sugarcane nor rice, 57 had neither cane nor vegetables, and 41 had neither rice nor vegetables. On the other hand, only 10 had neither rice nor nonagricultural income, 9 neither cane nor nonagricultural income, and 8 neither vegetables for market nor nonagricultural income. These data suggest that the crucial element of the diversified livelihood type of Trinidad is the extravillage job.

In rural Trinidad it is thus rare to find a household deriving total income from a single economic pursuit. Such livelihood diversification represents an unwillingness to concentrate on one economic activity for quite logical reasons. Part-time jobs come and go, and agricultural prices fluctuate, for instance. This diversification, with different elements making up total livelihood, is similar to village economics at the turn of the century in Trinidad.

The economic diversity found in Trinidad villages is not without theoretical significance. A subsistence-market dualism has characterized rural areas of the Caribbean since slave emancipation in the 1830's. Yet much of the current literature dealing with developing areas suggests that the relationship between subsistence and market activities is fleeting or ephemeral. The terms so common in titles or subtitles, such as "change," "development," "progress," "transition," imply an inflexible evolutionary path leading from subsistence activity to market production. Moreover, some of the current research in cultural ecology stresses how primitive subsistence systems are being disrupted by the encroachment of metropolitan-based market systems, further suggesting an invariant subsistence-to-market change in which large economic systems destroy small.

The destruction and modification of small, primitive, subsistence systems by metropolitan market systems have been documented in several cases. Yet it is too early to formulate theory from this evidence. An equilibrium between market (extravillage work) and subsistence (internal village agriculture) in rural Trinidad is shown by both historical and contemporary evidence. This is characteristic of much of the Commonwealth Caribbean, and it appears that in this region either the market sector or the subsistence sector is capable of expansion in light of continually changing economic conditions.

BONHAM C. RICHARDSON

The Flax Genus *Linum*

Principal Investigator: Claude M. Rogers, Wayne State University, Detroit, Michigan.

Grant No. 943: In support of research on the genus *Linum* (flax).

Linum is a worldwide genus of plants composed of perhaps 150 species, of which *Linum usitatissimum* L., the source of both linen fibers and linseed oil, is the best known. I have been studying the distribution and relationships of the New World flaxes, which constitute about one-third of the genus. Through the use of a variety of data, such as comparative pollen structure, floral pigment biochemistry, geographical distribution, chromosome number, and interbreedability, together with classical comparative morphology, a number of conclusions have been reached regarding relationships among themselves and to the Old World species. Some knowledge has also been gained about those features that may be considered less and those that are more specialized in the genus (Rogers, 1969).

The North American species are distributed among three sections. One *(Cathartolinum),* comprised of the single species *L. catharticum* L., is otherwise widespread in Europe. Its sporadic occurrence in various parts of eastern North America, mostly in disturbed places such as roadsides and pastures, suggests that it is an introduction, possibly in recent times, from Europe. A second section *(Linum),* with but two native North American representatives, is widely distributed in Eurasia, with as many as 30 to 40 species. The American species, confined to the western portion of the Continent, are closely related to Siberian plants, and it is likely that they spread from Asia via the Bering Strait route. The third section *(Linastrum)* is by far the largest in the New World. There are nearly 40 North American taxa (Rogers, 1963, 1968), while all the 15 to 20 species native to South America belong to this genus as well. The North and South American species displaying the greatest array of features thought to be primitive closely resemble certain South African plants. Whether this group migrated eastward or westward across the Atlantic is not entirely clear, but the section is well represented in the Old World. Certainly some of the most highly specialized species in the whole genus are among those found in the New World, and North and South America appear to be most logically interpreted as secondary centers of diversification.

Thus, information derived from the study of the New World flaxes has indicated that some part of the Old World is the geographical center from which the genus has spread to other parts of the world, and it became necessary, if one were to trace out the migrations and relationships of this important group of plants, to learn more about the distribution of the genus in the Old World. In order to accomplish this, the principal published floras and collections of plants housed at the Royal Botanic Gardens at Kew, the British Museum (Natural History) in London, the Muséum National d'Histoire in Paris, and the Conservatoire et Jardin Botanique at Geneva were examined. The greatest concentration of species of *Linum* is in the eastern Mediterranean region. For example, Turkey has the highest number of kinds of wild flax for any area of comparable size. Not only are a large number of species of flax native to this region, but also representatives of all the usually accepted sections of the genus, including the three that grow in the New World, are found there. It is clearly an area of importance in deciphering relationships in the genus and is the one selected in which to do the fieldwork supported by the National Geographic Society.

The fieldwork was carried out during the summer of 1971 and had specific aims: the observation of the plants in their natural habitat and the collection of specimens, not only of whole plants but also especially floral buds placed in preserving fluid for cytological study and seeds for the production of plants in the greenhouse for a variety of future studies, particularly genetic and biochemical. Except for the traditional morphological data derived from the use of pressed and dried specimens, most Old World species are poorly known. For one example, of the 48 taxa recognized for Turkey (Davis, 1967), only 9 have had chromosome numbers determined, and of these more than half are subject to conflicting reports. Biochemical and breeding data are even more sparse.

After considering the various alternatives, I thought that travel by car would provide the most nearly complete and continuous collecting opportunities. Therefore an automobile was leased in Paris and ultimately returned there after completion of the fieldwork and subsequent study at the Royal Botanic Gardens Herbarium and Library at Kew. More than two months were spent in the field. The itinerary included southern France and Spain, northern Morocco, Algeria and Tunisia, Sicily and mainland Italy, Greece, Turkey, Bulgaria, and Yugoslavia. About half of the field-trip time was spent in Turkey. Approximately 125 collections were made, comprised of several thousand specimens. Examination of chromosomes in floral bud material was made upon return to the laboratory; seeds were started and a variety of genetic and biochemical analyses are currently underway.

The chromosome complements of a number of species have been counted, most of them for the first time (Rogers et al., 1972). Some useful information about infrageneric relationships is emerging. The Mediterranean species of the section *Linastrum* prove to have $n=10$ and $n=9$. Those with $n=10$ appear also frequently to have heterostylous flowers, while $n=9$ plants do not. If there is a direct relationship between the plants of the Mediterranean area and those of South Africa and, ultimately, to those of the New World, it would likely be with those with $n=9$. The latter are homostylous and have chromosome numbers of multiples of 9. The only non-Mediterranean species of Africa for which the chromosome number is known is *L. holstii* Engl. of East Africa, which has $n=27$, while the basic chromosome number for both North and South American species is $n=18$. These numbers are most likely to have been derived via doubling of chromosome complement from a primitive plant with $n=9$. More such study needs to be made on the African species in order to help demonstrate whether they are, as they appear to be, intermediate between the Mediterranean species on the one hand and the New World plants on the other. It should be noted also that although the North American species are now quite well known cytologically, additional studies among the South American species, especially those of southern Brazil, Uruguay, and eastern Argentina, need to be made.

The base chromosome numbers for the other sections are also becoming established, with *Dasylinum* having $n=8$ and *Syllinum* having $n=14$. Of some interest here is *L. seljukorum* Davis, an unusual, highly localized, and very rarely collected species of central Turkey. It was placed, but with some doubt, in the subgenus *Dasylinum* (Davis, 1957). Its chromosome number of $n=8$ supports this disposition. The present work throws no additional light on the relationship of the cultivated species, *L. usitatissimum,* to wild species. Its chromosome number has for some time been known to be $n=15$. A few others, notably its putative wild ancestor, *L. bienne* Mill., have this number also. Others of this section *(Linum),* including those collected in the present study, have $n=9$.

Comparative biochemical work has only just begun. Analysis of fatty acids contained in the seeds and of floral and other pigments has proved to be constructive in the assay of relationships in this genus (Giannasi and Rogers, 1970; Rogers, 1972). It seems likely that pigment chemistry of the Old World plants should prove especially helpful since floral pigmentation is one of the principal features used to distinguish the several sections.

Although much more information is needed and the work that has come out of the present research is largely exploratory, on the basis of data thus far accumulated a very tentative worldwide distribution and migration pattern for the genus *Linum* is beginning to emerge. From southeastern Europe and the Mediterranean region have dispersed the major sections of the genus: *Cathartolinum* throughout Europe to North America; *Linum* northward throughout most of Europe and eastward through Asia and into western North America; *Dasylinum* and *Syllinum* throughout the Near East and northern Africa; and *Linastrum,* southward through eastern Africa, thence to North and South America.

REFERENCES

Davis, P. H.

1957. Materials for a flora of Turkey, II: *Linum* Linn. Notes Roy. Bot. Gard. Edinburgh, vol. 22, pp. 135-161.

1967. Flora of Turkey, vol. 2: Linaceae, pp. 425-450. Edinburgh University Press.

Giannasi, D. E., and Rogers, Claude M.

1970. Taxonomic significance of floral pigments in *Linum* (Linaceae). Brittonia, vol. 22, pp. 163-174.

Rogers, Claude M.

1963. Yellow flowered species of *Linum* in eastern North America. Brittonia, vol. 15, pp. 97-122.

1968. Yellow flowered species of *Linum* in Central America and western North America. Brittonia, vol. 20, pp. 107-135.

1969. Relationships of the North American species of *Linum.* Bull. Torrey Bot. Club, vol. 96, pp. 176-190.

1972. The taxonomic significance of the fatty acid content of seeds of *Linum.* Brittonia, vol. 24, pp. 415-419.

Rogers, Claude M.; Mildner, R.; and Harris, B. D.

1972. Some additional chromosome numbers in the Linaceae. Brittonia, vol. 24, pp. 313-316.

Claude M. Rogers

Energy and Water Budget Studies in the Tundra

Principal Investigator: Wayne R. Rouse, McMaster University, Hamilton, Ontario, Canada.

Grant No. 962: To study the microclimate of subarctic plant systems and water conservation.[1]

The open tundra near the west coast of Hudson Bay (lat. 57°N., long. 88°W.) is flat and treeless and comprises a series of beach ridges created by rapid isostatic uplift of the Hudson Bay shoreline. These well-drained sites are typically dominated by nontranspiring ground lichen cover, mixed ground lichen and moss, and lower order vascular plants (Kershaw and Rouse, 1973). The vegetation shows a successive development as one moves inland from partial plant cover on the youngest ridges to mature spruce-lichen woodland in the oldest. The depth of the peat layer underlying the vegetative mat also increases with the development of the plant cover. This whole treeless zone lies in the area of continuous permafrost as defined by Brown (1970) and represents the most southerly incursion of the continuous permafrost zone in North America.

The plants comprising the surface vegetation all exhibit a diffusive resistance to the movement of water vapor from the moisture source in the soil to the atmospheric sink and thus are not able to evaporate as freely as temperate plants under conditions of abundant moisture supply. In a detailed study of the evaporation behavior a simple evaporation model has been derived (Rouse and Stewart, 1972) in the form

$$LE_M = (0.403 + 0.011T)(Q^* - G), \quad (1)$$

when LE_M is the latent heat flux predicted by the model, T is air temperature measured in a meteorological screen, Q^* is net radiation, and G is the heat flow into the soil. This model gives high correlation coefficients of 0.95 on an

[1]In preparing the final reports of this research I have had the generous collaboration of Dr. K. A. Kershaw and R. B. Stewart of McMaster University. In addition to the grant from the National Geographic Society the program was supported by research grants from the Canadian National Research Council and the McMaster University Research Board.

hourly basis and 0.98 on a daily basis with low standard deviations when compared to the measured latent heat of evaporation. In a test on an independent set of data in the subarctic lichen woodland (Rouse and Kershaw, 1971) the model also performed well. On a daily basis the G term will tend toward zero, so that only the two measured parameters of Q^* and T are needed to make the model operational.

In the course of the fieldwork associated with this project routine measurements of soil moisture were made by means of neutron attenuation techniques over a variety of terrain types ranging from well-drained upland sites to a poorly drained lowland site. The measurements included two sites that had been subjected to pronounced changes due to known activity by removal of the surface vegetation through burning and through the impact of Caterpillar tractors. The detailed results of this study are reported by Rouse and Kershaw (1973). There was a great range in the average seasonal moisture content SM (percent volumetric) for the different sites, which was associated in a linear fashion with the amount of organic matter $OM(\%)$ in the surface soils in the form

$$SM = 15.74 + 1.98\, OM \tag{2}$$

which yielded a correlation coefficient of 0.89 with low standard deviation. This greater moisture conservation associated with the lusher vegetative development and greater organic debris has implications for the behavior of the active layer above the permafrost, as the thermal conductivity of the soil is strongly influenced by its moisture content. Thus the surface organic layer plays a twofold role affecting both the amount of heat energy entering the soil and the amount of moisture retained in the soil. When the surface vegetation is destroyed and incorporated into the mineral soil through burning or the grinding of the Caterpillar tractor, it increases the surface organic content of the soil and enhances its moisture holding ability.

In conclusion, these studies provide evidence that the evaporation rates from upland tundra sites can be determined accurately using simple data and that the amount of soil water in the active layer above permafrost is closely related to the degree of accumulation of surface organic matter.

REFERENCES

Brown, R. J. E.

1970. Permafrost in Canada, 234 pp. University of Toronto Press.

Kershaw, Kenneth A., and Rouse, Wayne R.

1973. Studies on lichen-dominated systems, V: A primary survey of a raised-beach system in northwestern Ontario. Can. Journ. Bot., vol. 51, no. 7, pp. 1285-1307.

ROUSE, WAYNE R., and KERSHAW, KENNETH A.
1971. The effects of burning on the heat and water regimes of lichen-dominated systems. Arctic Alpine Res., vol. 3, pp. 291-304.
1973. Studies on lichen-dominated systems, VI: Interrelations of vegetation and soil moisture in the Hudson Bay lowlands. Can. Journ. Bot., vol. 51, no. 7, pp. 1309-1316.
ROUSE, WAYNE R., and STEWART, ROBERT B.
1972. A simple model for determining evaporation from high-altitude upland sites. Journ. Appl. Meteorol., vol. 11, no. 7, pp. 1063-1070.

WAYNE R. ROUSE

Archeological Research on the Island of Cozumel, Mexico

Principal Investigators: Jeremy A. Sabloff, University of New Mexico, Albuquerque, New Mexico; and William L. Rathje, University of Arizona, Tucson, Arizona.

Grant Nos. 1021, 1124, 1280. For a study of Pre-Columbian culture change on Cozumel Island, Mexico.

The over-all aims of the Cozumel Archeological Project are to test both a series of general hypotheses about the role of trading ports in the development of ancient civilizations and several specific hypotheses concerning the growth of Postclassic Maya civilization.

The extensive surveys and excavations of the 1972 and 1973 field seasons uncovered much new and exciting information that should have a significant impact upon our knowledge of the role of trade in the development of ancient Maya civilization. Analyses of ceramics, artifacts, settlement data, architectural information, and historic sources are currently nearing completion. The results will be edited and assembled for publication (by the Arizona State Museum, University of Arizona).

Until very recent times studies of ancient trade in the Maya area have been insufficient in their attempt to explain the role of trade in the development of Maya civilization. That is not to say that studies of trade have been ignored or neglected, but rather that most works, written prior to the past decade, have been either descriptive in nature or quite superficial in their explanatory scope.

We, the project's co-directors, came to feel that a study of the shifting patterns of trade among the ancient Maya might throw some fresh light on such old problems as the collapse of the Classic Maya and the nature of the so-called "Decadent" period. Furthermore, we believed that oft-used archeological concepts such as "port-of-trade" needed closer examination and that the material and behavioral correlates of such concepts had to be defined in order to give them greater utility. With the clarification of these concepts, hypotheses about recurrent trends in changing commercial patterns might be tested.

The Island of Cozumel (see fig. 1) was chosen for detailed analysis for several reasons. First, it was known from the rich ethnohistoric literature that the island was a pivotal trading center between Honduras, Yucatán, and Tabasco in pre-Conquest times. Second, the archeological remains had a time depth from at least 300 B.C. through the 16th century A.D., with large surface remains from the Postclassic (post-9th-century A.D.) period. Third, because of its position on a heavily used Postclassic trade route, the cultural system on Cozumel was constantly exposed to and constantly reacted to changing informational stimuli.

Under the joint sponsorship of the Peabody Museum, Harvard University, and the University of Arizona and with the support of the National Geographic Society, the Ford Motor Co., the Ford Foundation, the American Can Co., Mrs. C. Ayling, and other private donors, field research was begun in February 1972. The archeological work was carried out with the cooperation and authorization of the Instituto Nacional de Antropología e Historia of Mexico, whose representatives were of great aid to the project at all times. The first field season lasted from February through June 1972. A small group of graduate and undergraduate students from Harvard University, the University of Arizona, and Brandeis University participated in the fieldwork. The second field season lasted from February through June 1973, but a much larger group of students, numbering over 20, participated in both the field and laboratory research. Additional field assistance was provided in both years by local Cozumeleños. Without the enthusiastic participation of the students and local workers and without the active cooperation of local officials, none of our work would have been possible.

The data uncovered by the surveys and excavations of the 1972 and 1973 field seasons will enable the project to make contributions on several fronts. In relation to the culture history of Cozumel, the project's discoveries have greatly amplified the only previous excavations on the island, which were undertaken by W. T. Sanders in 1955 and have established a full culture sequence for Cozumel. Moreover, the excavations have been related to the chronological and architectural research of the late E. W. Andrews IV on the east coast of Quintana Roo as well as to the ongoing research of Arthur Miller at Tancah.

The cultural sequence that the project has pieced together indicates that the island was first occupied by the time of Christ (that is, in the late Formative Period). The occupation from this time until A.D. 700-800 was relatively sparse. However, it appears as if the island began to grow in prominence during the Florescent Period, just about the time of the 8th to 9th century A.D. collapse of Classic Maya civilization in the Southern Lowlands. Cozumel's population and importance continued to grow until they reached their height during the Decadent Period (A.D. 1250-1519). The population declined drastically during the 16th century A.D., owing to diseases brought in by the Spanish *conquistadores* and through migration to the mainland.

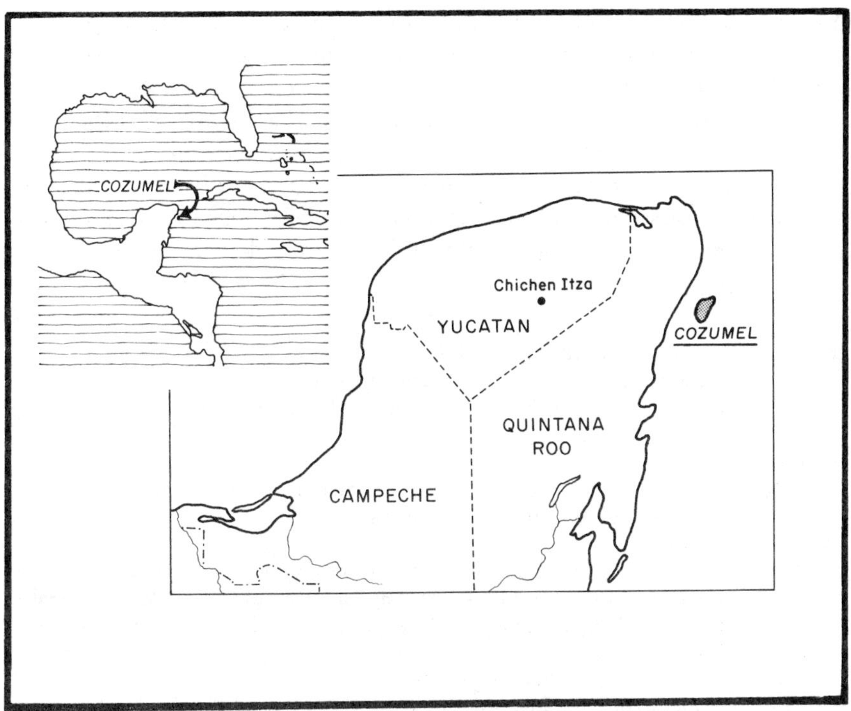

FIG. 1. Map locating the island of Cozumel, Quintana Roo, Mexico.

In relation to the so-called "Decadent" or late Postclassic Period, the project has provided a new interpretive view of this period, which can be contrasted with the previous interpretation made by the Carnegie Institution of Washington on the basis of its important research at the site of Mayapán. The economic viewpoint taken by the project has enabled it to argue against earlier views that this period was one of cultural decay.

It would appear that although monumental art and architecture, as well as elite craft production, lost their previous esthetic brilliance, the civilization of the "Decadent" Period reached new heights in economic growth and complexity, especially as regards long-distance trade. A mercantile viewpoint, rather than a theocratically controlled esthetic ethos, seemed to dominate the cultural scene. Mass production, particularly of pottery, grew in importance and began to replace the older production of individual pieces. The general populace had a greater access to goods formerly restricted to the elite and the general standard of living seemed to rise. These new interpretations have important implications for our view of the development of ancient Maya civilizations and their potential significance has begun to be explored in a series of papers produced by members of the project (see References that follow).

Finally, in relation to general models of trade, the discoveries of the project have allowed it to define some unique material correlates of ancient Maya trading centers. Moreover, the project's research has further enabled it to make some suggestions about the cross-cultural behavior of trading centers that, it is hoped, will be of some value in future archeological studies.

REFERENCES

CONNOR, J. G., and RATHJE, WILLIAM L.

1973. Mass production and the ancient Maya: Experiments in cracking Maya pots. Paper read at annual meeting of Society for American Archaeology, San Francisco.

FREIDEL, DAVID A.

1973. The IxChel shrine. Paper read at annual meeting of American Anthropological Association, New Orleans.

RATHJE, WILLIAM L.

1975. Last tango at Mayapán: A tentative trajectory of production-distribution systems. Pp. 409-448 *in* "Ancient Civilization and Trade," J. A. Sabloff and C. C. Lamberg-Karlovsky, eds. University of New Mexico Press. (In press.)

RATHJE, WILLIAM L., and SABLOFF, JEREMY A.

1972. A model of ports-of-trade. Paper read at annual meeting of Society of American Archaeology, Miami Beach.

1973. Ancient Maya commercial systems: A research design for the Island of Cozumel, Mexico. World Archaeol., vol. 5, no. 2, pp. 221-231.

RATHJE, WILLIAM L.; SABLOFF, JEREMY A.; and GREGORY, D. A.

1973. El descubrimiento de un jade Olmeca en la isla de Cozumel. Estudios de Cultura Maya, vol. 9, pp. 85-92.

SABLOFF, JEREMY A.

1977. Old myths, new myths: The role of sea traders in the development of ancient Maya civilization. Pp. 67-97 *in* "The Sea in the Pre-Columbian World," E. Benson, ed. Dumbarton Oaks, Washington, D. C.

SABLOFF, JEREMY A., and FREIDEL, DAVID A.

1975. A model of a Precolumbian trading center. Pp. 369-408 *in* "Ancient Civilization and Trade," J. A. Sabloff and C. C. Lamberg-Karlovsky, eds. University of New Mexico Press.

SABLOFF, JEREMY A., and RATHJE, WILLIAM L.

1973. A study of changing Pre-Columbian commercial patterns on the island of Cozumel, Mexico. Atti XL Congr. Int. Americanisti (Roma-Genova, 1972), vol. 1, pp. 455-463.

1975a. The rise of a Maya merchant class. Sci. Amer., vol. 233, no. 4, pp. 72-82, illus.

1975b. A study of changing Pre-Columbian commercial systems: The 1972-1973 seasons at Cozumel, Mexico, J. A. Sabloff and W. J. Rathje, eds. Monographs of the Peabody Museum, Harvard University, No. 3.

SABLOFF, JEREMY A.; RATHJE, WILLIAM L.; FREIDEL, DAVID A.; CONNOR, J. G.; and SABLOFF, PAULA L. W.

1974. Trade and power in Postclassic Yucatán: Initial observations. Pp. 397-416 *in* "Mesoamerican Archaeology: New Approaches," N. Hammond, ed. University of Texas Press.

SABLOFF, PAULA L. W.

1972. The power of land. Paper read at annual meeting of American Anthropological Association, Toronto.

JEREMY A. SABLOFF
WILLIAM L. RATHJE

Excavation of Oligocene Marine Fossil Beds Near Charleston, South Carolina

Principal Investigator: Albert E. Sanders, Charleston Museum, Charleston, South Carolina.

Grant Nos. 954, 1074: For excavation of an Oligocene fossil site near Charleston.

Fossil cetacean remains have been found in the vicinity of the Ashley River near Charleston, South Carolina, for more than a century, several forms having been described from Oligocene marine beds and from Pleistocene marine sediments that have furnished reworked rostral fragments of extinct beaked whales of late Miocene(?) or early Pliocene(?) age. Containing heavy concentrations of phosphate, these deposits were mined extensively from 1867 to the 1920's and are familiarly known as "the Ashley River phosphate beds." Their importance as a source of marine-mammal remains has been cited by numerous authors. Commenting on the geographic distribution of the squalodonts (an extinct group of toothed whales), Remington Kellogg (1923a) noted that "in the Northern Hemisphere the squalodonts appear in considerable numbers during the Miocene. Their geological history in this region prior to the Miocene is unsatisfactory, resting as it does upon the occurrence of cetaceans in the Ashley River phosphate beds of South Carolina and . . . an imperfectly known squalodont . . . in the Upper Oligocene of Germany." Although Oligocene squalodonts have since been described from Germany, Russia, and the Pacific coast of the United States, these discoveries have not diminished the importance of the South Carolina beds.

In most cases, however, cetacean remains from the Ashley River phosphate region have been found during commercial mining operations or after having been washed from the beds in which they were originally buried; consequently, accurate determination of their stratigraphic position and associated fauna usually has not been possible. Heretofore, virtually no attempt has been made to locate fossil cetacean remains in place in the Charleston beds despite the attention the latter have drawn in the literature. The vast potential of such investigations has now been amply demonstrated by the results of the first organized paleontological excavation of marine deposits in the Charleston area. Conducted during the summers of 1970, 1971, and 1972, this project evolved from the curiosity of two alert youngsters.

In August 1969 James Nicholson and Ricky Seagroves telephoned the Charleston Museum to report a "string of backbones" that they had discovered in a newly cut ditch on the north side of County Road S-230 near Chandler Bridge Creek in Dorchester County, South Carolina, some 20 miles (3.2 kilometers) northwest of Charleston (fig. 1). Meeting the boys at the ditch I found that they had encountered several fossil cetacean vertebrae that had been exposed in the south bank. After gathering these remains I inspected the ditch and noted that the banks contained large numbers of vertebrate and invertebrate fossils of marine origin. Displaced clam casts, shark teeth, fish vertebrae, turtle-shell fragments, and a few cetacean vertebrae and rib fragments were scattered about the sides and bottom of the ditch. A small cetacean mandible protruded from one of the banks as if thrust there like a dagger. Some distance away from the mandible the remains of a small sea turtle were found in place in the south bank.

Subsequent trips to the ditch produced sirenian rib fragments, bird bones, remains of another small sea turtle, and the braincase of a cetacean now tentatively regarded as a new species of the genus *Squalodon.* The two boys avidly assisted in collecting material from the ditch. Prowling the banks in their spare time they eventually discovered portions of three skulls representing the primitive odontocete genus *Xenorophus,* previously known only from the type specimen, *Xenorophus sloanii* Kellogg (1923b), in the Smithsonian Institution's National Museum of Natural History.

Toward the end of 1969 Roger Lambert, an amateur fossil collector, found a large, virtually complete cetacean skull in the north bank of the ditch. Now in the Charleston Museum collection, this specimen represents an undescribed genus among the toothed whales.

All the determinate cetacean material from the ditch was referable to the superfamily Squalodontoidea, an extinct group of toothed whales comparable in size to the modern porpoises and dolphins. Members of this group are characterized by double-rooted molariform teeth in which the crown is triangular in shape and is laterally compressed. Usually there are three or four accessory cusps on the cutting edges of the crown, creating a serrate effect. Ranging from the late Eocene or early Oligocene through the Miocene, the squalodonts occupy a major position in the phylogeny of the odontocetes.

Assessing the impressive body of material from the ditch, Dr. Frank C. Whitmore, Jr., of the U. S. Geological Survey, and I agreed that the presence of *Xenorophus* strongly indicated that the exposed beds were Oligocene in age. One of the most distinctive toothed whales known, *Xenorophus* was described from a partial skull found in the Cooper marl, an Oligocene marine formation underlying the entire Charleston area. Although the Cooper marl was exposed

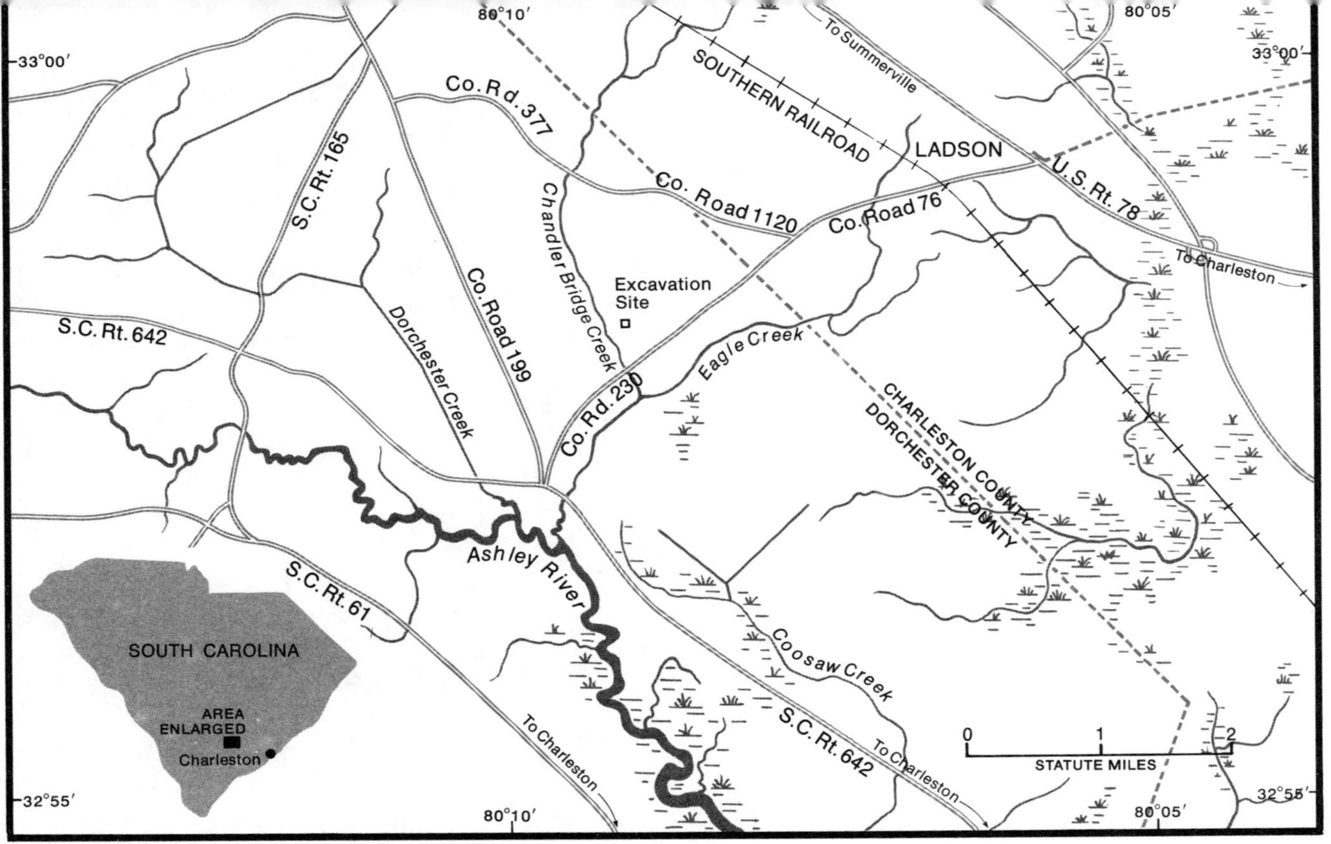

FIG. 1. Geographic location of the Chandler Bridge Excavation site, Dorchester County, South Carolina.

in the bottom of the ditch, our *Xenorophus* material was found in the beds overlying the marl, suggesting that these units were of the same age as the Cooper.

The availability of marine deposits apparently of Oligocene age and rich in fossil cetacean remains was of profound significance. The Oligocene epoch is a critical period in the phylogeny of the whales because it was during this time that the last major steps in cetacean evolution were accomplished. Unfortunately it is also one of the poorest known chapters in the history of the cetaceans. Cetacean remains from the Oligocene are rare and have consisted almost entirely of accidental discoveries of isolated specimens. Feeling that the exposed deposits presented an unparalleled opportunity to obtain Oligocene cetacean remains in number under conditions that allowed complete stratigraphic control, Dr. Whitmore and I concluded that a portion of these beds should be systematically excavated as soon as possible.

1970 Season. Ed Riley, of Trolley Enterprises, Inc., owners of the property adjoining the ditch, generously granted permission to excavate an area on the north side of the oxidation pond bordering the ditch, and in July of 1970 the trustees of the Charleston Scientific and Cultural Educational Fund approved my application for a grant to finance the excavation. I am deeply grateful to Mr. Riley and to the trustees of the Charleston Fund for their vital contributions to the project.

The site selected for excavation was cleared of underbrush and second-growth timber by a bulldozer and operator provided by Westvaco Corporation. To expose the fossil-bearing beds a dragline furnished by Charleston County removed approximately 4 feet (1.2 meters) of overburden from an area of about 70 by 70 feet (21.4 by 21.4 meters). Intersecting drainage ditches were cut along the north and east sides of the excavation area, and a shorter ditch of about 30 feet (9.2 meters) in length was dug outward from the southeastern corner to drain that sector of the site. The excavation area was then staked off in a grid system of 6-foot (1.8-meter) squares to provide a means of recording the horizontal position of all specimens found. Square rows were designated alphabetically from east to west (A-K) and numerically from north to south (1-12). Dirt from the excavation was to be carried out of the work area in wheelbarrows rolled along a wooden track, which would serve as an avenue through the mud during wet weather. A crew of six college students was employed and excavation with hand tools was begun on July 13, 1970.

On July 17 the stratigraphy of the beds was analyzed in an on-site conference between Dr. Donald J. Colquhoun, of the University of South Carolina, Druid Wilson, of the U. S. Geological Survey, Dr. Whitmore, and myself. Three distinct stratigraphic zones were recognized above the Cooper Formation, the basal unit exposed in the ditches bordering the site: (1) an 8-12-inch

(20-30-centimeter) layer of brown, fine quartz-phosphate sand disconformably overlying the Cooper Formation; (2) a 15-inch (38-centimeter) bed of gray, poorly compacted fine sand and phosphate nodules overlying Bed 1; and (3) a 22-inch (56-centimeter) bed of gray, well compacted medium sand, beach pebbles, and phosphate nodules overlying Bed 2 (fig. 2). These determinations made it possible to employ complete stratigraphic control in the removal of all material recovered during the excavation.

To obtain adequate samples of the fauna of all three beds above the marl, squares A-1 through A-5 were excavated from the top of bed 3 to the top of the Cooper marl. Excavation in other squares was eventually limited to bed 3 because of the abundance of cetacean remains discovered in that unit. Many very small fossils (primarily fish remains) were obtained by washing sediments from bed 1 through a screen. This technique was not feasible in beds 2 and 3 because of the higher clay content in these units.

During the course of the excavation small vertebrate and invertebrate material was found in great abundance. Specimens of this nature were placed in 40-dram plastic bottles with labels denoting the squares and zones from which they were recovered. Larger vertebrate remains were encased in plaster jackets and marked with appropriate positional data. When activities were suspended on August 28 nearly 200 bottles of specimens and approximately 35 plaster jackets had been accumulated.

The results of this exploratory investigation were truly astounding. During the last five weeks of the excavation the remains of six squalodonts were encountered in bed 3. Among these are four skulls and related skeletal material representing a new squalodont genus. Temporarily designated as Genus X, this form was about the size of the modern bottlenose dolphin *(Tursiops truncatus).* A massive complex of bones in squares B-9, B-10, and C-9 consisted of the skull, right mandible, and most of the axial skeleton of another individual of the new genus represented by the large skull found earlier in the roadside ditch (fig. 4). The excavation specimen appears to be not only the largest squalodont on record but also the most nearly complete squalodont skeleton yet reported. In life the animal was at least 20 feet (6 meters) in length. This previously undescribed form has been temporarily designated as Genus Y.

Square C-12 produced one of the most important fossil cetacean finds in many years. From near the bottom of bed 3 we recovered the first skull of *Xenorophus* to be found with the braincase present. Possessing certain features formerly known only in the most primitive types of early cetaceans, this specimen drastically revises previous concepts of the postorbital region of the skull in *Xenorophus.* Discussed and figured by Whitmore and Sanders (1976:307-308, fig. 1a) as *Xenorophus sloanii,* the C-12 skull has recently been

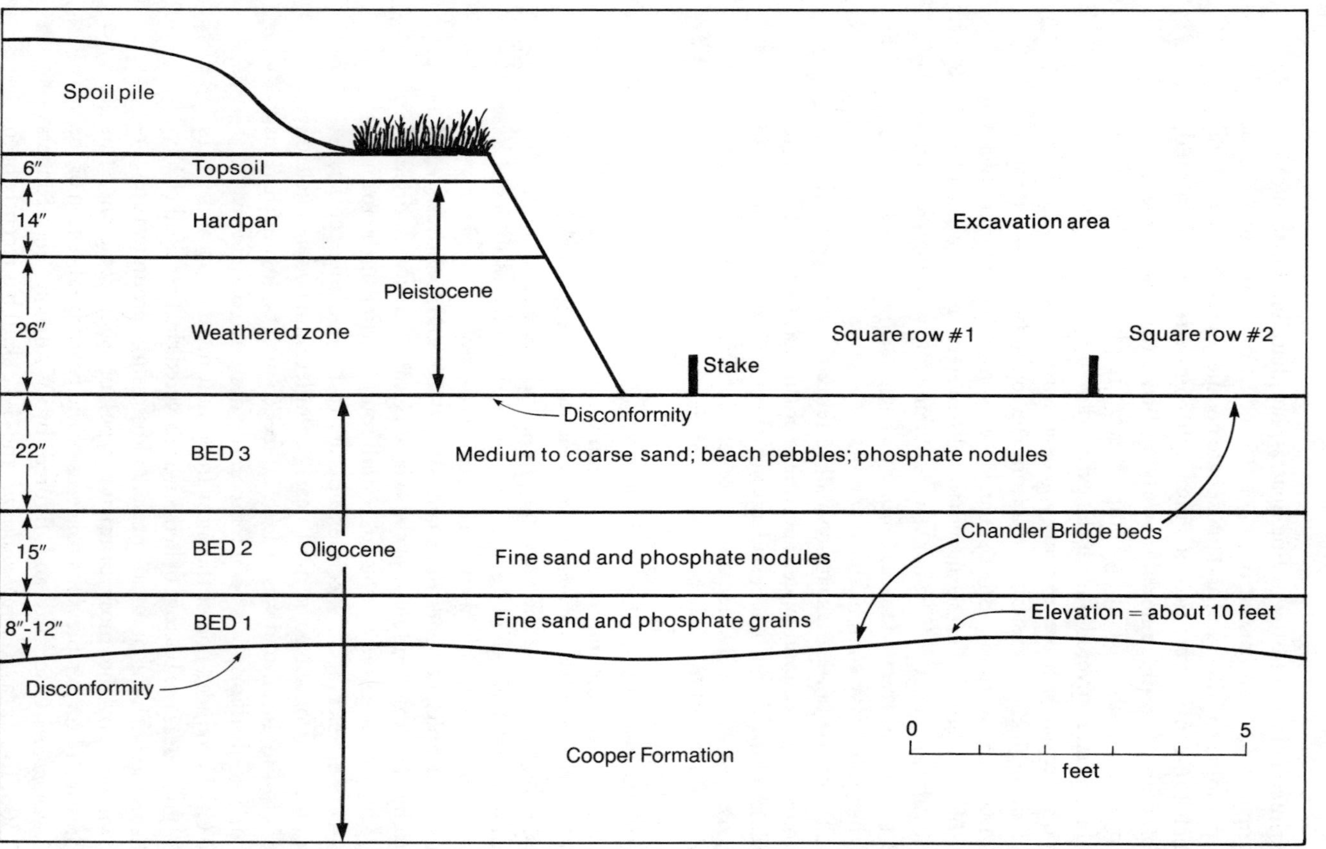

FIG. 2. Stratigraphy of the Chandler Bridge beds and overlying units as seen in section along west wall of ditch on east side of excavation area.

FIG. 3. Northeast view of site, fourth week, 1970 season. Foreground is top of Bed 3, uppermost unit of fossil-bearing deposits. Exploratory squares were dug along east side of ditch (square row A). Four skulls of an apparently new squalodont temporarily designated as Genus X were found in squares A-4, A-7, A-9, and B-10.

redetermined as a new species of *Xenorophus,* previously unnoticed features of diagnostic value being evident on the ventral side of the specimen. Five vertebrae and three rib fragments found near the skull are the first known examples of the postcranial anatomy of *Xenorophus.*

During Dr. Whitmore's two-week sojourn with the excavation we made several trips into the surrounding countryside to look for outcrops that would give us some idea of the full extent of the beds under investigation. Time did not permit a truly thorough search, but we did discover that the beds are also exposed in the banks of Eagle Creek at a point about 1 mile due south of the site. Subsequent investigations in Charleston, Dorchester, and Berkeley counties have revealed six additional localities for these beds, which will be described as a new formation. Mentioned by Whitmore and Sanders (1976) as the "Eagle Creek" beds, this formation will hereinafter be referred to as "the Chandler Bridge beds" pending publication of the formal description. Lithologic distinctions between this unit and the underlying Cooper Formation have been briefly summarized by Sanders, Lemon, and Weems (1979), and

FIG. 4. Discovery of remains of Genus Y individual in square B-10, Bed 3, 1970 season. The skull and most of the postcranial skeleton were present. This new squalodont appears to have been slightly larger than the modern Pilot Whale (*Globicephala*).

Lemon (1976) has analyzed textural and clay mineral differences between these deposits and Pleistocene sediments overlying them.

1971 Season. On the basis of the extraordinary success of the 1970 excavation the National Geographic Society generously granted funds to conduct a second season of work at the site. The return of most of the 1970 crew enabled us to begin the new season with five experienced members among the seven college students hired for the excavation.

Before operations could be resumed it was necessary to overcome a major problem which had developed at the site. Over the winter of 1970-71 seepage water filled the ditches on the north and east sides of the site and overflowed into the excavation area, filling it with about 12 inches of standing water. This was removed by a large heavy-duty pump brought in by the City of Charleston along a road cleared by a bulldozer and operator furnished by Westvaco Corporation. The site was undamaged and was in excellent condi-

FIG. 5. Squalodont mandible found in square B-4, Bed 3, 1971 season. Six teeth are in place in this specimen, which has been tentatively referred to Genus X.

tion when digging was begun on July 5. While the excavation was in progress the constant seepage of ground water into the ditches was controlled with a 3-horsepower gasoline pump purchased under the Society's grant.

Field methods employed in 1970 were continued in 1971, but the plan of excavation was altered considerably. Although cetacean remains occur in all three beds above the Cooper marl, activities of the previous summer indicated that they were most abundant in bed 3. Excavation work in 1971 was therefore confined to that unit. To cover as much ground as possible the squares were dug in rows forming a network of intersecting trenches. During the 7 weeks of work the excavation of bed 3 was completed over approximately one-half of the site, a volume of about 49 tons of earth having been hauled out of the work area in wheelbarrows.

Though not quite as spectacular as the year before, the 1971 season yielded vital supplementary material. A complex of 12 vertebrae and 9 rib fragments found in squares C-9 and C-10 appears to be the remains of another individual of Genus X. Square C-11 furnished the atlas vertebra for the *Xenorophus* skull found in the adjoining square C-12 in 1970.

FIG. 6. South view of site at beginning of 1972 season. Excavated area shows pattern of trenching activities conducted in 1971.

The remains of another small squalodont were discovered in square J-10. Fourteen vertebrae were clumped in one corner of the square and three more were found nearby. Despite a thorough search in adjoining squares the skull of this animal was not found, but four additional vertebrae were located. In size and general morphology these vertebrae greatly resemble those of Genus X and are almost certainly referable to that form.

One of the most significant discoveries of the summer was made in the southeast sector of the site, where the greater portion of the right mandible of a small squalodont was found in square B-4 (fig. 5). One single-rooted premolar and five double-rooted molariform teeth are in place. Alveolae for five other single-rooted teeth and seven more double-rooted teeth are present. The teeth clearly match those of Genus X. This specimen is the only virtually complete mandible of Genus X found during the three summers of excavation.

1972 Season. In view of our continued success at the site in 1971 the Society granted funds for 7 more weeks of work during the summer of 1972. The grant also included a substantial allowance for preparation of the huge quantity of fossil material that the beds were producing. The field crew was increased to eight members to improve our chances of completing the excavation of bed 3, which was unexplored over fully one-half of the site. The City of Charleston pump crew again removed the winter accumulation of water, and activities were resumed on July 5. The trenching method of exploration was continued, and with two students working in each square it was possible to dig four squares simultaneously as opposed to our previous rate of only three squares at a time. With this extra margin the remaining portion of bed 3 was completed on schedule and fieldwork at the site was terminated on August 20, 1972.

Rivaling the remarkable results of the first season, the 1972 excavation produced five more squalodont bone complexes and cranial elements of at least three other individuals. A complex found in square C-7 consisted of 7 vertebrae, fragments of 12 ribs, and part of a mandible. Another complex, in square E-7, contained 18 vertebrae, 5 rib fragments, and a bulla. Farther west along square row 7 a small complex of 4 vertebrae, 2 ribs, and 2 as-yet-undetermined bones was found in square J-7. Preliminary observations indicate that all the above material is referable to Genus X.

An extremely important supplement to the specimen found in 1970, the remains of another individual of *Xenorophus* were discovered in squares B-2 and C-2. This complex was composed of 11 vertebrae, portions of 11 ribs, and most of the posterior half of the skull. The second skull of *Xenorophus* to be found with the braincase present, this specimen also furnished the first examples of the periotic bone and auditory bulla in the new species of *Xenorophus* from the Chandler Bridge beds. A mandible and 2 vertebrae from B-1, a cervical vertebra and 2 rib fragments from C-1, and a vertebra from C-3 probably are additional elements of this skeleton.

One of the most significant discoveries of the entire three years of excavation was made in almost melodramatic fashion during the last two weeks of the 1972 season. To achieve better drainage in a trench through bed 3 along the westernmost edge of the site (square row J) a narrow channel was dug into the upper half of bed 2. In the process, an extensive bone complex was encountered in square J-4. Eventually, a large section of the bank adjoining the square had to be removed to permit the recovery of these remains, which consisted of the skull, both mandibles, 12 vertebrae, and 6 rib fragments. This individual is unlike any of the other squalodont forms from the Chandler Bridge beds. Morphological features of the skull were not discernible in the field and have not been fully restored in the laboratory, but several teeth associated with it are quite different from those of Genus X, Genus Y, and *Xenorophus*. Temporarily designated as Genus Z, the J-4 specimen represents another previously undescribed squalodont. Its remains constitute the first large bone complex found in bed 2 and infer that this unit is much richer than the exploratory work in 1970 had indicated. (See fig. 7.)

An isolated skull found in square I-1 appears to represent another individual of Genus X. A rib and a mandible fragment in I-1 probably are related to the skull, as may be eight vertebrae from H-1 and H-2. A braincase found with two vertebrae in square C-5 seems to be still another example of Genus X. A fragment of a skull of Genus Y was found in square H-5, and a cranial fragment from H-3 also may be referable to this genus. A large number of isolated squalodont vertebrae and ribs were recovered from various points about the excavation area, but these specimens cannot be evaluated until all material from the site has been examined. The great abundance of cetacean remains in the Chandler Bridge beds is graphically illustrated by the fact that of the 54 squares excavated in 1972 only 11 were devoid of fossil cetacean material.

Associated Biota

Although cetacean remains are by far the most significant fossils occurring in the Chandler Bridge beds, they represent only one aspect of the paleobiology of these deposits. The variety and abundance of associated material found during the excavation have in fact revealed the Chandler Bridge fauna to be one of the most comprehensive marine assemblages known from the Oligocene.

Vertebrate Remains. Skeletal elements of cetaceans and sirenians were the only marine-mammal fossils encountered. The sirenian remains consisted almost entirely of isolated ribs, which are of little or no diagnostic value. However, the 1972 season did furnish a sirenian humerus that has been referred to the genus *Halitherium* and a tooth that matches the upper third molar of a U. S. National Museum specimen of the genus *Metaxytherium.* These specimens were the first determinate sirenian fossils recovered from the Chandler Bridge beds.

Bed 3 produced a small but highly valuable assemblage of bird remains in the form of isolated limb bones and fragments thereof. Formerly under examination by the late Dr. Alexander Wetmore, these specimens are now being studied by Dr. Storrs Olsen of the National Museum of Natural History. Virtually all the forms determined to date are sea birds, notably boobies and albatrosses. This material is providing our first knowledge of the avifauna of the Western Atlantic Coast during Oligocene time; furthermore, it appears to be the only marine bird fauna known from Oligocene beds.

FIG. 7. Cetacean remains in square J-4, Bed 2, 1972 season. The skull, both mandibles, 12 vertebrae and 6 rib fragments were present. Temporarily designated as Genus Z, this individual appears to represent a new genus among the squalodonts.

The excavation also yielded the first Oligocene marine turtle fauna from the Atlantic Coast of North America. Sea-turtle shell fragments were commonly encountered in all three beds but were especially abundant in beds 1 and 3. Preliminary examinations by Dr. Robert E. Weems of the U. S. Geological Survey, who will report on the reptile material from the excavation, have shown that four chelonian genera are represented in the Chandler Bridge beds: (1) an as-yet-undetermined species of the genus *Procolpochelys,* possibly a descendant of *P. (=Carolinochelys) wilsoni* (Hay, 1923) or possibly that species, the type of which is now known to have come from the Cooper Formation at Ingleside, Berkeley County, S.C. (Weems, 1974); (2) a new species of the genus *Syllomus;* (3) the extinct leatherback turtle *(Psephophorus,* possibly *P. rupeliensis;* and (4) a form that seems to represent an undescribed genus in the Cheloniidae. Morphological details of the humerus of the new species of *Syllomus* suggest that this form is an ancestor of *S. aegyptiacus* (Lydekker, 1889) from the Calvert Formation (middle Miocene) of Maryland and Virginia, the Miocene of Japan, and from Tertiary beds in Egypt. *Procolpochelys* and *Psepho-*

phorus also are known from the Calvert Formation (Weems, 1974), and it is probable that the Chandler Bridge representatives of these two genera are precursors of the Calvert forms, *Procolpochelys grandaeva* (Leidy, 1851) and *Psephophorus calvertensis* Palmer (1908). Comparison with European material will be necessary to determine the taxonomic status of the fourth, and apparently new, sea turtle occurring in the Chandler Bridge beds.

Crocodilians were the only other reptile group represented. One of the most impressive specimens found at the site is a gigantic crocodilian femur recovered from bed 3 during the 1972 season. Measuring 355 millimeters in length, this bone obviously came from an individual at least 30 feet (9 meters) long. More complete remains of two other individuals, excavated from the Cooper Formation by the Charleston Museum in 1978, now permit assignment of the 1972 specimen to the genus *Gavialosuchus,* an extinct group of large, narrow-snouted crocodiles that appears to be ancestral to the modern False Gavial, *Tomistoma schlegeli.*

Ray dental plate segments and teeth and vertebrae of sharks and bony fishes occurred in great profusion, numerous forms being represented in the fish material and the shark teeth. During the 1971 season the posterior portion of the skull of a large billfish and the skull and entire spinal column of a fish approximately 75 centimeters in length were found in bed 3. The shark teeth are being studied by Robert W. Purdy of the National Museum of Natural History. Purdy's preliminary observations indicate that the Chandler Bridge material will provide new data on the degree of dental variation within certain species of extinct sharks.

Invertebrate Remains. Clam casts constituted the greatest majority of the invertebrate macrofossils but some gastropod casts and a large number of solitary corals also were found. As determined by Dr. J. W. Wells of Cornell University, all the corals represent a single species of the genus *Balanophyllia,* a group found from Paleocene to Recent times in mostly shallow temperate and tropical waters. Ruth Todd, U. S. Geological Survey, identified 19 species of Foraminifera from bed 1 but found the foraminifers in beds 2 and 3 to be scarce, poorly preserved, and identifiable only at the generic level.

Plant Remains. The 1970 season yielded a number of surprisingly well-preserved nuts found in bed 1. Hickory nuts were most prevalent in this assemblage. A seed from bed 1 was identified by Jack A. Wolfe, U. S. Geological Survey, as representing an indeterminate species of grape (genus *Vitis).* These remains of flowering plants indicate a temperate climate along this portion of the Atlantic coast at the time that the Chandler Bridge beds were being laid down.

Summary and Preliminary Conclusions

The remains of at least 17 individuals representing 4 different genera of extinct toothed whales belonging to the superfamily Squalodontoidea were found during the three summers of excavation at the Chandler Bridge site. A fifth squalodont genus is documented by a partial skull from the roadside ditch where the beds were first discovered. Such a large concentration of individuals might not be so unusual if we were dealing with terrestrial vertebrates in nonmarine deposits, but these animals were marine forms that presumably ranged along a good portion of the Atlantic coast of North America and most assuredly were not members of a faunal community confined to a few square miles of territory.

Why, then, were the remains of so many individuals of such generic diversity found within an area of no more than 70 by 70 feet? The answer to this question is suggested by the lithology of bed 3, in which skeletal elements of all but one of the seventeen squalodonts were found. The sand and flat, water-worn pebbles occurring in this unit are typical of the lithic materials deposited in shallow, inshore waters, demonstrating that bed 3 was laid down on a former shoreline of the Atlantic Ocean. Therefore it seems logical to conclude that the cetacean fossils in bed 3 are the remains of animals that were stranded on this ancient shore at various times. Strandings of sick or dying individuals and even entire schools are common among Recent cetaceans, and there is no reason to believe that this was not true also of their Mid-Tertiary ancestors. The large number of isolated vertebrae that were widely distributed in bed 3 probably are remnants of incompletely buried squalodont skeletons broken up and scattered along the shore by tidal currents.

Other aspects of the lithology of bed 3 indicate an environment somewhat different from that of an open beach front. The presence of clay (characteristic of a low-energy, quiet environment) as well as sand (typical of a high-energy, turbid environment) suggests that bed 3 was deposited in an embayment receiving clay-mineral sediments from inland sources and sand particles from wave-struck beaches on one or both sides of the embayment (E. M. Lemon, Jr., pers. comm.). Studies by the U. S. Army Corps of Engineers have found that a similar situation exists in Charleston Harbor today, i.e. "sand size sediment suspended by the wave action and carried by littoral and flood tidal currents project this material for deposition in the lower energy east harbor area" (U. S. Senate Doc. 88, p. 25, July 1, 1968). Although these observations of a Recent depositional pattern do not prove that bed 3 was laid down in the manner described above, they do qualify the mechanical aspects of our interpretation. Thus, the tidal currents that carried sand-size sediments into the embayment in which bed 3 seems to have been deposited evidently brought with them an occasional squalodont which was cast ashore and eventually buried by subsequent tidal fluctuations.

Significance of the Cetacean Material. Although a detailed analysis of the cetacean remains must be reserved for the formal description of the new forms, it is possible to offer some preliminary observations regarding the significance of this material. Basically, the skulls of the squalodontids from the Chandler Bridge beds represent four different stages in the telescoping of the cranial elements in the odontocetes. Most primitive of these is the skull of *Xenorophus.* In the skulls of modern toothed whales the parietal bones are restricted to the sides of the braincase, having been eliminated from the roof of the skull during the evolutionary "telescoping" process, which moved the nasal opening backward to a position well behind the orbits. In *Xenorophus* telescoping of the rostral elements is well advanced, but the braincase is still constructed in normal mammalian fashion, the parietals meeting at the midline to form the posterior portion of the skull roof (Whitmore and Sanders, 1976, fig. 1a). These and other previously unknown features of the cranial morphology of *Xenorophus*—notably a transversely curved braincase, a nearly vertical occiput, and a prominent sagittal crest—have made it clear that this genus does not belong in the family Agorophiidae, of which it has long been considered a member. Accordingly, *Xenorophus* was removed from the Agorophiidae and placed in *incertae sedis* by Whitmore and Sanders (1976, p. 310).

The skull of Genus Y exhibits a more advanced stage of telescoping in which the parietals are still in place in the skull roof but have been covered by a forward thrust of the supraoccipital and are no longer visible in dorsal aspect except for small triangular areas at the outer edges of the skull roof (Whitmore and Sanders, 1976, fig. 4). The maxillaries have overspread the greater portion of the frontals but do not come in contact with the supraoccipital as in the more progressive genus *Squalodon.* The supraoccipital is in contact with the frontals, and there is a pronounced intertemporal constriction, the latter feature being a primitive trait that was eliminated in later stages of telescoping in the Odontoceti. Genus Y compares most closely with *Patriocetus ehrlichi* (van Beneden, 1865) from the late Oligocene of Austria, but the length of the intertemporal constriction is not as great as that of *Patriocetus* and there are radical differences in the teeth of these two forms.

In Genus Z, as in Genus Y, the parietals are present in the skull roof and form a prominent intertemporal constriction, the supraoccipital is in contact with the frontals, and the maxillae do not achieve contact with the frontals. However, Genus Z differs from Genus Y in dental morphology, in width and shape of the anterior margin of the supraoccipital, and in size, Genus Z being a smaller animal approximately the size of modern *Kogia breviceps.* As noted by Whitmore and Sanders (1976, p. 312), "Genus Y and Genus Z . . . represent a stage of telescoping in which the supraoccipital and the frontals have achieved contact, but the maxillae cannot reach the supraoccipital because the parietal region is too narrow to accommodate them." The skulls of these two squalodonts effectively demonstrate that in halting the backward progress of the maxillae the intertemporal constriction was a major obstacle to the completion of the telescoping process, the maxillae being in broad contact with the supraoccipital in odontocetes with fully telescoped crania. Thus, had natural selection not favored the gradual elimination of the parietals from the skull roof, telescoping in the odontocetes would not have proceeded beyond the stage seen in Genus Y and Genus Z.

In Genus X the telescoping process is much farther advanced than in Genus Y and Genus Z but is still a step or two away from the completed stage exemplified in *Squalodon.* The parietals are in place in the skull roof but have been overridden by the supraoccipital and are concealed from dorsal view except in small, triangular areas at the sides of the skull roof, as in Genus Y and Genus Z. However, in Genus X the parietal region is shorter and broader, producing a less conspicuous intertemporal constriction and permitting the anterior margin of the supraoccipital to assume a broadly rounded shape that places it within reach of the posterior tips of the maxillae, which achieve contact with the supraoccipital at the apex of the interior angle of the parietal triangles (Whitmore and Sanders, 1976, fig. 5). Specimens from the excavation have shown that in young individuals of Genus X the parietals were exposed across the entire width of the skull roof but were eventually covered by forward growth of the supraoccipital in succeeding stages of ontogeny (Whitmore and Sanders, 1976, p. 313, figs. 6-8). Genus X represents the same stage of telescoping as that of *Eosqualodon langewieschei* Rothausen (1968) from the late Oligocene of Germany, but Genus X is a smaller animal with teeth that are similar to those of taxa that have been assigned to the genus *Microcetus.* This stage of telescoping, which has been called the "eusqualodontid" stage by Rothausen (1968), is also represented in the skull of *Agriocetus incertus* (Brandt, 1874) from late Oligocene sands near Linz, Austria. *Agriocetus* has long been regarded as a close ally of *Patriocetus ehrlichi,* also from the Linz sands, but my observations of the holotypes of these two forms do not support that view.

Completion of the major steps in the telescoping of the cranial elements in odontocetes is displayed in the partial skull found in the roadside ditch in 1969. As noted previously, this specimen is provisionally regarded as a new species of the genus *Squalodon.*

The skulls of the three new genera from the Chandler Bridge beds have provided the first clear indications of the manner in which the parietal bones were eliminated from the skull roof in the odontocetes. From studies of these specimens and the holotypes of Oligocene odontocetes in western Europe and the Soviet Union, it now seems evident that the parietals were crowded out of the skull roof by a forward thrust of the supraoccipital, which gradually overrode the parietalia and eventually made contact with the frontals. Pressed from behind by the advancing supraoccipital and blocked anteriorly by the frontals, the parietal region became progressively shorter and broader until, in later stages of telescoping (e.g., Genus X and *Eosqualodon),* it was compacted into a narrow strip across the skull roof beneath the anterior portion of the supraoccipital. Reduced to only a fraction of their former size and value as structural elements, and with space for their embryonic development steadily decreasing, the parietals continued to diminish until they eventually disappeared from the skull roof. With their departure the supraoccipital achieved sutural union with the frontals and the maxillae came into broader contact with the supraoccipital, thus completing one of the last major steps in the telescoping process.

Two of the specimens from the excavation have furnished information on progress in the evolution of echolocation in late Oligocene ondontocetes. Dr. Gerald Fleischer's studies (1976, pp. 142-143) of a broken periotic from Genus Z disclosed that the cochlea in this squalodont "is an intermediate form in most aspects, between a dolphin-type (high frequency echolocator) and a cochlea not specialized for high-frequency sonar" and that the mode of coiling "is intermediate between Odontoceti and Mysticeti," although Genus Z is clearly an odontocete. Fleischer (1976, p. 143) also examined fragments of the cochlea of a badly shattered periotic from the *Xenorophus* skull from square B-2 but could determine only that the mode of coiling "is the same as in Odontoceti." From his analysis of the cochlear structure in Genus Z Fleischer (1976, p. 150) was able to conclude that "the adaptation of the cochlea for high-frequency echolocation occurred in Squalodontoidea during the Oligocene."

Age of the Chandler Bridge Beds. Morphological details of the squalodont skulls discussed above suggest that the Eagle Creek beds were laid down during Oligocene times. The archaic *Xenorophus* and the new genera from these deposits represent evolutionary stages that have not been recorded from later horizons. Telescoping of the cranial elements is complete in the skulls of all known odontocetes from the Miocene, the survivors of earlier stages of odontocete evolution (e.g., *Xenorophus)* having disappeared by the end of the Oligocene (Kellogg, 1928, p. 50; Rothausen, 1970, p. 187). The telescoping

FIG. 8. West view of site at end of 1972 season, last of the three summers of fieldwork. During the seven weeks of work in 1972 the excavation of Bed 3 was completed over the entire site.

process is complete in only one of the five genera from the Chandler Bridge beds.

The invertebrate remains contribute additional evidence that these deposits are Oligocene in age. Druid Wilson examined samples of the molluscan fauna and found them to be typical Cooper marl forms. As determined by Ruth Todd, the Foraminifera of bed 1 appear to constitute an Oligocene fauna. Of the 19 species from this bed, 10 are known to occur in the Cooper marl, and 1 of these forms has not been recorded from younger beds.

In general, however, foraminifers, ostracodes, and calcareous nannoplankton are scarce and poorly preserved in the non-calcareous Chandler Bridge beds and thus have been of virtually no value for biostratigraphic correlation. At present, the cetaceans provide the best indication of a specific horizon within the Oligocene. The evolutionary levels represented in the skulls of the odontocetes so far recorded from these beds are—with the exception of *Xenorophus*—essentially the same as those seen in squalodonts from

Chattian-age (late Oligocene) beds in Europe, but the high percentage of Chandler Bridge forms with incomplete telescoping argues against a very late Oligocene date for this assemblage. In fact, recent biostratigraphic correlations in Europe indicate that the deposits that furnished the holotype of *Eosqualodon langeweischei*—an evolutionary counterpart of Genus X—are of early Chattian age (K. Rothausen, 1979, priv. comm.), having been assigned to the upper part of nannoplankton zone NP 24 of Steininger, Rögl and Martini (1976). Furthermore, the Chandler Bridge beds are now known to contain the remains of archaeocetes, skulls and postcranial elements of three individuals representing at least two different species having been collected by the Charleston Museum in 1975 and 1978 at other localities near Charleston. Most primitive of the three recognized suborders of Cetacea, Archaeoceti are known primarily from Eocene beds, records from the Oligocene being exceedingly rare. The presence of these archaic forms and the predominance of odontocetes with incomplete telescoping, coupled with the early Chattian date for *Eosqualodon,* suggests that the Chandler Bridge beds are no younger than middle Chattian.

Having provided the largest and most diverse assemblage of squalodont remains yet recorded from an Oligocene formation, the Chandler Bridge beds must be regarded as one of the most important fossil cetacean localities in the world. Doubtless there are other localities of equal potential, and it is hoped that the results of the present investigation will encourage similar explorations of accessible Oligocene marine fossil beds wherever they may occur.

REFERENCES

FLEISCHER, GERALD

1976. Hearing in extinct cetaceans as determined by cochlear structure. Journ. Paleont., vol. 50, no. 1, pp. 133-152, illus.

KELLOGG, REMINGTON

1923a. Description of two squalodonts recently discovered in the Calvert cliffs, Maryland; and notes on the shark-toothed cetaceans. Proc. U. S. Nat. Mus., vol. 62, art. 16, pp. 1-69, illus.

1923b. Description of an apparently new toothed cetacean from South Carolina. Smithsonian Misc. Coll., vol. 76, no. 7, 7 pp., illus.

1928. The history of whales—their adaptation to life in the water. Quart. Rev. Biol., vol. 3, no. 1, pp. 29-76, illus.

LEMON, EARL M., JR.

1976. Textural and clay-mineral differentiation of Oligocene and Pleistocene deposits in the Stallsville quadrangle, South Carolina. Geol. Soc. America Abstracts with Programs, vol. 11, no. 4, p. 186.

MALDE, HAROLD E.
1959. Geology of the Charleston phosphate area, South Carolina. U. S. Geol. Surv. Bull. 1079, 105 pp., illus.

MILLER, GERRIT, S., JR.
1923. The telescoping of the cetacean skull. Smithsonian Misc. Coll., vol. 76, no. 5, 70 pp., illus.

ROTHAUSEN, KARLHEINZ
1968. Die systematische Stellung der europäischen Squalodontidae (Odontoceti, Mamm.). Pal. Zool., vol. 48, pp. 83-104, illus.
1970. Marine Reptilia and Mammalia and the problem of the Oligocene-Miocene boundary. Giorn. Geol. ser. 2, vol. 35, fasc. 1, pp. 181-189.

SANDERS, ALBERT E.; LEMON, EARL M., JR.; and WEEMS, ROBERT E.
1979. A newly recognized post-Cooper/pre-Hawthorn stratigraphic unit in the Lower Coastal Plain, Dorchester County, South Carolina. Geol. Soc. America Abstracts with Programs, vol. 11, no. 4, p. 210.

STEININGER, FRITZ; RÖGL, FRED; and MARTINI, ERLEND
1976. Current Oligocene/Miocene biostratigraphic concept of the Central Paratethys (Middle Europe). Newsl. Stratigr., vol. 4, no. 3, pp. 174-202, illus.

WEEMS, ROBERT E.
1974. Middle Miocene sea turtles *(Syllomus, Procolpochelys, Psephophorus)* from the Calvert Formation. Journ. Paleont., vol. 48, no. 2, pp. 278-303, illus.

WHITMORE, FRANK C., JR., and SANDERS, ALBERT E.
1976. Review of the Oligocene Cetacea. Syst. Zool., vol. 25, no. 4, pp. 304-320, illus.

ALBERT E. SANDERS

The Taiwan Pheasant Project

Principal Investigator: Sheldon R. Severinghaus, Cornell University, Ithaca, New York.

Grant No. 994: To study Taiwan's mikado and Swinhoe's pheasants.[1]

The Taiwan Pheasant Project was initiated in August 1972 for the purpose of studying the mikado and Swinhoe's pheasants (*Syrmaticus mikado* and *Lophura swinhoii,* respectively) in the high mountains of Taiwan. Both species are endemic to the island (Severinghaus and Blackshaw, 1976) and were listed as rare and endangered in the *Red Data Book* of the International Union for the Conservation of Nature (I.U.C.N., 1966). Only a handful of scientists have ever seen either species in the wild. Prior to this study, therefore, little detailed, first-hand ecological information on these wild pheasants had been gathered.

The objectives of the project were to determine the present status and distribution of the pheasants, to study their ecology and behavior, to evaluate the natural and man-induced pressures operating upon their populations, and to delineate the web of scientific, economic, and cultural interests that man has spun around them, thus making them the important resources that they are. Detailed results of these field studies with an extensive bibliography are presented elsewhere (Severinghaus, 1977). This report summarizes the observations made and provides some general conclusions.

Logistics and Methods

Headquarters for the project in Taiwan was the Environmental Research Center at Tunghai University in Taichung. In October 1972 the project was

[1] The pheasant project was supported by the following organizations and institutions, to whom sincerest thanks are here expressed: National Geographic Society, New York Zoological Society, International Council for Bird Preservation, Fauna Preservation Society, Tunghai University Environmental Research Center, Taiwan Provincial Forestry Bureau, National Science Council (Taipei), and National Science Foundation (Washington, D. C.).

accepted for inclusion under the U. S.–Republic of China Cooperative Science Program. Dr. Chi-lu Chen, professor of anthropology at National Taiwan University, became the Chinese co-investigator under this arrangement. Both the project's objectives and its administrative structure, therefore, reflected the interdisciplinary nature of the research: the biology of the pheasants on one hand and their socio-economic importance to people on the other. The field-research team consisted of four persons: the author as principal investigator, his wife, an assistant from the Ami tribe on the east coast, and a Hakka assistant from southern Taiwan, all college graduates. The team had a proficiency in five languages, which was useful in dealing with the variety of ethnic groups on the island.

In order to achieve project objectives, information and data were gathered in four ways: (1) review of the literature, (2) study of museum specimens, (3) direct field observations of wild pheasants, and (4) interviews with people who have had personal experience with the pheasants.

Following a short period of orientation in Taiwan (Aug.-Sept. 1972), a 4-month preliminary islandwide survey was conducted (Oct. 1972-Jan. 1973) to test field-research capabilities in the rugged mountains, to make contacts with aborigine guides, to become familiar with habitat and land-use conditions, and to observe wild pheasants. Results of this trial run were evaluated in February 1973. From March through July 1973 extensive field trips were made into the eastern half of the island's mountains. The western half of the mountains was covered during the same period in 1974 (Mar.-July). In between these two periods of spring research, related lowland research was carried out (Aug.-Sept. 1973) and cold-season field trips were made (Oct. 1973-Feb. 1974).

During the 10 months spent in the mountains (about 300 field days), the team traveled some 6,700 kilometers: 2,000 on foot, 4,000 by jeep, 400 by narrow-gauge logging railroad, and 300 by logging truck. Interviews were conducted among all ethnic groups, including the nine different aboriginal tribes. Using colored pictures of the pheasants to avoid confusion, the team gathered supplementary information on the natural history of the pheasants and on their economic and cultural value to the people.

In November 1974, project operations were shifted to Japan where a month-long review of extensive Japanese materials was undertaken with particular attention to the mikado and Swinhoe's pheasants. Specimens in museums and private collections were studied, library materials were reviewed, Japanese ornithologists who have had personal field experience in Taiwan were interviewed, and animal dealers were questioned.

Pheasant Ecology and Behavior

The natural history of the two pheasants is a broad subject and a particularly difficult one to study. The pheasants live in the forest interior, often where the undergrowth is impenetrable and the slopes steep. Even in areas where pheasants are fairly common, as judged from indirect signs, they are rarely seen and rarely flush. They can slip easily and quietly out of range on foot in advance of an approaching person or party. Vocalizations, which are useful in locating and counting other pheasant species, are infrequent and almost inaudible for these species. Nevertheless, 95 direct sightings of wild pheasants were made by members of the field team. Length of observations ranged from 1 second to 20 minutes. Food plants utilized by both species were collected and identified. Behavioral differences were noted and on-site habitat descriptions were taken.

Status. Although both the mikado and Swinhoe's pheasants are listed as rare and endangered, results from this research suggest that neither species is as rare in the wild as previously thought. Their current status might more accurately be described as fairly common but "threatened with endangerment" by various man-induced factors. The Swinhoe's pheasant faces more immediate danger than the mikado (see *Environmental Pressures* below). The previously reported rarity of these pheasants is probably due, in part at least, to the difficulty of access to their favored haunts and the retiring nature of their habits.

Distribution. The most notable finding made with regard to distribution was the discovery of Swinhoe's pheasants inhabiting the long, narrow, coastal mountain range hugging the eastern edge of the island. As far as is known, they have never been reported there before. This low-lying range is completely isolated from the massive, towering central mountains by a cultivated and populated lowland valley. Swinhoe's pheasants are also reportedly still found in the isolated mountains just north of Taipei as well as at elevations close to sea level in a few places where habitat remains suitable. Otherwise, the distribution of this species and of the mikado pheasant is confined to the higher regions of the central mountain ranges, as earlier ornithological literature has reported (e.g., Hachisuka and Udagawa, 1951).

Habitat Requirements. Mikado pheasants have usually been considered as inhabiting virgin, coniferous, or mixed conifer-hardwood forests with a dense undergrowth of dwarf bamboo above 2,000 meters in elevation. Although this has been confirmed, mikados were also observed at lower elevations and in other types of habitat, including road construction slides, natural secondary hardwood forest, replanted conifer monocultures, and dense second growth of brush and grass on open slopes.

In contrast, Swinhoe's pheasants seem to prefer, if not depend exclusively on, virgin broadleaf forests at lower elevations between 500 and 2,000 meters. There is fragmentary evidence that they may live also in areas of second growth, but no direct observations of this were made. An interesting and possibly limiting factor is slope, or something related to slope. Mikados seem to prefer slopes steeper than 40°; Swinhoe's the gentler slopes less than 40°.

Courtship and Breeding. No courtship of wild pheasants was observed and no active nests were found. Sufficient other observations of behavior were made, however, to begin to suggest the behavioral "inclinations" of free-living, wild pheasants. In this regard, mikados may be monogamous under natural conditions and male-female pairs may maintain territories. Swinhoe's pheasants, on the other hand, may be polygamous, with perhaps only the male holding a territory. Reliable hatching records for wild Swinhoe's were obtained and one possible tree nest was documented for this species.

Environmental Pressures. The most easily discernible environmental pressures acting upon wild pheasant populations are man-induced. The mikado pheasant has a rather broad habitat tolerance, being able to live in man-disturbed areas as well as in tracts of virgin forest. Hunting and trapping for various reasons seem to be the primary factor affecting the mikado (see *Socioeconomics* below). Given effective protection from hunting and trapping, therefore, the mikado's chances for survival would seem to be quite good.

Prospects for long-range survival of the Swinhoe's pheasant are more precarious. This species seems to live almost exclusively in virgin broadleaf forests with gentle slopes. Since such areas are generally found below 2,000 meters in elevation, these pheasants are confronted with an array of encroaching land-use practices. First, hunting pressure is heavier in these regions because they are more easily accessible than the higher, steeper regions where mikados live. Second, the gentler slopes below 2,000 meters are gradually but steadily being converted to various forms of mountain agriculture. Third, the low-economic-value native hardwood forests are being cut and replaced with faster-growing, higher-value conifer plantations. Fourth, mining of various kinds occurs more frequently at lower elevations within the range of the Swinhoe's pheasant. And finally, the opening of mountainous regions for these various purposes brings associated disturbances. The building of roads, railroads, and cableways is destructive to habitat. Increased access brings in more people to areas they would not otherwise reach. This leads to increased pressure from sustained and unrestricted hunting. All these factors pose a particularly serious threat to Swinhoe's pheasants in light of their distribution and habitat requirements. Although they seem to be fairly common at the present time, the current trends in land-use practices and hunting, if left unchecked, could eventually cause the birds' extinction.

Socioeconomic Values of the Pheasants

In addition to studying the natural history of the pheasants, project personnel also investigated their economic and cultural value. The pheasants, on a relatively small scale, mirror the tremendous economic value of the island's wildlife resources as a whole. The rarity of the pheasants combined with their stunning plumage has made them popular as ornamental birds among aviculturists the world over. This has created an international market for the birds and a chain of "retailers" starting in the high mountains. The aborigines live-trap the birds, bring them down to the lowlands, and sell them to Chinese animal dealers. They in turn sell them to foreign buyers for approximately US $50 a pair. In Japan, prices quoted for a pair of mikados start at more than $150. As a source of income the sums involved are relatively small but do carry considerable purchasing power for the people on the local market.

The Japanese have long had a particular interest in the mikado pheasant. It was discovered in 1906 during the Japanese occupation of Taiwan. It was given the Japanese name for "emperor" and presented to the Emperor himself. Locally in Taiwan, the Chinese seem to prefer the more colorful Swinhoe's pheasant. Many of these were found locally in private bird collections. Mortality is high, and captive breeding in Taiwan is rarely successful. This puts a constant demand on wild populations for replacement of captive birds when they die.

Among the island's aborigines, the pheasants have played various cultural roles. People in some villages of the Ami tribe considered the Swinhoe's pheasant as the king of birds. Its feathers were commonly worn in the Ami headdress. Among other tribes the tail feathers of both species were worn ornamentally in headdresses. For one tribe each feather indicated an enemy head decapitated by the wearer. In weaving, some traditional garments of the Atayal tribe have been designed after the black-and-white barred tail pattern of the Mikado.

The pheasants, as well as other wild game in the mountains, are always a welcome source of fresh meat. A surprisingly large number of people who live and work in the mountains (e.g., aborigines, loggers, miners, construction workers) take advantage of the proximity to wildlife by hunting in their leisure time. Trap lines can be laid out easily and then checked from time to time in off-hours or on the way back to camp from work. Much of what is trapped is eaten and never brought to the lowlands for sale. This practice is easy to appreciate since fresh domestic meat from the lowlands is difficult to obtain in the mountains. Roasted pheasant and other wild game form a refreshing change from the steady diet of salted fatty pork, dried fish, and canned meat. It has the added appeal of being considered more nutritious than domestic meats.

Pheasant Conservation

Among the steps taken toward the development of wildlife conservation in Taiwan was the 3-year total ban on hunting, promulgated in 1972 and renewed in 1975. Export of wildlife has also been prohibited. In addition, in July 1974 the Taiwan Provincial Forestry Bureau approved the establishment of a 3,680-hectare high-mountain wildlife reserve (Severinghaus, 1978a). This developed out of a recommendation based on the pheasant project's field research in the area. The reserve is comprised largely of virgin hardwood forest at the lower elevations and mixed hardwood-conifer forests at higher elevations. Both mikado and Swinhoe's pheasants have been observed within the boundaries, the Swinhoe's being relatively common. Many other bird species are present, as are a variety of larger mammals, including the serow *(Capricornis crispus),* muntjac *(Muntiacus reevesi),* two species of giant flying squirrel (the white-bellied, *Petaurista alborufus,* and the red, *P. petaurista*), and the endemic Formosan macaque *(Macaca cyclopsis).*

Since 1974, however, economic development activities have increased dramatically in Taiwan with plans to build three more cross-mountain highways (three major ones already exist) and, for the first time, to establish an around-the-island railroad (Severinghaus, 1977). These developments will lead to a rapid exploitation of resources in heretofore relatively isolated mountain areas. The resulting increased accessibility and disturbance to these areas are bound to have a detrimental impact on wildlife, including the pheasants, if action is not taken.

Given the current circumstances, therefore, I published a series of recommendations for the conservation of the mikado and Swinhoe's pheasants and for the development of a coordinated wildlife management program in Taiwan (Severinghaus, 1978b). The International Council for Bird Preservation reviewed these recommendations at its 17th World Conference in Ohrid, Yugoslavia, in June 1978 and subsequently wrote letters to the Taiwan government urging consideration of the recommendations (I.C.B.P. Resolution #9). I have also proposed plans for follow-up studies on the pheasants. This is where events stood as of July 1979.

Secondary Results of Project

During the course of the research on pheasants, several other discoveries were made. In the mountainous interior of the southeast an old aboriginal skull rack with the remains of nine human skulls was found in a village abandoned 30 years ago and overgrown with jungle vegetation. As far as is known, this is the only such shelf extant.

A stand of Taiwan beech *(Fagus hayatae)* was discovered high in the mountains southwest of Taipei (Severinghaus and DeVol, 1974). This species is highly localized in distribution and has seldom been seen or collected by scientists. The discovery postulates a wider distribution for the species than has been thought and reports the occurrence of black bears *(Selanarctos thibetanus)* in apparent association with the beech.

A tick was collected in the mountains on the east coast and given to the United States Naval Medical Research Unit (Taipei) for identification. It was only the second individual of this species *(Ixodes acutitarsus)* ever collected in Taiwan. The first one was collected in 1937 by a Japanese scientist.

Edible wild plants eaten by the research team on field trips were collected and given to botanists at National Taiwan University to be included in the *Flora of Taiwan* now being compiled.

Observations were made on many other birds and mammals. Although no species new to science were discovered, new information on the status, distribution, and ecology of Taiwan's avian and mammalian fauna was gathered. Some of this information has been incorporated in various publications to date (Severinghaus, 1978a-d; Severinghaus and Blackshaw, 1976). Other publication are forthcoming.

REFERENCES

HACHISUKA, M., and UDAGAWA, T.

1951. Contributions to the ornithology of Formosa, part 2. Quar. Journ. Taiwan Museum, vol. 4, nos. 1 & 2, pp. 1-180.

I.U.C.N.

1966. Red data book, *Aves.* International Union for the Conservation of Nature and Natural Resources, Morges, Switzerland.

SEVERINGHAUS, S. R.

1977. A study of the Swinhoe's and mikado pheasants in Taiwan with recommendations for their conservation. Ph.D. thesis, Cornell University, Ithaca, N.Y., 364 pp.

1978a. Conservation of the Swinhoe's and mikado pheasants in Taiwan. Pheasant Trust Annual Report, 1976.

1978b. Recommendations for the conservation of the Swinhoe's and mikado pheasants in Taiwan. World Pheasant Assoc. Journ. III (1977-78), pp. 79-89.

1978c. Diurnal behavior of an Eurasian Woodcock *(Scolopax rusticola).* Auk, vol. 95, no. 4, p. 748.

1978d. Aerial feeding by Bulbuls. Ibis, vol. 120, no. 4, pp. 514-516.

SEVERINGHAUS, S. R.—Continued

1978e. Field research and captive breeding: a look at two endangered species of pheasants. First International Birds in Captivity Symposium: in press.

1979. The ecology and behavior of Swinhoe's pheasant in Taiwan. Living Bird. (In press.)

1980. A review of some problematic avian taxa in Taiwan. Zool. Meded. (In press.)

SEVERINGHAUS, S. R., and BLACKSHAW, K. T.

1976. A new guide to the birds of Taiwan, 222 pp. Mei Ya Publications, Inc., Taipei.

SEVERINGHAUS, S. R., and CHANG, JAMES W. F.

1979. Notes on the Yellow Tit *Parus holsti* of Taiwan with discovery of its nest. Bull. British Orn. Club. (In press.)

SEVERINGHAUS, S. R., and DEVOL, C. E.

1974. Notes on the distribution of Taiwan beech. Taiwania, vol. 19, no. 2, pp. 235-237.

SHELDON R. SEVERINGHAUS

Asian Woodpecker Studies

Principal Investigator: Lester L. Short, American Museum of Natural History, New York, New York.

Grant No. 1012: In support of a behavioral, ecological, and taxonomic study of Asian woodpeckers.

The avian family of woodpeckers (Picidae) numbers about 200 species, distributed over all the continents except Australia and Antarctica. About a third of the species and genera occur in Asia, and most species in that region have been known only through reports of casual observations. Faced with a dearth of behavioral and other information about this sizable portion of the world's woodpeckers in preparing a monograph of the family, I traveled to parts of Asia from early February to mid-May 1972, with the support of a National Geographic Society grant. Areas visited were Okinawa, Malaya, Thailand, and India. This report summarizes my results; for further details see the publications cited below.

The first part of the trip was devoted to locating and studying the endangered Okinawa woodpecker *(Sapheopipo noguchii)*. A grant from the International Council for Bird Preservation helped to support this portion of my studies, and the United States Marine Corps also aided me logistically. Behaviorally virtually unknown, the Okinawa woodpecker represents a very distinct species, comprising a genus of its own; its range is limited to a few hills on northern Okinawa that still bear sufficient native forest and undergrowth. I studied up to eight birds and was able to estimate that 20 to 60 pairs are all that remain of this endemic woodpecker. Observations of feeding habits and some social behavior, and tape recordings of five vocalizations and instrumental drumming (signal tapping on tree trunks), provided new data useful in comparing the species with its relatives and in plans for its preservation. The data show clearly that *Sapheopipo* is related to the widespread genus *Picus* and to the South Asian *Blythipicus* (I later studied the latter in Malaya). I have made various suggestions (Short, 1973a) to minimize and stop forest destruction and fragmentation in the area where the woodpecker occurs. While on Okinawa I observed various other birds, leading me to analyze and reevaluate the zoogeography of Okinawa and the Ryukyu Islands, stressing the complex origins (from Japan, from Taiwan and China, from the Pacific islands and Philippines) of the avifauna (Short, 1973b).

From Okinawa I proceeded to Malaya where, thanks largely to the help of Dr. David Wells of the University of Malaya, I had an extremely productive stay. I concentrated on repetitive visits to study sites along the coast (Rantau Panjang, Kuala Selangor), in forested lowlands (the Krau Game Reserve in Kuala Lompat, Pahang, and the International Biological Program's lowland rainforest study site at Pasoh, Negeri Sembilan), in foothills (Ulu Gombok Forest Preserve, Selangor), and in montane forest (Fraser's Hill, 4,100 feet, Selangor-Pahang border). The diversity of the habitats insured that I would see the greatest number of species, and repetitive visits enabled me to check breeding and other situations progressively. An enormous volume of new data was obtained on the habits, including aggressive and other social behavior, of 25 Malayan woodpeckers. Most of this information has been discussed elsewhere (Short, 1973d); I have prepared (1978) a treatise on the ecology and morphological variation relating to sympatry of 13 species of woodpeckers in the forest sites at Kuala Lompat and Pasoh. Woodpeckers are specialized for feeding on tree trunks and branches; hence usually rather few species with sharply distinct habits occur at any one site. The richness of the Malayan lowland forest and evolutionary factors involving the local woodpeckers have permitted an unusually great number of woodpeckers to coexist there (only a few parts of South America approach Malayan forests in the number of sympatric woodpeckers).

The studies in Malaya gave me an insight into the urgency of preserving large tracts of the incredibly rich tropical forests of the world. Despite its relatively small population, lowland forest destruction in Malaya (and elsewhere in the region) is proceeding rapidly. It is appalling to contemplate the loss to future generations that is occurring for small financial gains at present. Forest preserves and parks in the region are too small and too scattered to protect the major segment of at least the larger fauna, and once isolated such areas are subjected to intense disturbance and poaching pressures at their edges. One can only hope for a rapid change in attitude, a hope for which there is all too little basis.

Especially interesting to me was the opportunity provided by the tree ladder at Pasoh to study birds at different heights in the forest. The ladder arrangement provides platforms at various heights to 115 feet above the ground. A quick trip up or down is a never-to-be-forgotten experience, for the climatic shift (in humidity, temperature, air movements) is dramatic. I spent a night alone on the top platform, sampling the sounds and sights of the canopy.

In Malaya I investigated nesting of white-bellied woodpeckers *(Dryocopus javensis),* banded red woodpeckers *(Picus miniaceus),* laced green woodpeckers

(Picus vittatus), the olive-backed woodpecker *(Dinopium rafflesii),* common golden-backed woodpeckers *(Dinopium javanense),* buff-rumped woodpeckers *(Meiglyptes tristis),* and great slaty woodpeckers *(Mulleripicus pulverulentus).* At the nest of the olive-backed woodpecker I obtained movies, photographs, and tape recordings; this is the first described nesting of this little-known species. Several nests of great slaty woodpeckers, a large species, were taken over by other animals, and so the nests failed. The fact that nesting failure seemed very great for all forest woodpeckers perhaps accounts for their supposedly long nesting seasons (birds may have to try two or three times to nest successfully). Although no nests were studied of these species, some breeding data (courtship, attempted nesting, parent-young foraging and interactions) were obtained for speckled piculets *(Picumnus innominatus),* rufous woodpeckers *(Celeus brachyurus),* crimson-winged woodpeckers *(Picus puniceus),* greater golden-backed woodpeckers *(Chrysocolaptes lucidus),* maroon woodpeckers *(Blythipicus rubiginosus),* orange-backed woodpeckers *(Reinwardtipicus validus),* buffnecked woodpeckers *(Meiglyptes tukki),* and gray and buff woodpeckers *(Hemicircus concretus).* Vocal and foraging data were secured for other woodpeckers not studied in detail.

I left Malaya for several weeks in late March to visit peninsular Thailand with the main purpose of studying interactions between coastal laced green woodpeckers and a montane form of that species often considered specifically distinct (as *Picus viridanus*). With the help of Kitti Thonglongya of Bangkok I was able to survey coastal and interior Prachuap, even reaching the Burmese border (escorted by a noisy platoon of Thai soldiers). The lowland monsoonal forests in the region have been largely cut and burned, however, and plantations of exotic trees, cultivated fields, and bamboo scrub preclude a forest connection that would allow contact of these woodpeckers. Therefore I concentrated on behavioral study of available woodpeckers, which was rewarding because I found a number of species common that had been rare or lacking in the areas of Malaya visited. Especially noteworthy was the bamboo woodpecker *(Gecinulus viridis)* that I photographed and observed, obtaining tape recordings of various calls. Poorly known, this woodpecker never had been photographed previously (fig. 1). Rufous woodpeckers, greater yellow-naped woodpeckers *(Picus flavinucha),* gray-headed woodpeckers *(Picus canus),* and common and greater golden-backed woodpeckers also were studied in detail.

Returning to Malaya in April, I continued investigations at my study sites. Aside from brief meetings with cobras and sun bears, I encountered no hazards more bothersome than ubiquitous leeches and was able to observe numerous birds other than woodpeckers. One observation led me to pay particular attention to barbets (Capitonidae), close relatives of woodpeckers but fruit-eaters with a very different bill. I was surprised to find that red-throated barbets *(Megalaima mystacophanos)* occasionally peck at dead tree trunks, feeding on insects secured in the manner of woodpeckers (Short, 1973c). This observation suggests that barbets and woodpeckers may compete to some extent and probably did so even earlier in their evolution.

After concluding the Malayan activities in mid-April, I proceeded to Calcutta. There I visited the Indian Museum and went about securing permits to enter the "restricted area" about Darjeeling. With the help of West Bengal forestry officials and other personnel, I worked in several forest areas; namely, at Sukna, north of Siliguri at the base of the Himalayas, and near the Nepalese border 8 miles southwest of Darjeeling (elevation 6,900 to 9,500 feet). At the lower site the woods were largely managed sal forest. Here I found gray-capped woodpeckers *(Picoides canicapillus),* streak-breasted woodpeckers *(Picoides macei),* rufous woodpeckers, lesser yellow-naped woodpeckers *(Picus chlorolophus),* greater yellow-naped woodpeckers, greater golden-backed woodpeckers, heart-spotted woodpeckers *(Hemicircus canente),* and great slaty woodpeckers. Movies provided a means of analysis of complex displays in aggressive interactions of gray-capped and streak-breasted woodpeckers. The voices of most species were recorded on tape.

In the mountain forests west of Darjeeling I found crimson-breasted woodpeckers *(Picoides cathpharius),* Darjeeling woodpeckers *(P. darjellensis),* scaly-bellied green woodpeckers *(Picus squamatus),* and bay woodpeckers *(Blythipicus pyrrhotis)* and obtained movies, photographs, and tape recordings of all but the scaly-bellied green woodpecker. The fog-bound laurel and rhododendron forest partly was managed, but good tracts of relatively undisturbed forest remain, especially on steeper slopes. Plans to visit a site deeper in the mountains fell through when someone at the forestry station involved came down with smallpox, and the area was closed to outsiders.

The trip home by way of Europe permitted a brief visit to the British Museum (Natural History), where I examined specimens of some Asian woodpeckers.

New information about 30 Asian woodpeckers, representing 15 of 16 genera occurring on that continent, provided comparative data most useful in studies of woodpecker behavior and relationships. This information has been incorporated into a book (in press) on the world's woodpeckers emphasizing their behavior (as a result of the Asian studies I have gained field experience with over 120 species, representing all woodpecker genera except Cuban *Xiphidiopicus*). Treatment of the data included audiospectrographic analysis and comparison of resulting sonagrams, and frame-by-frame study of motion

FIG. 1. Female bamboo woodpecker *(Gecinulus viridis)* in southern Thailand. Never photographed previously, this woodpecker frequents bamboo growth. Despite this preference it encounters difficulty moving on the bamboo stalks, slipping and clasping the stalk peculiarly with its three-toed feet and assuming a more typical woodpecker posture only when gripping the rough nodes, as shown here.

pictures where appropriate. Some behavioral and taxonomic results of these studies are highlighted here.

Active competition was observed between the larger *Picoides macei* and smaller *P. canicapillus* in India (Short, 1975). The larger species tends to forage on large branches and trunks of trees, the smaller one on branchlets and twigs, but there is some overlap. When both happen to feed in the same tree, however, I found that *macei* ignores *canicapillus* so long as it stays in the twigs and outer branches, but attacks and drives it away whenever *canicapillus* ventures onto the trunk. This occurred even when the birds involved were at widely separate points in a tree; i.e., *macei* on the lower trunk quickly moved to displace *canicapillus* if it caught sight of *canicapillus* foraging high on the trunk of that tree. Other instances were observed that seemed to indicate competition of an indirect nature. A white-bellied woodpecker that had taken to roosting nightly in a certain tree gave up that tree as a roosting site when a great slaty woodpecker started to use a different hole in the same tree as its roosting chamber. This occurred with no apparent interactions, although the birds saw each other. A white-bellied woodpecker was observed to work at enlarging a prospective nesting cavity being excavated by a crimson-winged woodpecker, rendering it unusable by the latter, even though the branch in which the cavity was being constructed was too narrow for a white-bellied woodpecker nesting or roosting cavity.

No clear case of competitive interaction was noted in *Picus,* except for slight interactions between *P. puniceus* and *P. miniaceus;* as many as three species *(mentalis, puniceus, miniaceus)* of this genus were observed sympatrically. However, these species do differ markedly in their foraging habits and feeding sites, suggesting adaptive interplay resulting from competition. Sympatric *Meiglyptes tukki* and *M. tristis* forage similarly, but they tend to use different foraging sites, *tukki* favoring more dense forest and lower parts of trees and *tristis* preferring forest edges and clearings, where it feeds chiefly in the canopy.

Very closely related species, similar in habits, are allopatric and form species pairs (most are superspecies). Some of these are *Blythipicus rubiginosus* and *B. pyrrhotis, Hemicircus concretus* and *H. canente, Picus puniceus* and *P. chlorolophus, Picus mentalis* and *P. flavinucha,* and *Sasia abnormis* and *S. ochracea.* Detailed comparisons of the species of *Blythipicus* and *Picus* are reported elsewhere (Short, 1973d).

Among other behavioral highlights are the: (a) Cluster roosting of families of *Chrysocolaptes lucidus,* with each bird excavating a hole of its own, the cavities often side by side or only a few feet apart; (b) courtship feeding of *Dinopium rafflesii,* documented on film; (c) demonstration of the minute movements of a drumming white-bellied woodpecker, through film analysis; (d) peculiar advertising calls of *Picus puniceus* and *P. chlorolophus;* (e) odd whiny call and ungainly courtship display of the long-necked *Mulleripicus pulverulentus;* (f) apparent nest robbery and predation by a greater yellow-naped woodpecker on a hole-nesting bird (or mammal) of indeterminate species; and, (g) ant-feeding habits of many (about half) of the observed woodpecker species, agreeing with results of South American investigations (Short, 1970).

Vocal data gathered for the several species of *Picoides* provided an important basis for an analysis of vocal communication in this, the largest genus of woodpeckers (Winkler and Short, 1978). This is one of the few studies treating in this way an entire genus of birds.

Asiatic *Picumnus innominatus* and *Celeus (Micropternus) brachyurus* appear correctly placed in these otherwise Neotropical genera. Among Eurasian (and African) woodpecker genera other than *Picumnus* and *Celeus,* only the cosmopolitan *Dryocopus* and *Picoides* also are represented in the New World. Southern Asian species of *Picoides*, especially *macei* and *canicapillus*, behaviorally are more like American species of that genus than are most European *Picoides*. Earlier museum study by my colleague Walter Bock and me had suggested that *Chrysocolaptes validus* was misplaced within that genus, and the Asian field studies not only corroborated this view but also rather strongly suggested that its relationship is with the genus *Blythipicus;* for the time being I place it in a monotypic genus *Reinwardtipicus*.

Some genera of woodpeckers exhibit very similar, complex plumage patterns but differ markedly in structure of the bill and degree of morphological specialization for "woodpecking" habits. Among these generic pairs, considered by some to be convergent in plumage coloration, are *Dinopium* and *Chrysocolaptes*, and *Meiglyptes* and *Hemicircus*. The data on vocalizations and displays of species of these genera that I observed clearly indicate great behavioral resemblance concordant with the plumage pattern resemblances between species of these generic pairs. These resemblances I consider to reflect the close relationship of the genera, that is, of *Chrysocolaptes* to *Dinopium*, and of *Hemicircus* to *Meiglyptes*, and hence convergent evolution is not involved.

The genera *Gecinulus*, *Blythipicus*, *Reinwardtipicus*, *Sapheopipo*, *Dinopium*, and *Chrysocolaptes* show behavioral similarities with *Picus*, and these genera probably are closely interrelated. *Mulleripicus*, in some ways the most distinctive of Asian woodpeckers, nonetheless shows behavioral similarities with *Meiglyptes;* and *Meiglyptes*, *Hemicircus*, and *Mulleripicus* seem to form a discrete woodpecker assemblage (related probably to *Celeus* through *Meiglyptes*). *Picus* and its assemblage of genera also are related to *Celeus;* i.e., *Picus miniaceus* is morphologically and behaviorally almost intermediate between *Celeus* and *Picus*. Interestingly, although the southern Asian *Dryocopus javensis* and *Celeus brachyurus* are distinct and differ considerably, *Dryocopus* too shows clear relationship with *Celeus* in the New World through the South American *Dryocopus galeatus*, which shows a mixture of traits of the two genera.

REFERENCES

SHORT, LESTER L.

1970. Notes on the habits of some Argentine and Peruvian woodpeckers (Aves, Picidae). Amer. Mus. Novitates, no. 2413, 37 pp.

1973a. Habits, relationships, and conservation of the Okinawa Woodpecker. Wilson Bull., vol. 85, pp. 5-20.

1973b. Notes on Okinawan birds and Ryukyu Island zoogeography. Ibis, vol. 115, pp. 264-267.

1973c. "Woodpecking" by a red-throated barbet. Auk, vol. 90, pp. 909-910.

SHORT, LESTER L.—continued

1973d. Habits of some Asian woodpeckers (Aves, Picidae). Bull. Amer. Mus. Nat. Hist., vol. 152, pp. 253-364.

1975. Interspecific competition in woodpeckers. Emu, vol. 74 suppl., p. 301.

1978. Sympatry in woodpeckers of lowland Malayan forest. Biotropica, vol. 10, pp. 122-123.

——. Woodpeckers of the world. Delaware Mus. Nat. Hist. (In press.)

WINKLER, HANS, and SHORT, LESTER L.

1978. A comparative analysis of acoustical signals in pied woodpeckers (Aves; Picidae). Bull. Amer. Mus. Nat. Hist., vol. 60, pp. 1-110.

LESTER L. SHORT

Biology of the Precambrian genus *Kakabekia:* Geographic and Microenvironmental Determinations in the Distribution of Living *K. barghoorniana*

Principal Investigator: Sanford M. Siegel, Professor of Botany, University of Hawaii, Honolulu, Hawaii.

Grant No. 976: To study the biogeography of *Kakabekia,* a microorganism with precambrian affinities: Icelandic microhabitats.

The genus *Kakabekia* consists of two recognized species, *K. umbellata* and *K. barghoorniana* (fig. 1). The former is known only as a microfossil from the Gunflint Range in southern Ontario (Barghoorn and Tyler, 1965). Cherts containing *Kakabekia* (as well as other microfossils) have been assigned to the mid-precambrian, about 2 x 10^9 years of age. *K. barghoorniana* is a rare living member of the genus and was first discovered in soils from Harlech, Wales, in 1964 (Siegel and Giumarro, 1966). Since its discovery, *Kakabekia* has routinely been grown in 15 M aqueous ammonia and is considered an ammonophile (Siegel et al., 1967; Siegel and Siegel, 1968). In a rigorous sense, however, it has never been cultured in pure form independent of the initial soil inoculum. Further, growth is slow and yields of biomass so low that it has never been obtained in sufficient yield for biochemical analyses. It has been possible, nevertheless, to establish a number of characteristics. These include some details of cytomorphology; presence of heme-enzymes; growth requirements (e.g., ammonia, oxygen, temperature); and its probable procaryotic nature (Siegel and Siegel, 1970; Siegel, 1977).

In 1969, after unsuccessfully surveying many Caribbean, North American, and western European soil samples, *K. barghoorniana* was again found in two collections from Alaska—one from the flanks of the Mendenhall Glacier (Juneau) and the other from Point Barrow north of the Arctic Circle (Siegel and Siegel, 1970). The location of the sites suggested a distribution restricted to higher latitudes—at or above 48° N. The possibility that *Kakabekia* flourished at low temperature was supported when living *Kakabekia* was found in Iceland in 1970 (Siegel and Siegel, 1970, 1971a, 1971b). With the "cryophile" hypothesis as a guide, *Kakabekia* has been sought in the higher elevations of temperate and tropical latitudes and its distribution in Iceland reexamined in 1972.

Methods

Soil samples were obtained from a number of sites including: the continental United States; north and southeastern Alaska, Hawaii; east-central Mexico; Panama and the Guayanas; Iceland, Wales, France, Belgium, and West Germany; Japan and Malaysia.

These sites ranged from 3° to 71° N. latitude and from sea level to nearly 5,000 meters.

Samples were sealed in plastic, dried, and cooled or refrigerated when possible until use.

Routine cultures consisted of 0.5 gram of soil in 10 milliliters of 15 M aqueous ammonia containing 0.5 percent glucose. Inoculated media were incubated at 20° C in filled, stoppered vials, excluding most free air space. Experimental variation in temperatures, alkali, etc., will be described as appropriate below.

Mercury analyses were carried out by standard nitric acid-perchloric acid digestion and flameless atomic absorption. This procedure yields "available" Hg in the organic soil fraction; it does not release Hg immobilized in the silicate rock matrix.

Results

BIOGEOGRAPHIC CONSIDERATIONS

The distribution of *Kakabekia* suggested that the limiting latitudinal factor might be temperature-related. At lower elevations, *Kakabekia* has not been found south of about 45° N, and is limited to regions of relatively cool summers. This restriction does not apply to higher elevations, but the presence of *Kakabekia* at sites more than 2,000 meters above sea level in tropical and low temperate latitudes is fully consistent with the concept of cryotolerance, since air temperature decreases about 1° C for each 140–195 meters of altitude (higher lapse rates at higher latitudes).

The high latitude "rule" seems to fit the Japanese samples quite well, although its narrow zone on Mt. Fuji (table 1) indicates that there are other factors operating as well.

FIG. 1. Fossil and living specimens of *Kakabekia. a, b,* two specimens of fossil *K. umbellata* in Gunflint chert (photographed at 1050X); the mantle of *a* is about 10 μm in diameter; ray structures and stipe are also show. *c, d,* two specimens of culture *K. barghoorniana* (photographed at 960X); *c* is from Harlech, Wales, soil; *d,* from edge of Solheimajökull, south Iceland. Note comparable structural detail in *a* and *c*.

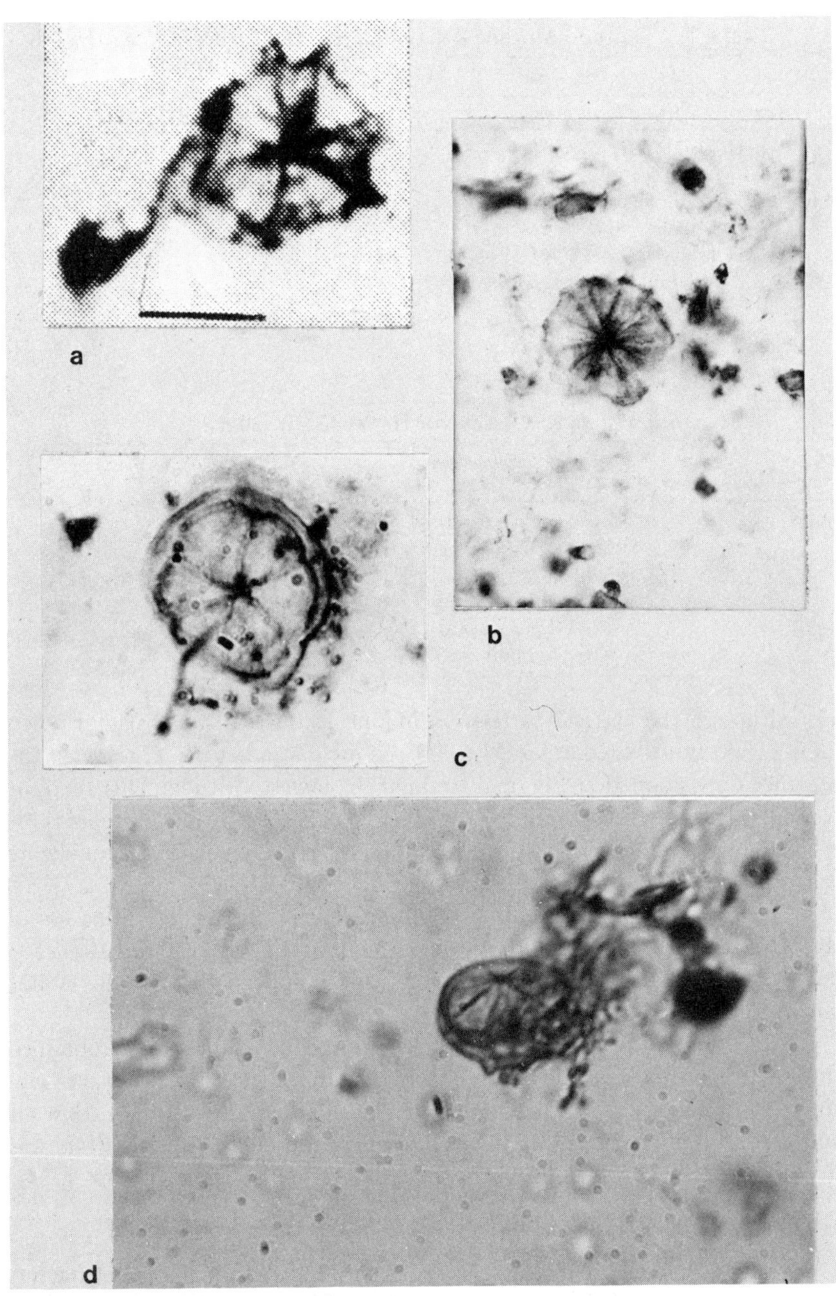
a
b
c
d

TABLE 1. Latitude-Altitude Relations in the Occurrence of *Kakabekia*

JAPAN		
Island location	*Presence of* Kakabekia	
Hokkaido (lat. ca. 45° N)	-	
Lake Toya	+	
Mount Showa Shinzan	+	
Sapporo	-	
Honshu (lat. ca. 35° N)		
Akiyoshido (cave)	-	
Mount Fuji 2300 meters	+	
3000 meters	-	
3300 meters	-	
3750 meters	-	
MAUNA KEA, ISLAND OF HAWAII (lat. ca. 20° N)		
Elevation (meters)	*Incubation temperature (°C)*	
	-7	*30*
2140 (Saddle Road)	-	+
2840 (Hale Pohaku)	+	+
3200	+	-
3670 (Adze factory)	+	-
3944 (Lake Wai'au)	+	-
4160 (Summit area)	+	-

Although the vertical pattern on Mauna Kea was also consistent when samples were incubated at –7° C to 20° C, incubation at 30° C revealed the presence of an anomalous thermal strain at the lowest altitude. This aberrant strain has not been further studied. It is evident, however, that the more typical form of *Kakabekia* grown at –7° C (and 20° C) is quite sensitive to moderate warmth.

The operation of factors other than temperature in the determination of the vertical distribution pattern is evident on Mount Haleakala; *Kakabekia* has only been found at or above 2,800 meters, and it appears that certain habitat factors affect the distribution.

Additional data confirming heat sensitivity in *Kakabekia* was obtained from sediment flanking the runoff channels from the geyser Stokkur, at Geysir, Iceland (table 2). The area is rich in alkaline thermal waters, but low air and ground temperatures lead to steep temperature gradients. *Kakabekia* was in evidence only at locations where the temperature had fallen below 30° C.

REGIONAL VARIATIONS IN MORPHOLOGY

It was previously reported that distribution of morphological characters in populations of *Kakabekia* varied with the collection site (Siegel and Siegel,

TABLE 2. Occurrence of *Kakabekia* in Runoff Streams at Geysir, Iceland
Sampling on 24 June 1972. Air temperature ca. 7°C, pH of runoff water ca. 10.

Approximate distance from source (meters)	*Water temperature (°C)*	Kakabekia *in sediment edging stream bed*
50	48-50	-
100	35-38	-
200	22-24	+

TABLE 3. Morphological Patterns in Populations of *Kakabekia* from Various Sources

	Mantle (%)			*Rays (%)*		*Stipe (%)*
Source	*Incised*	*Lobed*	*Entire*	*1-3*	*> 4*	*Present*
Fossil (Ontario)	57	20	23	20	80	50
		PACIFIC GROUP				
Mendenhall Glacier, Alaska	0	67	33	20	80	21
Mount Fuji (2,300 m), Japan	0	59	41	14	86	17
Mauna Kea (3,200 m), Hawaii	0	55	45	11	89	22
Haleakala (2,800 m), Maui	0	40	60	12	88	12
		ATLANTIC GROUP				
Reykjanes Pen., Iceland	0	27	73	10	90	25
Harlech Castle Site, Wales	0	24	76	8	92	36

1970). Continued attention has been given to this feature (table 3). The most conspicuous feature is the absence of deeply incised mantles except in fossil specimens.

This condition may represent an artifact of fossilization, however; the incised specimens may represent a strain or subspecies now extinct. Fossil populations are also distinguished by fewer individuals with minimal numbers of rays (1–3) and more retaining stipes.

Among living *Kakabekia*, regional populations may form two series, here designated the Pacific and Atlantic groups.

ENVIRONMENTAL PHYSIOLOGY

Evidence for temperature limits have been based on sampling in tropical alpine and subarctic thermal gradients, together with laboratory variations in incubation temperature. Comparisons have involved widely separated geographical sources, hence contain an additional variable.

The culture of different source materials using a standard protocol shows that the field-based picture is accurate (table 4), but that large differences are

TABLE 4. Low Temperature Tolerance in *Kakabekia*

Based on 7-day cultures in routine ammonia water-glucose medium. Counts derived from sampling 10-15 fields on triplicate safranine-stained smears at 1250X magnification (oil).

Incubation temperature °C	*Number of* Kakabekia *per cm*^{2}		
	Mendenhall Glacier, Alaska	*Mauna Kea (3,200 m), Hawaii*	*Reykjanes Pen. Iceland*
35	0	0	0
25	25	4	9
4	22	4	4
−7	9	<4	<4

TABLE 5. Comparative Performance of *Kakabekia* Soil Samples in Ammonia Water and Other Alkaline Media at pH 12

Sample	*Source*	NH_3 15 *M*	*NaOH* 0.01 *M*	Na_2SiO_3 0.01 *M*
Al-5	Mendenhall Glacier, Alaska	21	17	9
Al-6	Mendenhall Glacier, Alaska	17	13	0
Al-B-1	Point Barrow region, Alaska	4	4	0
Al-B-2	Point Barrow region, Alaska	4	4	0
Il-16-2	Reykjanes Pen. Iceland	9	9	4
Mk-4000	Mauna Kea (4,000 m), Hawaii	4	4	4
HK-2800	Haleakala (2,800 m), Maui	8	8	4

present among sample sites. The observations support the concept that *Kakabekia* is a heat-sensitive organism with respectable cryophile.

The question of alkaline requirements is perhaps more critical than thermal limits. Is ammonia required per se for culture, or can it be replaced by other alkaline media? Certainly there are many ammoniacal microhabitats; however, our routine culture medium offers no possible association with natural ammonia levels.

The organic constituents of soil inocula could serve in a low but continuous NH_3-generator under alkaline conditions. A number of *Kakabekia* samples have now, however, been grown in 0.01 N NaOH (pH 12) nearly as well as they were in 15 M aqueous NH_3 (table 5). The replacement of NaOH by

TABLE 6. Icelandic Soil Mercury Level in Relation to Occurrence of *Kakabekia*

Hg level in soil (ppb)	*Occurrence of* Kakabekia
< 35	usually +
35-80	variable but reduced
≧ 100	always 0

TABLE 7. Sensitivity of *Kakabekia* to Mercury and Fluoride

Inhibitor		Kakabekia *sample density (No./cm²)*		
Hg^{2+} ppb	*F^- ppm*	*Solheim (glacier)*	*Skogar (falls)*	*Ave.*
0	0	6	6	6.0
10	0	6	6	6.0
100	0	4	3	3.5
1000	0	0	0	0.0
0	10	5	6	5.5
0	100	5	5	5.0
0	1000	4	5	4.5
10	10	5	6	5.5
100	100	3	4	3.5

sodium metasilicate provides nearly the same pH, but growth was quite diminished or completely suppressed. The exceptions were some of the samples that show poor growth under "normal" conditions. Although we have long associated silica with *Kakabekia* structure, this is the first indication of a toxic response. Presumably the normal SiO_2 requirement of *Kakabekia* is met by the silica in the inorganic fractions of the soil.

The toxicity of organic structures was encountered earlier during efforts to obtain *Kakabekia* in pure culture (Siegel et al., 1967). Beef blood, urine, and milk all inhibited growth completely. Metal ion toxicity was not considered until geothermal mercury became an issue in Iceland.

Field collections in Iceland during June and July of 1970 and 1972 established a general distribution pattern for *Kakabekia*.

Upon comparing this pattern with that of soil Hg, an inverse relationship was evident (table 6). Hg toxicity was demonstrated further using two soil samples from southern Iceland (table 7). The addition of F-media failed to inhibit per se or to alter the Hg response.

Acknowledgments

Aspects of this study relating to mercury involved the assistance of Mr. Freyr Thorarinson and the cooperation of Dr. Godmundur Sigvaldason, Nordic Institute of Vulcanology.

Thanks are also due for the support provided by National Geographic Society, the Research Corporation (Cottrell Foundation), National Aeronautics and Space Administration, and the University of Hawaii Foundation.

REFERENCES

BARGHOORN, ELSO, and TYLER, STANLEY

1965. Microorganisms from the Gunflint chert. Science, vol. 147, pp. 563-577.

SIEGEL, BARBARA Z.

1977. *Kakabekia,* review of its physiological and environmental features and their relation to its possible ancient affinities. Pp. 143-154 *in* "College Park Colloquium on Chemical Evolution," 221 pp. C. Ponnamperuma, ed. Academic Press Inc., New York.

SIEGEL, BARBARA Z., and SIEGEL, SANFORD M.

1970. Biology of the Precambrian genus *Kakabekia.* New observation on living *Kakabekia.* Proc. Nat. Acad. Sci. (U. S.), vol. 67, pp. 1005-1010.

1971a. A search for a pre-cambrian relict microorganism, *Kakabekia barghoorniana.* Nat. Aeronaut. Space Admin. Tech. Memo. X-62, 009, Sect. 8.11, pp. 117-121.

1971b. Cryobiology of the relict form *Kakabekia barghoorniana* Siegel. Abstract, Cryobiology, vol. 8, p. 388 (3rd Int. Congr. Cryobiology, Washington, September 1971).

SIEGEL, S. M., and GIUMARRO, CONSTANCE

1966. On the culture of a microorganism similar to the Precambrian microfossil *Kakabekia umbellata.* Barghoorn, in NH_3 rich atmosphere. Proc. Nat. Acad. Sci. (U. S.), vol. 55, pp. 349-353.

SIEGEL, S. M.; ROBERTS, KAREN; NATHAN, HENRY; and DALY, OLIVE

1967. Living relative of the microfossil *Kakabekia.* Science, vol. 56, pp. 1231-1234.

SIEGEL, S. M., and SIEGEL, B. Z.

1968. A living organism morphologically comparable to the Precambrian genus *Kakabekia.* Amer. Journ. Bot., vol. 55, pp. 684-687.

B. Z. SIEGEL
S. M. SIEGEL

In Search of the Primitive Bamboos

Principal Investigators: Thomas R. Soderstrom and Cleofé E. Calderón, Smithsonian Institution, Washington, D. C.

Grant Nos. 1014, 1547: For studies of bambusoid grasses in eastern Brazil.

Grass is the most important of all plants to man: sugarcane, bamboos, rice, millet, sorghum, corn, and the cereals—barley, oats, wheat, rye—all are grasses. Of these, for example, rice provides a major part of the diet in southeast Asia, as do the cereals and corn in Europe and America, and the sorghums in Africa. Almost one-fourth of the earth's vegetation is grassland; in numbers of individual plants spread over the globe the grasses are unsurpassed. Hence, any research on grasses—apart from yielding information of theoretical interest—may ultimately have practical value because of the economic importance of the family.

Tree grasses, or bamboos, are important in the economy of certain parts of tropical America and southeast Asia, where they provide not only food but construction material as well. Although bamboos are easily recognized, smaller non-woody grasses related to them ("herbaceous bambusoid grasses") mostly go unnoticed. Their flowers are usually borne in an inconspicuous manner, either under the blades or in some cases underground. Their appearance is not that of a typical grass but more often that of a seedling palm, fern, or even moss. Especially abundant in the forests of tropical America, they are seldom collected, even by the experienced botanist.

On an expedition to Kaieteur Fall (Guyana, formerly British Guiana) in 1962 and the Wilhelmina Mountains (Surinam, or Dutch Guiana) in 1963, Soderstrom collected plants of two then-unknown genera of these grasses, *Piresia* and *Rehia (Bulbulus),* growing in the densely shaded undergrowth of the humid rain forest. Apart from the unusual morphology of the plants themselves, the locality was an unexpected one in which to find grasses, which are plants that normally prefer open situations where sunlight is plentiful.

Although the relationships of these grasses were imperfectly understood at that time, our subsequent research on them has shown that these and similar grasses are closely related to bamboos. They share many features with them and in all likelihood represent the kind of grass from which the woody bamboos have evolved.

Observations of the herbaceous bambusoid grasses in the Guianas elicited some intriguing questions, especially concerning their manner of pollination.

While grasses are generally wind-pollinated, the herbaceous bambusoid members, which grow in the lower stratum of the forest where there is no wind, cannot be pollinated by that means. In most plants of *Piresia,* for example, the flowers are borne on modified branches that spread out along the ground where they are buried beneath the fallen leaves.

In 1967, in Maracay, Venezuela, Soderstrom made a collection of insects found on the inflorescences of *Pariana,* an herbaceous bambusoid grass common throughout Amazonia. The insects turned out to represent a new genus of flies (Diptera) with individuals of two species in the gathering. Since it appeared that these flies might be instrumental in pollination of the plant—a phenomenon previously unreported in the grass family—we decided to study this question in greater depth, making observations on as many bambusoid grasses as possible, and over as broad a range of localities as feasible. Accordingly Calderón, in late 1967 and early 1968, made collections of insects on bambusoid grasses in Brazil, Colombia, Venezuela, and Panama. Interestingly, flies belonging to the same genus of Diptera were found on *Pariana* inflorescences in Belém, a locality over 2,500 kilometers east of Maracay (Soderstrom and Calderón, 1971).

The trip made by Calderón was rewarding in other ways besides corroborating our ideas of the Diptera-*Pariana* relationship, for it was the occasion for the discovery of several bambusoid grasses previously unknown to science. Among the most interesting were the gatherings from Bahia, where several new species were found of *Piresia,* the genus till then known only from the Guianas. This finding drew attention to a relationship that exists between the forest floras of eastern coastal Brazil and the Amazon Basin, one that we have been able to substantiate from further collections we have since made in both regions.

Another curious bambusoid genus found on that trip was *Eremitis,* which had been collected only one time previously, the original collection made by the German botanist, Riedel, who traveled through Bahia in 1821. Studies on the genus *Eremitis* revealed that it is related to the Amazonian *Pariana,* an additional clue to a floristic relationship between eastern Brazil and Amazonia.

Studies of the 1968 collections of herbaceous bambusoid grasses led to a better understanding of this fascinating group of plants and their relationship to the bamboos. A thorough investigation that we made on a new herbaceous bambusoid genus (Calderón and Soderstrom, 1973) showed how closely related are the herbaceous bambusoid grasses and the woodier members, commonly known as bamboos. For our studies we were fortunate to be able to discuss bamboos with our late colleague, Dr. F. A. McClure (1897-1970), who established at the Smithsonian Institution the finest and most complete collection of world bamboos. To this great colleague we dedicated our new genus, *Maclurolyra*.

With our accumulated experience in the field and laboratory, and the investigations on *Maclurolyra,* we became increasingly convinced that the bamboos and herbaceous bambusoid grasses evolved from a common stock and should therefore be regarded as comprising a single natural subfamily of grasses, technically known as the Bambusoideae. Although we were able to define this subfamily as a whole, the delimitation of genera within it and their relationships to one another were not clear and became our chief concern; we had excellent collections of Asiatic bamboos made by McClure and others, as well as substantial ones from Mexico, Central America, and the Andes, but we lacked good material from the Guianas, Amazonia, and eastern coastal Brazil. Critical to our understanding of evolution of the Bambusoideae was material of primitive members of the group: our studies to date had given all indications that eastern Brazil harbored those elements.

Two genera of herbaceous bambusoid grasses, apparently among the most primitive of all grasses, were known only from cultivation and their rediscovery would be of great interest to our studies and to the botanical sciences as a whole. One, *Anomochloa,* had been collected in Brazil in the early 1800's and was cultivated in the great conservatories of Europe during the 1850's. For over a century *Anomochloa* has figured in the literature as one of the most primitive grasses, and its bizarre morphology and non-grasslike appearance have prompted some botanists to question whether it might even belong to another family. A seed of this grass had been sent from Brazil to Paris and was there cultivated in the early 1800's and all specimens in herbaria date back to plants propagated in the mid-1850's from that original plant. By the 1860's all plants had died out in cultivation and it was never found in the wild. The famous plant morphologist, Agnes Arber, wrote (1934, p. 133), "*Anomochloa,* if a member of the Gramineae [grass family], is a most erratic one. Its rediscovery is much to be desired; a complete study of its structure and development would be of deepest interest."

The other, *Diandrolyra,* has been in cultivation since early in this century, when a plant was received at the Royal Botanic Gardens, Kew, England. Since that time plants have been cultivated at Kew, but never found again in the wild state. *Diandrolyra* had been received along with a shipment of orchids by the English horticultural firm of Saunders in Chelsea, and presented to Kew, where botanists recognized it as a new genus of grasses. As was so often the case in the early days of orchid collectors in South America, the plants were shipped to Europe but without information on the exact locality, for fear that other collectors would seek out the same place to gather more plants to sell.

We were particularly interested in *Anomochloa* and *Diandrolyra,* since both were bambusoid grasses. On the basis of the fact that such bambusoid grasses are most abundant in tropical America, we assumed they had come from there. Since they were primitive grasses and a study of them would be of inestimable value to our work on bamboos, we set out to relocate both genera.

During February through May of 1972 we carried out studies of the Bambusoideae in eastern Brazil and worked under the auspices of Dr. Raulino Reitz, then director of the Jardim Botânico of Rio de Janeiro, and with permission to make these studies from Brazil's National Research Council (Conselho Nacional de Pesquisas). As a base of operations Soderstrom used the Jardim Botânico and Calderón the Cacao Experimental Station (CEPLAC) in Itabuna, Bahia, where the director, Dr. Paulo de Tarso Alvim, offered all facilities for the research. Our idea was to cover as many places as possible in the forests of eastern coastal Brazil, with Calderón working in the large state of Bahia, and Soderstrom working south in the states of Espírito Santo, Guanabara, Rio de Janeiro, and São Paulo. In our fieldwork we were accompanied by local botanists or botanical assistants, Calderón with Srs. R. S. Pinheiro and Talmón, and Soderstrom with Sr. Dimitri Sucre.

Our purpose was not to collect every grass we encountered but rather to locate all bambusoid grasses and make thorough collections and studies of them. In most cases to make a thorough collection of one plant required as much as four or five hours. For each plant, specimens were taken and pressed and dried between newspapers. Often as many as 20 to 30 sheets were prepared, allowing us sufficient dried material for later study and examples of each to be sent at a later date to major herbaria of the world. In addition to the normal herbarium specimens, we collected material for morphological and cytological study. Leaves, roots, culm sections, flowers, and fruits were collected and preserved in FAA (a mixture of formalin, alcohol, and acetic acid) in plastic vials. Flowers were also preserved in Bocquet solution (glycerine and lactic acid mixture) for studies of vascularization. And young anthers were preserved in a special preservative for chromosome studies.

Besides the collection of plant material, soil samples were collected at each site and these analyzed in Brazil. Some ecological measurements were also made at each site, such as maximum-minimum temperature, atmospheric pressure and temperature, soil temperature, and light quality.

Numerous photographs were taken of each plant, both in color (using Kodachrome 25 and High Speed Ektachrome films) and in black and white (using Tri-X film, ASA 400).

Living plants were also collected and are now in cultivation at CEPLAC in Bahia, the Jardim Botânico in Rio, and the Smithsonian greenhouses in

Washington. This unique collection of forest grasses allows us to continue to make observations on the living plants throughout the year, and some of the more striking and easily cultivated ones will someday find a place in horticulture.

On the 1972 trip, we were successful in finding *Diandrolyra,* not only one species but at least six new to science. The species exhibit a great range in size, from the smallest type located in Bahia (flowering plants no more than a few inches tall) to the largest in the state of São Paulo, which reach about one foot in height. The plants grow in densely shaded habitats, in moist woods, often above small mountain streams, in Bahia south through the states of Espírito Santo, Rio de Janeiro, and São Paulo.

Several new species of *Piresia* were found in Bahia, but nowhere to the south. Like the two species known previously from the Amazon region, the new ones have inflorescences that spread out from the parent plant and creep into the leaf litter and fallen debris that covers the forest floor. So concealed are these inflorescences that plants of this genus seem never to be in flower.

Another genus with strange inflorescences is *Eremitis,* of which we found several new species, both in Bahia and Espírito Santo. The genus was originally described in 1877 from a fragmentary specimen and later botanists considered it to be a member of the Amazonian genus *Pariana.* Our collections of several additional species show it unquestionably to be a distinct genus. In *Eremitis,* the inflorescence can be terminal to the leafy shoot, or borne on separate bladeless shoots that burrow into the sandy soil. Such burrowing shoots may turn upward and poke through the soil, where flowering takes place just above the soil and far from the parent plant, or they may remain deep within the soil and produce a seed there, much in the fashion of a peanut.

A grass that has long been considered of extreme interest to morphologists since the 1800's because of its many primitive features is the genus *Streptochaeta.* Only two species are known and both occur only in tropical America, the common *S. spicata,* which ranges from Mexico to Argentina, and *S. sodiroana,* which is confined to a narrow area from Costa Rica to Ecuador. Both of these species have very broad leaves, and have characteristic flowering units (spikelets) with twisted awns that aid in their dispersal by passing animals. We were indeed surprised to find a third species of that genus, one with very narrow leaves, growing in a small woodland in Espírito Santo.

While many kinds of bamboos were collected, the most interesting ones came from Bahia, especially the genus *Atractantha.* Fragmentary material of two species in flower had been collected in Bahia in 1943 and 1950 and described as a new genus by McClure in his posthumous publication of 1973. Full collections were made of McClure's two species and six new ones were found, adding significantly to this very unusual genus of bamboos. In Bahia a further new genus of bamboos was found, unusual in that its rhizomes may reach two or three meters in length, allowing the plants to travel snakelike through the forest and send up an occasional stalk here and there among the trees.

Our 1972 collections included many new genera and species, and a study of the material and that of herbaria made it abundantly clear that we were confronted with a group of grasses of which a very large percentage is unknown. Only a few of the more interesting finds have been pointed out above; much of the material remains to be studied critically.

Studies of these collections have shown that certain places in tropical America have an especially high concentration of genera and species of bambusoid grasses. In these regions are also many endemics, some of them with features considered primitive for the whole family. The major region is Bahia, an area that we have designated as the "Bahian refugium," and shown to be a source of bambusoid elements that colonized Amazonia (Soderstrom and Calderón, 1974).

As examples of the relationships that we have found between the Bahian refugium and Amazonia, the genus *Piresia* is represented in both areas. Species of *Piresia* from Bahia retain bisexual flowers while those of Amazonia have male and female flowers, a more recent and advanced condition. Within the tribe Parianeae, the more primitive genera are endemic to the Bahian refugium, *Eremitis* with seven species and a new genus with four. Neither of these genera is found in Amazonia but the closely related *Pariana* is widespread throughout Amazonia, with some forty species, all of which are clearly advanced over any of those from the Bahian refugium.

To test further the interesting Bahian-Amazonian relationship, we spent four months in both regions, during February through May of 1976. The first two months were spent in southwestern Amazonia (state of Acre), where further collections were made of Bambusoideae that are now under study. But the most interesting and doubtless significant discoveries were made during the fieldwork in Bahia in the latter two months, again under the sponsorship of the National Geographic Society.

This time in Bahia we both worked under the auspices of CEPLAC in Itabuna, where we were provided all facilities of the research institute and transportation for two parties, with a driver and botanical assistants in each case, Calderón leading one group and Soderstrom the other. Each group made separate trips of 1-2 weeks each within Bahia, returning to Itabuna for three days each time to process the material and prepare for another trip. Thus we were able to make eight trips to different locations in Bahia in 1976 and increase our inventory of bambusoid grasses and field observations.

After years of searching, our long sought-after bambusoid genus, *Anomochloa,* was found by Calderón growing in a single locality in Bahia. Plants were taken to Itabuna for growing outdoors and to Washington for cultivation in the greenhouse. After more than one century this rarest of all grasses has come to light and we will now be able to study it thoroughly and determine its relationships not only to bamboos and other grasses but to the flowering plants in general.

Besides *Anomochloa,* the fieldwork in Bahia of 1976 turned up many additional new species of herbaceous bambusoid grasses and bamboos. A most peculiar new bamboo genus with a fleshy fruit was found and is being described (1979). Two of the three species of this new genus were in flower, and one of these in fruit, events in themselves of rare occurrence in bamboos. The fruits of the new bamboo were fleshy and the size of small olives. This is remarkable, as the condition of fleshy fruits is unknown in any of the other 28 genera of New World bamboos which, like most grasses such as wheat, have a dry kernel called a "caryopsis." The relatively few genera of bamboos with fleshy fruits are endemic to the Old World, in such distant places as Africa, Madagascar, and southeast Asia.

Our understanding of the bambusoid flora of eastern Brazil has changed dramatically as a result of the two trips made there during 1972 and 1976. While it will take years to study all of the collections, we can make some general statements at this time. We collected at least 162 different species of Bambusoideae, of which 80 are undescribed, or new to science, so that we have doubled the known number of species from the whole region. While many of the new species can be assigned to known genera such as *Bambusa, Merostachys,* and *Raddia,* others belong to genera previously unknown to science.

In all there are six new genera in our collections, two of bamboos and four of herbaceous bambusoid grasses, an extraordinary number for so small an area. Eastern coastal Brazil, particularly northern Espírito Santo and Bahia, contains the richest inventory of bambusoid grasses in the Americas, if not in the world. This wealth of material collected in tropical America is of interest not only because it provides material for taxonomic description, but because these additional plants are giving us new insights into the relationships of this whole group of forest grasses. They are helping us to decipher pathways of evolution in the Bambusoideae, and in turn to recognize the natural limits of the genera within the subfamily.

Discovery of the fleshy-fruited bamboo in Bahia, along with *Anomochloa,* supports the hypothesis that the Bahian region harbors relicts of ancient grasses. There is little doubt that further fieldwork will uncover even more. Studies on the material at hand will be aimed at describing the new genera and species, and also at discovering the relationships of the bambusoid grasses of eastern Brazil with those of Amazonia. And having looked at this westward relationship, we must now also look to the East where other bamboos with fleshy fruits occur.

Thus, as we continue to work in Bahia and Amazonia, we must now explore the forests of tropical West Africa for our bambusoid grasses, for while some herbaceous bambusoid grasses are known from there, we must look more carefully for these grasses that so easily go unnoticed by even the experienced collector. Could there be a relative, as yet undiscovered, of our new bamboo growing along the coast of tropical West Africa? After all, such an area as Cameroon—where some bambusoid grasses are known—was contiguous with the region of Bahia prior to Continental Drift. This separation of continents isolated the Bahian region to the east. Later, desiccation cut the region off to the north and west, and mountain building and major ecological changes isolated it from the south. The narrow tropical forest belt of eastern Bahia is probably all that remains of a once much larger region where plants of such genera as *Anomochloa* thrived in greater abundance. Our studies, supported by the National Geographic Society, are leading to a recognition of this Bahian refugium, and to the discovery there of the world's most primitive grasses.

REFERENCES

ARBER, AGNES

1934. The Gramineae, a study of cereal, bamboo, and grass, 480 pp. Cambridge, Cambridge University Press.

CALDERÓN, CLEOFÉ E., and SODERSTROM, THOMAS R.

1973. Morphological and anatomical considerations of the subfamily Bambusoideae, based on the new genus *Maclurolyra.* Smithsonian Contr. Bot., no. 11, iii + 55 pp., 24 figs.

MCCLURE, FLOYD A.

1973. Genera of bamboos native to the New World (Gramineae: Bambusoideae), ed. by T. R. Soderstrom. Smithsonian Contr. Bot., no. 9, xii + 148 pp., 48 figs.

SODERSTROM, T. R., and CALDERÓN, C. E.

1971. Insect pollination in tropical rain forest grasses. Biotropica, vol. 3, no. 1, pp. 1-6.

1974. Primitive forest grasses and evolution of the Bambusoideae. Biotropica, vol. 6, no. 3, pp. 141-153.

THOMAS R. SODERSTROM
CLEOFÉ E. CALDERÓN

Aspects of Mbotgate Life Style

Principal Investigator: E. Richard Sorenson, Smithsonian Institution, Washington, D. C.

Grant No. 1006: In aid of grantee's cinema research studies of New Hebridean child behavior.

In the interior of the island of Malekula, of the New Hebrides, where the mountains of the interior jut above the coastal region, the warm moist air of the South Pacific is forced upward to cooler elevations where it condenses to create a persistent cover of cloud and rain. Hidden under these clouds were four surviving Mbotgate villages. They were last remnants of a once widespread traditional inland New Hebrides way of life.

I search out such remnants for they each represent some kind of independent expression of human adaptation. Many have brought into being some special expression of basic human potential. Unique behavioral adaptations and social patterns are created through the independent cultural evolution once fostered by the many isolated separate regions of the earth. Each of these emergent human experiments in living tells us something more about the nature and potential of our very complex human species. Most have now disappeared.

Thanks to the generosity of the National Geographic Society, I was able to follow up the lead I had been given on the Mbotgate by my friend Dr. Kal Muller, who first stumbled into these villages in 1968. It was a great stroke of luck, for I had wanted to find another isolated divergent Melanesian traditional culture to compare with the Fore of New Guinea. The Fore were an unusual Melanesian people whose behavioral adaptations I had found to be unique and intriguing during earlier expeditions to New Guinea.

I expected that the Mbotgate would be different. They had been reported to be organized around exclusive men's secret cults—the Nimangi—maintained by an elaborate system of graded initiations. To be sure, the Fore also had initiations, but the elaborateness of the Mbotgate system put them into quite a different class. Related to the initiation system was a highly developed art representing the ancestors and the beliefs of the society. The art helped to sustain the way of life by anchoring meaning to abstractions with personal significance. There was nothing like this among the Fore. The Mbotgate were also much less territorially fluid than the Fore; they jealously guarded their traditional lands both by force of arms and with the help of their ancestor spirits. The Fore continually moved to new lands.

As different as they appeared on the surface, both the Fore and Mbotgate had an unmistakable Melanesian character. So, in spite of the newness of the place, I felt at home at once, for many of their manners, responses, and movements reminded me of the Fore.

Without film it is very difficult to inquire into this kind of difference or similarity. With film one can see and isolate the behavioral patterns that make up a people's character. The visual record, once made, captures data unnoticed and unanticipated during actual fieldwork. Difficult-to-spot subtle patterns and fleeting nuances of manner, mood, and human relations become clear through repeated examination of related filmed events, sometimes by slow motion and stopped frame. When the characteristic behavioral patterns sustaining a way of life become known, another expression of human adaptive creation is revealed.

There were six villages in these mountains, four of Mbotgate speakers and two of Nabwol. They were scattered and small. Hamlets did not exceed six houses. Total population was less than 150, density not more than 2 per square mile. But it was not always so uncongested here. Older Mbotgate remember a quite different time, when more people and villages dotted these mountains and more languages were spoken.

It was not so easy to tell where the boundaries of a village began or ended. There were no precise limits, just a fading away from the main center out into the jungle beyond. To be sure, there was a clear and unambiguous center; but residential offshoots scattered somewhat centrifugally into the surrounding countryside. This seemed very Melanesian also.

Most of the village offshoots had been established to be near new gardens. So they were temporary, since gardens were moved when fertility declined (very much like the Fore in New Guinea). Only major ceremonial centers seemed to have any aura of permanency. These anchored the political geography.

Out from the main ceremonial center of Lendombwey, residential clusters more than about a 10-minute walk away would begin to have place-names of their own. Some even had "small," or nonsecret, ceremonial houses, which

---

FIG. 1. Much as among the Fore people of New Guinea, a benign and protective physical presence of older hamlet mates provides a secure envelope of consensual and tactile social relation for infants and toddlers. This leads to a different type of social and cognitive development than exists normally in Western cultures.

FIG. 2. One of the effects of the "tactile system" of handling young children is a remarkable capability of handling such potentially dangerous objects as knives without much danger. The above scene and the scene on the opposite page are what one normally might encounter any day in any Mbotgate hamlet.

served as collective men's residences. But these were considered minor ceremonial houses. I even heard them called "children of Lendombwey." Farther out there were larger ceremonial centers with their own centrifugal pattern of community dispersal around them.

But Lendombwey was the uncontested dominant center, both spiritually and ceremonially. It seems likely that all the present Mbotgate villages were originally settled by people dispersing out even farther from Lendombwey.

I focus my attention on children, because, as children grow up and into a way of life, one can see how their activity and responses begin to become patterned and to melt into the life-style of their culture.

Several things about the children here caught my eye and the eye of my camera: a remarkable physical competence characterized even young children. They could deal with the objects and material of their surroundings with an effectiveness that would surprise any Westerner—including use of potentially

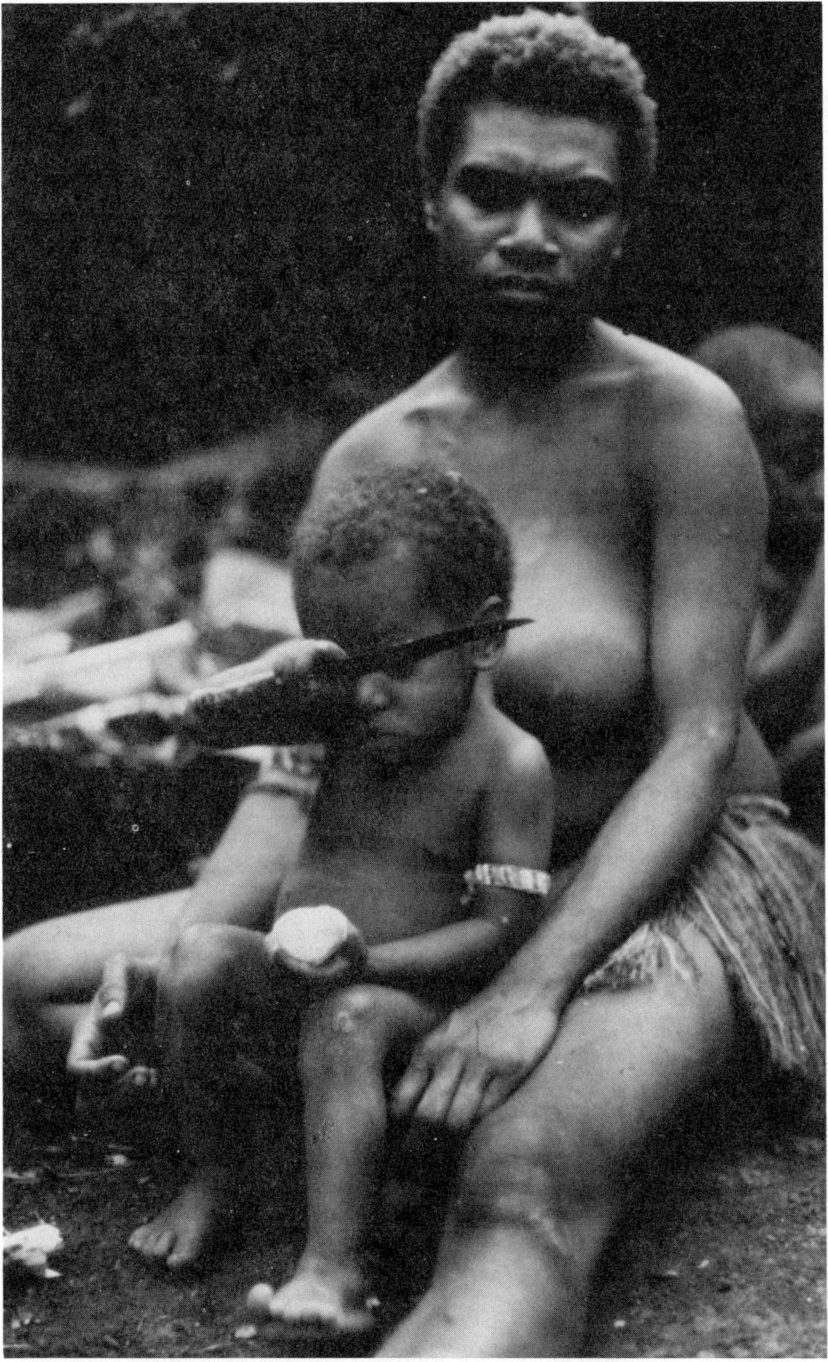

FIG. 3. Unlike the Fore of New Guinea, the Mbotgate young adopt stances of competitiveness and aggression during normal play. Unstructured and without the formal rules of the play of Fore children, the Mbotgate stances have no established "rules of fairness." Yet the encounters are managed so that even small children can "tilt" with older children as part of the mutually rewarding game. As the children grow older this type of play involves wrestling, sham attack, and group stand-offs.

dangerous things like axes, knives, and fires. In this they closely resembled the Fore.

But unlike the Fore they were shyer of strangers, not unfriendly, just shyer. And unlike the Fore the Mbotgate children played informal competitive games. They would seek out their friends for playful bouts of challenge and provocation, of push and pull, and of thrust and evasion. And whereas Fore children tended to explore together, Mbotgate would do so more often alone.

But like the Fore the Mbotgate infants were provided considerable close physical touch with older hamlet mates. And like the Fore they were clever in responding advantageously and effectively to novel challenges and opportunities. And, they were also adept with the materials of the world around them.

A day in the life might go much like the following: Yelik and Gelitnaman (10 and 12 years of age) would try to entice Sari (7 years) into chasing them and jumping on them. But while the game was clearly one of challenging skill, the older boys would not run so fast that Sari could not catch them from time to time.

With its elements of provocation, deception, and surprise, this had the superficial look of an aggressive play, but it never erupted in squabbles or hostility. Nor did I see clear efforts to excel—as is the case so often among American children. It was a friendly tilting that sharpened their adroitness and strength. It fostered agility, alertness, and cunning. It suited a culture where hunting contributes a sizable proportion of the food and fighting is required to keep one's land.

Later Sari could be found at the edge of the village clearing—alone and quiet, preoccupied with "hunt." He was stalking lizards with Yelik's bow and arrow. Stealthily, in total silence, slowly, he skirted bushes and trees, each movement perfectly controlled. Spying a quarry, he drew his bowstring, muscles taut for a moment—and then the arrow flew. A miss. No sign of regret or disappointment. He simply retrieved his arrow and resumed his hunt. Another shot nailed a lizard to the ground, impaled on one of the four prongs of the arrow. Not a trace of childlike exuberance at this success; no cries of "I got him!" Nor did he even look around to see who might have witnessed the great deed. Instead, with head slightly bowed and feet stamping, he rhythmically executed a tight circle and then retrieved the arrow with the lizard.

Nearby a woman, with her infant son strapped to her back, handed him a sharp knife to hold for her as she got up. This is not in the least uncommon. And toddlers frequently grab knives, machetes, and burning sticks, waving them around and carrying them about without so much as a blink from nearby elders. Even babies snatch knives from their mothers. The Mbotgate view all this as normal. Only rarely do their children hurt themselves.

Then there was Gelitnaman, a boy of about 12, in the rain outside my house, playing at plaiting flattened bamboo into wall sections, as he had just seen the coastal natives who had accompanied me do. It was a technique alien to the Mbotgate. Yet he was handling the bamboo with a remarkable adeptness. I "knew" the principle of plaiting, he knew the reality. I could explain, he could do.

The great advantage of the motion-picture record was to permit comparison of the styles and expressions of behavior seen. Smiles, anger, rejection, sadness, disgust, pleasure, were much like the Fore (Sorenson, 1976b); so was their collective approach to unity.

By examining and re-examining the motion-picture record I eventually began to see differences. The facial expressions during Mbotgate children's play often included fleeting expressions of standing-one's-ground, victoriousness, provocation, and deception. Was this a behavioral key underlying the need for an elegantly formalized secret men's cult to manage the society? We are verging on just such a hypothesis. More work needs to be done to see just how this works.

The Mbotgate are the last traditional inland Melanesian culture remaining in the New Hebrides. And they are now threatened. Their lands have been penetrated—opened up—and like all other pre-technological peoples they change quickly in the face of the powerful materials, commerce, and government that follows. Even my own very presence was changing them; they very quickly tried and adopted the things I brought and the things we did.

So with mixed feelings, I watched as this culture—one that had evolved over thousands of years in isolation—began to vanish in front of my very own eyes. I could not help but sympathize with their excitement over new things I had; but I regretted that this strange and spirited people would soon shed their exotic way of life to adopt in its stead the more dispirited market culture emerging throughout the New Hebrides around access to Western products.

The film record we were able to obtain is small. What it shows us is the value of more. We can only hope that the behavioral forms of this unique way-station of human adaptation do not disappear before we can continue this sample. Unlike the materials of cultures, which can be dug up later, behavioral

---

FIG. 4. Development of a style of human interaction which includes elements of physical contest provides a basic behavioral foundation on which skills useful in warfare, such as chasing and evading or practice spear throwing, are gained in the course of play.

patterns vanish without a trace. Only our film can preserve "fossils" of behavior for future study.

REFERENCES

SORENSON, E. RICHARD

1976a. The edge of the forest: Land, childhood and change in a New Guinea protoagricultural society, 278 pp., illus. Smithsonian Institution Press, Washington.

1976b. Social organization and facial expression of emotions. Nat. Geogr. Soc. Res. Rpts., 1968 Projects, pp. 389-409, illus.

1978. Cooperation and freedom among the Fore of New Guinea. Pp. 12-30 *in* "Learning Non-Aggression," Ashley Montague, ed. Oxford University Press.

1979. Early tactile communication and the patterning of human organization: A New Guinea case study. Pp. 289-306 *in* "Before Speech," M. Bullowa, ed. Cambridge University Press.

E. RICHARD SORENSON

Crown-of-thorns Starfish (*Acanthaster planci*) Investigations in Micronesia, July 1971 through March 1972

Principal Investigator: Walter A. Starck II, Marine Research Foundation, Key West, Florida.

Grant No. 965: For study of the biology and epidemiology of the crown-of-thorns starfish.

Serious coral destruction by the crown-of-thorns starfish *Acanthaster planci* was first reported in 1963 on the Great Barrier Reef of Australia. Subsequent reports from other areas indicated that the phenomenon was widespread, and after reports of extensive damage to the reefs around Guam a crash survey program was organized by the Westinghouse Ocean Research Laboratory for the U. S. Department of the Interior. The Westinghouse survey was carried out in the summer of 1969 by 10 teams of scientists who covered 16 islands within the U. S. Trust Territory (Micronesia). As a result of the survey 10 islands were considered to be infested.

The general conclusions of the Westinghouse report (Chesher, 1969) were that the phenomenon was unprecedented and offered a potentially serious and widespread threat to the ecology of Indo-Pacific coral reefs. An immediate control program and further research were recommended. Two suggested causes for the outbreak were considered most promising. One involved reduced predation on *Acanthaster* larvae due to coral destruction by human activities; the other involved reduced predation on adults because of the collection of tritons by shell collectors.

Subsequent to the Westinghouse survey and continuing at present (1972) the University of Guam has surveyed additional islands in the Trust Territory and resurveyed most of the islands reported on by Westinghouse. Their findings (Tsuda, 1971) will be discussed in more detail below.

The suggestion that *Acanthaster* posed a serious, widespread, and unprecedented threat to the ecology of Indo-Pacific coral reefs generated considerable controversy among scientists. Skeptics dismissed the phenomenon simply as some natural fluctuation or cycle, and alarmists vehemently proclaimed the seriousness of the problem. Unfortunately, the former offered virtually no solid information or broad experience to support their disclaimers, while the evidence offered by the latter group was far from conclusive.

The objectives of the present study were to begin to obtain a better personal feeling for the biology of Indo-Pacific coral reefs in general, to ascertain if present conditions in the Trust Territory indicate a serious and growing problem with *Acanthaster* or simply natural fluctuations in populations, and to investigate more fully certain other aspects of the biology of *Acanthaster planci*.

Our work began with arrival at Eniwetok Atoll on July 30, 1971, and continued there until October 1, when we departed Eniwetok for Ponape. We then island hopped westward, spending 11 days at Ponape, 5 at Ant Atoll, 8 at Truk, 4 at Kuop Atoll, 2 at Puluwat, and 4 at Yap, arriving in Palau on November 16 and remaining there until late March 1972.

Abundance

The idea that in the past *Acanthaster* was a great rarity and that the recent outbreaks are unprecedented is without substantial basis. Dana (1970) has pointed out several older references to *Acanthaster* as a common or even abundant organism in certain locations. More importantly it has been only in the past 10 to 15 years, with the increasing amount of SCUBA diving for sport and in research, that we have had any basis at all to discuss the abundance or rarity of reef animals. In our own work in the West Indian region we have found literally dozens of species of fishes and invertebrates to be common and even abundant that in the past had been considered rare or were even undescribed and unknown.

Acanthaster, like most of the mobile invertebrate macrofauna, is normally nocturnal and stays hidden in the day. At Eniwetok we never observed *Acanthaster* in the open during the day, yet it was quite common at night. At one location where none were normally seen in the day as many as 10 specimens could be found within a radius of 15 meters at night. No noticeable destruction of coral occurred at that location during our 2-month stay, though that population density would be classified as an "infestation," using the Westinghouse survey criteria.

Four conditions make *Acanthaster* visible diurnally. During a true epidemic, involving thousands of individuals in a limited area of reef, they are reported to feed actively in the day and remain in the open. Such a condition has been documented only from Guam and on the Great Barrier Reef.

More limited aggregations of a few dozen to several hundred individuals may appear rather suddenly, remain for weeks or a few months, and then disappear. Such a population appeared at the east pass at Eniwetok in early 1971, but when we examined the area we found the population had completely dispersed. Vine (1970) has suggested that such aggregations are associated with breeding, a phenomenon known for other echinoderms.

Populations living in loose thickets of branching *Acropora* are also visible in the day simply because there is no place to hide completely. Such situations were observed in shallow lagoon areas at Truk and Palau.

Finally, populations in certain areas may remain in the open during the day. A similar phenomenon occurs in the West Indian echinoid *Diadema antillarum,* which in certain areas is cryptic diurnally while in other locations it is active and in the open throughout the day. Such differences appear to be correlated with reduced predation. Scattered individuals of *Acanthaster* were observed in the open during the day at Ponape.

Surveys

The original Westinghouse survey classified all islands surveyed into six conditions with respect to *Acanthaster* populations, as shown by the following summary of results from the Westinghouse report:

Condition 1 – Few *A. planci,* reefs healthy and undamaged:

Yap, Woleai, Mokil, Ifalik, Lamotrek, Kwajalein

Condition 2 – Large populations of *A. planci* concentrated in one or more local shallow-water reefs; damage to reef slight; no extensive dead reef:

Palau, Kapingamarangi(?), Arno, Pingelap(?)

Condition 3 – Large populations of *A. planci* in all depths, damage to reef fresh and extensive; patches of live reefs interspersed with completely dead reef zones (this is a condition of short duration; Ponape may have recently passed from condition 3 to condition 4):

Condition 4 – Large populations of *A. planci* arranged into one or more fronts, separated by or leaving behind extensive, almost completely dead reefs:

Saipan, Guam, Ponape, Rota, Truk

Condition 5 – Entire island with primarily dead reefs:

Tinian, Ant, Kuop

Condition 6 – Population expansion of *A. planci* failed to pass condition 2 and it dispersed following localized coral kill (hypothetical answer to conditions reported in field, requires confirmation after a year or more of development):

Kapingamarangi(?), Pingelap(?), Nukuoro

This classification unfortunately implies that any condition other than a lush reef with virtually no *Acanthaster* is some stage in an *Acanthaster* population explosion. It also classifies entire reef areas that may include over 100 miles of reef by a condition that may occur in only very restricted locations.

Resurveys, one to two years later, by teams from the University of Guam confirmed the continued existence of rich reefs and low populations of *Acanthaster* at Yap, Ifalik, Woleai, and Lamotrek. Pulap, Puluwat, Pulusuk, Satawal, Elato, Olimarao, Eauripik, and Faraulep Islands, as well as atolls in the central Caroline Islands, were also surveyed by the Guam team though not included in the original Westinghouse survey. Healthy reefs are reported at all locations, and the greatest number of *Acanthaster* seen was 11 during a 10-minute tow at Pulusuk. On most tows, none or occasionally 1 or 2 were reported. As in the Westinghouse survey, populations approaching one per minute of tow were considered evidence of infestation. White feeding sites on coral were similarly considered, though a single starfish may be responsible for multiple feeding sites and the pincushion starfish *(Culcita)* and possibly other organisms may also be involved. On this basis four islands were considered to show evidence of "minor infestations." At a mean speed of 2 knots, however, a towed observer covers 200 feet in a minute and with two observers scanning opposite sides a path at least 60 feet wide is scanned. One starfish per 12,000 square feet of reef, though much more than is normally seen, is still a very low population density and certainly within the capacity of the reef to support.

With the absence of coral damage reported, I would consider none of the islands to be "infested" and none in serious ecological danger from *Acanthaster*.

Kapingamarangi, listed in the Westinghouse report as questionably condition 2 or 6, and Nukuro, listed as condition 6, were resurveyed by the Guam team and found to have healthy reefs with *Acanthaster* well scattered. The largest groups contained only 3 to 4 animals.

Four large populations of *Acanthaster* concentrated in herds and clearly damaging the reefs were reported by Chesher (1969; p. 48) for Palau. All were in the lagoon. The most recent and extensive resurvey by the University of Guam was conducted in January 1972, while we were in Palau. Starfish were virtually absent in all but one limited location, where the maximum count was 14 individuals during a 10-minute tow.

Control efforts of divers with formalin guns account for only part of the population decline, as it occurred also in locations where control efforts had not been made. In general coral growth is very rich throughout the Palau Islands.

Arno Atoll and Pingelap, listed in the Westinghouse report as condition 2 or 6, have not been resurveyed.

All the islands listed as condition 4 in the Westinghouse report were covered by University of Guam resurveys. At Saipan they found that the large populations of *Acanthaster* had virtually disappeared and they could account for only part of the disappearance as due to control efforts. At Rota only a relatively small population of starfish was found to remain. At Guam the situation was essentially static, with large numbers of starfish still present but with little additional coral damage. At Truk a general decline in starfish populations was found, again accountable only in part by control efforts. Around Ponape the fronts described in the Westinghouse report were found to have dispersed, though several areas were considered to be seriously infested on the basis of counts of 1 to 2 starfish per minute of tow. My own observations were concentrated along the northern and northeastern reefs, two of the three locations originally reported to be heavily infested. The outside reefs generally supported good though not lush coral growth. No infestations of *Acanthaster* were seen over 6 miles of reef examined and there was no evidence of extensive coral damage due to *Acanthaster*. Ponape is a high island with over 300 inches of rain per year in the interior. On an outgoing tide during rainy weather visibility in the harbor area was reduced to 1 or 2 feet and very dirty water blanketed even the outer northern reefs. Patch reefs in the harbor were barren on top but fringed around the sides by several silt-resistant species of coral. These reefs were described as "dead" in the Westinghouse report, as were the portions of the outer reef adjacent to the pass leading into the harbor. Both were considered to have been killed by *Acanthaster*. Neither were actually dead, and the lack of rich growth is undoubtedly due to the silt-laden low-salinity water periodically flooding them.

Aguijan Island in the Marianas Islands was also resurveyed for the first time by the Guam team and found to be infested by *Acanthaster*, like nearby Saipan and Tinian. A population of 3,000 to 4,000 starfish was estimated to occur around the coast of the island.

Three islands in the Westinghouse survey were considered to have primarily dead reefs, killed by *Acanthaster* (condition 5). Tinian was resurveyed by the Guam team, which found limited areas of additional dead coral and greatly reduced populations of starfish. The Guam team, however, considered the coral areas around Tinian, Saipan, and Aguijan generally to be not true coral reefs but simple coral communities growing on a rock substrate; thus, what has been attacked by starfish in these areas must largely be isolated coral colonies, not actual coral reefs.

Ant and Kuop Atolls were the remaining two reefs considered to be killed by *Acanthaster*. At Ant we found considerable coral growth in the areas reported killed by starfish. The Guam report remarked that the eastern and northern sections of the atoll possess one of the most beautiful reefs that their team leader had ever seen and concluded that the atoll is not as dead as the Westinghouse report states. In the Westinghouse report two locations in the lagoon and two on the outside of the reef are indicated as dead. Patches of dead coral are common in lagoons, even in the West Indian Region where *Acanthaster* does not occur. The very existence of lagoons is a result of poor conditions for coral growth there. The areas on the outside reef were not dead but simply areas with dead coral interspaced with considerable living coral and no evidence of *Acanthaster* infestation. Lack of the usual clouds of plankton-feeding fishes that usually hover over outside reefs was indicative of a scarcity of planktonic food. Some feature of local hydrography is possibly responsible for this phenomenon.

At Kuop Atoll we found that the eastern side, reported as dead, supported only sparse coral growth. Very poor development of typical spur-and-groove formations in the surge zone and general scarcity of coral colonies either alive or dead on the reef flat were indicative that coral growth has been poor here for a very long time. Again plankton-feeding fishes were much scarcer than normal, and some feature of local hydrography is probably responsible for a reduced supply of nutrients in the form of plankton. Possibly Kuop's position immediately adjacent (about 1 kilometer) to the much larger barrier reef around the Truk Islands results in its being located in a current eddy that deprives it of a normal flow of planktonic food.

Predation

Virtually no reef animal is immune to predation. The echinoid *Diadema antillarum* of the West Indies is covered with needle sharp, toxic spines 6-12 inches long, yet it is preyed upon by at least 15 species of fishes, a crustacean, and two gastropods (Randall, Schroeder, and Starck, 1964, p. 429). Coral-reef communities are characterized by a tremendous diversity of organisms with limited numbers of individuals of most species; consequently reef predators take a wide variety of species within their general type of prey, the actual prey at a given time depending upon availablility. Populations of predators are therefore not tied to any one prey, and for a given prey species a large population of predators is always in existence, supported by other organisms. A substantial increase in abundance of a particular prey results in increased predation on it even greater than its proportional increase. This phenomenon is due to the greater proportion of prey forced into less ideal habitats and, even more important in many cases, the conditioning of predators that leads them to seek more actively the abundant prey. In extreme cases a wide variety of predators will concentrate on a temporarily abundant organism to the exception of all other prey. This is commonly observed in predatory reef fishes, when large schools of herrings or engraulids move into an area.

Because of the nature of predation on reefs, regular interrelated cycles of abundance of prey and predators are not known to occur, and the effects of random fluctuations in larval success are greatly dampened. To explain a radical increase in a population of *Acanthaster* some release from predation must be found. The normally nocturnal habits of *Acanthaster* are highly indicative of substantial predation on it, and its remaining in the open during the day where large populations are present is likewise indicative of greatly reduced predation.

The previously known predators on *Acanthaster,* the triton *(Charonia tritonis)* and the shrimp *Hymonocera elegans,* are both too uncommon everywhere to alone control populations of *Acanthaster.* Various fishes would seem to be potentially more important predators, and our efforts were concentrated on the giant wrasse *Chelinus undulatus,* which appeared to be a likely candidate. *Chelinus* reaches a weight of over 100 pounds and occurs throughout the Indo-Pacific. It is a solitary species, and the normal population densities we observed by submarine were generally 1 to 3 fish per linear kilometer of reef. The greatest number seen at one time was 12 fish in one location at Eniwetok. *Chelinus* is a shy fish and difficult to approach, but by chasing them with the submarine until they holed up in the coral we were eventually able to take 5 specimens with bangsticks. One contained remains of *Acanthaster,* three were virtually empty, having only fragments of gastropod shell in the gut, and one contained a moray eel about 400 millimeters long and a bivalve mollusk.

A recent report from Fiji (Owens, 1971, p. 17) reported fishermen to have found *Acanthaster* remains in the stomachs of green triggerfish *(Pseudobalistes flavimarginatus).*

Other balistids and labrids, diodontids, tetrodontids, gaeterinids, sparids, lethernids, and other fishes are also potential predators; but to verify this, examination of hundreds of stomachs will be required. The only practical way to obtain the number and variety of species needed would be to examine catches brought in by fishermen. This unfortunately proved impossible in Micronesia. The U. S. Government currently subsidizes the Micronesian economy to the extent of approximately $70,000,000 per year for a total population of 100,000 Micronesians, who now prefer buying canned fish to catching them. As a consequence, subsistence fishing is now at a very low level.

Reduction of predation on *Acanthaster* larvae was hypothesized in the Westinghouse report as the most probable cause of population explosions. Destruction of coral through human activities was suggested to have created predation-free settling places for the starfish larvae. Settling areas free of coral appear to be normally abundant on reefs, but most importantly an increase in success of larval settlement would be largely offset by increased predation unless predators on juvenile and adult *Acanthaster* were also reduced. Random fluctuation of a few percent in survival of larvae in organisms like *Acanthaster* that produce hundreds of thousands or millions of eggs would result in continuous astronomical fluctuations in populations, were it not for the dampening effect of predation on later stages. Blasting and dredging, considered to be the most important cause of coral destruction, would, however, also result in killing or driving off the predators that control larger *Acanthaster.*

Ecological Effects

Relatively few animals feed on coral, and it is not a significant item in the nutritional budget of reef communities. Its most important function is in furnishing diverse and constantly renewing shelter for reef dwellers. The immediate ecological effects of *Acanthaster* eating away the film of living polyps are therefore not drastic. Over a period of years the dead coral would be eroded away, however, if new growth did not occur. Little information is available in the scientific literature on the rate of recovery of reefs. In the areas we examined, *Acanthaster* had attacked *Acropora, Poecillopora,* and other smaller corals and left untouched massive heads of *Porites.* At Eniwetok we observed table *Acropora* up to 4 feet in diameter growing on submarine cables less than 15 years old. From this and observations on recovery from storm damage at Alligator Reef, I would estimate that barring continued predation by *Acanthaster,* substantial regrowth of small coral colonies will be effected in about 5 years and essentially complete recovery will take about 15 years. Also, a period of about 15 to 30 years seems to be involved between massive destruction of *Acropora* and other fragile corals by severe hurricanes or typhoons and their subsequent recovery.

Conclusions

Populations of *Acanthaster* vary greatly in density on individual reefs and between different reefs. Fluctuations in population at given locations also frequently occur. There are no clearly defined "normal" or "infestation" conditions, but rather all degrees of density. Declines in reported infestations are only partially attributable to control efforts. Epidemics of *Acanthaster* lasting several years and doing extensive and severe damage to coral reefs have apparently occurred only at Guam and in a limited region inside the Great Barrier Reef. Reports of population explosions and reef destruction from Micronesia have been greatly exaggerated by inexperienced observers, and the erroneous concept that anything more than one starfish per 200 feet of reef involves some stage of an epidemic.

Increased predation by fishes and other organisms normally dampens the extent of random population fluctuations. Any activity by man that serves to reduce predation on the adult stages of *Acanthaster* will result in exaggerated population fluctuations and if severe enough will result in sustained high populations limited then only by available food. Spear fishing, shell collecting, commercial fishing, blasting and dredging, and possibly pesticides all contribute to reducing populations of predators.

While the seriousness of the problem has been greatly exaggerated, I believe occasional future outbreaks sustained by reduced predation and doing considerable localized coral damage can be expected.

Recommendations

Further work on predation on *Acanthaster* is needed. Feeding experiments offering *Acanthaster* to various predators, extensive stomach-content examination of potential predators, and population censuses of predators would all be fruitful. The pesticide problem is potentially much more complex, but analysis of tissue samples of predators from various areas should give strong indication if the problem is a real one.

Other Work

During the course of the present work we selectively collected unusual fishes with small multipronged spears. Fourteen undescribed species and several others that are probably new were collected. Specimens of several species have been turned over to specialists in the groups to which they belong, and a manuscript describing a new deep-water butterflyfish has been completed with Dr. Gerald R. Allen of the Trust Territory Marine Resources Office.

Collections also were made of commensal shrimps living on corals, sea anemones, crinoids, and a 10-foot-long synaptid holothurian. Several of these are almost certainly new and will be turned over to Dr. Raymond B. Manning of the Smithsonian Institution.

Surveys of local distribution and population density of four species of reef sharks were carried out with the submarine and observations made on behavior. About 20 percent of the gray reef sharks *(Carcharhinus menisorrah)* when approached attacked the submarine, some repeatedly. One attack broke a window and another sheared the propeller drive pin. In all instances gray sharks when approached began exhibiting an exaggerated lateral swimming motion at a distance of 10 to 15 meters. Upon closer approach the back was arched posteriorly, pectoral fins extended downward, and the jaws worked in a biting motion. If an attack was not carried out, this display became so exaggerated that forward swimming motion was lost and the tail sank, leaving the animal writhing about in a diagonal head-up position. Observations carried out on attacks on large bait indicated that this display was essentially similar to the motions involved in tearing chunks from large prey, and thus may be a displaced attack. Attack on the submarine in some instances seemed to be directed at ourselves inside, and in others, at the sub itself. Frequently an attack involved a rapid circle, with the attack coming from behind but so rapidly that a diver in similar circumstances could not have turned around in time to face the attack.

Population densities of gray sharks averaged one to two per kilometer of reef. This apparently very high density, compared to large terrestrial predators, is evidently possible because of the low food requirement of sharks. Currently I am analyzing growth data from returns on 1,000 lemon sharks that we tagged in the Florida Keys. Growth in this species, which attains a length of 9 feet, seems to average only a few inches per year. Several instances are known of sharks living and remaining active for over a year in captivity without food. Everything indicates a very low rate of metabolism. In Palau we captured two gray sharks and made oxygen consumption measurements in a fiberglass tank on deck. These data, while very preliminary, indicate a metabolic rate about half, or less, that of bony fishes, as recorded in the literature. Converted to pounds of protein, the rate measured is roughly equivalent to a meal of one 10- to 12-pound fish per month.

REFERENCES

CHESHER, RICHARD H.
1969. *Acanthaster planci:* Impact on Pacific coral reef, 152 pp., illus. Final report to U. S. Department of the Interior. Research Laboratories, Westinghouse Electric Corporation, Pittsburgh, Pennsylvania.

DANA, THOMAS F.
1970. *Acanthaster:* A rarity in the past? Science, vol. 169, p. 894.

OWENS, D.
1971. *Acanthaster planci* starfish in Fiji: Survey of incidence and biological studies. Fiji Agr. Journ., vol. 33, pp. 15-23, illus.

RANDALL, JOHN E.; SCHROEDER, ROBERT E.; and STARCK, WALTER A., II
1964. Notes on the biology of the echinoid *Diadema antillarum.* Caribbean Journ. Sci., vol. 4, nos. 2-3, pp. 421-433, illus.

TSUDA, ROY T., *compiler*
1971. Status of *Acanthaster planci* and coral reefs in the Mariana and Caroline Islands, June 1970 to May 1971. Mar. Lab. Univ. Guam Techn. Rpt. no. 2, 127 pp. illus.

VINE, PETER J.
1970. Field and laboratory observations of the crown-of-thorns starfish *Acanthaster planci*. Nature, vol. 228, pp. 341-342.

WALTER A. STARCK II

Excavation of Protohistoric Arikara Indian Cemetery Near Mobridge, South Dakota, 1971

Principal Investigator: T. Dale Stewart, National Museum of Natural History, Smithsonian Institution, Washington, D. C.

Grant No. 984: In support of excavations yielding skeletal remains and information on burial customs of the Arikara Indians.

Back in 1923 Dr. M. W. Stirling—then a new employee of the Smithsonian Institution—spent the month of June excavating Indian cemeteries at four localities within 8 miles of one another in the vicinity of Mobridge, north-central South Dakota. The approximately 110 skeletons or parts of skeletons comprising his collection have been valued ever since for research purposes on account of their unusually fine state of preservation. Yet in spite of this, no further intensive excavation of these cemeteries was undertaken until 1965 when Prof. William M. Bass of the University of Kansas (now of the University of Tennessee) began work at the Leavenworth site (39C09)—Stirling's site no. 4, also known as the Lewis and Clark site. In two field seasons there Professor Bass recovered the remains of 285 individuals. Subsequently, he spent part of his 1968 and 1969 field seasons and most of his 1970 field season at the Mobridge site (39WW1)—Stirling's site no. 1 and the subject of the present report. This work produced a total of 371 burials. Stirling's sites nos. 2 and 3, now known as the Nordvold sites, have not received further attention.

Professor Bass had intended to return to the Mobridge site in 1971 to extend the excavation of the cemetery area.[1] However, when he failed to obtain the necessary grant funds he generously offered (1) to relinquish his excavation rights to the Smithsonian Institution, (2) to lend his field equipment stored in Mobridge, and (3) to serve as project consultant. It was on this basis that the grant from the National Geographic Society was arranged. As it happened also, Douglas Ubelaker, a member at various times since 1965 of Professor Bass's field crews and the designated field director of his planned 1971 field season, joined the Smithsonian's staff in the spring of 1971. The successful

[1] In 1968 Professor Bass designated this area "Feature 102." Each year thereafter he increased the first digit in the number by one, therefore providing a means of identifying the excavation year. In conformity with this system the feature was numbered 402 in 1971.

outcome of the rearranged 1971 field season is due in large measure to Ubelaker's availability to direct the field work and to his exceptional experience in cemetery exploration.

The field crew assembled by Ubelaker, although small in number, proved to be highly motivated and therefore willing to spend long hours in excavating, both with shovels and with small hand tools. The large number of recovered specimens listed below attests to their efforts. Serving as assistant field director was James Yost of the University of Kansas. Under him were five excavators: David Meditz, also of the University of Kansas; Clark Larsen and Teri Johnson of Kansas State University; Charles Bass of Knoxville, Tennessee; and Steven Potts of Worthington, Minnesota. Marla Sloan of Kansas State University served as cook and part-time excavator. Only Ubelaker, Yost, and Meditz had had previous field experience of the sort required at the Mobridge site.

By the scheduled date for beginning the field season—Monday, June 14—the rented headquarters in Mobridge was in order, the crew and principal investigator were on hand, and only the elevated scraper for removing the sterile topsoil from the site was missing. The scraper operator was under contract elsewhere and consequently was unable to coordinate his schedule with ours. Rather than waste time, however, Ubelaker took the crew several miles north of Mobridge to the Rygh site (39CA4) on the east shore of the reservoir known as Lake Oahe. Lake Oahe was created in recent years by damming the Missouri River at Pierre, 100 miles south of Mobridge. Therefore, what was originally the river valley is now flooded, and the bordering bluffs where the Indians lived and buried their dead form the present shores of the lake.

On a visit to the Rygh site the preceding day crew members had found an Indian skeleton eroding from the bank along the lake shore. Using it as an example, the experienced excavators in the crew demonstrated the technique of exposing and removing a typical Arikara burial (figs. 1, 2). The most unusual feature of such a burial is an inclined wood covering of cedar sticks or planks. At the time of burial a circular pit was dug to an appropriate depth (in this case 32 inches), the flexed body placed in it, and the wood covering arranged over the body so as to slope from well above the head to the level of the feet. The wood covering may have protected the body during the back-filling of the earth, but in any event the earth ultimately filled every space within the pit. The point is that the excavator's knowledge of this burial custom enables him to remove the earth at the top of the pit until he encounters the wood covering. Thereupon he knows where the head and feet are located.

While this demonstration was in progress, and a second skeleton was being discovered and removed (a third incomplete skeleton was recovered later),

FIG. 1. Partly excavated burial exposed in the bank of Lake Oahe at the Rygh site (39CA4) near Mobridge, South Dakota. The diagonal element above the skeleton is a wood covering. Note that it slopes downward from above the skull.

Ubelaker returned to town and arranged for a local owner of a front loader to come to the Mobridge site in the afternoon and remove enough topsoil to make it possible for the work to get under way there and continue until the elevated scraper became available. It is sufficient here to record that this preliminary trenching was accomplished by late Monday afternoon.

Beginning on Tuesday and continuing through most of Thursday the crew excavated as many as possible of the detected disturbances in the subsoil. Actually, 10 graves yielded the remains of 15 individuals. Then, late Thursday afternoon, the original contractor arrived unexpectedly with his elevated scraper and worked the rest of that day and all day Friday. As a result of this operation a total of 47 graves were tentatively identified and mapped, mainly northwest of the 1970 excavations. Tested areas west and south of the 1970 excavations produced no signs of graves.

I left for Washington at the end of the first week and did not return to Mobridge until the last week in July when Professor Bass also joined the group. However, weekly reports from the field told me that the recovery of skeletons was progressing steadily and that the crew was gaining in experience. The

FIG. 2. The same burial pit shown in figure 1 as seen from above after the surface of the wood covering was cleaned. The latter—a rather constant feature of Arikara burials—is sometimes composed of cedar sticks, as here, and at other times of cedar planks.

FIG. 3. The setting of the Mobridge site (39WW1) as seen from the air near the end of the 1971 field season. The site is between the railroad and Lake Oahe in the angle formed by the railroad and the approach to the highway bridge. The mottled dark area on the near side of the approach to the highway bridge is the site of the Indian village. Below this the scraped areas of the cemetery show up in lighter color. The present city of Mobridge is out of view to the lower right.

weekly production figures for the field season are as follows: 18, 38, 24, 40, 30, 46, 61, 26—total 283. By comparison with the figures given at the beginning, it can be seen that this total exceeds that of any previous season, and this in spite of the small size of the crew.

To appreciate these figures fully one should understand one of the complicating factors. The cemetery area under investigation is only a few hundred yards from, and in full view from, the highway leading to the bridge across Lake Oahe (fig. 3). This means that it has been exposed to amateur diggers for years. Evidence of this was seen in the form of incompletely filled holes all over the field. Since the previous diggers usually worked unsystematically, they often failed to explore completely the graves they entered. It was thus found profitable to reopen their pits. At the least, one might expect to find enough of a skeleton in situ to determine original burial position. But not infrequently most of the bones would still be present and only partly disturbed.

At the most, only the skull would be missing or only the uppermost of the two or more superimposed skeletons would be disturbed. Actually, 56 (51 percent) of the explored pits had been previously disturbed, and yet 21 (38 percent) of these disturbed pits contained enough articulated skeletal material to give a clear indication of head direction and burial position (see below).

Of course, the wood coverings usually were completely disrupted by the amateurs' digging. Nevertheless, traces of the covering almost invariably could be found. The records show that 238 (85 percent) of the individuals recovered from the Mobridge cemetery area this year were from pits with wood coverings. In eight instances (3 percent) the wood covering had been partially burned for some unexplained reason.

The amateurs probably expected to find a rich assortment of objects buried with the dead, and if so they must have been disappointed about as often as rewarded for their efforts. Grave goods were encountered by our crew in 57 (52 percent) of the graves investigated and then were usually limited to unexciting objects of native manufacture, such as shell or bone beads, chipped stone tools, and broken pottery. In only 2 (4 percent) of the 57 pits containing grave goods were the artifacts of European manufacture: small blue and white glass beads. Beads of this sort were introduced by the fur traders during the 18th century. These facts lead to the conclusion that the Mobridge cemetery area 402 dates from the protohistoric period; that is, from just before and just after initial European contact.

Anyone who attempts to explore an Arikara burial is likely to be in for a lot of digging (table 1). As measured from the present surface with a string and line level, the depth to the most superior part of the skeleton commonly was between 2 and 3 feet, but ranged from just below the surface to 6 feet. The shallow burials tended to be those of infants.

As for the skeletons themselves, the preferred head direction in all age groups was northwest, according to the indication of the 124 yielding this observation (table 2). The same group also showed the variant positioning of the body parts. In 91 (73 percent) the trunk rested on its back, with almost equal numbers having the legs flexed to the right and left, and very few having the legs in other positions (figs. 4, 5). For views of 10 other burials from this cemetery, see the book by D. H. Ubelaker entitled *Human Skeletal Remains: Excavations, Analysis, Interpretation* (Aldine Publishing Co., Chicago, 1978).

Age and sex determinations as shown in tables 1 and 2 should be regarded as tentative since they were made under field conditions. Nevertheless, it is clear that subadults considerably outnumber adults and among adults (the only ones that could be sexed) males outnumber females. The high mortality

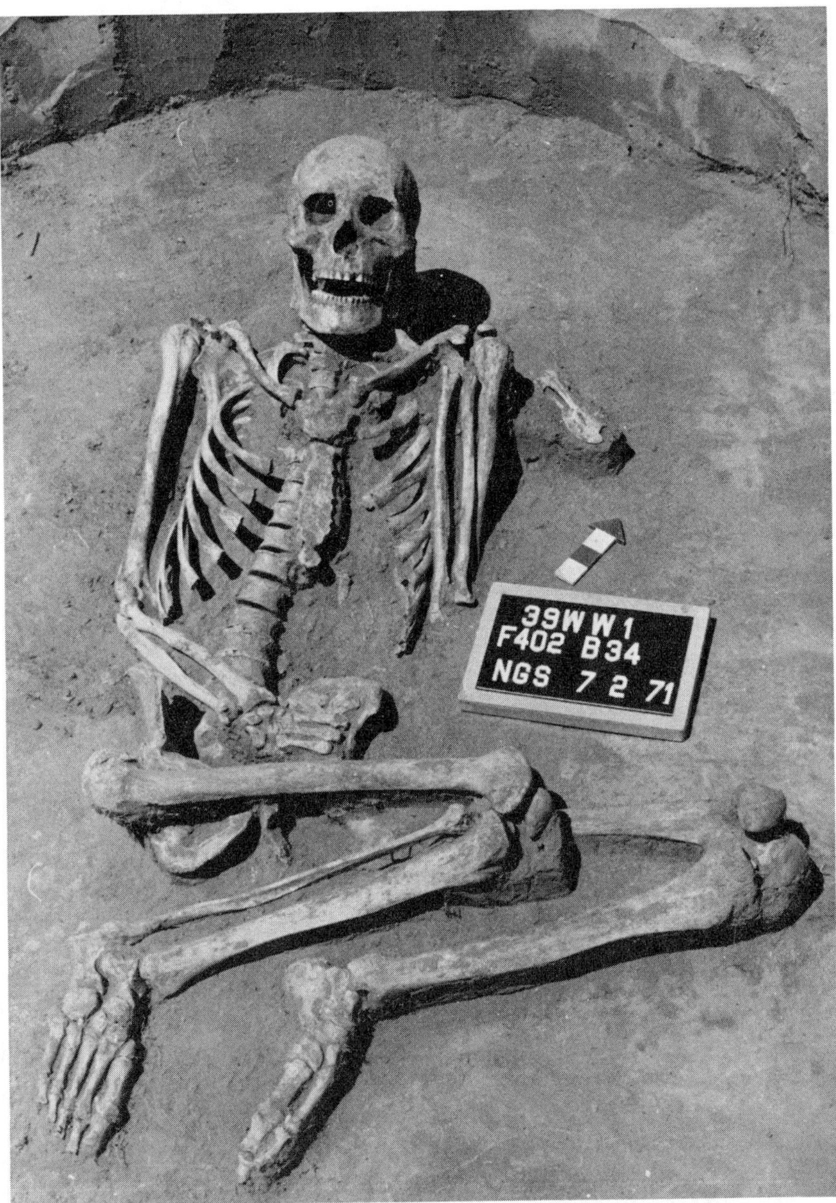

FIG. 4. Burial 34 in cemetery area 402 of the Mobridge site (39WW1) as exposed on July 2, 1971. The position of the skeleton—on back, with head to the northwest and knees flexed to left—is typical of Arikara burials.

TABLE 1. Depth to Top of Skeleton by Age and Sex

Depth	Adults													
	Males		*Females*		*Sex?*		*Adolescents*		*Children*		*Infants*		*Totals*	
(ft.)	*No.*	*Pct.*	*No.*	*Pct.*	*No.*	*Pct.*	*No.*	*Pct.*	*No.*	*Pct.*	*No.*	*Pct.*	*No.*	*Pct.*
0-1	—	—	—	—	1	9.1	—	—	—	—	5	12.5	6	4.9
1-2	5	16.7	4	23.5	1	9.1	4	36.4	4	28.6	11	27.5	29	23.6
2-3	10	33.3	7	41.2	2	18.2	5	45.4	5	35.7	21	52.5	50	40.6
3-4	9	30.0	3	17.6	5	45.4	2	18.2	5	35.7	2	5.0	26	21.1
4-5	5	16.7	3	17.6	1	9.1	—	—	—	—	1	2.5	10	8.1
5-6	1	3.3	—	—	1	9.1	—	—	—	—	—	—	2	1.6
TOTALS	30	100.0	17	99.9	11	100.0	11	100.0	14	100.0	40	100.0	123	99.9

TABLE 2. Direction of Head in Burial by Age and Sex

	Adults													
	Males		*Females*		*Sex?*		*Adolescents*		*Children*		*Infants*		*Totals*	
Direction	*No.*	*Pct.*	*No.*	*Pct.*	*No.*	*Pct.*	*No.*	*Pct.*	*No.*	*Pct.*	*No.*	*Pct.*	*No.*	*Pct.*
North	2	6.4	1	5.9	—	—	—	—	3	21.4	6	14.2	12	9.7
Northwest	20	64.5	12	70.5	7	77.8	11	100.0	7	50.0	20	47.6	77	62.1
West	1	3.2	1	5.9	—	—	—	—	—	—	7	16.7	9	7.3
Southwest	—	—	2	11.8	—	—	—	—	—	—	1	2.4	3	2.4
South	3	9.7	1	5.9	—	—	—	—	2	14.3	1	2.4	7	5.6
Southeast	3	9.7	—	—	1	11.1	—	—	1	7.1	2	4.8	7	5.6
East	—	—	—	—	—	—	—	—	1	7.1	2	4.8	3	2.4
Northeast	2	6.4	—	—	1	11.1	—	—	—	—	3	7.1	6	4.8
TOTALS	31	99.9	17	100.0	9	100.0	11	100.0	14	99.9	42	100.0	124	99.9

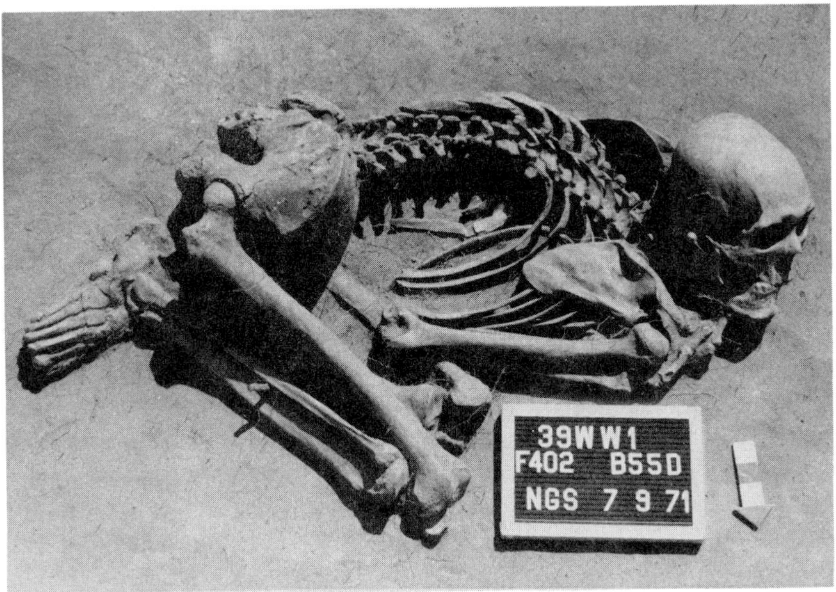

FIG. 5. Burial 55D (a multiple interment) in cemetery area 402 of the Mobridge site (39WW1) as exposed on July 9, 1971. The twisted position of the upper half of this Arikara skeleton is atypical.

rates for subadults, especially infants, are the usual finding among Amercian Indians.

A dozen or so spectacular cases of bone pathology were observed in the course of handling the skeletons and gave the impression of having resulted mainly from trauma. Considered in the setting of the whole collection, these cases should go far in establishing the health status of the population.

To conclude, following the termination of the project on Friday, August 6, Ubelaker and Yost delivered the collection to the National Museum of Natural History in Washington on schedule. The cleaning and cataloging of the specimens were promptly carried out by the personnel of the Museum's Processing Laboratory.

T. DALE STEWART

Biography of Joseph Francis Rock (1884–1962): Scientist-Explorer

Principal Investigator: Stephanne B. Sutton, Arnold Arboretum, Harvard University, Cambridge, Massachusetts.

Grant No. 1011: In support of the preparation of a biography of Joseph F. Rock, explorer and ethnographer of western China.

This grant helped support my work on a biography of Joseph F. Rock, botanist, explorer, ethnologist, and cantankerous human being. I had become aware of Rock in the course of research on a previous book and was particularly interested in the little-known areas and aspects of China disclosed in his letters and diaries. I decided, therefore, to concentrate my study on the years that Rock had spent in western China, 1922-1949, and to treat both the evolution of the man and the picture of China that emerged in his eye-witness accounts and extraordinary photographs. Rock's reports on the hinterland provinces of Yunnan, Szechwan, Kansu, and Sikang; his ethnological studies of non-Han tribes; his letters to the West composed during the Mohammedan-Tibetan feud of 1926, the Long March, the Second World War, and the Communist take-over—all of which he saw from an unusual geographical perspective—seemed to me important contributions to our understanding of the vast and complex Middle Kingdom, especially since no Westerners (the redoubtable Edgar Snow excepted) had been permitted to visit Rock's old stamping grounds since his forced but dignified departure in 1949. As far as I know, Chinese authorities have still permitted only a handful of foreigners to poke around these regions, and so I continue to find Rock's writings relevant.

I completed the manuscript of the biography in 1972. It then entered the merry-go-round of publishing houses, only to emerge therefrom, in book form, in 1974 under the title *In China's Border Provinces*. As a postscript, *Harvard* magazine plans to publish my article about Rock and Nakhi manuscripts sometime in 1978.

The late Dr. Leonard Carmichael, whom I admired very much, explained to me that the Society did not customarily support publication projects per se but had been moved to do so in my case because Rock had made several important expeditions on its behalf (Oehser, 1975). The Society's photographic and correspondence archives, which proved immensely valuable to my study, must, I imagine, conceal a great many other secrets to be revealed by other scholars.

REFERENCES

OEHSER, PAUL H., ed.

1975. Explorations in west and southwest China, 1923-1930 [by Joseph F. Rock]. Nat. Geogr. Soc. Res. Rpts., 1890-1954 Projects, pp. 277-279.

SUTTON, STEPHANNE B.

1973. J. F. Rock, a Na-Khi-English encyclopedic dictionary (a review). Harvard Journ. Asiatic Stud., vol. 33, pp. 277-282.

1974. In China's border provinces: The turbulent career of Joseph Rock, botanist-explorer, 334 pp., illus. Hastings House, New York.

——. [Untitled article.] Harvard Mag. (In press.)

STEPHANNE B. SUTTON

Desert Gazelles: Energetic and Water Cost of Locomotion

Principal Investigator: C. Richard Taylor, Countway Laboratory, Museum of Comparative Zoology, Bedford, Massachusetts.

Grant No. 1015: In support of a study of desert gazelles.

In this project we set out to answer two questions: (1) What is the energetic cost of locomotion in a gazelle; and (2) how does exercise affect water loss from desert gazelles? We now have answers to both of these questions. Two papers have appeared describing our findings (Taylor et al., 1974, see References). A short summary follows.

Energetic Cost of Locomotion in a Gazelle

Functional anatomists have argued convincingly that animals like gazelles are built in a manner that minimizes the amount of energy expended in moving. Terrestrial animals, unlike birds and fishes, do little "external work" on the environment as they move. Most of the work is internal: accelerating and decelerating limbs and body and changes in center of gravity. Gazelle limbs are light and very fragile, and most of the muscle mass is located around the pivot point, contrasted to cheetah limbs, which are heavy and used to club down prey. The amount of work to accelerate or decelerate a limb is proportional to the mass of each small segment of limb times the square of its velocity. This work can be minimized by decreasing the mass of limbs and by moving the muscle mass close to the pivot point, where it moves more slowly for a given ground speed. From dissections and weighing of limbs, we found that about 30 times as much energy would be required to accelerate and decelerate cheetah limbs as gazelle limbs.

To our surprise, we found no difference between energy expended while running by the cheetah and the gazelle at any given speed up to 30 km h^{-1}. Steady-state oxygen consumption increased linearly with increasing speed at the same rate in both species. The greater kinetic energy required to accelerate and decelerate a cheetah limb compared to that for a gazelle must be compensated for by either greater elastic storage of energy or by some other factor.

Taylor, Schmidt-Nielsen, and Raab (1970) have found an empirical relationship between energy cost of running and body weight for quadrupedal running in a number of mammals. The slope of the relationship between oxygen consumption and body weight can be predicted from body weight using this simple equation: $M_{run} = 8.46\ W^{-.4}$ where M_{run} is the slope in milliliters of oxygen $(g \cdot km)^{-1}$ and W is the weight in grams. The observed slopes of gazelles and cheetahs were very close to those predicted on the basis of body weight: 0.15 ml O_2 $(g \cdot km)^{-1}$ for the cheetah compared to the predicted slope of 0.15 and observed slope of 0.14 ml O_2 $(g \cdot km)^{-1}$ versus the predicted of 0.13 for the cheetah.

Thus, the equation of Taylor, Schmidt-Nielsen, and Raab for calculating the slope appears valid for a great number of quadrupedal animals even though they differ greatly in the structural arrangement of their limbs. The explanation of this empirical relationship still remains unclear; it is useful, however, in calculating the amount of energy animals use in their environment while moving from place to place.

Water Loss from Gazelles During Exercise

A number of species of gazelles live in hot deserts, apparently without having to drink. Investigations over the past five or six years have uncovered special physiological mechanisms that these animals use for minimizing water loss in hot desert environments. By grazing at night, when water content of plants is higher, gazelles can meet their low requirements for water. Experiments, however, have been limited to resting animals. In this study we wanted to extend these studies to exercising animals.

The additional food eaten and digested by exercising animals will increase the intake of free water in the food and also increase the amount of water formed by oxidation of the food. These gains, however, could be more than offset by greater losses if the heat generated by exercise was lost mainly by evaporation. In this study we compared the amount of heat produced with the amount of heat lost by evaporation, by nonevaporative means, and the amount of heat stored as animals ran at different speeds.

One might expect that desert gazelles would have adopted a strategy, or strategies, to reduce evaporative dissipation of heat during exercise, perhaps even to the point where exercise would improve their water balance. Different strategies have been utilized by running animals to increase nonevaporative heat loss. The African hunting dog, infamous for doggedly running down its prey, increases nonevaporative heat loss while it runs by operating at a very high body temperature, thereby increasing the temperature gradient between itself and the environment. In this way it can run much farther before dehydration becomes a problem. Cheetahs, gazelles, and ostrichlike rheas have adopted another strategy when they travel at high speeds. Body temperature increases during the sprint, and the stored heat is dissipated after stopping.

We found that heat production increased nearly linearly with increasing running speed and up to about 15 times resting level (at 21 km/hr). Water balance of gazelles was unchanged as metabolic rate increased from resting levels to about three times that at rest (the ratio of evaporative water loss to metabolic rate was the same). This would enable gazelles to walk from plant to plant as they graze without altering their water balance. As metabolic rate increased from four to seven times above resting level, 30-40 percent more water was lost per calorie of heat produced than at rest. Thus when gazelles travel at a fast walk or a trot their water balance is adversely affected. When metabolic rate was greater than 10 times resting level most of the heat was stored and the gazelle cooled slowly after stopping, utilizing mainly nonevaporative means. Thus when gazelles canter or gallop their water balance is improved.

It seems reasonable to conclude that exercise does not drastically alter the water balance of desert gazelles, and the results obtained on resting animals are applicable to animals as they move about to find food in nature.

REFERENCES

TAYLOR, C. RICHARD; DMI'EL, RAZI; SHKOLNIK, AMIRAM; BAHARAV, DANIEL; and BORUT, ARIEH

1974. Heat balance in running gazelles: Strategies for conserving water in the desert. Amer. Journ. Physiol., vol. 226, no. 2, pp. 439-442.

TAYLOR, C. RICHARD; SCHMIDT-NIELSEN, KNUT; and RAAB, J. L.

1970. Scaling of energetic cost of running to body size in mammals. Amer. Journ. Physiol., vol. 219, pp. 1104-1107.

TAYLOR, C. RICHARD; SHKOLNIK, AMIRAM; DMI'EL, RAZI; BAHARAV, DANIEL; and BORUT, ARIEH

1974. Running in cheetahs, gazelles, and goats: Energy cost and limb configuration. Amer. Journ. Physiol., vol. 227, no. 4, pp. 848-850.

C. RICHARD TAYLOR

Biotic Succession of Lodgepole-pine Forests of Fire Origin in Yellowstone National Park

Principal Investigator: Dale L. Taylor, South Florida Center for Research, Everglades National Park, Homestead, Florida.

Grant No. 942: In support of a study of biotic succession of lodgepole-pine forests of fire origin in Yellowstone National Park.

A forest fire serves the purpose of preparing a seedbed and stimulating lodgepole-pine *(Pinus contorta)* cones to open, thus allowing the establishment of a lodgepole-pine forest. Succession is an orderly progress of community change. By measuring populations in successive older postfire areas, the establishment and development of a lodgepole-pine forest can be documented. This paper is a report on a long-term study of lodgepole-pine succession being conducted in Yellowstone National Park.

Previous Study

A study that attempted to document natural succession of lodgepole-pine forests in Yellowstone National Park was conducted during the summers of 1965, 1966, and 1967 (Taylor, 1969). Study areas that were selected and years since being burned were 1966 (1), 1960 (7), 1954 (13), 1942 (25), 1910 (57), 1856 (111), and oldest (approximately 300 years). The only apparent difference in the areas was time since they were burned.

The extent of pesticide usage, lumbering, predator control, and forest-fire history were documented in an attempt to determine how the study areas were affected by man's activities.

Environmental factors that were measured included air temperatures (36-inch and 18-inch levels), soil temperatures (1-inch and 6-inch levels), relative humidity, evaporation rates, and precipitation rates. Little successional change was shown by air temperatures and relative-humidity values. One-inch and 6-inch maximum and minimum soil temperatures showed a progressive decrease in average values from the youngest to the oldest study area. Evaporation rates showed a definite relationship with closure of the forest canopy.

Composite soil samples from the upper 4 inches were classified as sandy loam. Litter depth ranged from 4 millimeters in the 7-year area to a maximum of 46 millimeters in the 300-year area. Organic-matter content, extractable sodium, conductivity, and cation-exchange capacity did not show successional trends. Soil pH, extractable potassium, and phosphorus values were thought to be correlated with time since being burned and the number of snags or basal area per acre of timber present.

Lodgepole pines were the predominant tree in both the over 4-inch and under 4-inch d.b.h. categories in all study areas except the 300-year area, where limber pines outnumbered lodgepole pines in the under 4-inch category. The number of trees per acre, the average height of trees, and the total basal area per acre increased from the youngest stands to the 111-year area and decreased from the 111-year area to the 300-year area. Average basal area, the number of age categories, the number of diameter breast-height categories, and the percent of damaged lodgepole-pine trees increased from youngest to the oldest study area. Lodgepole-pine seedlings occurred in all seven study areas. Limber pines and subalpine firs were of significance only in the under 4-inch category in the 300-year area. The percent of trees affected by dwarf mistletoe *(Arceuthobium americanum), Letharia vulpina,* and *Alectoria jubata* showed successional trends associated with forest development.

The 1971 Study

The purpose of the 1971 study, supported by the National Geographic Society, was to compare birds, small mammals, plant species, and population and biomass changes with the 1966-67 averages. Since forest-canopy closure was deemed an important item in the establishment of the lodgepole-pine forest, an area was added that gave some measurement of the phenomenon.

The Study Areas. The six study areas, selected previously, were again used. An additional area, burned in 1966, was added in 1967 but was not studied intensively until 1971. The previous study established that the forest canopy closes between 25 (1942 area) and 57 (1910 area) years postfire (Taylor, 1969). Accordingly, the 40-year area, burned in 1931, was sampled during 1971 to determine the kind and coverage of herbaceous plant species in an intermediately closed forest canopy.

All study areas were located on the Central Plateau of Heart Lake-Flat Mountain Arm regions of the Park (fig. 1) at 8,000 to 8,200 feet elevation. All areas were located on soils of rhyolite origin (Boyd, 1961) and all had been glaciated (Love, 1961). Postfire age represented by each study area is shown in table 1. Areas were sampled from the same locations as sampled in 1966-67.

Herb Succession. We sampled each area quantitatively using 2 x 5 decimeter quadrats and six coverage classes for herbs and shrubs (Daubenmire,

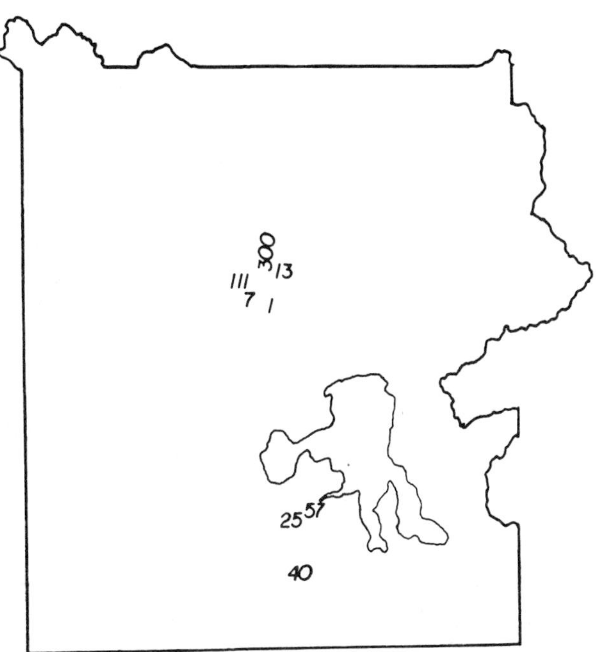

FIG. 1. Location of study areas within Yellowstone National Park. Numbers refer to years postfire when the area was first studied.

1959). Species that occurred within 40 plots and all species observed within each area were recorded (table 2).

Within one year postfire, eight plant species had become established. This number increased to a maximum of 81 species at 25 years postfire, then declined precipitously to 25 species with closure of the forest canopy at 57 years. Fewer than 25 herbaceous plant species were encountered in any area where forest canopy had closed.

The number of plant species in the 40-year postfire area fits the general series of data (table 2). The reduction in species is expected in an intermediately closed forest canopy as compared to an open canopy area. On the basis of these data, it can be predicted that forest-canopy closure is sufficient by 40 years postfire to cause a reduction by one-third from the maximum number of plant species encountered 25 to 30 years postfire when the forest canopy is still open. When the forest canopy closes, a stable and low number of species will occur for about 300 years.

TABLE 1. Postfire Age and Location of the Study Areas

(Data for 1966 and 1967 were averaged. Years postfire marked with asterisk represent 1971 data.)

Study area	*Date sampled**	*Years postfire*	*Identified on map by*	*Location*
1966	1967	1	1	Central Plateau
	1969	3		
	1971	5*		
1960	1967	7	7	Central Plateau
	1971	11*		
1954	1967	13	13	Central Plateau
	1971	17*		
1942	1967	25	25	Flat Mountain-Heart Lake
	1971	29*		Flat Mountain-Heart Lake
1931	1971	40*	40	Flat Mountain-Heart Lake
1910	1967	57	57	Flat Mountain-Heart Lake
	1971	61*		Flat Mountain-Heart Lake
1856	1967	111*	111	Central Plateau
	1971	115*		
1667? (oldest area)	1967	300?	300	Central Plateau
	1971	304*		

One objective of this study was to estimate the amount of soil lacking plant cover (table 3). The amount of exposed soil varied inversely with the number of plant species present. In the very early seral stages where plants were becoming established, 60 to 88 percent of the soil was exposed. As plants became established the amount of exposed soil decreased, but as the forest canopy closed and plants were eliminated by trees shading the soil, exposed soil increased to 85 percent. Amount of exposed soil decreased in the 300-year area where the decadent forest was breaking up, allowing greater light penetration and a greater coverage by plants.

Mosses (at least four species) reached the highest level of establishment in the 25- to 40-year postfire areas (table 3), while lichens (at least two species) provided coverage of 2 percent or greater in only the oldest seral stages.

Avifauna. The census technique employed walking a predetermined tract of 800 to 1,200 yards. All birds 75 feet on each side of the observer were

TABLE 2. Number of Plant Species Observed in Lodgepole-pine Forests of Various Ages

Years postfire	*Total plant species*	*Plant species in 40 plots*
1	8	6
3		8
5	18	9
7	35	9
11		16
13	44	24
17		25
25	81	31
29		30
40		20
57	25	17
61		16
111	23	11
115		11
300?	20	12
304?		7

counted (Kendeigh, 1944). Data from 1966 and 1967 were averaged. The 1971 data are from the single season.

The greatest number of species occurred in the youngest seral areas where 13 to 19 species were observed (table 4). In areas where the forest canopy had closed, only 9 to 13 species were present. White-crowned sparrows *(Zonotrichia leucophrys),* the third most numerous species in the 25-year area during 1966-67, were absent from the area in 1971 (29 years postfire). This apparently was due to the increased height of trees that made the area less favorable to these birds.

Not only were more bird species present, but also there was a greater number of breeding pairs per 100 acres in the youngest areas (table 4). Values from the younger seral stages ranged from 96.5 pairs per 100 acres in the 5-year postfire area to 234.9 pairs in the 13-year area. Values in areas where the forest canopy had closed ranged from 30.4 in the 57-year area to 60.9 pairs in the 304-year area. This shows that forest canopy closure results in breeding pairs being reduced by 37 to 87 percent.

Salt (1957) measured bird weights in Grand Teton National Park. These weights were used to determine standing crop biomass from census data in this study. Avifaunal standing crop biomass ranged from 10,000 grams to

TABLE 3. Coverage Estimates of Vascular Plant Species, Mosses, and Lichens, and the Amount of Soil Exposed

Years Postfire	*Vascular plant species**	*Mosses**	*Lichens**	*Exposed soil (Pct.)*
1	0			81
3	1			88
5	2	x		78
7	3	x		60
11	4	x		66
13	12	x		23
17	6	x		19
25	11	x		6
29	12	x		12
40	5	x	x	44
57	6	x		49
61	3	x		56
111	2	x	x	72
115	3		x	85
300?	2	x	x	42
304?	3	x	x	60

* Coverage 2 percent or more.

over 19,000 grams per 100 acres in youngest areas (table 4). Forest-canopy closure was accompanied by a drop of from 6,210 grams to more than 17,000 grams biomass per 100 acres as compared to youngest areas. This represents a 57 to 91 percent biomass decrease associated with forest canopy closure.

Mammals. Mammals were censused by snap trapping for three nights (Calhoun and Casby, 1958). The 1966-1967 data represent 1,440 trap nights while data for 1971 are for 720 trap nights. Owing to the single-year data with fewer trap nights, some of the rarer species were not collected (table 4).

Species numbers increased from 4 in the earliest seral stands to 12 in the 25-year postfire area. The decrease from 12 to 6 in the 29-year area was because some rarer species were not collected in the single season sample. Once forest canopy closed, the number of species remained fairly stable at three to five species. Closure of forest canopy favors only red squirrels and red-backed voles and is apparently unfavorable to six mammal species.

There was little relationship between number of individuals trapped and succession, although the general trend was toward fewer individuals in the older areas until the 300-year postfire area where highest numbers were collected.

TABLE 4. Avifaunal and Small Mammal Data for the Various Study Areas

	Avifauna				Mammals	
Years postfire	*Species*	*Breeding pairs*[1]	*Total biomass*[1]	*Total species observed*	*Individuals*[2]	*Biomass*[2]
5	13	96.5	11,926	4	4.0	135.3
7	15	209.8	17,538	5	4.7	115.4
11	13	137.0	11,295	6	3.5	105.3
13	16	234.9	19,139	9	4.7	153.6
17	15	162.5	13,754	8	5.4	189.1
25	19	199.8	13,536	12	3.6	107.4
29	18	155.9	10,037	6	3.2	103.5
57	10	30.4	1,852	4	4.7	102.6
61	10	38.5	1,677	5	2.9	95.7
111	10	48.6	3,827	5	1.9	45.8
115	9	48.4	2,162	3	2.4	56.9
300?	13	50.8	3,381	5	5.6	156.9
304?	10	60.9	2,481	5	9.3	209.3

[1]Per 100 acres [2]Per 100 trap nights.

Greatest species diversity in an area does not mean that the greatest number of individuals or greatest biomass will be trapped there (table 4). The greatest number of species trapped was in the 25-year area, but the 3.6 individuals per 100 trap nights was in the midrange for mammals trapped. The 111-115-year postfire areas consistently yielded lowest collections but were also areas where fewest species occurred. The greatest number of individuals trapped per 100 trap nights was 9.3, which occurred in the 304-year area where *Cleithronomys gapperi* (red-backed vole) made up 87 percent of the collection.

Biomass values ranged from 45.8 grams trapped per 100 trap nights to 209.3 grams (table 4). These two divergent values were from the two oldest study areas. *Cleithronomys gapperi* made up 81 percent of the 209.3 grams of biomass collected in the 304-year area.

Discussion. Whittaker (1970) has stated that species diversity increases from the simple communities of early succession to the richer communities of late succession. Odum (1962) describes a Margalef model of succession that shows species diversity to be low in early stages with a gradual increase in species with progression in time.

The data from this study do not fit the above general theories but are more in line with Loucks (1970) and Margalef (1963), who suggest that diversity

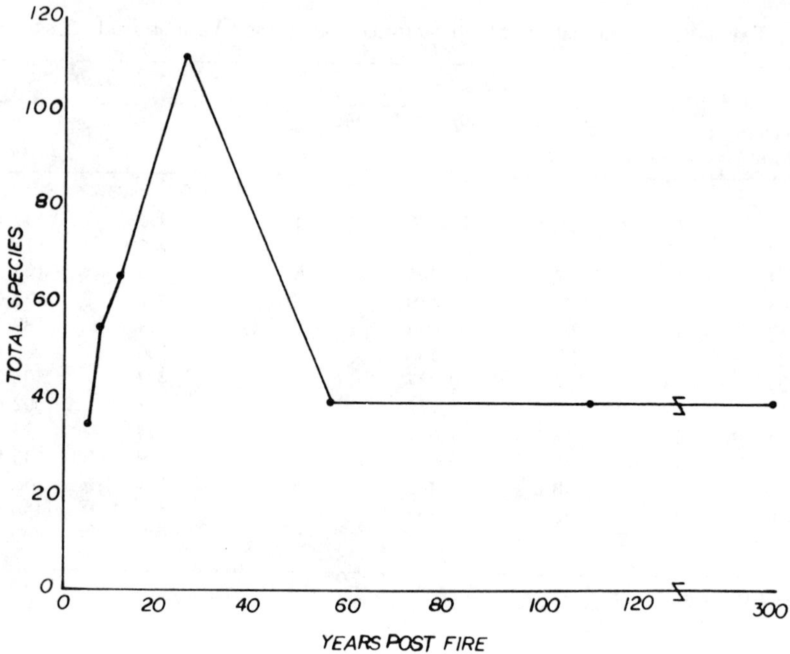

FIG. 2. Successional trend shown by the total number of plant, bird, and small-mammal species.

increases to a certain point and then stops, perhaps declining in the climax community.

Odum (1971) states that an increase in size of organisms and an increase in length and complexity of life histories may be involved in reducing the number of species that can live in a given area. Closure of the lodgepole-pine forest canopy with the resultant shading of the soil leaves only large long-lived tree species. As shown in figure 2, closure of the forest canopy was the most important factor affecting species diversity. Once forest canopy has closed, the depauperate condition will persist for 300 or more years, or until a fire occurs. A forest fire does result in a drastic change in composition, but increases in species diversity, and in some categories, biomass, in the developmental seral stages where smaller plants and shorter life cycles exist, compensates for the loss.

Forest-fire control favors lodgepole pine and a few shrubs but is apparently unfavorable for over 50 other plant species. Eight to ten species of birds are eliminated with forest-canopy closure, whereas only three to five species are favored by canopy closure. Closure of the forest canopy favors only two small mammal species and is unfavorable to six other species. In addition, 74 percent of the study area observations of deer, elk, moose, and black bears were in the three youngest-aged stands (Taylor, 1969). General observations indicate large mammals feed in the younger seral stages and usually use the older areas as avenues for travel and escape.

Odum (1971) states higher diversity means longer food chains, more cases of symbiosis, and greater possibilities for negative feedback control, which reduces oscillations and increases stability. Diversity in species composition is related to the degree of community stability (Odum, 1971; McArthur, 1955). If this is true, then we have the paradoxical situation in lodgepole-pine succession of "more stable" communities (the younger seral stages) being replaced by "less stable" communities (those areas where forest canopy has closed). Fire must have played an important role in the development of such communities.

If higher diversity is desirable, then it is necessary that fire be regarded as a natural and important environmental factor in Yellowstone Park. Lightning is a natural part of the ecosystem and was a part of the primitive environment in which the flora and fauna of Yellowstone Park evolved. Lightning-caused forest fires must have been an influential factor in the perpetuation of the biotic communities that exist in Yellowstone. Since about 1954, there has been little correlation of acreage burned with the number of forest fires as found in past years (Taylor, 1969, 1974). This reduction in acreage burned is attributed to fire control.

Results from this study indicate that *some* older lodgepole-pine forests must be burned periodically to perpetuate the community life cycle and promote biotic diversity. If this is not done the Park will become more and more uniform and will become subject to devastating fires. Certain natural (lightning-caused) fires should be allowed to burn, with fire control exercised in only those areas where fire may endanger Park facilities and human lives.

Yellowstone Park was partially zoned in 1972. The zones are in two units, one of 191,078 acres, and the other 149,606 acres. Wildfires within the zone areas are being monitored rather than controlled.

REFERENCES

Boyd, F. R.
1961. Welded tufts and flows in the Rhyolite Plateau of Yellowstone Park, Wyoming. Bull. Geol. Soc. Amer., vol. 72, pp. 387-426.

Calhoun, John B., and Casby, James
1958. Calculation of home range and density of small mammals. Public Health Monogr. 55, 24 pp. U. S. Department of Health, Education, and Welfare.

Daubenmire, Rexford
1959. A canopy-coverage method of vegetation analysis. Northwest Sci., vol. 33, no. 1, pp. 43-64.

Kendeigh, S. Charles
1944. Measurement of bird populations. Ecol. Monogr., vol. 14, pp. 67-106.

Loucks, Orie L.
1970. Evolution of diversity, efficiency, and community stability. Amer. Zool., vol. 10, pp. 17-25.

Love, J. David
1961. Reconnaissance study of Quaternary faults in and south of Yellowstone National Park, Wyoming. Bull. Geol. Soc. Amer., vol. 72, pp. 1749-1764.

Margalef, R.
1963. Succession in marine populations. Adv. Front. Plant Sci., vol. 2, pp. 137-188.

McArthur, Robert H.
1955. Fluctuations of animal populations, and a measure of community stability. Ecology, vol. 36, pp. 533-536.

Odum, Eugene P.
1962. Relationships between structure and function in ecosystems. Jap. Journ. Ecol., vol. 12, pp. 108-118.
1971. Fundamentals of ecology, ed. 3, 575 pp. W. B. Saunders Co., Philadelphia.

Salt, George W.
1957. An analysis of avifaunas in the Teton Mountains and Jackson Hole, Wyoming. Condor, vol. 59, no. 6, pp. 373-393.

Taylor, Dale L.
1969. Biotic succession of lodgepole pine forests of fire origin in Yellowstone National Park. Ph.D. thesis, University of Wyoming.
1974. Forest fires in Yellowstone National Park. Journ. Forest Hist., vol. 18, no. 3, pp. 68-77.

Whittaker, Robert H.
1970. Communities and ecosystems, 158 pp. Macmillan Co., New York.

Dale L. Taylor

Systematics, Ecology, and Distribution of Annual Killifish in Northern South America

Principal Investigator: Jamie E. Thomerson, Southern Illinois University, Edwardsville, Illinois.[1]

Grant No. 1019: In support of a study of the systematics, ecology, and distribution of annual killifish in northern South America.

Annual killifishes are cyprinodont fish species with an array of characteristic adaptations that allow them to live in temporary bodies of water. These include rapid growth, early sexual maturity, high fecundity, exuberant reproductive activity, and strong sexual dimorphism. Even more striking are the drought-resistant eggs and unique pattern of embryonic developments (Wourms, 1972a,b,c). These fishes live in seasonal drought areas of Africa and South America; regions called llanos, pampas, savannas, or even (in Venezuela and Colombia) semideserts. South American annual species are distributed from Argentina to Colombia.

These fishes avoid permanent streams and lakes with two results: (1) They avoid the intense competition characteristic of South American fish faunas and (2) they are seldom seen by ichthyologists pursuing studies in permanent water.

Many of the annual species are very beautiful fishes and are avidly sought by expert aquarists who specialize in their breeding and maintenance. There is thus an interest in their taxonomy, behavior, ecology, etc., among nonscientists comparable to that of some of the specialized horticultural areas. From a scientific point of view these fishes may furnish answers to fascinating evolutionary and zoogeographic questions. They provide a particular opportunity for study of adaptation to an environment that is harsh and unlikely for most fishes. In addition, their unique properties have stirred the interest of scientists working on such diverse problems as mosquito control (Bay, 1966), patterns of aging (Walford and Liu, 1965), and cellular movement (Wourms, 1972b). All these studies should rest on a firm foundation, now lacking, of

[1] The cooperation, hospitality, and assistance of Sr. Francisco Mago-Leccia, Universidad Central, Caracas, and Dr. Plutarco Cala, Universidad Nacional, Bogotá, made it possible to carry out this research. Assistance in the field by E. Hoigné, L. Aquana, G. Lofstead, D. Taphorn, and R. Yacano is also greatly appreciated.

knowledge of the systematics, ecology, and distribution of these fishes. Weitzman and Wourms (1967) documented the sorry state of taxonomy of the New World annual cyprinodonts by showing that none of the genera as presently defined could be recognized!

At onset of this study the following species were known from Venezuela and Colombia: *Austrofundulus transilis* Myers, 1935 (described from a single specimen); *Pterolebius zonatus* Myers, 1937 (described from a single specimen); *P. maculipinnis* Radda, 1954 (described by accident); and *A. dolichopterus* Weitzman and Wourms, 1967 (described from specimens collected by the Venezuelan aquarist Emilio Hoigné), known to occur in the Orinoco Basin llanos of Venezuela. Other Venezuelan species included *Rachovia hummelincki* de Beaufort, 1940 (based on six specimens collected on the Peninsula de Paraquana); *A. stagnalis* and *A. transilis limnaeus,* both described by Schultz (1949) from series of specimens collected in the Lake Maracaibo Basin. Colombian species included *Rachovia brevis* (Regan), 1912, from "Colombia." Dahl (1958) described *R. splendens* and *A. myersi* from the Caribbean coastal llanos of Colombia. Turner (1967) reported *R. hummelincki* from the Magdalena River Basin.

In 1969 I visited Venezuela and, with the enthusiastic assistance of Sr. Hoigné, made collections from the Orinoco Basin, Maracaibo Basin, and a coastal plain area in Estado Falcón. We discovered an undescribed *Austrofundulus* species in the Maracaibo Basin and found *R. hummelincki* at several Maracaibo localities (Thomerson, 1971). We also obtained several Orinoco Basin species that were either undescribed or difficult to identify.

Support from this grant allowed a collecting expedition to Venezuela in 1972. We were able to work both the eastern and western sides of the Maracaibo Basin, to explore the Venezuelan Orinoco Basin along its northwestern margin, and to revisit some localities in the central basin. Annual fishes often colonize roadside ditches and borrow pits or live in swampy areas along the roads. Efficient exploration for annual species is thus possible where roads traverse suitable habitat. We simply drive down the road and stop to check every likely looking wet place. Usually a few swipes with a dip net are sufficient to show whether or not annual fishes are present.

Collections from the western Maracaibo Basin show that *R. hummelincki* and *A. t. limnaeus* are common there. We also collected the first *A. stagnalis* seen since the original description. On the eastern side of the lake we collected additional specimens of an undescribed *Austrofundulus* species and revisited four localities collected in 1969 (Thomerson, 1971, for localities). In less than three years the following had happened: (1) The road was changed so that we spent over an hour searching for V69-5. This locality is on private land and was essentially unchanged. (2) V69-6, a roadside ditch, was completely obliterated by road improvements. (3) V69-7, a swamp at the outskirts of Lagunillas, was dotted with piles of dirt, obviously in the process of being filled. (4) V69-9, a borrow pit on private land, had a dam built right across it to form a permanent lake for cattle water. Obviously a great deal of stress is being placed on annual fishes by human activities in the Maracaibo Basin. On the other hand, two out of the four altered habitats mentioned above were man-made, and the digging of roadside ditches and borrow pits often provides new habitat for annual fishes.

We made exploratory collections along the northeastern margin of the Orinoco llanos in the states of Barinas and Portuguesa and documented considerable range extensions for *P. maculipinnis* and *P. zonatus*. Later we documented the distribution of these species in Guárico and Cojedes and then visited the area around Caño Benito in Estado Cojedes where we collected specimens and made observations contributing to the description of two new species: *Rivulus stellifer* Thomerson and Turner, 1973, and *Pterolebias hoignei* Thomerson, 1974.

This area around Caño Benito has the richest and most complex annual fish fauna known. All six species known from the Orinoco Basin occur there, and two *(R. stellifer* and *P. hoignei)* are known only from Caño Benito. In spite of fairly extensive exploration of the Orinoco llanos, we have not found an area of similar richness. This area is obviously deserving of further study of the ecology and life histories of the annual fauna to clarify how so many species can live together in a niche-depauperate habitat (Turner, 1967).

Specimens and observations made during this expedition also contributed to a paper providing a key for identification of the Orinoco Basin species and summarizing present knowledge of their ecology and distribution (Taphorn and Thomerson, 1975).

A second expedition to Colombia, supported by this grant, made collections in the Colombian coastal llanos and in the semidesert of the Guajira Peninsula. We found *A. stagnalis* (first record for Colombia) in borrow pits along the highway from Río Hacha to Maicao in Guajira and made a number of collections of *R. brevis* in the coastal llanos. We visited Sincelejo, the type locality of Dahl's *R. splendens* and *A. myersi,* but were unsuccessful in finding annual species there. In several places we found *R. brevis* less than a week old. These I took alive and reared to adulthood at my university, using funds supplied by the grant. With this and other material we have been able to show (Thomerson et al., 1976) that *R. splendens* is a synonym of *R. brevis*.

The investigations made under this grant make clear that we are dealing with two quite different faunas.

The Orinoco Basin. This fauna includes *A. dolichopterus, A. transilis, P. hoignei, P. zonatus, P. maculipinnis,* and *R. stellifer.* The species are highly differentiated and it is likely that the fauna is an old one. The slope of the Orinoco Basin is such that it was not flooded during Pleistocene interglacial high sea-level periods. The species are of diverse origin not reflected by present taxonomy. *A. transilis* and *P. maculipinnis* have their closest relatives in the Maracaibo Basin. *P. hoignei, P. zonatus,* and *A. dolichopterus* seem closely related to species from southern South America. *R. stellifer* may be a relict species. None of the species is known to occur outside the Orinoco Basin.

The Coastal Fauna. The Sierra de Perijá and the Guajira Peninsula seem to act as partial barriers between the Maracaibo Basin and the Colombian coastal llanos faunas. All the species involved are closely related and none occur outside this area. Much of the area now occupied by annual fishes was obviously flooded during the Pleistocene interglacial periods and the present distribution is largely post-Pleistocene. The Maracaibo Basin fauna includes *A. stagnalis, A. t. limnaeus* (not the same species as the Orinoco Basin *A. transilis*), *A.* new species, and *R. hummelincki* ssp. The Colombian coastal llanos fauna includes *A. myersi* (probably a synonym of *A. t. limnaeus*), *R. brevis,* and *R. hummelincki* ssp. *A. stagnalis* occurs on the Guajira Peninsula but is not known from the Colombian coastal llanos. No more than two species have been found syntopic (in contrast to as many as five in the Orinoco Basin), and the combination is always a *Rachovia* sp. and one of the other species.

In addition to the research papers cited above, data obtained under this grant form the major basis for a revision of the genera *Austrofundulus* and *Rachovia* (Taphorn and Thomerson, 1978) and will contribute greatly to a revision of the subfamily rivulinae.

In 1973 I presented two papers based in large part on this research: "The Genus *Austrofundulus,*" at the American Killifish Association annual meeting, Detroit, Michigan, and "Origins and Relationships of the Orinoco Basin Annual Killifish Fauna," at the American Society of Ichthyologists and Herpetologists annual meeting, San José, Costa Rica.

REFERENCES

Bay, Ernest C.

1966. Adaptation studies with the Argentine pearl fish *Cynolebias bellottii,* for its introduction into California. Copeia, 1966, no. 4, pp. 839-846.

Dahl, George

1958. Los peces del Río Sinu; informe preliminar, 47 pp. Secretaría de Agricultura y Ganadería de Córdoba, Montería, Colombia.

De Beaufort, L. F.
1940. Freshwater fishes from the Leeward group, Venezuela and eastern Colombia. Stud. Fauna Curaçao, Aruba, Bonaire and Venezuelan Islands, vol. 2, pp. 109-114.

Myers, George S.
1927. An analysis of the genera of Neotropical killifishes allied to *Rivulus.* Ann. Mag. Nat. Hist., ser. 9, vol. 19, pp. 115-129.
1932. A new genus of funduline cyprinodont fishes from the Orinoco Basin, Venezuela. Proc. Biol. Soc. Washington, vol. 48, pp. 7-14.

Radda, A.
1964. Die Gattung *Pterolebias* Garman 1895. DATZ, vol. 17, no. 2, pp. 39-41.

Regan, Charles T.
1912. A revision of the poeciliid fishes of the genera *Rivulus, Pterolebias* and *Cynolebias.* Ann. Mag. Nat. Hist., ser. 8, vol. 10, pp. 494-508.

Schultz, Leonard P.
1949. A further contribution to the ichthyology of Venezuela. Proc. U. S. Nat. Mus., vol. 99, pp. 1-211.

Taphorn, Donald C., and Thomerson, Jamie E.
1975. Annual killifish of the Orinoco Basin of Venezuela. Journ. Amer. Killifish Assoc., vol. 8, no. 3, pp. 67-73.

Thomerson, Jamie E.
1971. Distribution and biology of the annual cyprinodontid *Rachovia hummelincki* in Venezuela. Journ. Amer. Killifish Assoc., vol. 7, no. 2, pp. 21-28.
1974. *Pterolebias hoignei,* a new annual cyprinodontid fish from Venezuela, with a redescription of *Pterolebias zonatus.* Copeia, 1974, no. 1, pp. 30-38.

Thomerson, Jamie E., and Turner, Bruce J.
1973. *Rivulus stellifer,* a new species of annual killifish from the Orinoco Basin of Venezuela. Copeia, 1973, no. 4, pp. 783-787.

Thomerson, Jamie E.; Taphorn, Donald C.; Foster, Neal R.; and Turner, Bruce J.
1976. *Rachovia splendens* Dahl, a synonym of the annual killifish *Rachovia brevis* (Regan). Copeia, 1976, no. 1, pp. 204-207.

Turner, Bruce J.
1967. Discovery of the rivuline cyprinodontid teleost *Rachevia hummelincki* near Barranquilla, Colombia, with notes on its biology and distribution. Copeia, 1967, no. 4, pp. 843-846.

Walford, Roy L., and Liu, R. K.
1965. Husbandry, life span and growth rate of the annual fish, *Cynolebias adloffi* E. Ahl. Exp. Geront., no. 1, pp. 161-171.

Weitzman, Stanley H., and Wourms, John P.
1967. South American cyprinodont fishes allied to *Cynolebias* with the description of a new species of *Austrofundulus* from Venezuela. Copeia, 1967, no. 1, pp. 89-100.

WOURMS, JOHN P.

1972a. The developmental biology of annual fishes, no. 1: Stages in the normal development of *Austrofundulus myersi:* Dahl. Journ. Exp. Zool., vol. 182, no. 2, pp. 143-168.

1972b. The developmental biology of annual fishes, no. 2: Naturally occurring dispersion and reaggregation of blastomeres during the development of annual fish eggs. Journ. Exp. Zool., vol. 182, no. 2, pp. 169-200.

1972c. The developmental biology of annual fishes, no. 3: Pre-embryonic and embryonic diapause of variable duration in the eggs of annual fishes. Journ. Ex. Zool., vol. 182, no. 3, pp. 389-414.

1978. A revision of the South American cypriodont fishes of the genera *Rachovia* and *Austrofundalis,* with the description of a new genus. Acta Biol. Venezuela, vol. 9, no. 4, pp. 377-452.

JAMIE E. THOMERSON

Photographing Pre-Columbian Gold Artifacts of Panama

Principal Investigator: Reina Torres de Araúz, Director, Patrimonio Historico Nacional, Panama.

Grant No. 935: For a graphic catalogue of the Pre-Columbian gold artifacts of Panama.

The collection of pre-Columbian gold in Museo Nacional de Panama, although not large, includes very important masterpieces representative of the several techniques developed by the goldsmiths of Panama before the conquest. Also, it is representative of the different archeological regions of the country during the period from A.D. 300 until the arrival of Europeans. Accurate photographs in color of this collection were needed to complete the internal catalogue of the institution, which previously consisted solely of verbal descriptions of the objects.

Staff photographer Victor Boswell of the National Geographic Magazine accomplished with great skill the task of providing these photographs, the cameras, film, and processing being supplied by the Society.

The work began in July 1971 at the old building of the Museum in Panama City, with the Head of the Museum, Professor Marcela Camargo, in charge of the accession and control of the collection while the photographing was going on.

Seven hundred gold pieces were photographed, each in several positions. This was necessary for various reasons: The casting techniques, for example, required an accurate close-up of both sides of an object; hammering and repoussé techniques required special angles; and gold wire and joining required close-ups. Also, such pieces as necklaces and pendants made with gold or tumbaga, inlaid with quartz, cerecite, agate and other precious and semiprecious stones, each required a special set-up because of the ornaments' intricacies.

Before the end of the mission two private collectors gave permission for their collections to be photographed, and special trips were made to the Provinces of Colón and Veraguas for this purpose.

After the fieldwork had ended, and Mr. Boswell had returned to Washington, a complete collection of color slides was sent back and was immediately used in compiling the new catalogue of the gold collection. This catalogue includes the color slides of the object, and also measurements, description and other pertinent data.

With the building and organization of the new Museo del Hombre Panameño, this collection of slides has been of enormous value because it has permitted an accurate study of all the gold objects, so that selection could be made for the present display in the Gold, or Treasure, Room of the Museum. The slides also offer a means of control without the need of handling the actual objects. In addition, they are currently being used for lectures given in the Museum auditorium and for special programs.

REINA TORRES DE ARAÚZ

Observations on the Biology of Marsupials in Colombia and Venezuela

Principal Investigator: C. Hugh Tyndale-Biscoe, Australian National University, Canberra, Australia.

Grant No. 927: For a study of the reproductive biology of South American marsupials.

Marsupials are indigenous to the Australasian and Neotropical regions of the world. Isolation of both regions throughout the Tertiary resulted in two independent radiations of species and some remarkable parallels. Whereas the Australasian radiation is today the more diverse, the Neotropical marsupials are the remnant of a much greater radiation, which flourished in South America before the land connection with North America formed in the Pleistocene.

According to Cabrera (1940) there are 15 genera of living marsupials in the Americas, represented by about 70 species. However, 10 of the genera are monotypic, while the single genus *Marmosa* contains 36 species, so that the group as a whole may be thought to be evolutionarily conservative.

The majority of species is found in the Brazilian zone of equatorial forest, while a few species occur in the grasslands and a few in the highlands. Because Colombia and Venezuela contain all three habitats, most of the marsupial genera and many of the species are found in these two countries.

As a student of Australian marsupials, I was particularly interested to see as many of the Neotropical marsupials alive and in their own habitats as I could during a short visit. I also prepared to make closer studies on three species. These were to investigate the reproduction of *Caenolestes obscurus* and to compare reproduction in two species of *Didelphis*. As the collections were to be made at several sites, I proposed also to examine the effects of altitude on blood values and reproduction.

The fieldwork was done at seven localities, ranging from sea level to 3,500 meters and representing the main habitats for marsupials, as follows:

Colombia, April 16 - October 30, 1971
- Buenaventura, Depto Valle, 10 meters:
  - Coastal tropical, second-growth forest, and habitation, September 25-26, 1971.
    - *Philander opossum* - 4 male, 2 female
    - *Didelphis marsupialis* - 1 male

Cali, Depto Valle, 1,000 meters:
Orchards and gardens surrounding the city, April 20 - September 18, 1971.
Chironectes minimus - 1 female
Didelphis marsupialis - 29 male, 32 female

Pichinde, Depto Valle, 1,600 meters:
Forest and orchard, August 4 - 10, 1971
Didelphis albiventris - 1 male
Didelphis marsupialis - 6 male, 4 female
Marmosa impavida - 1 male, 1 female
Philander opossum - 4 male, 1 female

Pilimbala, Depto Cauca, 2,900 meters:
Montane forest, April 29 - June 22, 1971 (5 four-day trips).
Didelphis albiventris - 2 male, 4 female

Páramos de Puracé, Depto Cauca, 3,500 meters:
Elfin forest bordering grassland - *Espeletia* association, April 16 - June 24, 1971 (5 four-day trips).
Caenolestes obscurus - 12 male, 3 female

Finca El Bosque, Villavicencio, Depto Meta, 500 meters:
Orchard, September 15 - 16, 1971.
Didelphis marsupialis - 3 male, 3 female
Philander opossum - 2 female

Venezuela
Rancho Grande, Edo Aragua, 1,100 meters:
Subtropical cloud forest, July 13 - 14, 1971
Monodelphis brevicaudata - 2 male, 3 female

In addition to my own collections I was able, through the courtesy of Dr. R. B. Mackenzie, to examine the large series of specimens of marsupials collected in Colombia by his team during 1967-1970, which is housed in the Virus Section, Department of Microbiology, Universidad del Vallé, Cali.

Results

Three species of small marsupials were collected in which the adults weighed less than 100 grams (table 1). As with similar sized Australian marsupials, the females of these three species lack a pouch and the young, when attached to the teats, are exposed.

Monodelphis brevicaudata (Erxleben): The short-tailed opossum occurs in forest throughout Venezuela and the Guianas and is presumed to occur in northern Colombia. I collected 5 specimens at Rancho Grande, near Maracay, in northern Venezuela, in Sherman box traps baited with mince and set in tall grass or forest adjacent to a road. The *Monodelphis* females were larger in all dimensions than the two males collected (table 1). Three females were collected, one had 9 naked young each attached firmly to a nipple; another, without young, had 9 developed teats and was lactating; while the third was in proestrus. Thus breeding was in progress in early July.

Marmosa impavida (Tschudi): An adult male and female were caught at Pichinde, near Cali, at 1,600 meters. The female was suckling 8 young. The female and 6 of her young were kept in captivity for 7 weeks, by which time the young were furred and almost independent.

Caenolestes obscurus (Thomas): This is a small shrewlike animal, representative of a quite distinct family of marsupials, the Caenolestidae, found only in the high-altitude wet páramos and some islands off southern Chile. All caenolestids are rare, because they are difficult to catch, and for this reason very little is known of their biology.

The largest series have been collected in Colombia (table 2). In February and March 1911, W. H. Osgood (1912) collected 11 specimens in the Páramo de Tama, near San Antonio on the Colombia-Venezuelan border; in July and September 1969 Dr. R. B. Mackenzie collected 16 specimens in the Páramos el Soche near Bogotá; while in August 1969 Dr. J.A.W. Kirsch collected 25 in the Páramos de Puracé, near Popayán. Four of the 6 females in Kirsch's collection were lactating, and so it seems possible that the species might have a restricted breeding season a few months earlier than August. In order to examine this I began trapping in the same locality in April, and on April 30 I collected an estrous female and a breeding male in adjacent traps. The ovaries of the female contained 4 Graafian follicles, but none had ovulated. As Kirsch's animals each had 3 or 4 lactating teats, 4 may be the normal litter size in this species. In three subsequent collecting trips through May and June to the Páramos de Puracé I failed to trap any other adult female but caught 9 more males, all in breeding condition.

Mackenzie did not catch any adult females in July, and in his September collection none was breeding. Osgood, conversely, collected at least one pregnant female, but none of the others was lactating. The evidence from these scattered records covering three localities and spanning 60 years leaves open the question whether *Caenolestes obscurus* has an annual pattern of breeding or whether individuals breed at any time. The climate of the wet páramos is similarly cold and wet throughout the year, so that no special advantage is readily apparent for the species to breed episodically. In all samples, except Osgood's, males considerably exceeded females, a fact that may reflect a real sex ratio of 69 percent or may reflect a different response of the sexes to the traps used.

Examples of two species of marsupials in the middle size range, less than 1 kilogram body weight, were collected. These were *Philander opossum* and

TABLE 1. Measurements of Adult Marsupials Collected

Marsupial	*Number*	*Sex*	*Age*	*Body Weight (g)*	*Total Length (mm.)*	*Head 1*	*Tail 1*	*Pes*	*Comments*
Caenolestes	12	♂	A	28.7±7.9	236.2±14.2	35.4±1.6	123.2±3.9	22.2±0.6	
obscurus	3	♀	A	20.5±4.8	205.0±21.2	31.4±2.1	112.3±11.7	19.6±0.4	
Chironectes	1	♀	Y	170	—	56	230	45	
minimus	1	♀	A	450	626	—	356	42	4 pouch young
Marmosa	1	♂	A	61	345	40	190	24	
impavida	1	♀	A	52	315	39	190	21	8 young attached
Monodelphis	2	♂	A	30.5±5.0	180.0±7.1	34.0	65.0	14.9±3.0	
brevicaudata	2	♀	A	57.5±10.6	220.0±7.1	39.2±1.7	80.0	18.2±1.1	9 teats lactating
Philander	8	♂	A	416.9±132.1	530.6±59.2	76.98±8.0	272.5±33.5	41.6±2.9	
opossum	4	♀	A	323.8±65.2	513.8±30.1	71.5±5.7	270.0±14.7	38.6±1.1	3 had 5 pouch young each
Didelphis	3	♂	A	1525.0±294.8	830.0	115.7±3.8	415.0±22.9	62.3±1.2	
albiventris	4	♀	A	1608.8±381.3	863.3±11.6	113.1±4.0	412.5±37.5	60.1±3.2	Avg. litter 4.2
Didelphis	22	♂	A	1487.73±399.04	771.67±44.39	113.05±10.35	382.86±25.77	61.25±2.87	
marsupialis	23	♀	A	1273.70±353.55	776.75±62.48	107.88±11.86	381.14±27.81	57.50±2.72	Avg. litter 4.5

TABLE 2. Combined Data on Breeding in *Caenolestes obscurus* in Colombia

Site and Collector	*Date*	*Males*		*Females*		*Reproductive state of adult females*
		<20 g.	*>20 g.*	*<20 g.*	*>20 g.*	
Páramos de Tama (W. H. Osgood)	Feb.-Mar. 1911		5	1	5	1 pregnant; none lactating
Páramos de Puracé (C. H. Tyndale-	April 1971		3	1	1	1 estrus
	May 1971	1	4	1		
Biscoe)	June 1971	1	3			
Páramos el Soche (R. B. Mackenzie)	July 1969		2	3		
Páramos de Puracé (J.A.W. Kirsch)	Aug. 1969	2	10	1	5	4 lactating; 1 not breeding
Páramos el Soche (R. B. Mackenzie)	Sept. 1969	2	6	2	1	1 not breeding
		6	33	9	12	
TOTALS		39 (65%)		21 (35%)		

Chironectes minimus, which are considered to be closely related on the grounds of similarity of chromosomes, blood proteins, and appearance. Both species live very close to streams or irrigation canals and feed on small animals found in or near the water.

Philander opossum (Linnaeus): The gray four-eyed opossum, or chucha gris, is widespread from Central America to Argentina, several subspecies being described. During August and September I collected 12 adult specimens from 3 localities; 5 taken near Buenaventura at sea level, 2 near Villavicencio at 500 meters, and 5 near Cali at 1,600 meters. The 8 males ranged in weight from 230 to 675 grams (table 1), and all were sexually mature. All four females (275-420 grams) were breeding; one pregnant and 3 suckling 5 pouch young each.

All these animals were caught in second-growth forest close to streams, in several cases less than a meter from water. It was thus interesting to observe that a pair in captivity would invariably defecate into the water container rather than elsewhere in the enclosure. They would eat fruit and vegetables provided as well as meat. Chicken bones were held in the hands and the ends chewed.

Chironectes minimus (Zimmermann): The water opossum, or chucha de agua, is distinguished from all other marsupials by its webbed hindfeet and general adaptation to water. It occurs throughout the northern parts of the continent, but we had great difficulty in either seeing or catching any. One young female was obtained near Cali and kept in an aquarium tank for one week. It ate live frogs, earthworms, and carp that it caught in the water and took to a dry shelf. Like *Philander,* it also defecated into the water, and one may conclude that this is a normal behavior of both these species that live near flowing streams.

In South America there are two distinct species of large opossums, weighing as adult 1-2 kilograms (table 1). The common opossum, *Dipelphis marsupialis,* is the most widespread marsupial in South and Central America, where it extends from sea level to nearly 2,000 meters. The North American opossum, *Didelphis virginiana,* has recently been shown to be a separate species, which probably evolved from *D. marsupialis* during the Pleistocene in Mexico and has since invaded North America (Gardner, 1973). The second species in South America is the white-eared opossum, or chucha del monte *(Didelphis albiventris),* which occurs from 1,600 to 3,500 meters. We collected both species from 5 sites, and I examined also a large series of both species collected by Mackenzie in eastern Colombia.

Didelphis marsupialis (Linnaeus): Females were breeding throughout the whole time we spent in Cali. Since the gestation period is 13 days and lactation lasts 3 months most females caught were carrying pouch young. Some that were not carrying young but in full lactation were presumed to have an associated litter in the vicinity of the trap, and on several occasions young of the appropriate age were caught at the same time in nearby traps. Since several females in this condition were found to be pregnant, it is evident that they return to estrus and conceive about the time that their young leave the pouch. Other females from which I removed pouch young returned to estrus, became pregnant, and gave birth 21-23 days later.

The average litter size near Cali was 4.5 and in eastern Colombia 6.5. There was no reduction in mean litter size with increasing age of pouch young, as would occur if they died in the pouch. Similarly, the sex ratio remained equal, and so there was no differential mortality of one sex.

A method of aging animals by their teeth was devised, and this enabled an analysis of the populations near Cali and in eastern Colombia to be made.

In eastern Colombia breeding occurs from January through August, but none occurs in the remaining 4 months of the year. The onset of breeding in January coincides with the beginning of the 3-month dry season and extends into the following wet period. It is possible for a female to produce two litters in that period. The average litter size of 6.5 is similar to that found in Panama by Fleming (1973) and by Burns and Burns (1957) for *D. virginiana* in Florida, where two litters are produced each year.

By contrast, the opossums around Cali at an altitude of 1,000 meters appear to breed throughout the year and a female may produce three litters, one in January, one in April, and one in August. However, the average litter size of 4.5 is the smallest recorded for any population of *Didelphis marsupialis* or *D. virginiana*. The climate at Cali does not change markedly during the year, so that there are no extremes of wet or dry periods, which might impose restriction on breeding.

When these results are compared to those from Central and North America for both species they fit a trend that is related to latitude. Thus in the most northerly populations of *D. virginiana* only one litter per year is produced, but the average size is 9.0, whereas in Texas and Florida two litters are produced and the litter size is 6.2.

A paper by me and Dr. R. B. Mackenzie, incorporating the detailed analyses of this study and discussing the breeding patterns of all three species in relation to latitude and climate, was published in the *Journal of Mammalogy* in 1976.

Didelphis albiventris (Lund): The white-eared opossum is not nearly so abundant as the common opossum in Colombia. The latter species is commensal with man and is readily trapped near houses and in orchards and cultivated land. It has a high fecundity, so that there is a high proportion of young animals in the population. In contrast to this species, *Didelphis albiventris* has a smaller average litter size (4.2) and a higher proportion of old animals in the population. At Pilimbala the species was not caught near houses, but in montane forest where caves were common. The density seemed to be much lower than that of *D. marsupialis* and the area occupied by an individual much greater. The numbers of animals caught are too few for one to be more precise than this, but it does suggest that there may be some interesting differences in the ecology of these two species.

Blood Values

Blood samples were collected by heart puncture from all our specimens of *Didelphis albiventris, D. marsupialis,* and *Philander opossum.* From these the hematocrit, hemoglobin concentration, and red-cell diameter were measured and blood films were examined by Dr. Stephen Ayala, Universidad del Vallé, for blood parasites.

Correlations were apparent with age and with altitude in all three species. Hemoglobin concentration and hematocrit values were lowest at the lowest altitudes and highest in *Didelphis albiventris* from Pilimbala, but no differences could be found in the diameter of red cells. The values from pouch young of *D. marsupialis* and *Philander opossum* were lower than adult values, but not in one litter of *D. albiventris* measured. In the large series of *D. marsupialis* collected near Cali the lactating females generally had lower hemoglobin than other adults and there was some correlation also with the level of infection with blood parasites. However, the over-all values for both parameters are similar to other mammals and to values reported for *Didelphis virginiana* (Giacometti, Berntzen, and Bliss, 1972).

Other studies in progress or completed have used the material collected on this expedition. The growth of oocytes and ovarian follicles has been described by Lintern-Moore, Moore, Tyndale-Biscoe and Poole (1976) and the anatomy and histology of the testes and accessory organs of the males are being studied by Dr. J. C. Rodger and Dr. P. Woolley. Fleas from the animals collected in Colombia have been described by Méndez (1977). Apart from a representative series of specimens, whch were deposited with the fauna authorities (INDERENA) in Bogotá, all the skins, skulls and spirit material have been lodged with the Australian National Mammal Collection in Canberra.

Acknowledgments

Collection of the specimens in Colombia was made under license issued by INDERENA, Bogotá, and in Venezuela by the permission of the Fauna Division, Ministry of Agriculture, Caracas.

The Australian National University allowed me to spend sabbatical leave on this project and provided funds for travel to Colombia: these were augmented by a grant from the National Geographic Society that made it possible to obtain a very full photographic record of the animals encountered and their habitats, and to undertake additional travel within Colombia. In Cali I was most generously helped by staff of the Universidad del Vallé in the departments of Anatomy, Biology, Hematology, and Microbiology, and I especially thank Dr. Antonio D'Alessandro, head of the International Center for Medical Research and Training, for his help and support. Finally I thank my wife, Marina, for her help with catching and caring for animals and, by her fluency in Spanish, making friends with everyone we encountered in Colombia.

REFERENCES

BURNS, R. K., and BURNS, L. M.

1967. Observations on the breeding of the American opossum in Florida. Rev. Suisse Zool., vol. 64, pp. 595-605.

CABRERA, ANGEL, and YEPES, JOSÉ

1940. Mamíferos sud-americanos, 370 pp., illus. Compañia Argentina de Editores, Buenos Aires. (Marsupialia, pp. 17-50.)

FLEMING, THOMAS H.

1973. Reproductive cycles of three species of opossums and other mammals in the Panama Canal Zone. Journ. Mamm., vol. 54, pp. 439-455.

GARDNER, A. L.

1973. The systematics of the genus *Didelphis* (Marsupialia: Didelphidae) in North and Middle America. Spec. Publ. Mus. Texas Tech. Univ., vol. 4, pp. 1-81.

GIACOMETTI, L.; BERNTZEN, A. K.; and BLISS, M. L.

1972. Hematologic parameters of the opossum *(Didelphis virginiana).* Comp. Biochem. Physiol., vol. 43A, pp. 287-292.

LINTERN-MOORE, SUE; MOORE, G.P.M.; TYNDALE-BISCOE, C. H.; and POOLE, W. E.

1976. Growth of the oocyte and follicle in the ovaries of Monotremes and Marsupials. Anat. Rec., vol. 185, no. 3, pp. 325-332.

MENDEZ, EUSTORGIO.

1977. Mammalian-siphonopteran associations, the environment and biogeography of mammals of Southwestern Colombia. Quaestiones Entomologicae, vol. 13, pp. 91-182.

Osgood, Wilfred H.
1912. Mammals from western Venezuela and eastern Colombia. Field Mus. Nat. Hist. Publ. Zool., vol. 10, pp. 31-66.

Tyndale-Biscoe, C. H. and Mackenzie, R. B.
1976. Reproduction in *Didelphis marsupialis* and *D. albiventris* in Colombia. Journ. Mamm., vol. 57, no. 2, pp. 249-265.

C. Hugh Tyndale-Biscoe

Migration Studies of the Monarch Butterfly in North America

Principal Investigator: Fred A. Urquhart and Norah R. Urquhart, Scarborough College, University of Toronto, Toronto, Canada.

Grant Nos. 920, 1030, 1503, 1669. In aid of field investigations of the migratory routes of the monarch butterfly (*Danaus p. plexippus*) in North America.

In our previous report (1976b) the methods we used in following the migrations of the monarch butterfly were discussed. The conclusions reached on the data available at that time were presented. Since that report a number of monarch-study expeditions have been sent out to various parts of the North American Continent with special reference to Mexico, with the result, together with the return of alar-tagged specimens (fig. 1), that it is now possible to

FIG. 1. Tagging method now used extensively to study the movements of many species of Lepidoptera, consists of an identifying-instructive label placed over the leading edge of the front wing and glued to the membrane of the wing by removing the scales from the area. This method of following the movements of the migrants was responsible for tracing migratory routes and for the discovery of the overwintering areas of monarch butterflies in Mexico.

plot accurately the migration routes and to delineate the overwintering site of these butterflies in Mexico, as here presented.

An analysis of numerous release-recapture lines, taken from our previous publications (see Urquhart citations in *References*), together with recent significant recaptures, indicated four distinct flight patterns (fig. 2). Migrants originating from breeding areas in the Plains regions (long. 95°-105° W.) move southward in a direction between long. 195° and 210° W. Migrants from breeding areas east of long. 95° W. form three flight patterns: Pattern C shows a southwestward movement between long. 215° and 225° W.; pattern D shows a southward movement between long. 185° and 205° W.; flight pattern E shows a westward movement between long. 255° and 260° W. (fig. 2).

Flight patterns B and D show a high degree of parallelism as distinct from pattern C for the following reasons: Migrants moving southward along pattern D upon reaching the coast of the Gulf of Mexico move westward to follow the coastline. In addition to the release-recapture lines indicating this movement, numerous field observations were made during 1970-1977, in October-November, when countless thousands of migrants were observed flying westward following the coast. This change of direction from a southward to a westward movement is due to an apparent antipathy on the part of the migrants to travel over large bodies of water where distant landmasses are beyond the optical range of the butterflies (Urquhart, 1960). The occasional migrant would fly out over the water only to return again to the land. This mass movement along the coast of the Gulf of Mexico has been referred to previously as a "Gulf Coast Population" (Urquhart, 1966). Flight pattern C results from the two vector patterns, D and E. Thus, a migrant released at point F (fig. 2), and following flight pattern D, upon reaching the coast of the Gulf of Mexico would then follow flight pattern E. At being recaptured at some point G a line connecting the two points would result in flight pattern C. Therefore, flight patterns C, D, and E form a vector flight triangle.

Data from numerous field observations and reports from associates and others (Urquhart, 1960) have shown that the largest breeding population of the monarch butterfly in North America lies between long. 70° and 95° W. and between lat. 37° and 45° N. (fig. 3). This is owing to the great abundance of milkweed, particularly of the species *Asclepias syriaca* (Woodson, 1954) that abounds along roadways and submarginal lands supplying an unlimited amount of food for the larvae (Urquhart, 1960). Migrants from the Plains regions of the midwestern United States of America and the extreme southern parts of Canada represent a much smaller migrating population (fig. 2). This is due to the less abundant food supply represented by relatively few species of *Asclepias* together with the nature of the plants, which instead of growing in

FIG. 2. Flight patterns based on numerous release-recapture lines: Pattern D, southward movement; pattern E, westward movement; pattern C, resulting from flight vectors D and E; A, a flight record from point of release to point of recapture in the overwintering site and a flight direction combining patterns D and E; pattern B, from the Plains region. Symbols: Arrow shows direction of flight; ▼ release point; ■ recapture point.

thick clusters are widely separated, with the result that a larva dislodged from one plant is unable to locate a second one, and hence the mortality rate is high (Urquhart, 1960).

By extrapolating the release-recapture lines into Mexico together with recaptures at the overwintering or near-overwintering site it has become clear that the overwintering site occupies various locations along the entire range of the Neo Volcanic Plateau (fig. 3).

As the result of numerous observations recorded along the Rio Grande area of the Texas-Mexico border, together with observations of mass flights in Mexico and the recapture of tagged specimens, it is concluded that the migrants enter Mexico along the Rio Grande between long. 97° and 103° W. and overwinter along the Neo Volcanic Plateau between long. 97° and 102° W. (fig. 3) extending along a line between lat. 19° and 20° N.

Extensive field expeditions along the Neo Volcanic Plateau have disclosed five overwintering areas (fig. 2): Area 1 has two loci of concentration; Area 2 has three loci; Area 3 has four loci; Area 4 has three loci; and Area 5 has one locus (further field investigations now in progress will no doubt reveal more loci in this area). Hence a total of 13 loci in five areas have been located to date. (Explanation of terms used: *Site* refers to the Neo Volcanic Plateau; *Area* refers to a particular volcanic mountain; *Locus* refers to a particular area of concentration within an Area.)

The various loci are located at altitudes between 3,000 and 3,500 meters, regardless of the height of the mountain, which in some cases may be as much as 4,680 meters. Some of the loci are more accessible than others. In Area 5, a logging road passes directly through the colonies that occupy trees on each side of the road. In Area 3 the mountain is steep and strewn with large, smooth volcanic boulders, which necessitated the employment of a surefooted Mexican and his two horses to pull members of the field party up the slope (fig. 4). In Area 2, it was possible to drive by jeep to the 3,280-meter height and then climb down the side of the mountain to where the locus of the overwintering monarchs was located at a height of 3,000 meters.

FIG. 3. Flight lines, taken from many release-recapture lines, showing direction of flights from the breeding grounds to the overwintering grounds in the Neo Volcanic Plateau of Mexico. A, area of maximum population growth; B, area of maximum migrant population; C, direction of flight from the plains regions; D, direction of flight for areas east of the Plains regions with maximum migrant population; E, five areas (1-5, from left to right) now known to harbor overwintering monarchs in Mexico. Heavy arrows = area of maximum migration through Mexico; lighter arrows = area of minimal migration through Mexico from the Plains regions.

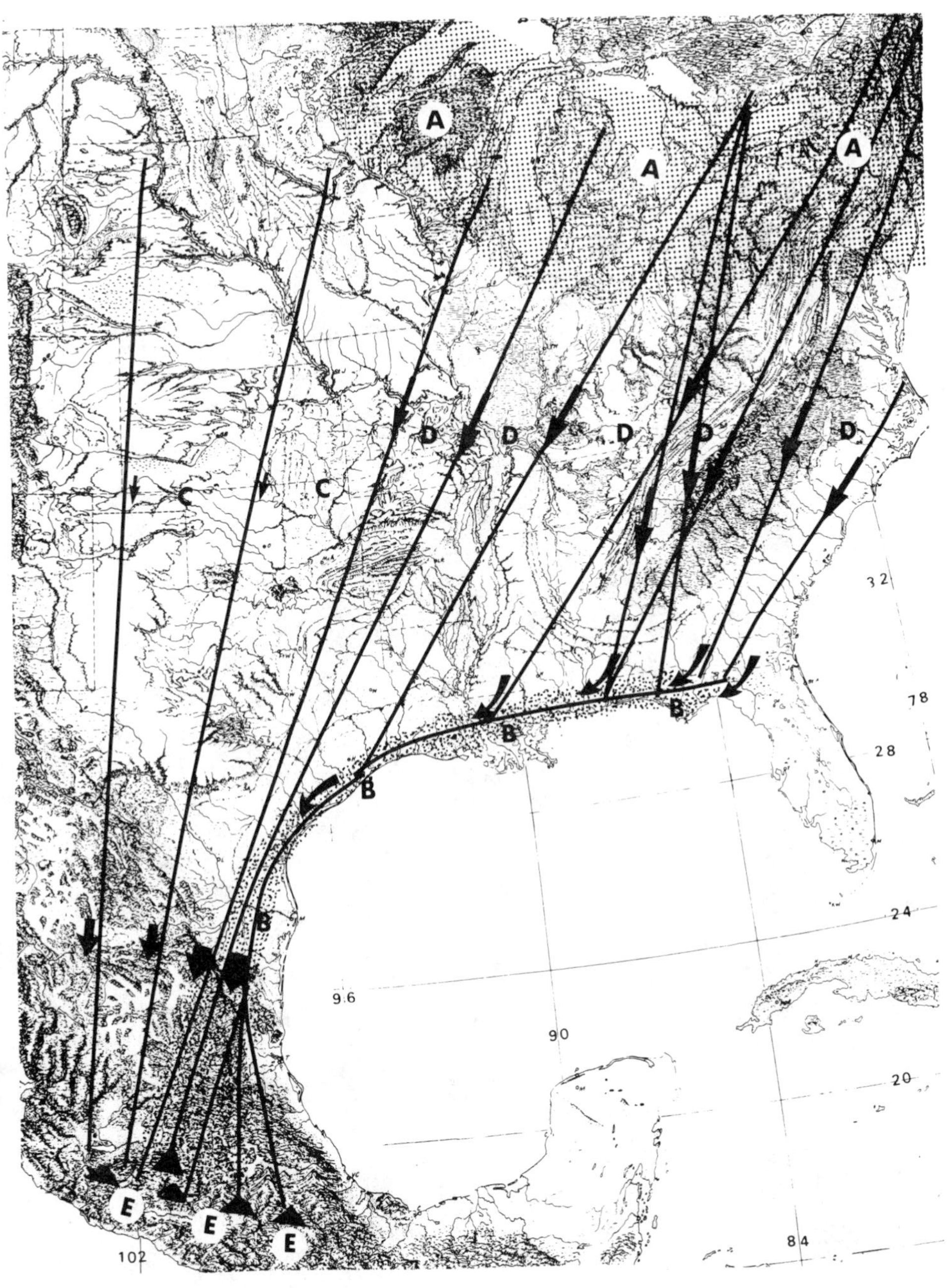
A
A
A
D
D
D
D
D
C
C
B
B
B
B
E
E
E
32
78
28
24
96
90
20
84
102

FIG. 4. In Area 3 a guide and his horses were employed to assist the field party in reaching the locus of the migrants at a height of 3,000 meters.

The population density in the various loci varies considerably: in one locus in Area 3 the population extended over 8 hectares with dense clusters on the branches and trunks of 1,117 *oyamel* trees; in another locus the extent was less than 1 hectare and clusters occurred on the branches and trunks of 52 trees; in Area 5 the single locus so far located represents clusters on 8 trees.

In addition to the variation in the size of a population in any one locus, the area occupied by the monarchs varies from the time the migrants arrive in December until departure in late February or March. When the migrants first arrive they cluster on trees at an altitude of approximately 3,000 meters and remain in a semitorpid condition during January to mid-February (fig. 5). After mid-February, when the temperature begins to rise and the daylight period increases, the monarchs move down the slope of the mountain, reducing the size of the clusters on the trees but increasing the area occupied. It is conjectured that this movement is to warmer areas in the valleys in preparation for the vernal migration. It is during this period that thousands of monarchs are seen imbibing water from valley ponds and streams and visiting the few flowering plants that are present on the slopes.

The floor of the forest is partly covered with monarchs. In one locus in Area 3 there were places where the monarchs were piled one upon another to a depth of 20 centimeters. Numerous dead monarchs lie upon the forest floor, having been dislodged from the trees by strong mountain winds accompanied by heavy snow and hail storms. Those near the summit of the mountain, where such storms are more prevalent, suffer to a greater degree, with the result that dead monarchs are more prevalent in this area than farther down the mountainside.

Temperature varied markedly over a period of 6 weeks in some loci from a low of 4°C. during the night to a high of 26°C. during the day. Occasionally the temperature dropped to -4°C. with frost on the ground. Snow flurries were common, particularly in those areas where the summit of the mountain was over 4,000 meters and snow-capped throughout the winter months.

The migration routes of the eastern population of the monarch butterfly that overwinters in the Neo Volcanic Plateau of Mexico is now well documented as a result of over 40 years of research. However, further field expeditions and continuing alar tagging will eventually reveal many more loci in the various overwintering Areas of the Mexican Site which are as yet unknown. Also, other migratory routes leading to parts of Central America will eventually be worked out and the overwintering site revealed.

FIG. 5. Cluster of overwintering migrant monarchs on the limb of a cypress tree in Area 2. This was a relatively small area of slightly over 2 hectares and with clusters on 52 trees.

REFERENCES

HOLLAND, WILLIAM J.

1898. The butterfly book, 369 pp., illus. William Briggs, Toronto.

KLOTZ, ALEXANDER B.

1951. A field guide to the butterflies, 349 pp., illus. Houghton Mifflin Co., Boston.

MOFFATT, JAMES A.

1900. *Anosia archippus* yet again. 31st Ann. Rpt. Ent. Soc. Ontario, pp. 45-51.

RILEY, CHARLES VALENTINE

1877. Migratory butterflies. Sci. Amer., vol. 38, p. 215.

SCUDDER, SAMUEL H.

1889. The butterflies of the Eastern United States and Canada, with special reference to New England, 3 vols., 1,958 pp., illus. Published by the author, Cambridge, Massachusetts.

URQUHART, FRED A.

1941. A proposed method for marking migrant butterflies. Can. Ent., vol. 73, pp. 21-22.

1952. Marked monarchs. Nat. Hist., vol. 61, pp. 226-229, illus.

1955. Report on the studies of the movements of the monarch butterfly in North America, 40 pp. Royal Ontario Museum of Zoology and Paleontology, Toronto.

1958. A discussion of the use of the word "migration" as it relates to a proposed classification for animal movements. Contr. Roy. Ontario Mus. Zool. Palaeont., vol. 50, pp. 1-11.

1960. The monarch butterfly, 361 pp., illus. University of Toronto Press.

1964. Travels of the monarch. Massachusetts Audubon, vol. 48, no. 4, pp. 190-193.

1965a. A population study of a hibernal roosting colony of the monarch butterfly *(D. plexippus)* in northern California. Journ. Res. Lepidoptera, vol. 4, no. 4, pp. 221-226.

1965b. Monarch butterfly *(Danaus plexippus)* migration studies: Autumnal movement. Proc. Ent. Soc. Ontario, vol. 5, pp. 23-33.

1966. A study of the migrations of the Gulf Coast populations of the monarch butterfly *(Danaus plexippus* L.) in North America. Ann. Zool. Fenn., vol. 3, pp. 82-87.

1971a. La mariposa *(Danaus plexippus)* a México. Hist. Nat. y pro Natura, vol. 3, no. 4, pp. 126-127.

1971b. Monarch butterfly peak. Smithsonian Inst. Center for Short-lived Phenomena Ann. Rpt. 1971, pp. 220-222. Cambridge, Massachusetts.

1973. The migrating monarch. News (Mexico City), February, p. 2.

1976a. Migration of butterflies along the Gulf Coast of northern Florida. Journ. Lepidoptera Soc., vol. 30, no. 1, pp. 59-61.

1976b. Found at last: The monarch's winter home. Nat. Geogr. Mag., vol. 150, no. 2, pp. 161-173, illus.

URQUHART, FRED A., and URQUHART, NORAH R.

1970. A study of a continuously breeding population of *Danaus plexippus* in southern California compared to a migratory population and its significance in the study of insect movement. Journ. Res. Lepidoptera, vol. 7, no. 4, pp. 169-181.

1973. The migrating monarch butterfly. Mexican World, vol. 7, no. 2, pp. 14-30.

1976a. Monarch butterfly *(Danaus plexippus* L.) overwintering population in Mexico (Lep. Danaidae). Atalanta, vol. 7, no. 2, pp. 56-60.

1976b. Ecological studies of the monarch butterfly *(Danaus p. plexippus).* Nat. Geogr. Soc. Res. Rpts., 1968 Projects, pp. 437-443, illus.

1976c. A study of the Peninsular Florida populations of the monarch butterfly *(Danaus p. plexippus* L.: Danaidae). Journ. Lepidoptera Soc., vol. 30, no. 2, pp. 73-87.

1976d. The overwintering site of the eastern population of the monarch butterfly *(Danaus p. plexippus:* Danaidae) in southern Mexico. Journ. Lepidoptera Soc., vol. 30, no. 3, pp. 153-158.

1977. Overwintering areas and migratory routes of the monarch butterfly *(Danaus p. plexippus;* Lepidoptera: Danaidae) in North America, with special reference to the western population. Can. Ent., vol. 109, pp. 1583-1589.

1978. Autumnal migration routes of the eastern population of the monarch butterfly *(Danaus p. plexippus* L.; Danaidae; Lepidoptera) in North America to the overwintering site in the Neovolcanic Plateau of Mexico. Canadian Journ. Zool., vol. 56, no. 8, pp. 1759-1764.

1979a. Breeding areas and overnight roosting locations in the northern range of the monarch butterfly *(Danaus plexippus plexippus)* with a summary of associated migratory routes. Canadian Field-Naturalist, vol. 93, pp. 41-47.

1979b. Vernal migration of the monarch butterfly *(Danaus p. plexippus,* Lepidoptera: Danaidae) in North America from the overwintering site in the neovolcanic plateau of Mexico. Canadian Entomologist, vol. 111, pp. 15-18.

WILLIAMS, C. B.; COCKBILL, G. F.; and GIBBS, M. E.

1942. Studies in the migrations of Lepidoptera. Trans. Roy. Soc. London, vol. 92, pp. 101-280.

WOODSON, ROBERT E.

1954. The North American species of *Asclepias* L. Ann. Missouri Bot. Gard., vol. 41, pp. 1-211.

FRED A. URQUHART
NORAH R. URQUHART

Investigation of Cave Deposits of Quaternary and Holocene Origin: The Muleta Expedition, 1971–1973

Principal Investigator: William H. Waldren, Donald Baden-Powell Quaternary Research Centre, Pitt Rivers Museum and Department of Ethnology and Prehistory, University of Oxford, United Kingdom.

Grant Nos. 928, 1027, and 1144. In support of cooperative cave research program of Quaternary and Holocene origin.

An investigation of Pleistocene and Holocene cave deposits on the Balearic Island of Mallorca, and of other research related to the extinct endemic ruminant *Myotragus balearicus* Bate (1909) and to the collection and preservation of evidence demonstrating the animal's co-existence with man and its ultimate extinction by man, has been in progress since 1962. Under this program, the field operation of a hydraulic sedimentological system for the treatment of the various soils, levels, and sectors of the deposit, in order to extract the maximum fossil microfauna and ancient floral information and specimens, was one of the aspects supported by National Geographic Society grants during the period 1971-73.

The excavational operation was located principally in the cave of Son Muleta, but also at the rock shelter of Son Matge (long. 6° 25′E. lat. 39° 35′N.) in Mallorca's northern Jurassic Sierras.

Until the present time a final report on the project itself has not been possible, nor has it been possible to release in reasonable detail the results of many of the research program's findings. However, the principal investigator is currently engaged at the Baden-Powell Quaternary Research Centre, Pitt Rivers Museum, in the preparation of a thesis "Aspects in Balearic Prehistoric Culture and Ecology . . . The Muleta-Matge Corpus," which is the synthesis of 18 years of investigations in the Balearic Islands.

It is always rewarding when any aspect of a project's goals is realized, but it is even more so when one accomplishes all that one originally set out to do. Now that the present phase of the Muleta Expedition has terminated, certain concrete results, evidence, and information can be cited that are definite contributions to the knowledge of this Western Mediterranean area and that give a wealth of data where none existed prior to these investigations. As listed, these findings do not appear to be a formidable contribution; when examined separately, however, their individual implications can be seen to change considerably our understanding of the prehistoric events in this area. The investigations have shown that:

1. The artiodactyl *Myotragus balearicus,* thought by world authorities to have disappeared some 40,000 years ago, in fact survived until about 3000 B.C.

2. Man occupied the Balearic Islands as early as the 5th millennium B.C., whereas the former estimate of his time of arrival was no earlier than 1800 B.C.

3. Man and *Myotragus balearicus* certainly co-existed for at least two millennia and the extinction of *Myotragus* was directly due to its relationship to man and man's introduction into his economy of other animals with the same ecological function, so that a well-balanced competitive existence between *Myotragus* and its environment was not conducive to its survival.

4. The Muleta Cave deposits have presented science with an unprecedentedly rich collection of well-preserved study material of a rare and oddly evolved insular species not found elsewhere in the world.

5. Because of the nature of the deposits, the preservation of the materials involved, and their chronological period (in this case extending over 250,000 years), the study opportunities afforded by Muleta Cave are of great value to many disciplines.

6. Through the assets present in the cave environment, materials, cave stratigraphy and other advantages, a number of chronometric surveys, biometric programs, and other study projects have been possible that are currently and will for some time bear fruit. Other individual studies being inaugurated will entail years for their realization.

7. Muleta Cave has produced approximately 2,000 specimens of *Myotragus balearicus,* along with hundreds of thousands of specimens of microfauna in other categories, both vertebrate and invertebrate.

William H. Waldren

Ancient Environments and Age of Non-glaciated Terrain in Southeastern Alaska

Principal Investigator: Ian A. Worley, Department of Botany, University of Vermont, Burlington, Vermont.

Grant No. 945: For study of ancient environments and age of non-glaciated terrain in southeastern Alaska.

Evidence compiled in recent years indicates that there have been portions of the fiorded coastlands and archipelagos along the northern and eastern margins of the Gulf of Alaska that have remained ice-free during periods of glacial maxima. Since Heusser's (1960) summary, additional materials have been published: geological evidence is cited in this report for Forrester Island at the mouth of the Dixon Entrance, by Sainsbury (1961) for the highest peaks of Prince of Wales Island, by several workers (Miller, 1958, 1961; Goldthwait et al., 1963; Coulter et al., 1965; Worley, 1972) for parts of the shorelands from Icy Point to the mouth of the Copper River, and by Karlstrom (1957, 1964) for portions of the Kenai Peninsula and Kodiak Island. Biological evidence for ice-free terrain and refugia is given for the Queen Charlotte Islands by McCabe and Cowan (1945), Foster (1963), Klein (1965), Calder and Taylor (1968), and Schofield (1969); for the Alexander Archipelago (southeastern Alaska) by Harris (1965), Klein (1965), and Worley (1972); and for the coastal lands from Cape Decision to the Copper River by Heusser (1960), D. Bishop (pers. comm.), and Worley (1972).

Heusser (1952, 1954, 1960) summarizes pollen profiles and peat stratigraphy from the region, and his work provides the only systematic pollen analysis for it. However, all of the samples came from peatlands that have formed on recently glaciated terrain. Most of the biological data are based upon the contemporary distributions of organisms displaying strongly disjunct populations (for summaries see Schofield, 1969, and Worley, 1972). The purpose of the present study is to establish firm correlative data between geological phenomena and biological indicators.

The primary objectives are: 1, to locate positive evidence of terrain in southeastern Alaska that was not glaciated during, at least, the Wisconsin stage of the Pleistocene; and 2, to further substantiate the biological evidence for refugia.

I have recently concluded (Worley, 1972) that the most important refugia in southeastern Alaska and adjacent British Columbia are not high mountain nunatakas as sometimes suggested, but landforms immediately adjacent to the open ocean. This is inferred by Klein (1965). Three phenomena have been proposed: unglaciated islands, unglaciated sea facing slopes and forelands, and exposed areas of the continental shelf during periods of lower sea level.

In southeastern Alaska the first two of these can be investigated directly by means of dating and examination of supra-bedrock stratigraphy. The following two sites were chosen as the most desirable for this study:

Forrester Island

The Forrester Island National Wildlife Refuge (fig. 1) lies offshore the southwestern corner of the Alexander Archipelago at the mouth of the Dixon Entrance. The village of Craig is 50 miles to the north and Ketchikan 80 miles northeast. The island is 14.5 miles offshore from Dall Island, near latitude 50° 50′ N., and longitude 133° 30′ W.

The refuge is composed mainly of Forrester Island, which is about 5 miles long (lying almost directly north-south) and 1.5 miles wide, with a total area of approximately 4 square miles, and Lowrie and Petrel Islands, each less than 160 acres in area.

The highest point of Forrester Island now stands 1,340 feet above sea level. Moderate to steep slopes descend from a central ridge to the tops of 300-500-foot-high sea cliffs which nearly encircle the island. The southern end of the island is a prominent terrace at an elevation of 300 to 450 feet. Other similar terrace remnants occur on the western slopes.

Throughout the island marine erosion dominates geomorphological processes. Facing the force of the open sea, the cliffs on the westward face are the steepest and most undercut. Wave cut platforms extend several hundred feet westward along the seaward flank of the island group.

Except for the northeast corner of the island 80 percent of the bedrock is of intrusive igneous origin. Medium- to light-colored quartz monzonite predominates, with other phases ranging in composition from granite to biotite-hornblende diorite. Dikes and veinlets are relatively common, with pyrite, magnetite, molybdenite chalcopyrite, and pyrrhotite the most frequent minerals (Clark et al., 1971).

Except for the shorelines and seacliffs, Forrester Island is densely covered by trees, shrubs, or peatlands.

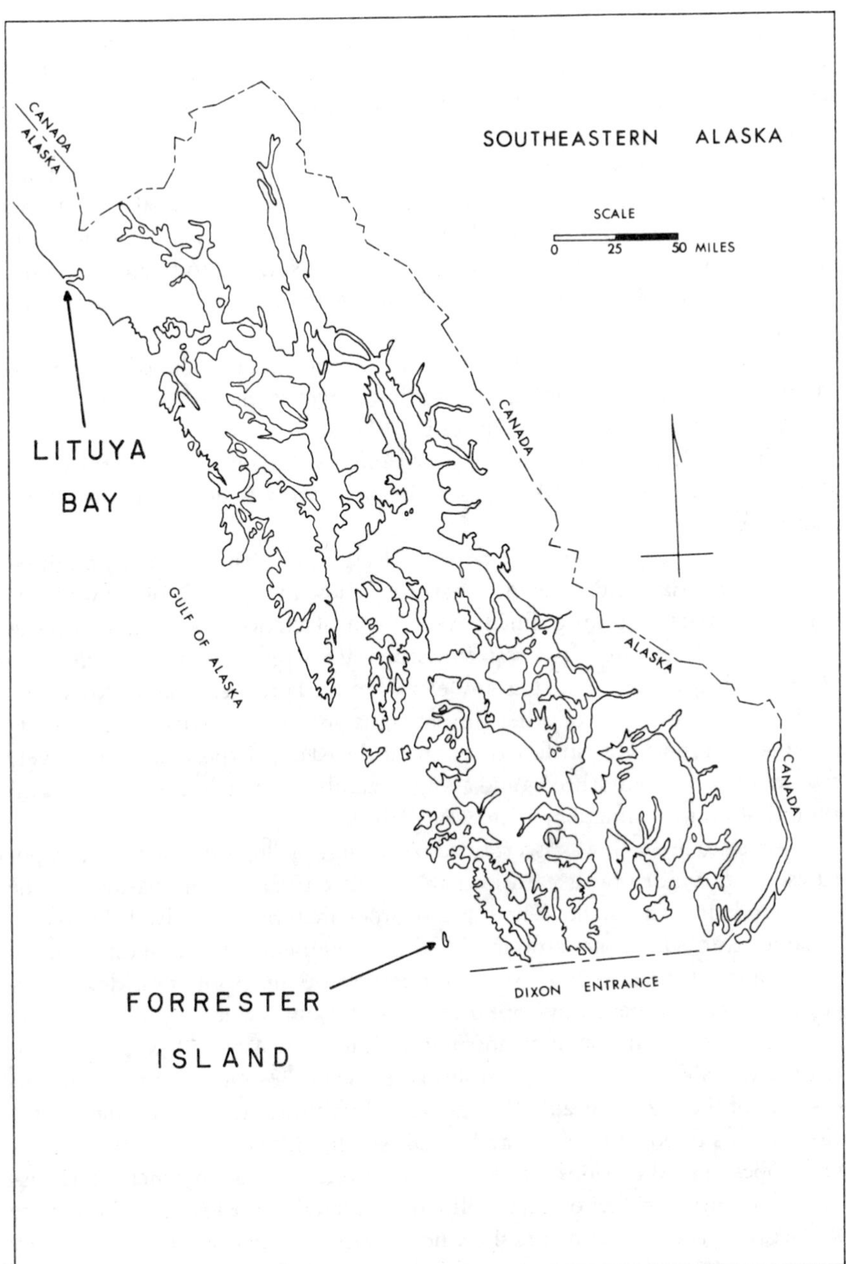

FIG. 1. Location of study sites, Forrester Island, and the Lituya Bay vicinity.

Two weeks were spent on the island during July of 1971. An encampment was made on the southern terrace, and most of the southern half of the island was visited on foot. A helicopter overflight of the entire island was made upon arrival.

Three major objectives were accomplished while on the island: a geomorphological search for evidence of glaciation; the securing of a basal peat sample for radiocarbon dating to establish the duration of organic accumulation; and collection of peat samples taken through several surfaces to bedrock profiles for subsequent pollen analysis and interpretation of previous ecosystems and environments.

There are no indications that the island has ever been glaciated. It is possible that some nivation, perhaps by a minute pocket glacier, occurred on the northeast face of the highest point of the island.

All surficial material on shore, in streamcuts, and on elevated terraces and slopes is of local origin. Although searched for with diligence no erratic materials were found.

Granitic rocks shaped and polished by glacial action occur throughout southeastern Alaska. For the most part they show little alteration by weathering since their smoothing during Wisconsin glaciation. Contoured surfaces are commonly exposed in forest zones beneath windthrown trees. No such sculptured rock was located at any elevation on Forrester Island. No striae, chattermarks, grooves, or other similar signs of glacial activity were located.

Bedrock is near the surface throughout the island. Exposures are relatively frequent beneath windthrows and along streamlets. All drift is of local origin, typical of humid climate granitic weathering.

Depth to bedrock was ascertained by coring, by dug pits, by stream exposures, or by windthrow excavations at several stations at all elevations on the southern half of the island. The supra-bedrock material is nearly always a thin organic layer, sometimes atop local bedrock fragments. The deepest peats located on the terraces were 9 feet. Forest derived organic soils are seldom in excess of 6 feet, and generally appear to average about 3 feet deep.

The gross geomorphology does not indicate glaciation. All ridges are well defined and sharp. With the possible exception of those adjacent to the northeast face of the highest peak, all ridges and cliffs appear to be of marine derivation, with subsequent stream and aerial weathering erosion. There are faces and slopes in all directions, no lee and stoss profiles occur anywhere on the island. No piles or ridges of unconsolidated materials were located. The terrace surfaces and their escarpments show no alteration by glaciation.

The constant level of the tops of the principal sea cliff escarpments and the conformation of terrace elevations indicate a common origin. The lack of cliffs above the terraces could have occurred through their obliteration in time, thus suggesting antiquity of the terrace surfaces; or the terraces and slopes may have formed during more-or-less continuous uplift of the island mass with respect to the sea. Direct evidence for either possibility was not found. Indeed, no materials of marine origin were located in any exposures on the island, nor in the peats of any of the core samples, although they might be located by a more intensive search.

A basal peat sample, beneath 9 feet of continuous peat, and lying near bedrock, from the southern major terrace has yielded a radiocarbon date of 6,470±160 B.P. This date is somewhat anomalous. There are no reports of significant sea level rise at that date, nor has there been significant sea level depression in the last 6,000 years (Mathews et al., 1970). Similarly, evidence for 500 feet of isostatic uplift during this time is generally lacking. Heusser (1960) has suggested a change in elevation with respect to sea level for terraces adjacent to Lituya Bay of similar age (dated by similar methods) of up to 3.7 feet per century. Such a calculation for Forrester Island yields an exposure rate of 5.7 feet per century.

Rapid post-Wisconsin isostatic rebound with initial rates in excess of 50 feet per century are known from near Vancouver, British Columbia, with total uplift with respect to the sea between 500 and 1,000 feet (Mathews et al., 1970). However, there is little possibility that ice could have surrounded or overtopped Forrester Island 4,000 to 6,000 feet in thickness as it did in the Vancouver vicinity. Consequently, any great change in sea level relationships must be accounted for by tectonic activity.

It is possible that Forrester Island has been exposed above the sea for only a brief duration. Uplift of 400-500 feet could have occurred during the last six millennia, at a rate substantial enough to cause the formation of the present sea cliffs. Even if the single radiocarbon date is in error, or is from an exceptionally young site, the shallowness of the organic accumulations and soil, and the lack of deeply incised streams indicate a youthful surface. Crustal movements are frequent in southeastern Alaska, and Forrester Island lies in a field of active major faults (Brew et al., 1966).

Bryophytes were collected thoroughly. The flora is depauperate, compared with southeastern Alaska as a whole and with nearby Dall Island. Only one (*Pleurozia purpurea,* a leafy liverwort of hyperoceanic peatlands) was found of the species suggested elsewhere (Worley, 1972) to be of relict origin. The restricted flora may be the result of a recent substrate origin, or the lack of bedrock diversity.

The lack of glacial evidence, the youthfulness of the peats, the uniformly thin organic mantle over a bedrock mass at all elevations, and the depauperate flora could all be accounted for by the relatively recent exposure of this land mass above the sea.

Could, then, Forrester Island have served as a refugium during maximum glacial stages in southeastern Alaska? The lack of glacial evidence supports this possibility, as does the presence of certain small mammals (Klein, 1965). However, the paucity of the flora, the date of the peat sample, and the possibility of a recent marine past would seem, at this stage of our knowledge, to limit its importance as a possible refugium.

In addition to these studies an investigation was undertaken to determine the dynamics of the peatlands on the southern terrace. A complex sequence of probings showed that the bedrock surface averages 3 to 9 feet below the peat surface and that it is remarkably free from drift, unconsolidated materials, or irregular structure. The peatland surface appears to undergo an involved sequence of rapid growth, long-term slow growth, erosion, and regrowth. Ponds abound, and bear no overt relationship to bedrock. Approximately 500 peat samples were collected from 15 holes located at strategic points in the peatland, in transition zones, and in the adjacent forest, to determine the historicity of the bog structure. The pollen sequences from these profiles should, when compared with published profiles from southeastern Alaska and nearby British Columbia, better place in context the radiocarbon date attained.

Lituya Bay

Between Icy Point and Cape Fairweather (north of the Alexander Archipelago in Glacier Bay National Monument, see fig. 1) are several relatively small, but geologically investigated (Goldthwait et al., 1963; Miller, 1958, 1961; Mertie, 1933) sites apparently never overridden by glacial ice.

The valley of the active Fairweather Fault separates the catchment basins and slopes of the Fairweather Range from a range of low mountains (3,000 to 4,000 feet high) that slope into the sea. The western outflow of ice from the massif is spread along the fault valley and breaches the foothill range in periodic valleys. The small piedmont lobes (notably the Fairweather, Lituya Bay, Crillon, Dagelet, la Perouse, and Finger glaciers) have been severely channeled, often leaving distinctive periglacial topographical features. Between these lobes are unglaciated slopes and forelands that are strikingly sculptured by a series of elevated marine-cut terraces and escarpments (Mertie, 1933; Miller, 1961).

There are some 85 square miles of non-glaciated land in this region rising from contemporary sea level to perhaps 3,000 feet or more. Several major terraces are recognizable, the highest averaging about 1,500 feet above present sea level. Large streams have dissected the terraces, producing canyons, cascades, and waterfalls. Lakes are few, but swampy ground is common near the shore, and peatlands are abundant on all terrace levels. Some 18 percent of the vegetated land is open peatland of "hyperoceanic" (Worley, 1972), physiognomy and species composition; typical spruce-hemlock forests appear to cover at least 50 percent of the available terrain; the remainder of the land being either alpine communities, a forest-peatland transition, or youthful vegetation.

It is tempting to correlate the major terraces with Pleistocene interglacial periods. The only conclusions regarding the rate of exposure of these hills and terraces from the sea have been made by Heusser (1954, 1960), who suggests a 300-foot uplift in the past 8,000 years, and Goldthwait et al. (1963), who conclude no major sea level changes at Lituya Bay since the late Wisconsin period.

The objectives of this investigation were to obtain stratigraphies from the peatlands atop the highest terrace north of Lituya Bay, to obtain a radiocarbon date of the basal peats, and to search for species of plants whose distributions require local refugia for explanation.

Two pits were dug on the extensive and highest terrace between Justice and Echo Creeks. At an elevation of 1,600 feet, 8.1 feet of a suspected 15 to 18 feet of unconsolidated organics and inorganics atop bedrock were exposed. Rising waters and time forced abandonment of the dig at that depth. The second pit, at 1,800 feet elevation, showed a similar, although condensed vertically, stratigraphic pattern through 3 feet of exposure. It is not detailed here.

The terrace sampled has a sloping surface rising from 1,400 feet at its northwestern edge to slightly over 1,900 feet along the southeastern boundary. The surface is divided into two levels at the 1,650-foot elevation by an escarpment some 200 feet high extending north-south, the lower, western subterrace being approximately one-third of the entire surface.

The entire terrace lies at the elevation of the natural upper limit of continuous forest, permitting a broad, expansive expression of the subalpine ecosystem. Except where drainage is good and woodlands of trees and shrubs prevail, open meadows extend continuously over flats and slopes up to 15 or even 20 percent. Below about 1,700 feet the meadows are dominated by narrow-leaf sedges, above 1,700 feet *Fauria* (deer cabbage) forms an almost continuous herbaceous canopy. Occasional erect trees of mountain hemlock and spruce give an attractive parklike aspect to the upper elevations.

At 1,600 feet dense tree and shrub growth mantles gully slopes and escarpments. This community interfingers with the wet meadows on flatter terrain. The sedge meadows are dominated by *Eleocharis* and *Eriophorum,* and are especially lacking in bryophytes, there being only occasional leafy hepatics

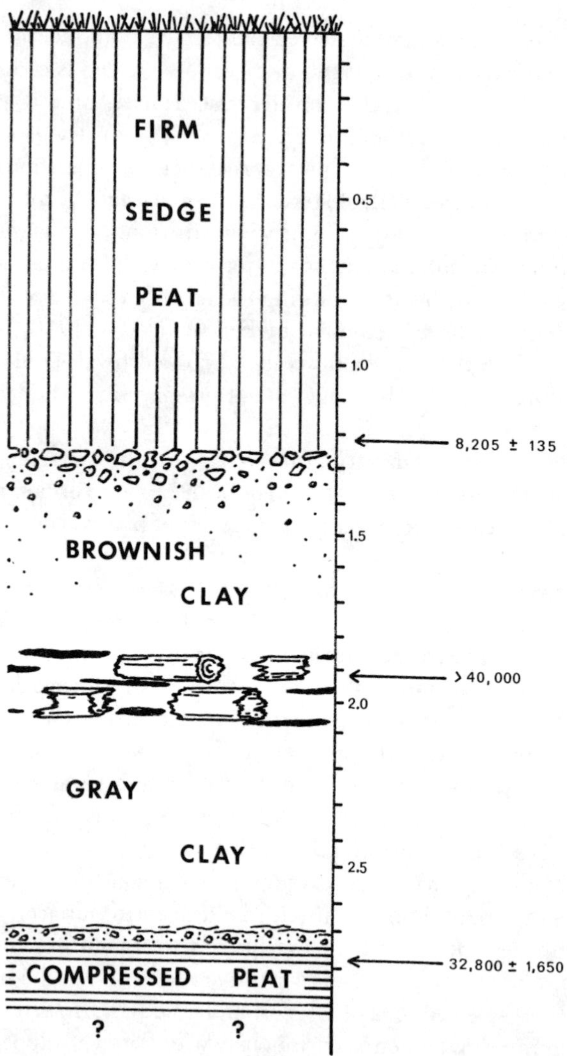

FIG. 2. Stratigraphic exposure at 1,600 feet elevation on terrace between Justice and Echo Creeks 7 miles northwest of Lituya Bay. Depths are in meters; the dates are years B.P. (1972). The zones are fully described in the text.

present. Pit ponds, so characteristic of peatlands in southeastern Alaska at lower elevations, are all but absent. Occasional surface streamlets meander through the meadows, but most watercourses are deeply incised. Where the water table is at or near the ground surface, as along some streamlets and in seeps, a lush broadleaf herbaceous community admixed with numerous bryophytes, including *Sphagnum,* forms a rich, productive growth.

The center of a large, relatively uniform flat surface about 400 by 500 feet was selected for the dig site. The slope at the site is about 5 percent, with an overall slope of 7½ steepening to 12 percent at its uppermost boundary. The sampling area receives groundwater and sheetflow from up-terrace, there being a forested zone immediately upslope from the site. Incised streams bound the surface laterally, their banks merging to form the bank across the lower edge of the peatland. Surface water occurs only at a minor shallow depression over 90 feet from the pit. Seeps appear along the bounding slopes, probably caused by the subsurface layer of compressed peat (see below).

The exposure (see fig. 2) can be divided into four zones (depths in meters):

Zone A (0.00 to 1.25 meters). The autotrophic surface community is simple, dominated by the sedges. *Sphagnum* and other mosses are absent; a few minute strands of a leafy hepatic grow among the sedges. Exceedingly dense, the turf is removable as blocks cut to shape. Firm sedge peat extends to a depth of 1.25 meters. The peat is darker and less fiberous with depth, but is without apparent color or texture zonation. No oxidative, inversion, recurrence, or ligneous surfaces or layers could be determined in the field.

Zone B (1.25 to 1.85 meters). At 1.25 meters a near-pavement of pebbles and cobbles free-standing in a sand (minor silt and clay fractions) matrix marks an abrupt transition horizon. The rocks of this hard till-like material, which may show minor water or frost reworking, are little rounded, are multifaceted with slightly worn angles, and are of diverse lithologies. Long axes and flat surfaces lie parallel to the ground surface. The coarse matrix materials and sands appear to be of decayed granitic origin (although such an origin is not necessarily inferred). From 1.25 to 1.45 meters the size of rock diminishes and the proportion of clay increases; from 1.45 to 1.85 meters clay predominates, minor sand is present, cobbles and most pebbles are absent, and a smoother texture prevails. The clay of this zone is tinted brown, perhaps from the addition of organic materials percolated downward from above.

Zone C (1.85 to 2.75 meters). Massive horizontal wood fragments cap this zone, which is characterized throughout by a pure, slimy, very fine, consistantly grey clay, devoid of brown coloration and without sands or pebbles. The uppermost layer of wood lies atop black, peaty organics which tend to be stratified horizontally. From 1.85 to 2.10 meters a series of wood and black organic peaty materials (with occasional imbedded rootlike fibers) lie as lenses in the clay, sometimes in contact one with another. Beneath these organics are pure clays, apparently laid down in still water, reminiscent of lake or lagoon sediments associated with Glacier Bay. At 2.70 meters minor stratifications with darker, possibly organic, layers begin. This merges with a rock-hard, massive, sandy clay containing a small number of angular pebbles. This layer is an aquifer; the artesianing water released by the digging forced termination of the exposure.

Zone D (2.75 meters to ?). At 2.75 meters a horizontal surface of highly compacted, hard, lustrous, strikingly layered peat was exposed. Penetration was exceedingly difficult. It is estimated that bedrock is another 2.25 meters deep.

Basal peat (I-6318) from Zone A, 1.25 meters deep, yielded a date of 8,205±135 B.P. A log fragment (I-5990) from Zone C, 1.90 meters deep, yielded a date of greater than 40,000 B.P. The lustrous peats (I-5991) of Zone D yielded a date of 32,800±1,650 B.P.

A suite of some 55 pebbles and two cobbles were recovered from between 1.30 and 1.75 meters in the clay zone; the largest being a 9 x 6 x 2.5-centimeter metaquartzite cobble. By percentage of weight the collection consists of 35.8 diorite, 22 amphibolites, 22 metaquartzite, 15.8 volcanics or dikes, and 4.4 granitic gneisses. The Tertiary units known (Miller, 1961; Karlstrom, 1964) at Lituya Bay and southward, as well as in the immediate vicinity of the Fairweather Glacier, are not reported from the sampling area. No bedrock outcrops were investigated during this study, thus the conglomerates of Tertiary and/or lower Pleistocene age may be present locally and may be a source of the collected rocks.

It is more likely, however, that the source was east of the Fairweather Fault. Active differential thrust movement by the fault has segregated the principal bedrock types on either side of the fault. Seaward volcanics prevail: predominately greenstone and volcanic graywacke with minor argillite, chert, and limestone, all of which are complexly deformed and mildly to moderately metamorphosed. Eastward of the fault the Fairweather mountains consist of a crystalline complex, including granite rocks, schist, gneiss, amphibolites, and marble, which is complexly deformed and moderately to intensely metamorphosed. Consequently, the bulk of the pebbles and cobbles collected in Zone B were apparently transported from the opposite side of the Fairweather Fault.

Discussion

The origin of the mineral zones could be lacustrine, fluvial, or landslide, with the principal agent either glacial, marine, or terrestrial. The stratification of the pebbles and cobbles, largest at the top, may indicate either a lag surface, turbidity action, or fossil frost features. The orientation of the individual cobbles may indicate stream or wave deposition, perhaps deltaic.

The principal assumptions ascribed to the late Pleistocene geomorphology of the seaward forelands west of the Fairweather Range is that: (1) glacial ice flowing westward from the catchment basins in the high mountains was distributed laterally within the valley of the Fairweather Fault (as it still is); (2) this ice passed through the lower mountains west of the fault in selected valleys; and (3) these mountains were never overtopped by ice, leaving ice-free the terrain on their seaward flanks.

The study terrace is midway between two of the principal glacial outlets, the northerly now occupied by the Fairweather Glacier, the southerly, now free from ice, Lituya Bay. Four valleys separate the major terrace segments between these outlets, each originating in the heights of the front range (which are 5 miles from the sea, dropping precipitously into the valley of the Fairweather Fault). These summits range between 3,500 and 4,500 feet in elevation; the elevation of the cols at the heads of the four valleys are (from the south) 2,129 feet, 2,600 feet, 3,000 feet, and 3,200 feet. If ice has passed through these cols (or, even less likely, also over the summits) it was either insignificant in amount or very long ago, for a glacial geomorphology is not apparent from either aerial photographs or from the air.

Consequently, direct transportation of the rocks to this site does not seem possible. If the Justice Creek valley were filled with locally derived ice, periglacial ponding would probably occur over the dig site. Such a mechanism could easily account for the mineral sedimentation and displaced logs.

An intriguing possibility requires a coastal process much like that now operative at sea level. Differential uplift, sea level changes, and deposition has created a sequence of wetlands nearly at sea level behind a high (50-100-foot) shoreline ridge deposition. Were present sea level to rise with respect to the land some 10 to 50 feet then extensive lagoons would form. Indeed, these lowlands may well have recently been lagoons. If there were such lagoons when the Fairweather and Lituya Bay glaciers were calving directly into the sea, icebergs would have frequently drifted into the lagoons, depositing their load of till as they melted. If a similar mechanism prevailed during the sea level phase of the study terrace, the pebbles and cobbles of the mineral zones (as well, perhaps, as the log) may have been rafted by ice whose origin was east of the Fairweather Fault.

The compressed peats at Zone D are assumed to be in situ, their layering is essentially horizontal. The age of 32,800 B.P. places their formation in mid-Wisconsin time. Dates of similar antiquity are unknown along the fiorded Pacific Coast of North America from Vancouver Island to the Copper River. All southeastern Alaskan dates are younger than 11,170 B.P. (McKenzie, 1970).

Both the interface between the compressed peats and the clay zones, as well as the interface between the clays and their overlying peats may be erosion surfaces and/or nonconformities. 24,600 years separate the two peats. If the clays are marine in origin, an average uplift rate with respect to the sea is between 6.6 and 19.5 feet per century. These rates indicate active movement, but are well within known rates for tectonic and isostatic uplift (Mathews et al., 1970; Miller, 1960).

The age of the initiation of the contemporary peatlands at 1,600 feet and on the next highest terrace at 300 feet (Heusser, 1960) is approximately 8,300 B.P. The initial ecosystem at the 300-foot elevation began with woody plants, which were replaced by herbaceous forms. This pattern still prevails at elevations below at least 1,500 feet. Ecosystem formation at 1,600 feet on shallow, poorly drained slopes apparently commences with herbaceous plants. This may account for the absence of ligneous layers in Zone A at 1,600 feet.

From these two dates, 1,300 vertical feet apart, with neither site possessing a glacial geomorphology, it must be concluded that some significant large-scale event occurred or terminated approximately 8,300 years ago. This date generally marks the initiation of the Hypsithermal interval (Heusser, 1953, 1960). It is possible to conceive that some catastrophic event prepared the terrain for the initiation of the present surface peats. The valley of the Fairweather Fault shows many signs of earthquake-caused massive landslides. Such an event may have similarly affected our 1,600-foot and 1,800-foot sites, and Heusser's 300-foot site. However, the regionality of this data is supported by the recent revelation by Ackerman (pers. comm.) of the onset of cultural materials at 8,230±130 years B.P. in a stratigraphy at Ground Hog Bay 15 miles east of the mouth of Glacier Bay.

The most notable biotic discovery was the finding of extensive populations of the minute liverwort *Treubia nana,* considered to have required local Alaskan-British Columbian Pacific refugia during maximum glaciations. Growing vigorously at an elevation of about 1,000 feet on the escarpment of the highest terrace in a rich *Chaemycyparis* forest are vastly more individuals than have heretofore been reported from North America.

Summary

Forrester Island shows no evidence of glaciation, but may be of recent origin. Only one bryophyte of biogeographic significance was located. These data minimize the probability of Forrester Island having been an important Pleistocene biotic refugium.

In over 1,200 miles of northwest coastal North America, the only Pleistocene materials predating the late Wisconsin to have been dated are now known from near Lituya Bay. However, age of formation of the terraces adjacent to Lituya Bay remains uncertain, but their existence during at least mid- to late-Wisconsin time of the late Pleistocene is confirmed. Although the evidence at hand does not directly support the concept of some local terrain being continuously ice free, and hence a likely refugium, the complexity of the landforms and stratigraphy underlines the uniqueness of the local Pleistocene history—and in that sense is support data for a refugium concept.

Populations of several local bryophytes are best biogeographically explained by considering the area to have been a continuous refuge, in one form or another.

Mertie's (1933) original curiosity has been justified. Furthermore, exposed sediments at an elevation of 1,600 feet have now been located, and their chronologies await reading. Their interpretation will lead to inferences about the extent of glaciation, the degree and type of ablation, the amount of accumulation in various basins and neves, and overall coastal glacial budgets. From the stratigraphic data certain sea level relationships can be determined. From these conclusions and from corresponding pollen profiles it is anticipated that the climatic and environmental conditions through at least the Wisconsin glacial interval can be reconstructed. Ackerman's recent (1968) discoveries stress the biological and cultural significance of the refugia and the distribution of organisms.

REFERENCES

ACKERMAN, R. E.
1968. The archeology of the Glacier Bay region, southeastern Alaska. Wash. State Univ. Lab. Anthr., Rep. of Investig. no. 44., 123 pp.

BREW, D. A.; LONEY, R. A.; and MUFFLER, L.J.P.
1966. Tectonic history of southeastern Alaska. Can. Inst. Min. and Metal., spec. vol. no. 8, pp. 149-170.

CALDER, J. A., and TAYLOR, R. L.
1968. Flora of the Queen Charlotte Islands, Part 1. Systematics of the vascular plants. Can. Dep. Agr. Monogr. 4, pt. 1.

CLARK, A. L.; BERG, H. C.; GRYBECK, D.; and OVENSHINE, A. T.
1971. Reconnaissance geology and geochemistry of Forrester Island National Wildlife Refuge, Alaska. U. S. Geol. Surv. Open File Report. 8 pp.

COULTER, H. W.; HOPKINS, D. M.; KARLSTROM, T.N.V., PEWE, T. L.; WAHRHAFTIG, C.; and WILLIAMS, J. R.
1965. Map showing extent of glaciations in Alaska. U. S. Geol. Surv. Map I-415.

DERKSEN, S. J.
1974. Quaternary Coleoptera as aids in the interpretation of environmental history. Rec. Adv. Brit. Quat. Stud., pp. 55-68.

FOSTER, J. B.
1963. The evolution of the native land mammals of the Queen Charlotte Islands and the problem of insularity. Unpubl. Ph.D. thesis, Univ. of British Columbia, Vancouver, 210 pp.

GOLDTHWAIT, R. P.; MCKELLAR, I. C.; and CRONK, C.
1963. Fluctuations of Crillon Glacier system, southeast Alaska. Bull. Int. Assoc. Sci. Hydrol., vol. 8, pp. 62-74.

HARRIS, A. S.
1965. Subalpine fir on Harris Ridge near Hollis, Prince of Wales Island, Alaska. Northwest Science, vol. 39, no. 4, pp. 123-128.

HUDSON, T.; PLAFKER, G.; and RUBIN, M.
1976. Uplift rates of marine terrace sequences in the Gulf of Alaska. U. S. Geol. Surv. Circ. 733, pp. 11-13.
1978. Tectonism and marine terrace development in the eastern Gulf of Alaska. Abstract, Geol. Soc. Amer. Cordilleran Section Meeting, April 1979.

HUESSER, C. J.
1952. Pollen profiles from southeastern Alaska. Ecol. Monogr., vol. 22, pp. 331-352.
1953. Radiocarbon dating of the thermal maximum in southeastern Alaska. Ecol., vol. 34, pp. 637-640.
1954. Additional pollen profiles from southeastern Alaska. Amer. Journ. Sci., vol. 252, pp. 106-119.
1960. Late Pleistocene environments of North Pacific North America. Amer. Geogr. Soc., Spec. Publ. 35, 308 pp.

KARLSTROM, T.N.V.
1957. Tentative correlation of Alaskan glacial sequences 1956. Science, vol. 125, pp. 73-74.
1964. Quaternary geology of the Kenai Lowland and glacial history of the Cook Inlet region, Alaska. U. S. Geol. Soc. Prof. Pap. 443, 69 pp.

KLEIN, D. R.
1965. Postglacial distribution patterns of mammals in the southern coastal regions of Alaska. Arctic, vol. 18, pp. 7-20.

MCCABE, T. T., and COWAN, I. MCT.
1945. *Peromyscus maniculatus macrorhinus* and the problem of insularity. Trans. Roy. Can. Inst., vol. 25, pp. 117-215.

McKENZIE, G. D.
1970. Glacial geology of Adams Inlet, southeastern Alaska. Inst. Polar Studies, Rep. 25, 121 pp.

MATHEWS, W. H.; FYLES, J. G.; and NASMITH, H.
1970. Postglacial crustal movements in southwestern British Columbia and adjacent Washington State. Can. Journ. Earth Sci., vol. 7, pp. 690-702.

MERTIE, J. B., JR.
1933. Notes on the geology and geography of Lituya Bay, Alaska. U. S. Geol. Surv. Bull. 836, pp. 117-135.

MILLER, D. J.
1958. Anomalous glacial history of the northeastern Gulf of Alaska region. Bull. Geol. Soc. Amer., vol. 69, pp. 1613-1614.
1960. Giant waves in Lituya Bay, Alaska. U. S. Geol. Surv. Prof. Pap. 354-C, pp. 51-86.
1961. Geology of the Lituya District, Gulf of Alaska Tertiary Province, Alaska. U. S. Geol. Surv. Open File Map 210.

SAINSBURY, C. L.
1961. Geology of part of the Craig C-2 quadrangle and adjoining areas, Prince of Wales Island, southeastern Alaska. U. S. Geol. Surv. Bull. 1058-H, pp. 299-362.

SCHOFIELD, W. B.
1969. Phytogeography of northwestern North America: Bryophytes and vascular plants. Madrono, vol. 20, pp. 155-207.

WORLEY, I. A.
1972. The bryo-geography of Southeastern Alaska. Unpubl. Ph.D. thesis, Univ. of British Columbia, Vancouver, 715 pp.

IAN A. WORLEY

APPENDIX

List of Grants for Research and Exploration Made by the National Geographic Society, 1977 and 1978

1977

1702: To Dr. Roger C. Green, University of Auckland, Auckland, New Zealand, for a study of Lau Island archeology: evidence for development of an ethnographic boundary.

1703: To Carl J. Clausen, Little Salt Spring Research Facility, Florida, for an investigation of submerged paleo-Amerind habitation area, Little Salt Spring, Florida.

1704: To Dr. William D. E. Coulson, University of Minnesota, Minneapolis, Minnesota, for a study of the Dark Age architecture and pottery of Nichoria (Greece).

1705: To Ian J. A. Graham, Harvard University, Cambridge, Massachusetts, for recording hieroglyphic inscriptions and figurative art in southeastern Campeche, Mexico.

1706: To Mrs. Rae N. P. Goodall, Ushuaia, Tierra del Fuego, Argentina, for research on the natural history of Tierra del Fuego (Argentina).

1707: To Dr. Bruce R. Dayton, State University of New York, Oneonta, New York, to study biomass production of selected woody species utilized by browsing game in Kruger National Park, South Africa.

1708: To Dr. Constantine H. Fernando, University of Waterloo, Ontario, Canada, for a study of freshwater zooplankton with special reference to southeast Asia (Indonesia).

1709: To Dr. Alan Lill, Monash University, Clayton Victoria, Australia, for a study of the comparative socioecology of three sympatric species of bowerbirds (Australia).

1710: To Dr. Knut Schmidt-Nielsen, Duke University, Durham, North Carolina, for a study of water balance of desert animals: evaporation from airways (Kenya).

1711: To Dr. Thomas B. Thorson, University of Nebraska, Lincoln, Nebraska, for a study of the evolution of freshwater adaptation in stingrays.

1712: To Dr. Kenan T. Erim, New York University, New York City, in continuation of the Society's support of the Aphrodisias archeological excavations, Turkey.

1713: To Dr. Rudolph H. Dornemann, Milwaukee Public Museum, Milwaukee, Wisconsin, in support of archeological excavations at Tell Hadidi, Syria.

1714: To Dr. Robert A. Bye, Jr., University of Colorado, Boulder, Colorado, for a study of evolutionary and ecological influences of the Tarahumara Indians on three plants in Mexico.

1715: To Dr. Kenneth W. Horch, University of Utah, Salt Lake City, Utah, to study the central processing of acoustic signals of the crab *Ocypode*.

1716: To Dr. Bernice M. Wenzel, University of California, Los Angeles, California, in support of study of olfaction in procellariiform birds.

1717, 1802: To Dr. John T. Emlen, University of Wisconsin, Madison, Wisconsin, in support of studies of island factors and density regulation on land bird populations in Hawaii.

1718: To Dr. James A. Jensen, Brigham Young University, Provo, Utah, in further support of the grantee's continuing study of a new Jurassic/Cretaceous dinosaur fauna from Colorado and Utah.

1719: To Mr. Bob H. Slaughter, Southern Methodist University, Dallas, Texas, in support of grantee's project for the recovery and study of the first microvertebrate fossils from the Miocene of Central America.

1720, 1801: To Dr. Richard D. Estes, Academy of Natural Sciences, Philadelphia, Pennsylvania, to study the variations in social organization of topi in East Africa.

1721: To Dr. Robert F. Martin, University of Texas, Austin, Texas, for study of reproduction, range expansion, and status of Texas cave swallows.

1722: To Dr. Robert J. Baker, Texas Tech University, Lubbock, Texas, for study of systematics and evolutionary strategy of the moles of America.

1723, 1781: To Dr. Mary D. Leakey, Nairobi, Kenya, for continuation of grantee's program at Laetolil and Olduvai Gorge.

1724: To Dr. Lautaro Nuñez A., Universidad del Norte, Chile, for study of Paleo-Indian archeology, paleoclimate, and paleontology at Quereo, Los Vilos, Chile.

1725: To Dr. H. Arthur Bankoff, for archeological investigations in the vicinity of Smederevska, Palanka, Yugoslavia.

1726: To Mr. Guy C. McLeod, Boston, Massachusetts, in support of grantee's bioluminescent and optical attenuation measurements in the Maui Basin.

1727: To Dr. George C. Gorman, University of California, Los Angeles, California, for study of the natural history, physiology, and genetics of Philippine sea snakes.

1728: To Dr. Ralph W. Brauer, University of North Carolina, Wilmington, North Carolina, for study of the physiology of abyssal freshwater fauna in Lake Baikal, central Siberia.

1729: To Dr. Gordon L. Kirkland, Jr., Shippensburg State College, Shippensburg, Pennsylvania, for faunal survey of the mammals of the Uinta Mountains, Utah.

1730: To Dr. Wayne R. Rouse, McMaster University, Hamilton, Ontario, Canada, in support of study of potential climatic modifications in the Hudson Bay lowlands.

1731: To Dr. Larry D. Agenbroad, Northern Arizona University, Flagstaff, Arizona, in support of excavation of a late Pleistocene mammoth locality in South Dakota.

1732: To Dr. Charles Walcott, State University of New York, Stony Brook, New York, for study of the southern right whale.

1733: To Dr. Wilmer G. Hunt, Chihuahuan Desert Research Institute, Alpine, Texas, for study of ecology of the peregrine falcon in the southern Chihuahuan Desert, Mexico.

1734, 1782: To Mr. Richard E. Leakey, Nairobi, Kenya, for continued exploration and investigation of extensive Plio/Pleistocene sediments in Kenya.

1735: To Dr. Ray A. Williamson and Dr. Florence H. Ellis, St. John's College, Annapolis, Maryland, in support of study of Pre-Columbian towers in the Four-Corners Area (Colorado and Utah).

1736: To Dr. George S. Korres, University of Athens, Athens, Greece, for study and publication of the Pylos archeological finds in southwestern Peloponnesus, Greece.

1737: To Dr. Jeffrey P. Brain, Harvard University, Cambridge, Massachusetts, in support of grantee's Tunica Treasure project.

1738: To Dr. Carlos Aguilar P., University of Costa Rica, Central America, for archeological reconnaissance in the Arenal Lake and Volcano Region, Costa Rica.

1739: To Dr. Gus W. Van Beek, Smithsonian Institution, Washington, D. C., in support of archeological investigations at Tell Jemmeh, Israel.

1740: To Dr. Paul W. Hodge, University of Washington, Seattle, Washington, in support of the Atlas of the Andromeda Galaxy.

1741: To Dr. Daphne F. Dunn, California Academy of Sciences, San Francisco, California, for study of systematics of actinians symbiotic with pomacentrid fishes.

1742: To Dr. Eugenie Clark, University of Maryland, College Park, Maryland, in support of study of behavior and biology of tropical sand-diving fishes.

1743: To Dr. Ronald A. Nussbaum, University of Michigan, Ann Arbor, Michigan, for the study of the origin, evolution, and ecology of the amphibian fauna of the Seychelles.

1744: To Dr. Thomas B. Croat, Missouri Botanical Garden, St. Louis, Missouri, for studies on classification of *Anthurium* (Araceae) of Central America.

1745: To Dr. Ted J. Case, University of California, San Diego, California, for study of behavioral ecology of the insular gigantic *Sauromalus* (Iguanidae) in the Gulf of California.

1746: To Mr. Jan Reese, St. Michaels, Maryland, in support of study of feral mute swans in Chesapeake Bay.

1747: To Dr. Richard H. Kesel, Louisiana State University, Baton Rouge, Louisiana, in support of Quaternary research in the General Valley, Costa Rica.

1748: To Dr. Storrs L. Olson, Smithsonian Institution, Washington, D. C., to study the Pleistocene birds of Puerto Rico.

1749: To Drs. Mary R. Dawson, Carnegie Museum of Natural History, Pittsburgh, and R. M. West, Milwaukee Public Museum, for continuation of study of Paleogene terrestrial vertebrate faunas in the Canadian high Arctic.

1750: To Dr. Roger E. Carpenter, San Diego State University, San Diego, California, for study of energetics of West African bats.

1751: To Mr. Gary L. Nuechterlein, University of Minnesota, Minneapolis, Minnesota, for study of breeding biology and social behavior of western grebes.

1752: To Dr. John S. Hall, Lowell Observatory, Flagstaff, Arizona, to establish basic standards of air quality from telephotometer measurements.

1753: To Dr. James M. Adovasio, University of Pittsburgh, Pennsylvania, in support of continued archeology and geomorphology of Meadowcroft Rockshelter and Cross Creek drainage, southwestern Pennsylvania.

1754: To Dr. Marvin J. Allison, Medical College of Virginia, Richmond, Virginia, for continuing study of Pre-Columbian American disease.

1755: To Dr. Graeme W. Barker, Sheffield University, Sheffield, United Kingdom, in support of the Molise project.

1756: To Dr. Eurico Th. Miller, Museo Arqueologico do Rio Grande do Sol, Brazil, for archeological investigations at Abrigo do Sol Rockshelter, Mato Grosso, Brazil.

1757: To Dr. Dennis J. Stanford, Smithsonian Institution, Washington, D. C., for archeological investigations at the Selby and Dutton mammoth-kill sites.

1758: To Dr. William B. Saunders, Bryn Mawr College, Bryn Mawr, Pennsylvania, for study of the ecology and growth of *Nautilus* in Palau (West Caroline Islands).

1759: To Dr. John J. Gaudet, University of Nairobi, Nairobi, Kenya, for study of nutrient release from papyrus swamps on Lake Naivasha, Kenya.

1760: To Dr. Donald Walker, Australian National University, Canberra, Australia, for study of Quaternary vegetation history in Papua, New Guinea.

1761: To Dr. Yael D. Lubin, Smithsonian Tropical Research Institute, Balboa, Canal Zone, for study of llanos ants and giant anteaters: an ecologic interaction (Venezuela).

1762: To Dr. Carl L. Johannessen, University of Oregon, Eugene, Oregon, for study of the magic-medicinal uses of the black-boned, black-meated chicken in Peru and Chile.

1763: To Dr. Robert M. Hunt, Jr., University of Nebraska, Lincoln, Nebraska, for study of paleontology and geology of the Agate National Monument and surrounding region.

1764: To Dr. Raymond F. Laurent, Universidad Nacional de Tucumán, Argentina, in support of study of herpetofauna of the forest remnants of northwest Argentina.

1765: To Dr. G. Causey Whittow, University of Hawaii, Honolulu, Hawaii, for study of thermal ecology of Hawaiian basking green sea turtles.

1766: To Dr. Tim W. Clark, Idaho State University, Pocatello, Idaho, in support of search for and critical habitat analysis of black-footed ferrets.

1767: To Dr. Peter R. Marler, Rockefeller University Field Research Center, Millbrook, New York, for study of vocal communication in primates.

1768: To Dr. Francine G. Patterson, Stanford University, Stanford, California, for study of linguistic capabilities and higher cognitive functioning of the lowland gorilla.

1769: To Dr. D. Bruce Means, Tall Timbers Research Station, Tallahassee, Florida, in support of study of the Eastern Diamondback rattlesnake.

1770: To Dr. G. Carleton Ray, Johns Hopkins University, Baltimore, Maryland, for studies of walrus and whales during the cruise of the Coast Guard Cutter *Glacier*.

1771: To Dr. Ralph M. Wetzel, University of Connecticut, Storrs, Connecticut, for continuing study of the mammals of Paraguay.

1772: To Dr. Birute M. F. Galdikas, University of California, in support of grantee's orangutan study.

1773: To Dr. Dagmar I. Werner, Charles Darwin Research Station, Guayaquil, Ecuador, for study of the Galápagos land iguanas.

1774: To Dr. Ann M. Tallman, Smith College, Northampton, New Hampshire, for study of palsa development in the Yukon Territory.

1775: To Dr. John M. Bird, Cornell University, Ithaca, New York, for study of native iron of Disko Island, Western Greenland.

1776: To Dr. Kenneth E. Campbell, Los Angeles County Museum of Natural History, Los Angeles, California, for study of late Tertiary vertebrates from southeastern Peru.

1777: To Dr. David C. Switzer, Plymouth State College, Plymouth, New Hampshire, for excavation of the Revolutionary War privateer, *Defence.*

1778: To Dr. Demetrius U. Schilardi, The University Museum, University of Pennsylvania, Philadelphia, Pennsylvania, for excavation of the Mycenaean Acropolis of Koukonaries.

1779: To Dr. Yosihiko H. Sinoto, Bernice P. Bishop Museum, Honolulu, Hawaii, for salvage excavation of an archaic habitation site on Huahine, Society Islands.

1780: To Drs. Jacques and Louise A. Bordaz, University of Pennsylvania, Philadelphia, Pennsylvania, for excavation at the Neolithic site of Erbaba, South-Central Turkey.

1783: To Dr. George A. Agogino, Eastern New Mexico University, Portales, New Mexico, for an investigation of Stolle, New Mexico, mammoth site.

1784: To Dr. William J. Rathje, University of Arizona, Tucson, Arizona, for study of animal utilization by the Cozumel Maya: interpretation through faunal analysis.

1785: To Dr. S. Jeffrey K. Wilkerson, University of Florida, Gainesville, Florida, for study of cultural ecology of the Mexican gulf coast.

1786: To Dr. E. Wyllys Andrews V, for publication of M.A.R.I. Publications 45, 46, and Occasional Papers 2 and 3.

1787: To Dr. Jay M. Pasachoff, Williams College, Williamstown, Massachusetts, in support of observations of the solar corona at the 1977 total eclipse.

1788: To Dr. James D. McCleave, University of Maine, Orono, Maine, in support of study of migratory mechanisms in larval and adult American and European eels.

1789: To Dr. Hartmut Walter, University of California, Los Angeles, California, for sociological studies of gregarious falcons.

1790: To Dr. Talbot H. Waterman, Yale University, New Haven, Connecticut, for study of the visual basis of spatial orientation in aquatic animals.

1791: To Dr. William J. L. Sladen, Johns Hopkins University, Baltimore, Maryland, in support of grantee's Northern Waterfowl Project of the US-USSR Environmental Protection Agreement.

1792: To Dr. Douglas W. Mock, Smithsonian Institution, Washington, D. C., for study of ecology and behavior of the goliath heron.

1793: To Dr. John Proctor, Stirling University, Stirling, Scotland, for study of production and nutrient cycling in Sarawak rain forests.

1794: To Dr. José F. Bonaparte, Universidad Nacional de Tucumán, Argentina, for study of Jurassic and Cretaceous terrestrial vertebrates of South America.

1795: To Dr. Ralph W. Schreiber, Los Angeles County Museum of Natural History, Los Angeles, California, for a study of the breeding behavior of the great white pelican *(Pelecanus onocrotalus).*

1796: To Dr. Geoffrey Lewis, University of Oxford, Oxford, United Kingdom, for survey of natural populations of polymorphic snails in North Africa.

1797: To Dr. Stanley H. Weitzman, Smithsonian Institution, Washington, D. C., for study of zoogeography of glandulocaudin fishes of South America.
1798: To Dr. Robert J. Sharer, University of Pennsylvania, Philadelphia, Pennsylvania, for completion of archeological investigations at Qurigua, Guatemala.
1799: To Dr. Patrick L. Colin, University of Puerto Rico, Mayagüez, Puerto Rico, for investigation of spawning by Atlantic Ocean surgeonfishes.
1800: To Dr. Martin L. Cody, University of California, Los Angeles, California, for study of convergent evolution of bird and plant communities.
1803: To Dr. George Kish, University of Michigan, Ann Arbor, Michigan, for bibliography of papers presented at the International Geographical Congresses, 1871-1976.
1804: To Dr. C. Vance Haynes, Jr., University of Arizona, Tucson, Arizona, for studies at Playa Lake in the Nubian Desert.
1805: To Dr. Mercedes S. Foster, University of South Florida, Tampa, Florida, for study of the social organization and behavior of the swallow-tailed Manakin.
1806: To Dr. John T. Polhemus, University of Colorado Museum, Boulder, Colorado, for zoogeographical studies of the Saldidae of the southern hemisphere.
1807: To Dr. Philip V. Tobias, University of the Witwatersrand, Johannesburg, South Africa, to assist in publication of volume four in the Olduvai Gorge series.
1808: To Dr. Geoffrey M. O. Maloiy, University of Nairobi, Kabete, Kenya, in support of a study to determine whether pastoral nomads of northern Kenya have any special desert physiology.
1809: To Mr. Walter F. Morris, Jr., Warren, New Jersey, for study of Chiapas Maya textile design symbols.
1810: To Dr. David P. S. Peacock, University of Southampton, England, to assist in an archeological study of the island of Pantelleria.
1811: To Dr. Janet H. Johnson, University of Chicago, Chicago, Illinois, in support of the Quseir Project.
1812: To Dr. Mario J. Sanoja, Universidad Central de Venezuela, Caracas, Venezuela, for study of preceramic sites in eastern Venezuela.
1813: To Drs. Bernd Heinrich and George A. Bartholomew, University of California, Berkeley, California, for research on dung beetles.
1814: To Dr. Craig G. MacFarland, Charles Darwin Research Station, Guayaquil, Ecuador, for study of population ecology of the East Pacific green turtle in the Galápagos Islands.
1815: To Drs. John W. Hardy and Bertram G. Murray, Jr., Florida State Museum, Gainesville, Florida, for study of ecological relationships of three sympatric populations of Mexican finches.
1816: To Dr. Peter Moller, The American Museum of Natural History, New York, New York, in continuation of study of ethology of electric fish in Lake Kainji, Nigeria.
1817: To Dr. Berthold K. Holldobler, Harvard University, Cambridge, Massachusetts, for study of establishment and maintenance of territory in the African weaver ant.
1818: To Dr. Dian J. Fossey, Karisoke Research Centre, Rwanda, Africa, for study of behavioral and ecological determinants of the free-ranging mountain gorilla.

1819: To Dr. Robert S. Kennedy, Chicago, Illinois, for conservation research of the monkey-eating eagle of the Philippines.

1820: To Dr. Kenneth L. Brown, University of Houston, Houston, Texas, for grantee's archeological-ethnohistoric study of the development of Central Quichean civilization.

1821: To Ms. Joan S. Gardner, Smithsonian Institution, Washington, D. C., for study of Pre-Columbian textiles from Los Ríos Province, Ecuador.

1822: To Dr. John A. Graham, University of California, Berkeley, California, for archeological investigations at Abaj Takalik, Guatemala.

1823: To Dr. Ivor Noel Hume, Colonial Williamsburg Foundation, Williamsburg, Virginia, for archeological investigation of seventeenth-century settlement sites at Carter's Grove, Virginia.

1824: To Dr. David J. Ligon, University of New Mexico, Albuquerque, New Mexico, for study of the adaptive significance of communality in the green woodhoopoe.

1825: To Dr. Lanna Cheng, Scripps Institution of Oceanography, La Jolla, California, for a study of the physiological ecology of the sea-skater *Halobates.*

1826: To Dr. Theodore W. Pietsch, California State University, Long Beach, California, for investigation of feeding mechanism of shallow-water anglerfishes.

1827: To Dr. Lytton J. Musselman, Old Dominion University, Norfolk, Virginia, for continuing study of the biology of giant spores of *Dryopteris* hybrids in the Dismal Swamp.

1829: To Dr. Eric R. Pianka, University of Texas, Austin, Texas, for study of the ecology and diversity of desert lizards in Western Australia.

1830: To Dr. Daniel J. Gade, University of Vermont, Burlington, Vermont, for study of native animal keeping in Amazonia.

1831: To Dr. John A. Breyer, Texas Christian University, Fort Worth, Texas, for study of the vertebrate biostratigraphy of Late Miocene sediments in western Nebraska.

1832: To Dr. William J. Mader, Brigham Young University, Provo, Utah, for study of ecology and breeding behavior of the laughing falcon in Venezuela.

1833: To Dr. John B. Heppner, Smithsonian Institution, Washington, D. C., for biological research and collection of small moths in Venezuela.

1834: To Dr. Daniel N. Torres, University of Chile, Santiago, Chile, for ecological studies on the Juan Fernandez fur seal.

1835: To Mr. Vikuosa O. Nienu, University of California, Berkeley, California, for studies of cultural development of the Nagas in Southeastern Asia.

1836: To Ms. Nicole Duplaix, New York Zoological Society, Bronx, New York, in support of study of the behavior and ecology of the giant otter in Surinam.

1837: To Dr. Sherwin J. Carlquist, Rancho Santa Ana Botanic Garden, Claremont, California, in support of study of the evolution of pollinating mechanisms in triggerplants.

1838: To Dr. Ian R. Swingland, Oxford University, Oxford, England, for study of reptile ecology in a Sarawak National Park.

1839: To Dr. Keir B. Sterling, Pace University, Pleasantville, New York, for a study of the history of ornithology in the Western Hemisphere.

1840: To Dr. Joel R. Gat, Weizmann Institute of Science, Rehovot, Israel, for a study of limnology of the Dead Sea.

1841: To Dr. Thomas H. Rich, National Museum of Victoria, Melbourne, Australia, in support of a search for Gondwana Cretaceous mammals and birds.

1842: To Mr. Renato O. Rimoli M., Universidad Central del Este, San Pedro de Macoris, Dominican Republic, for study of paleofauna from rock shelters and caves in the Dominican Republic.

1843: To Dr. John H. Ostrom, Yale University, New Haven, Connecticut, in support of a comparative study of paleontological materials.

1844: To Dr. John R. Krebs, Oxford University, Oxford, England, in support of a study of geographical variation in bird song.

1978

1845: To Dr. Ronald Singer, University of Chicago, Chicago, Illinois, in support of a search for the earliest humans in Great Britain.

1846, 1968: To Dr. Krzysztof M. Serkowski, University of Arizona, in support of search for other planetary systems in the universe.

1847: To Dr. John L. Creech, U. S. National Arboretum, Washington, D. C., for plant exploration to remote Japanese localities for valuable genetic resources.

1848: To Dr. Richard D. Estes, Academy of Natural Sciences, Philadelphia, Pennsylvania, for continuation of aerial census of Ngorongoro Crater, Tanzania.

1849: To Drs. Harold A. Mooney and Sherry L. Gulmon, Stanford University, Stanford, California, for a study of plant-water relations in an extreme desert.

1850: To Dr. Larry D. Agenbroad, Department of Geology, Northern Arizona University, Flagstaff, Arizona, for continuing excavation of a Late Pleistocene mammoth locality, South Dakota.

1851: To Dr. David M. Hopkins, U. S. Geological Survey, Menlo Park, California, in support of a workshop on paleoecology of the Arctic steppe mammoth biome.

1852: To Dr. Jane Goodall, Dar es Salaam, Tanzania, for continuing study of family relationships in free-living chimpanzees.

1853: To Dr. Robert E. Dewar, Jr., University of Connecticut, Storrs, Connecticut, in support of preliminary inquiry into the origins and prehistory of the Malagasy.

1854: To Dr. Thomas J. Riley, University of Illinois, Urbana, Illinois, in support of study of electron spin resonance spectroscopy for dating of archeological ceramics.

1855: To Dr. Marcio E. Veloz M., Santo Domingo, Dominican Republic, for investigations in Pedernales Province, Dominican Republic.

1856, 1967: To Mr. Norman Hammond, Rutgers University, New Brunswick, New Jersey, for archeological excavation of the Cuello (Belize) site.

1857: To Dr. Robert W. Wilson, University of Kansas, Lawrence, Kansas, for study of small mammal fossil fauna of Kohfidisch (Burgenland) Austria.

1858: To Dr. B. Miles Gilbert, University of Missouri, Columbia, Missouri, for study of paleontology and paleoecology of Natural Trap Cave, Wyoming.

1859: To Dr. Thomas B. Thorson, University of Nebraska, Lincoln, Nebraska, for continuing study of the evolution of freshwater adaptation in stingrays.

1860: To Dr. John L. Hoogland, University of Minnesota, Minneapolis, Minnesota, for study of sociobiology of the black-tailed prairie dog.

1861, 1886: To Dr. Mary D. Leakey, Nairobi, Kenya, for further exploration of Pliocene fossil beds and game tracks of Laetolil, Northern Tanzania.

1862: To Dr. G. Philip Rightmire, State University of New York, Binghamton, New York, in support of new studies of African *Homo erectus* from Olduvai Gorge.

1863: To Dr. Richard L. Hay, University of California, Berkeley, California, for study of stratigraphy of the Laetolil area.

1864: To Dr. Sterling P. Vinson, University of Arizona, Tucson, Arizona, for archeological exploration between Venosa and Potenza in Lucania, Southern Italy.

1865: To Dr. Kenneth G. Hirth, Western Michigan University, Kalamazoo, Michigan, in support of Xochicalco mapping project, Mexico.

1866: To Dr. Lautaro Nunez A., Antofagasta, Chile, in support of archeological project at Quereo, Los Vilos, Chile.

1867: To Dr. Branko Velimirov, University of Cape Town, Cape Province, South Africa, for study of growth, skeletal formation and mineralogy of the Blue Coral *Heliopora coerula*.

1868: To Dr. Samuel S. Goldich, Colorado School of Mines, Golden, Colorado, for study of the origin of aluminous laterite and bauxite.

1869: To Mr. William Melton, Jr., University of Montana, Missoula, Montana, for study of fossils and associated artifacts of Blacktail Cave, Montana.

1870: To Dr. Alan Lill, Monash University, Clayton, Victoria, Australia, in support of study of comparative socioecology of five Australian bowerbird species.

1871: To Dr. Jerome G. Rozen, Jr., American Museum of Natural History, New York, New York, for study of evolutionary relationships of the bee subfamily Panurginae.

1872: To Dr. Kenan T. Erim, New York University, New York, New York, for continuation of investigations and research of archeological material excavated at Aphrodisias, Turkey.

1873: To Dr. Christy G. Turner II, Arizona State Univeristy, Tempe, Arizona, for study of dental evidence for origin of the first Americans.

1874, 1948: To Mr. Richard E. Leakey, National Museums of Kenya, Nairobi, Kenya, for continuing investigations in Plio/Pleistocene sediments related to prehistory of mankind.

1875: To Dr. Charles W. McNett, Jr., The American University, Washington, D. C., in support of excavations at the Jeffrey-Harris rockshelter.

1876: To Dr. Lawrence Stager, University of Chicago, Chicago, Illinois, for excavations in the port and sacrificial precinct of Carthage.

1877: To Dr. Gus W. Van Beek, Smithsonian Institution, Washington, D. C., in support of archeological investigations at Tell Jemmeh, Israel.

1878: To Dr. W. Bruce Saunders, Bryn Mawr College, Bryn Mawr, Pennsylvania, for study of biology and ecology of *Nautilus* in Palau (West Caroline Islands).

1879: To Mrs. Rae Natalie P. Goodall, Tierra del Fuego, Argentina, for continuing research on the natural history of Tierra del Fuego.

1880: To Dr. Sandra L. Vehrencamp, University of California, La Jolla, California, for study of male incubation and communal nesting in anis.

1881: To Dr. Harold E. Edgerton, Massachusetts Institute of Technology, Cambridge, Massachusetts, for an underwater camera for the study of plankton in the sea.

1882: To Dr. Philip R. Bjork, South Dakota School of Mines and Technology, Rapid City, South Dakota, for the study of microvertebrates from the Chadron Formation in Nebraska and South Dakota.

1883: To Dr. Joseph R. Thomasson, Black Hills State College, Spearfish, South Dakota, in support of studies of fossil grasses from Ash Hollow Canyon, Nebraska.

1884: To Mr. Gary L. Nuechterlein, University of Minnesota, Minneapolis, Minnesota, for study of breeding biology and social behavior of western grebes.

1885: To Dr. Duane A. Schlitter, Carnegie Museum of Natural History, Pittsburgh, Pennsylvania, for systematic studies of small mammals of the United Republic of Cameroon.

1887: To Dr. Noel T. Boaz, New York University, New York, New York, in support of paleoanthropological research at Sahabi, northern Libya.

1888: To Mr. Richard L. Burger, Ancash, Peru, in support of Proyecto Huaricoto/Chupacoto, Callejon de Huaylas, Peru.

1889: To Dr. Don S. Rice, Florida State Museum, Gainesville, Florida, for an introductory survey of the Central Petén Savanna.

1890: To Drs. Jacques Bordaz and Louise Alpers-Bordaz, New York, New York, in support of analysis of material from Erbaba, Turkey.

1891: To Dr. James A. Tuck, Memorial University of Newfoundland, St. John's, Newfoundland, for study of Basque whaling stations in Labrador.

1892: To Dr. Graeme W. Barker, Sheffield University, Sheffield, United Kingdom, for the Molise project: early man and his environment in the Biferno Valley.

1893: To Dr. Rudolph H. Dornemann, Milwaukee Public Museum, Milwaukee, Wisconsin, in support of archeological excavations at Tell Hadidi, Syria.

1894: To Mr. John N. Postgate, Cambridge, England, for archeological excavations at Abu Salabikh, Iraq.

1895: To Dr. Robert H. Dyson, Jr., University of Pennsylvania, Philadelphia, Pennsylvania, in support of archeological excavations at Tal-i Malyan, Iran.

1896: To Dr. William M. Hurley, University of Toronto, Canada, and Dr. Peter Bleed, The University of Nebraska, Lincoln, Nebraska, for study of the Yagi Site, Japan.

1897: To Dr. George F. Bass, Texas A & M University, College Station, Texas, in support of excavation and restoration of eleventh-century shipwreck with glass cargo.

1898: To Dr. Eldon E. Ball, The Australian National University, Canberra City, Australia, for study of island colonization and biogeography in New Guinea.

1899: To Dr. Kentwood D. Wells, The University of Connecticut, Storrs, Connecticut, for study of social behavior and communication in neotropical frogs.

1900: To Dr. Ralph W. Brauer, University of North Carolina, Wilmington, North Carolina, in support of study of the physiology of abyssal freshwater fauna in Lake Baikal.

1901: To Dr. Hugh D. Wilson, Texas A & M University, College Station, Texas, in support of exploration for *Chenopodium* germplasm in southern South America.

1902: To Mr. Jan G. Reese, St. Michaels, Maryland, for a study of population ecology of feral mute swans in Chesapeake Bay.
1903: To Mr. David C. Oren, Harvard University, Cambridge, Massachusetts, for study of species area requirements in a patchy habitat in Amazonian Brazil.
1904: To Dr. Anthony G. Coates, George Washington University, Washington, D. C., for study of Cretaceous coral/rudist reefs from Turkey, Iran, Afghanistan and Israel.
1905: To Dr. H. E. Wright, Jr., University of Minnesota, Minneapolis, Minnesota, for study of climatic and vegetational changes in the Peruvian Andes.
1906: To Dr. Michael T. Voorhies, University of Nebraska, Lincoln, Nebraska, in support of study of a Miocene rhinoceros herd buried in volcanic ash.
1907: To Dr. George W. Uetz, University of Cincinnati, Cincinnati, Ohio, for study of the ecology and behavior of a colonial web-building spider.
1908: To Dr. Ralph S. Solecki, Columbia University, New York, New York, in support of study of the prehistory of Shanidar Cave, northern Iraq.
1909: To Dr. Bruce J. Bourque, Maine State Museum, Augusta, Maine, in support of the Fox Islands archeological project: analysis of faunal remains.
1910: To Dr. Clifford Evans, Smithsonian Institution, Washington, D. C., in support of the workshop of Paleo-Indian technology in South America.
1911: To Dr. Demetrius U. Schilardi, The University Museum, University of Pennsylvania, Philadelphia, Pennsylvania, in support of 1978 program of excavation of the Mycenaean palace of Paros.
1912: To Dr. Robert E. Ackerman, Washington State University, Pullman, Washington, in support of southwestern Alaska archeological survey: Akhlun-Kuskokwim Mountains.
1913: To Dr. William L. Franklin, Iowa State University, Ames, Iowa, for study of socioecology of the South American guanaco.
1914: To Dr. Frederick A. Mumpton, State University College, Brockport, New York, for a study of zeolite distribution in areas of high mesothelioma in central Turkey.
1915: To Dr. Roger C. Wood, Stockton State College, Pomona, New Jersey, in support of research on African and South American fossil turtles.
1916: To Dr. John E. Guilday, Carnegie Museum of Natural History, Pittsburgh, Pennsylvania, in support of exploration of Appalachian caves for Pleistocene Ice Age paleontological sites.
1917: To Dr. Russell W. Graham, Indiana University, Indianapolis, Indiana, in support of an excavation of the Dutton local fauna.
1918, 1947: To Dr. Dagmar I. Werner, Guayaquil, Ecuador, South America, for a study of Galápagos land iguanas.
1919: To Dr. George S. Korres, University of Athens, Athens, Greece, in support of an excavation of the Pre-Mycenaean tumulus at Voidokoilia near Pylos.
1920: To Dr. McGuire Gibson, University of Chicago, Chicago, Illinois, in support of a Yemen Arab Republic archeological-environmental survey.
1921: To Dr. Janice M. Stargardt, Cambridge, England, in support of study of environmental archeology on the Isthmus of the Malay Peninsula and Indonesia.
1922: To Dr. Alice L. Alldredge, University of California, Santa Barbara, California, for a study of demersal zooplankton on coral reefs.

1923: To Dr. Nicholas R. Hall, University of Florida, Gainesville, Florida, in support of a study of neurologic disease in cetaceans.

1924: To Dr. Mason E. Hale, Smithsonian Institution, Washington, D. C., for a study of control of biological growths on monuments at Tikal, Guatemala.

1925: To Dr. Francine G. Patterson, The Gorilla Foundation, Menlo Park, California, for a continuing study of linguistic capabilities and higher cognitive functioning of the lowland gorilla.

1926: To Dr. Frederick A. Urquhart, University of Toronto, West Hill, Ontario, Canada, for continuing study of monarch butterfly migrations through Yucatan.

1927: To Dr. Abraham Willink, National University of Tucumán, Argentina, in support of biosystematic studies on Andean and Patagonian fauna of eumenid wasps.

1928: To Dr. Robert D. Ballard, Woods Hole Oceanographic Institution, Woods Hole, Massachusetts, in support of investigations of the Galápagos Rift hydrothermal vents.

1929: To Dr. Jeffrey L. Bada, University of California, La Jolla, California, in support of amino acid dating of fossil bones from East Africa.

1930: To Dr. Patrick E. McGovern, The University Museum, University of Pennsylvania, Pittsburgh, Pennsylvania, in support of a cesium magnetometer and resistivity survey of Umm ed-Danānīr, Jordan.

1931: To Dr. Henry T. Wright, University of Minnesota, Minneapolis, Minnesota, for preliminary excavation of early IVth millennium strata at Susa, southwestern Iran.

1932: To Dr. Barbara Voorhies, University of California, Santa Barbara, California, in support of an archeological study of a portion of the coastal humid tropics in Chiapas, Mexico.

1933: To Dr. Merrick Posnansky, University of California, Los Angeles, California, in support of the Kramo Excavation, Begho, Ghana.

1934: To Dr. E. Wyllys Andrews V, Middle American Research Institute, Tulane University, New Orleans, Louisiana, in support of *Publication 48—Excavations at Dzibilchaltún.*

1935: To Dr. Frederick L. Colin, University of Puerto Rico, Mayaguez, Puerto Rico, for the final phase of an investigation of spawning by Atlantic Ocean surgeonfishes.

1936: To Dr. Daniel Otte, The Academy of Natural Sciences of Philadelphia, Pennsylvania, for a study of song evolution in relation to species formation in Hawaiian crickets.

1937: To Dr. John L. Creech, U. S. National Arboretum, Washington, D. C., in support of plant exploration to remote Japanese localities for valuable genetic resources.

1938: To Dr. Spencer G. Sealy, University of Manitoba, Winnipeg, Manitoba, Canada, for a study of the significance of feeding in mixed species flocks by marine birds.

1939: To Mr. Tepilit Ole-Saitoti, Tanzania, East Africa, for a study of the ecology of Maasailand.

1940: To Dr. John R. Clark, University of California, Los Angeles, California, for a study of population changes in Ankara since 1969.

1941, 1971: To Dr. C. Vance Haynes, Jr., University of Arizona, Tucson, Arizona, in support of the Playa Lake studies of the Western Desert (Egypt and Sudan).

1942: To Dr. Jose F. Bonaparte, Museo Argentino de Ciencias Naturales, Buenos Aires, Argentina, for a study of Jurassic and Cretaceous terrestrial vertebrates of South America.

1943: To Dr. Larry G. Marshall, Field Museum of Natural History, Chicago, Illinois, for a search for Cretaceous mammals and magnetostratigraphy of the Cretaceous-Tertiary boundary in South America.

1944: To Dr. Joyce R. Richardson, New Zealand Oceanographic Institute, Wellington North, New Zealand, in support of a study of evolutionary mechanisms in living brachiopods.

1945: To Dr. Austin E. Lamberts, Grand Rapids, Michigan, in support of a study of recolonization of a selectively denuded coral reef.

1946: To Dr. Fred G. Thompson, The Florida State Museum, University of Florida, Gainesville, Florida, in support of the final field season of a study of evolution and systematics of Hispaniolan urocoptid land snails.

1949: To Dr. Tom D. Dillehay, Universidad Austral de Chile, Valdivia, Chile, in support of archeological investigations at Monte Verde, Chile.

1950: To Dr. John A. Graham, University of California, Berkeley, California, for continuation of the Abaj Takalik excavation.

1951: To Dr. George C. Gorman, University of California, Los Angeles, California, in support of a sea snake study.

1952: To Dr. Ron Scogin, Rancho Santa Ana Botanic Garden, Claremont, California, for a study of the evolution and biochemistry of Hawaiian Island plants.

1953: To Dr. J. Alan Holman, Michigan State University, East Lansing, Michigan, for a comparative study of Pleistocene fissure fills at the Ladds Quarry, Georgia.

1954: To Dr. Mario C. Barberena, Federal University of Rio Grande do Sul, Brazil, for a study of Upper Permian and Triassic tetrapods of southern Brazil.

1955: To Dr. Eugene S. Morton, Smithsonian Institution, Washington, D. C., in support of a study of variation in communication within the monogamous avian pair bond.

1956: To Mrs. Yoshika O. Willis, Estado de São Paulo, Brazil, for a study of the current status of São Paulo birds.

1957: To Dr. Stuart H. Hurlbert, San Diego State University, San Diego, California, in support of comparative ecological studies of flamingos and lakes in the Andean antiplano.

1958: To Dr. Robert J. Sharer, The University Museum, University of Pennsylvania, in support of the follow-up investigations at Quirigua, Guatemala.

1959: To Dr. Ruth M. Shady and Dr. Hermilio Rosas, Surco, Lima, Peru, for a study of the cultural development in the north Peruvian highlands.

1960: To Dr. Ivor Noel Hume, The Colonial Williamsburg Foundation, Williamsburg, Virginia, in support of the 1979 archeological investigations at Carter's Grove, Virginia.

1961: To Dr. H. Carl Gerhardt, University of Missouri, Columbia, Missouri, for a study of mating call discrimination in *Hyla meridionalis* and *Hyla arborea*.

1962: To Dr. Thomas D. Seeley, Museum of Comparative Zoology, Harvard University, Cambridge, Massachusetts, for a study of predation, colony demography and social behavior of honey bees in Thailand.

1963: To Dr. Michael T. Madison, The Marie Selby Botanical Gardens, Sarasota, Florida, in support of botanical exploration of Cerro Sumaco, Ecuador.

1964: To Dr. Harry F. Shafer, Texas A & M University, College Station, Texas, in support of an archeological and botanical study of the Mimbres Mogollon, New Mexico.

1965: To Mr. John Carswell, The Oriental Institute, University of Chicago, Chicago, Illinois, in support of excavation of a 10th-12th century trading site in Sri Lanka.

1966: To Dr. George E. Stuart, National Geographic Society, Washington, D. C., for completion of the Coba archeological mapping project.

1969: To Dr. Glen E. Woolfenden, University of South Florida, Tampa, Florida, and Dr. John W. Fitzpatrick, Field Museum of Natural History, Chicago, Illinois, in support of a study of the demography of a communal breeder: the Florida scrub jay.

1970: To Dr. John Proctor, Stirling Univrsity, Stirling, Scotland, United Kingdom, in support of the analysis of materials collected during the Royal Geographical Society Mulu Expedition.

1972: To Mr. Yves A. Prevost, Edinburgh University, Scotland, for a study of the ecology of ospreys wintering in West Africa.

1973: To Mr. Steven L. Swartz, San Diego, California, in support of reproductive behavior and population studies of gray whales in Mexico.

1974: To Dr. Dian Fossey, Karisoke Research Centre, Rwanda, Central Africa, for studies of behavioral and ecological determinants of the free-ranging mountain gorillas.

Index

Acanthaster planci, crown-of-thorns starfish, investigations in Micronesia, 665
Afkodre, ethnographic research on, in Surinam, 565
Africa:
- behavior of indigobirds in, 541
- Botswana, demographic and social-anthropological study of the Hambukushu, 455
- early man research in East Africa, 459
- Kenya, ecology of golden-rumped elephant-shrew, 573
- Kenya, Lake Naivasha, effects of papyrus swamps on the ecology of, 267
- Rwanda, Mount Visoke (Parc des Volcans), mountain gorilla research, 237
- Tanzania, Olduvai Gorge, excavations, 459
- Uganda, Toro Game Reserve, conventionality of territorial leks in a population of kob, 75

Alaska, southeastern, study of ancient environments and age of non-glaciated terrain, 733
Albatross, Laysan, study of on Midway Atoll, 219
Alligator mississippiensis, thermal ecology of, 273
Allison, Marvin J., 1, 11
American alligator, thermoregulation and ecology of, 273
Anolis lizards, reproductive cycles and biogeographic relationships of, 283
Anolis limifrons, social displays, 377
Antelope. *See* Kob.
Aphrodisias, archeological site, Caria, Turkey, 185
Anthropology:
- Hambukushu of Botswana, demographic survey and social-anthropological study of, 455
- Pre-Columbian American diseases, 1
- Tlapanec Indians, Mexico, 517
- Trinidad, peasant livelihood behavior in, 579
- *See also* Archeology; Ethnography.

Architecture, in mainland Greece, ca. 2200-800 B.C., 463
Arctic:
- microflora of sea ice, 13
- polar-bear den surveys in Svalbard, 445

Arikara Indian, excavation of cemetery in South Dakota, 677
Arizona, Murray Springs Clovis site, archeological investigations, 347
Asia, woodpecker studies, 631
Astronomy, occultation of Beta Scorpii and Companion by Jupiter, May 13, 1971, observations of, 205
Auklet, Cassin's, study of nocturnal orientation in, 47
Austral Islands, seamounts in, 389
Archeology:
- Arikara Indian cemetery, Mobridge, South Dakota, excavation, 677
- Battle of Lepanto, Greece, sonar and diving search for site of, 161
- Bimini, Bahamas, underwater surveying, 21
- Chalcatzingo, Morelos, Mexico, investigations, 287
- Cozumel, Mexico, research on pre-Columbian culture change, 595
- Murray Springs Clovis site, Arizona, investigations, 347

Archeology *(continued)*:
Olduvai Gorge, Tanzania, excavations, 459
Rattlers Bight, Hamilton Inlet, Labrador, excavations, 223
Tell Keisan, Israel, excavations, 129

Bahamas, Bimini, study of offshore rock formations, 21
Bakhtiyārī Tribe, its organization and role in Iran, 257
Ball, Mahlon M., 21, 38
Batholith, Mount Stuart, Cascade Mountains, Washington, 175
Battle of Lepanto, search and survey mission, Greece, 1971-1972, 161-173
Beard, John Stanley, 39, 46
Beta Scorpii and companion, occultation of by Jupiter, 205
Bimini, Bahamas, study of late Quaternary geologic history, 21
Biology:
of marsupials in Colombia and Venezuela, 711
of snail-killing flies of the Pacific Northwest, 233
Birds:
ashy petrel, nocturnal orientation, 47
bald eagles, postfledgling activities of juveniles, 149
Cassin's auklet, nocturnal orientation, 47
Eocene flamingo nesting area, Sweetwater County, Wyoming, 473
finches, parasitic, behavior of, 541
fish-eating, Eagle Lake, California, reproduction study, 427
flamingos, population ecology of, 407
Laysan albatross, study of on Midway Atoll, 219
Leach's petrel, nocturnal orientation, 47
study of, in abandoned strip-mine areas, Mercer County, Pennsylvania, 71
Taiwan's mikado and Swinhoe's pheasants, 623
woodpeckers, Asian, 631
Botany:
bamboos, primitive, 647
fern gametophytes, geographic variation in frequency of spontaneous tumors in, 535
flax genus *Linum,* 587
flora of Tierra del Fuego, 275
genus Kakabekia, biogeography of a microorganism with precambrian affinities and Icelandic microhabitats, 639
lichens, family Thelotremataceae, in the Lesser Antilles, systematics and evolution of, 305
lodgepole-pine forests of fire origin, Yellowstone National Park, biotic succession of, 693
microflora of Arctic sea ice, 13
papyrus, Lake Naivasha, Kenya, 267
plant successions on Soufrière Volcano, 39
subarctic plant systems, microclimate of, 591
vegetation association on abandoned strip-mine areas, Mercer County, Pennsylvania, 70
Bowman, Robert I., 47
Brazil, bambusoid grasses in, 647
Brenner, Fred J., 67, 74
Briend, Jacques, 143
Buechner, Helmut K., 75, 90
Butterfly, monarch, migration in North America, 721

Calderon, Cleofé E., 647, 654
California:
  Eagle Lake, reproduction of fish-eating birds, 427
  Southeast Farallon Island, nocturnal orientation in Leach's and ashy petrels and Cassin's auklet, 47
Canada:
  Northwest Territories, study of ice flora, 13
  St. Elias Mountains, study of three surging glaciers, 103
Cascade Mountains, Washington, petrological and geochemical study of the Mount Stuart batholith, 175
Cave deposits of Quaternary and Holocene origin, investigation of, in Mallorca, 731
Cephalopods, photographic record in color of live deep-sea cephalopods, 145-147
Child behavior, Mbotgate, 655
China, explorations of Joseph Francis Rock (1884-1962) in, 687
Clark, Eugenie, 91, 102
Coenobita clypeatus, terrestrial hermit crab, study of, 361
Collins, Sam G., 103, 115
Colombia, petrology of Andean metamorphic rocks from, 213
Costa Rica, Nancite Beach, Santa Rosa National Park, mass-nesting of Pacific ridley turtles, 369
Cozumel, Island of, Mexico, archeological research on, 595
Crab, hermit, terrestrial, ethological study of, 361
Crown-of-thorns starfish, investigations in Micronesia, 665
Cruikshank, Dale P., 117, 123
Cyprus, Kyrenia, conservation of 2,000-year-old ship, 417

Delson, Eric, 125, 128
deVaux, Father Roland, 129
Dilly, P. Noel, 145, 147
Diseases, study of Pre-Columbian in Peru and Chile, 1
Dunstan, Thomas C., 149, 160

Eagles, bald, postfledgling activities of juveniles as determined by radio telemetry, 149
Ecology:
  effects of papyrus swamps on Lake Naivasha, 267
  of the American alligator *(Alligator mississippiensis),* 273
  of annual killifishes in northern South America, 703
  of complex ecosystems on abandoned strip-mine areas in Mercer County, Pennsylvania, 67
  of flamingos, 407
  of golden-rumped elephant-shrew of Kenya, 573
  of sponges in Pacific Reef caves, 339
  of yak in the Nepal Himalaya, 529
  paleoecology of Dry Cave, New Mexico, 331
  plant successions on Soufrière Volcano, 39
Ecuador, petrology of Andean metamorphic rocks from, 213
Edgerton, Harold E., 161, 173
Eel. *See* Red Sea garden eel.
Egypt, Theban Plain, engineering and petrographic study of colossi of Memnon, 355
Elephant-shrew, golden-rumped, of Kenya, ecology of, 573
Energy and water budget studies in the tundra, 591
Entomology. *See* Insects.
Erikson, Erik H., Jr., 175, 184
Erim, Kenan T., 185, 204

Ethnography:
Surinamese Creoles' magico-religious complex termed *Afkodre,* 565
Tlapanec Indians of Tlacoapa, Guerrero, Mexico, 517
Evans, David S., 205, 212

Feininger, Tomas, 213, 217
Ferns, geographic variation in frequency of spontaneous tumors in gametophytes, 535
Finches, parasitic, behavior of, 541
Fisher, Harvey I, 219, 222
Fishes:
annual killifishes in northern South America, 703
Crown-of-thorns starfish, Micronesia, 665
in strip-mine pools of abandoned areas in Mercer County, Pennsylvania, 72
live deep-sea cephalopods, colored photographic record of, 145
Red Sea garden eel, 91
tropical Pacific reef sharks, behavior of, 479
Fitzhugh, William W., 223, 231
Flamingos:
Eocene, nesting area, Sweetwater County, Wyoming, 473
population ecology, 407
Flax genus *Linum,* 587
Flora of Tierra del Fuego, collections, observations, and illustrations of, 275
Foote, Benjamin A., 233, 235
Fossey, Dian, 237, 255
Fossils:
Old World monkeys of the circum-Mediterranean region, 125
Oligocene marine fossil beds near Charleston, South Carolina, excavation of, 601
precambrian genus *Kakabekia,* 639

Galápagos Islands calderas, study of volcanic gas and petrology, 501
Garden eel. *See* Red Sea garden eel.
Garthwaite, G. R., 257, 265
Gaudet, John J., 267, 272
Gazelles, desert, energetic and water cost of locomotion, 689
Gehlbach, Frederick R., 273, 274
Geology:
ancient environments and age of non-glaciated terrain in southeastern Alaska, 733
late Quaternary geologic history of Bimini, 21
spectroscopy of volcanic flames and fume from Kilauea Volcano, Hawaii, 117
three surging glaciers, St. Elias Mountains, Canada, 103
Gifford, John A., 38
Gold artifacts, pre-Columbian, of Panama, graphic catalogue of, 709

Goodall, Rae Natalie Prosser, 275, 281
Gorilla, mountain, research, in central Africa, 237
Gorman, George C., 283, 286
Grasses, bambusoid, study of in eastern Brazil, 647
Greece:
domestic architecture and village layout, ca. 2200-800 B.C., 463
Lepanto, battle of, search for wrecks of, 161
Grove, David C., 287, 304

Hale, Mason E., Jr., 305, 308
Hall, William P., III, 309, 329

Hambukushu, of Botswana, demographic and social anthropological study of, 455
Harris, Arthur, 331, 338
Hartman, Willard D., 339, 346
Hawaii, Kilauea Volcano, spectroscopy of flames and fume, 117
Haynes, C. Vance, Jr., 347, 353
Heizer, Robert F., 355, 360
Henderson, Alex, 361, 368
Hughes, David A., 369, 376

Iceland, examination of genus *Kakabekia,* 639
Ichthyology. *See* Fishes.
Iguanid lizards, Mexican, chromosomes, speciation, and evolution of, 309
Indigobirds, Africa, behavior of, 541
Insects:
- monarch butterfly migration in North America, 721
- snail-killing flies (Diptera: Sciomyzidae) of the Pacific Northwest, study of biology of, 233

Iran, Bakhtiyārī Tribe, its organization and role, 257
Israel:
- Red Sea garden eel, distribution, mobility, and behavior of, 91-102
- Tell Keisan, excavation at, 129-143

Jenssen, Thomas A., 377, 388
Johnson, Rockne H., 389, 405

Kahl, M. Philip, 407, 415
Kakabekia, precambrian genus, biology of, 639
Kakabekia barghoorniana, living, geographic and micro-environmental determinations in the distribution of, 639
Katzev, Michael L., 417, 426
Killifish, annual, study of in northern South America, 703
Kob, Uganda, conventionality of territorial leks in a population of, 75
Koplin, James R., 427, 443
Kyrenia ship, conservation of, 417

Labrador, Rattlers Bight, Hamilton Inlet, excavations, 223
Lake Naivasha, Kenya, papyrus and the ecology of, 267
Larsen, Thor, 445, 454
Larson, Thomas J., 455, 458
Leakey, Louis S. B., 459
Leakey, Mary D., 459, 462
Leks, study of conventionality of in Uganda, 75
Lepanto, battle of, sonar and diving search for wrecks of, 161
Lichens, systematics and evolution of the Family Thelotremataceae in the Lesser Antilles, 305
Linum, flax genus, 587
Lizards:
- *Anolis,* in West Indies, study of, 283
- *Anolis limifrons,* social displays, 377
- iguanid lizards, Mexican, chromosomes, speciation, and evolution of, 309

Mallorca, Muleta expedition, 731
Mammals:
- gazelles, desert, 689
- kob, Uganda, conventionality of, in a population of territorial leks, 75
- marsupials, South American, reproductive biology of, 711
- monkeys, Old World, fossil, of circum-Mediterranean region, 125
- mountain gorilla research, 237

Mammals *(continued)*:
- polar-bear den surveys in Svalbard, 445
- vertebrate populations on abandoned strip-mine areas, behavior of, 67
- whales, behavior of, 551
- yak in Nepal Himalaya, field investigations of, 529

Manion, Bruce L., 47, 65
Marine fossil beds, Oligocene, excavation of near Charleston, South Carolina, 601
Marsupials, reproductive biology of, in Colombia and Venezuela, 711
Mbotgate life style, 655
McDonald, William A., 463, 471
McGrew, Paul O., 473, 478
Mediterranean region, study of fossil Old World monkeys, 125
Memnon, colossi of, engineering and petrographic study of, 355
Mercer County, Pennsylvania, behavior of vertebrate animals on abandoned strip-mine areas of, 67
Metamorphic rocks, Andean, from Colombia and Ecuador, 213
Mexico:
- Chalcatzingo, archeological investigations at, 287
- iguanid lizards of, 309
- Island of Cozumel, archeological research on, 595
- Tlacoapa, Guerrero, ethnographic study of Tlapanec Indians of, 517

Micronesia, crown-of-thorns starfish investigations, 665
Monarch butterfly, migration in North America, 721
Monkeys, a study of fossil Old World monkeys of the circum-Mediterranean region, 125
Morphology of sponges, in Pacific reef caves, 339. *See also* Biology.
Morrison, Dale P., 117, 123
Mount Stuart batholith, in Cascade Mountains, study of petrology and origin of, 175
Muleta expedition, 731

Nelson, Donald R., 479, 499
Nepal Himalaya, investigations of yak, 529
New Hebrides, island of Malekula, studies of Mbotgate child behavior, 655
New Mexico, Dry Cave, Pleistocene ecology study, 331
Nordlie, Bert E., 501, 516
North America:
- migration of monarch butterfly in, 721
- *See also* individual states of the United States; Canada; and Mexico.

Oettinger, Marion, Jr., 517, 528
Olduvai Gorge, Tanzania, excavations, 459
Olduvai Museum, 460
Ornithology. *See* Birds.

Pacific:
- reef sharks, tropical, behavioral study of (Rangiroa, French Polynesia), 479
- sponges in reef caves, morphological and ecological studies of, 339

Pacific Northwest, biology of snail-killing flies in, 233
Paleontology:
- ancient environments and age of non-glaciated terrain in southeastern Alaska, 733
- cave deposits of Quaternary and Holocene origin, 731
- fossil Old World Monkeys of the circum-Mediterranean region, 125

Olduvai Gorge, Tanzania, excavations, 459
Pleistocene ecology of Dry Cave, New Mexico, 331
Palmieri, Richard P., 529, 534
Panama, Pre-Columbian gold artifacts of, 709
Papyrus, effects of swamps of on the ecology of Lake Naivasha, Kenya, 267
Parsons, Patricia Amanda, 517, 528
Partanen, Carl R., 535, 540
Payne, Robert B., 541, 550
Payne, Roger S., 551, 564
Pennsylvania, Mercer County, behavior of vertebrate populations on abandoned stripmine areas of, 67
Petrel:
ashy, nocturnal orientation, 47
Leach's, nocturnal orientation, 47
Petrology:
Andean metamorphic rocks from Colombia and Ecuador, 213
colossi of Memnon on the Theban Plain, Egypt, 355
Galápagos islands calderas, 501
Mount Stuart batholith, Cascade Mountains, 175
See also Geology.
Pheasants, Taiwan's mikado and Swinhoe's, 623
Photography:
cinema research study of Mbotgate child behavior, New Hebrides, 655
of live deep-sea cephalopods, in color, 145
of pre-Columbian gold artifacts of Panama, 709
Physical anthropology, study of Pre-Columbian American diseases, 1
Pierce, B. Edward, 565, 571
Pine, lodgepole, biotic succession of forests of fire origin in Yellowstone National Park, 693
Radinovsky, Syd, 361, 368
Rathbun, Galen B., 573, 578
Rathje, William L., 595, 599
Red Sea garden eel, distribution, mobility, and behavior of, 91-102
Reiswig, Henry W., 339, 346
Reptiles:
American alligator, thermal ecology of, 273
Anolis limifrons, social displays, 377
Anolis lizards in West Indies, 283
iguanid lizards in Mexico, 309
turtles, ridley, field study of nesting in Costa Rica, 369
Rhynchocyon chrysopygus, golden-rumped elephant-shrew, of Kenya, ecology of, 573
Richard, Joseph D., 369, 376
Richardson, Bonham C., 579, 586
Rock, Joseph Francis, scientist-explorer, (1884-1962), biography of, 687
Rogers, Claude M., 587, 590
Rouse, Wayne R., 591, 593

Sabloff, Jeremy A., 595, 599
Sanders, Albert E., 601, 621
Seamounts, Austral Islands region volcanism study, 389
Severinghaus, Sheldon R., 623, 630
Sharks, reef, of Rangiroa, French Polynesia, behavior of, 479
Short, Lester L., 631, 638
Siegel, B. Z., 646
Siegel, Sanford M., 639, 646
Sociology:
livelihood mobility and economic diversity in three villages of Trinidad, 579
Mbotgate life-style, New Hebrides, 655
Tlapanec Indians, Mexico, 517
Trinidad, peasant livelihood behavior, 579
Soderstrom, Thomas R., 647, 654

Sorenson, E. Richard, 655, 664
Soufrière Volcano, St. Vincent Island, West Indies, study of plant successions on, 39
South America:
Chile, Pre-Columbian diseases, 1
Colombia, biology of marsupials in, 711
northern, annual killifishes in, 703
Peru, Pre-Columbian diseases, 1
Venezuela, biology of marsupials in, 711
South Carolina, excavation of Oligocene marine fossil beds near Charleston, 601
South Dakota, excavation of protohistoric Arikara Indian cemetery near Mobridge, 677
Southeast Farallon Island, nocturnal orientation in Leach's and ashy petrels and Cassin's auklet, 47
Sponges, morphological and ecological studies of in Pacific reef caves, 339
Starck, Walter A., II, 665, 675
Starfish, crown-of-thorns, biology and epidemiology of, Micronesia, 665
St. Elias Mountains, Canada, study of three surging glaciers, 103-115
Stewart, T. Dale, 677, 685
Subarctic plant systems, microclimate of, 591
Surinam, ethnographic research on *afkodre,* 565
Sutton, Stephanne B., 687, 688
Svalbard, polar-bear den surveys in, 445

Taiwan, pheasant project, 623
Taylor, C. Richard, 689, 691
Taylor, Dale L., 693, 702
Telemetry, radio, use in study of postfledgling activities of juvenile bald eagles, 149
Tell Keisan (Israel), excavations at, 129-143
Thomerson, Jamie E., 703, 708
Throckmorton, Peter, 161, 173
Tierra del Fuego, flora of, 275
Tlapanec Indians, ethnographic study of, 517
Toro Game Reserve, Uganda, study of leks in a population of kob, 75
Torres de Araúz, Reina, 709, 710
Trinidad, spatial analysis of peasant livelihood behavior in, 579
Tundra, energy and water budget studies in, 591
Turtles, ridley, field study of nesting in Costa Rica, 369
Turkey, Aphrodisias archeological site investigations, 1971-1977, 185
Tyndale-Biscoe, C. Hugh, 711, 720

Uganda, Toro Game Reserve, study of leks in a population of kob, 75
Underwater surveying:
Battle of Lepanto, Greece, search for, 161
offshore Bimini, 21
Urquhart, Fred A., 721, 730
Urquhart, Norah R., 721, 730

Vertebrate populations, behavior of on abandoned strip-mine areas in Mercer County, Pennsylvania, 67
Volcanology:
Austral Islands, seamounts, 389
Galápagos Islands calderas, volcanic gas and petrologic investigations, 501
Kilauea Volcano, Hawaii, spectroscopic study of the chemistry of flames and fumes, 117

Waldren, William H., 731, 732
Washington, Cascade Mountains, petrological and geochemical study of the Mount Stuart batholith, 175
Water budget studies in the tundra, 591

West Indies:
Anolis lizards of, 283
St. Vincent Island, plant successions on Soufrière Volcano, 39
Whales, behavior of various species, 551
Woodpecker, Asian, 631
Worley, Ian A., 733, 747
Wyoming, Sweetwater County, Eocene flamingo nesting area investigation, 473

Yak, field investigations of in the Nepal Himalaya, 529
Yalouris, Eletherios, 161, 173
Yellowstone National Park, biotic succession of lodgepole-pine forests of fire origin in, 693